Research in the Service of Mental Health

Report of the Research Task Force
of the National Institute of Mental Health

Prepared by Task Force Staff and Coordinating Committee
with
Herbert Yahraes

Editor-in-Chief: Julius Segal, Ph.D.

Associate Editors: Donald S. Boomer, Ph.D.
Lorraine Bouthilet, Ph.D.

National Institute of Mental Health
5600 Fishers Lane
Rockville, Maryland 20852

A summary of this report has
been prepared as a separate
publication and is for sale by
the Superintendent of Documents,
Government Printing Office,
Washington, D.C. 20402.
Order ADM 75-237.

DHEW Publication No. (ADM) 75-236
Printed 1975

November 1974

To:
Bertram S. Brown, M.D.
Director, National Institute of Mental Health

This report provides a detailed account of the findings and recommendations of the NIMH Research Task Force, established by you in May 1972 to conduct a comprehensive review and analysis of the Institute's scientific activities, and to make substantive and organizational recommendations for their future directions.

Contained here is both a review of past achievements and a framework for future efforts. The Research Task Force has fulfilled its mission with a sense of pride over the progress achieved to date, and of optimism over prospects for further advances in mental health research. The fact that the Task Force devoted over 2 years to accomplishing its mission reflects both the richness of the Institute's scientific achievements and the depth and thoroughness with which Task Force members approached their responsibilities. A less intensive analysis of the Institute's research programs could have been accomplished in a shorter period. Its results, however, would hardly have done justice either to the size and scope of the NIMH research investments to date or to the responsibilities with which you charged the Task Force.

The Task Force involved the efforts of more than 300 NIMH personnel and consultants. It should be pointed out, however, that the overall task could not have been completed without the contributions and support of countless other staff members, whose collaboration is embedded in this product.

The report is respectfully submitted in the hope that it will provide an important aid in administering the broad scientific programs of NIMH and a vehicle for creating within the entire mental health community an awareness of the richness, both in problems and in promises, of mental health research.

Julius Segal

Julius Segal, Ph.D.
Director, Research Task Force

Research Task Force Staff

Director	Julius Segal, Ph. D.
Associate Director	Donald S. Boomer, Ph.D.
Coordinator of Study Groups 1, 2, and 3	Patricia S. Goldman, Ph. D.
Deputy Coordinator of Study Groups 1, 2, and 3	Lyle W. Bivens, Ph.D.
Coordinator of Study Groups 4, 5, and 6	William Pollin, M.D.
Deputy Coordinator of Study Groups 4, 5, and 6	Phillippe V. Cardon, Jr., M.D.
Coordinator of Study Groups 7, 8, and 9	Morris B. Parloff, Ph.D.
Deputy Coordinator of Study Groups 7, 8, and 9	Irma Lann
Behavioral Science Coordinator	George V. Coelho, Ph.D.
Program Analysis Coordinator	Frank J. Sullivan, Ph.D.
Writer-Editors	Jacquelyn Hall, Ph.D. Bette Runck Paul Sirovatka
Staff Administrators	Michele Harvey Sherry Prestwich
Program Analysts	Michael Adler Vivian Isenstein
Program Assistant	Emily Barron
Systems Consultant	Bette Shannon
Art Director	William Bowman
Contributing Editors	Gay Luce Maya Pines Antoinette Gattozzi John Osmundsen Patricia McBroom Ellen Searcy Morton Werber
Secretaries	Margaret Salladay Lillian Becker Anne Cooley Sylvia Cunningham Mary Ravicini Shirley Watson Cindy Wells

Explanatory Note: Recent Reorganization of the National Institute of Mental Health

During the work of the Research Task Force, it became clear that organizational changes affecting the National Institute of Mental Health (NIMH) were impending.

Since neither the timing nor the exact nature of the changes could be foreseen, the Task Force decided to retain its original program descriptions. It was recognized that such descriptions are primarily valuable not because they reflect the details of Federal administration, but because they describe the nature of mental health research, the extent of Federal support, and the results.

Consequently, several organizational units described in this report are no longer part of NIMH. The principal change is that research on alcoholism and drug abuse is now the responsibility of separate institutes. In addition, some administrative offices are now offices of the Alcohol, Drug Abuse, and Mental Health Administration (ADAMHA), several with counterparts or near-counterparts in the new NIMH organization. For instance, the Office of Communications has been replaced by an NIMH Division of Scientific and Technical Information, and the Offices of Program Coordination and of Program Planning and Evaluation are now ADAMHA offices.

Within NIMH as of 1974, the Office of the Director is served by the Office of Program Development and Analysis and the Office of Program Support. Divisional organization has remained largely the same, but a new Division of Biometry carries out functions of branches formerly devoted to biometry and epidemiology.

With some exceptions, no attempt has been made to note these changes in this report.

Contents

Chapter 3. NIMH Support of Research Activities: An Overview

Chapter 4. Basic Research: I. Advances in Knowledge of the Biological Processes Underlying Behavior

Chapter 5. Basic Research: II. Advances in Knowledge of the Psychological Processes Underlying Behavior

Chapter 6. Basic Research: III. Advances in Knowledge of the Sociocultural Processes Underlying Behavior

Chapter 7. The Basic Research Activities of the National Institute of Mental Health

Chapter 8. Research on Mental Illness and Behavior Disorders

Chapter 9. Research on Alcohol Abuse and Alcoholism

Chapter 10.   Research on Drug Abuse

Chapter 12. Research on Treatment of Mental Disorders

Chapter 14. The Dissemination and Use of Research Information

Chapter 15. The Administration and Organization of NIMH Research Programs

CHAPTER 1

Purpose and Organization of the Research Task Force

THE MISSION

The Research Task Force of the National Institute of Mental Health was launched in May 1972 to conduct a comprehensive review and analysis of the Institute's scientific activities and to make substantive and organizational recommendations for future directions.

For roughly a quarter of a century, NIMH has been the Nation's major instrument of support for research in the broad domain of mental health. In the Institute's own laboratories and in research facilities throughout the country and the world, thousands of investigators under the auspices of NIMH have been at work on problems that span the entire range of mental health concerns and that involve the full spectrum of behavioral science disciplines. The number of research projects supported annually by the Institute has grown from 38 in 1948, when the first appropriations were made under the National Mental Health Act of 1946, to 1,497 in 1972. More than a billion dollars, approximately one-third of the Institute's total budget to date, has been invested in research.

This effort has produced a great yield. It has led to a substantial increase of information about the causes, treatment, and prevention of mental illnesses—and about the factors that help foster mental health. As detailed in this report, scientists in disparate fields have made significant progress toward the solution of a number of mental health problems, and the results of research conducted or supported by NIMH have been widely applied. This report makes abundantly clear also that many needs are still unmet—among them, for example, more nearly complete knowledge of the causes of major mental illness, better diagnostic and treatment methods, finer and more precise techniques for studying the operations of the brain and their effects on behavior, a clearer understanding of the relation between social and environmental factors and mental health, and more dependable ways both to determine the needs of a given population for mental health services and to measure the impact of such services.

Although unmet research needs do not decrease, resources for meeting them do; the decision to establish the Task Force was particularly timely in view of the reduction of funds for mental health research in recent years. As resources for research decline, their judicious allocation becomes more critical. Accordingly, the Task Force was confronted with such questions as these:

1

- What progress has been made in each of the many scientific fields involved in mental health research? What important questions remain unresolved? What dead ends have been reached?

- In the years ahead, what research investments are likely to be the most profitable—both through increased basic knowledge of the biological, psychological, and social mechanisms influencing human behavior and through improved methods of treating and preventing specific mental health problems?

- What research activities, though promising, now carry a lesser sense of urgency and opportunity?

- Among the many administrative and organizational support mechanisms that have accompanied the rapid growth and diversification of the Institute's research programs, which ones are still serviceable and which need to be modified or replaced?

Altogether, the Research Task Force was designed to undertake a thorough study of the Institute's research activities—substantive, organizational, managerial—as an aid in administering the broad scientific programs of NIMH.

SCOPE OF THE PROBLEM

The significance of the Task Force becomes more apparent when considered against the backdrop not only of the unsolved research problems in mental health, but also, and more important, of the unsolved human mental health problems that confront the Nation.

Although, as noted elsewhere in this report, fully reliable statistics describing the incidence and prevalence of mental and emotional disorders do not exist, overall estimates, even if in error by a generous margin, indicate that no less than 10 percent of the U.S. population, or at least 20 million people, suffer from some form of mental illness. About one-seventh of those afflicted receive psychiatric care of some sort.

Based upon those figures, and taking into account such factors as the mentally ill individual's loss of earnings and the cost of care both in and out of institutions, the annual cost of mental illness in this country is estimated at about $21 billion, or almost one-quarter of the national defense budget. This estimate may well be low; other estimates put the economic cost of alcoholism, alone, at $15 billion annually, and the annual cost of drug abuse at $10 billion.

The data below indicate how the overall statistics on treatment, excluding treatment outside of institutions, are distributed among the major categories of mental health problems. In 1971, the admissions to all psychiatric inpatient and outpatient services were at the rate of 1238.6 per 100,000 people. This total was distributed among the following diagnostic categories:

Schizophrenia	258.0
Depressive disorders	216.9
Alcoholism	127.9
Organic brain syndromes	54.9
Drug abuse	43.1

Mental retardation.. 28.9
Psychotic disorders not listed above........................... 18.9
Undiagnosed.. 88.9
All other diagnoses—among them, child behavior
  disorders, neuroses, psychosomatic disorders....... 401.1

These data scarcely suggest the suffering, economic loss, and social consequences of mental illness and behavior disorders. Steps to be taken to measure accurately the scope of the individual mental health problems faced by the Nation are presented elsewhere in this report. It should be pointed out here, however, that such data, although needed to assess the impact of specific interventions, are not required to conclude that the mission of NIMH carries with it the obligation and the prospect of reducing what may safely be regarded as the Nation's primary public health problem.

THE PROCESS

To initiate the Task Force, an informal planning group was convened by the Institute's Deputy Director; its members included the directors of the intramural and extramural research programs and the president of the Assembly of Scientists. This group determined that at least a year would be needed to conduct a project of such scope. It also decided that the basic work of the Task Force should be divided among 10 study groups, made up largely of working research scientists. The 10 study groups were as follows:

1. Biological and Physiological Processes
2. Psychological Processes
3. Social and Cultural Processes
4. Mental Illness and Behavior Disorders
5. Drug Abuse
6. Alcoholism
7. Social Problems
8. Treatment Techniques
9. Mental Health Services
10. Research Information and Utilization

The planning group nominated core members for the 10 study groups, largely from Institute personnel, and these persons were invited by the Director, NIMH, to participate. The study groups were given virtual autonomy; they chose their own chairpersons, enlarged their original membership as they wished, and set about their task in whatever ways they saw fit. The mission of each study group reflected the goals of the Research Task Force as a whole. These tasks were to:

1. Describe ongoing and past NIMH research activities and objectives, and related national efforts not supported by NIMH.

2. Evaluate the outcome of these activities.

3. Recommend emphases and deemphases for future research activities.

4. Recommend methods for managing the implementation of new initiatives and the continuation of ongoing programs.

5. Recommend changes in NIMH internal organizational structure, if necessary.

The study groups approached their work in ways that differed mainly in details and in sequence of steps. All the groups solicited the knowledge and opinions of other scientists and research administrators, both inside and outside the Institute. The groups also studied written information available within the Institute in the form of published and unpublished reports on activities and accomplishments in given areas and of summaries of individual research projects. For a view of current research, each group examined summaries of all the research projects in its area that had been recently funded as part of the Institute's extramural research program. All the groups used the expertise of their members, coupled in many cases with that of consultants, to sort out and pass judgment on the rich store of information brought to the surface. In almost every case the research field as a whole, and not the Institute's contribution alone, was considered.

More than 300 people were involved in Task Force activities. The 10 study groups comprised 88 men and women, who gave varying proportions of their working time to the project. Of the group members, 61 were NIMH employees, 22 came from outside of Government, and 5 were from Government agencies other than NIMH. More than 200 consultants assisted the groups in various ways, such as reviewing a research area, answering critical questions about an area, or reviewing and analyzing preliminary reports. A Task Force staff, numbering about 15 at any one time, supported and managed the enterprise.

General supervision of the overall task was provided by a Coordinating Committee, convened and chaired by the Deputy Director, NIMH and the Director of the Research Task Force. The membership of this committee included the directors of the operating divisions and offices, the 10 study group chairpersons, selected Task Force staff members, and a representative of the Assembly of Scientists.

During the planning stages of the Task Force, and during the early phase of its operation, a number of subtasks were undertaken that later proved to be unrealistically ambitious because of the time and the resources available. These tasks continue to be regarded as important in the context of any thorough assessment of mental health research programs, and it is hoped that efforts to pursue them will be undertaken in the future.

It was intended at the inception of the Task Force that the evaluation of NIMH research programs be accompanied by a similar description and analysis of the country's other research programs in the mental health field. Soon after the task was begun, it became apparent that such an analysis would be impossible, since there was a notable absence of comparable information storage and retrieval capacities across the various agencies supporting mental health research. It is a finding of the Task Force that within the Federal establishment no reliable mechanisms exist for describing and analyzing the sum of the research efforts pursued in fields related to mental health, and it is recommended that attempts be made to determine the feasibility and cost of organizing information systems yielding comparable descriptive data on mental health research pursued by various Federal agencies.

4

Also initiated during the course of the Task Force was a survey and analysis of ethical concerns in mental health research, resulting in the preparation of a preliminary chapter on the subject. Upon reflection and evaluation, this material was considered to fall short of a comprehensive summary of a complicated and controversial field; moreover, it was acknowledged that the subject is dealt with extensively in existing texts and articles and, therefore, that the Task Force energies would best be directed elsewhere.

Finally, it should be pointed out that the task of comprehensively describing the full substance of NIMH research programs to date has been achieved with varying degrees of detail and specificity in various chapters of this report. No report of limited size and scope can pretend to exhaust the rich store of findings and achievements embedded in the nearly three decades of productive, scientific effort. The descriptions contained in this report should be regarded, therefore, as reflecting examples and highlights of outcome rather than as comprehensive surveys.

THE REPORT

After extensive deliberations, each study group produced a voluminous report leading to recommendations both on substantive and on organizational and managerial matters pertaining to mental health research. The overall Task Force report was based largely on these individual study group reports. It was prepared by selected members of the Task Force staff and Coordinating Committee, acting for the Coordinating Committee as a whole. The Committee reviewed the report in its various stages and, as the work approached conclusion, debated the issues of organization and administration and made the decisions set forth in the final chapter.

The report was also reviewed, in semifinal form, by a number of authorities from outside NIMH—scientists, research administrators, and others active in the mental health or allied fields. It is addressed to the Director, NIMH, and by extension to all others who are concerned with the Nation's mental health for whatever clarification and guidance it may furnish them in advancing our common cause.

CHAPTER 2

An Organizational History of the NIMH Research Programs

INTRODUCTION

This chapter highlights the growth and diversification of the NIMH research enterprise. It gives particular attention to the major tides of budgetary, administrative, and organizational change that have brought the Institute's research activity to its present size and scope. The purpose is to provide background for subsequent descriptions of past and present research and for the recommendations affecting the substance and the organization of future programs.

The signing of the National Mental Health Act in July 1946 created the National Institute of Mental Health and marked the beginning of the Federal Government's large-scale support of research in mental health. The Act, which also called for support of clinical training and some services, specifically authorized a variety of mechanisms for supporting research: intramural studies, research fellowships, and grants to institutions and individuals. A National Advisory Mental Health Council was created to select projects that might make "valuable contributions to human knowledge with respect to the cause, prevention, or methods of diagnosis and treatment of psychiatric disorders."

Passage of the Act and creation of NIMH culminated several decades of planning and preparations by a handful of professional and lay persons devoted to improving the lot of the mentally ill. Until midcentury, voluntary organizations led the study of national mental health problems and raised public awareness to the need for action. The most active of these groups, the National Committee for Mental Hygiene, was founded by Clifford Beers in 1909. (In 1950 it merged with two other organizations—the National Mental Health Foundation and the Psychiatric Foundation—to form the National Association for Mental Health.)

Before the National Mental Health Act became law, the Public Health Service had been concerned with a few mental health problems—among them, drug addiction—and it also had responsibility for checking the mental, as well as the physical, condition of immigrants. Beginning in 1914, it conducted field studies that included an investigation of the mental health of school children and a special 3-year analysis of relationships between foreign-born parents and native-born offspring. The studies "also included an evaluation of State and local policies concerned with dependency, crime, delinquency, and other socially adverse behavior problems related to mental illness and mental defect. The investigations embraced samplings of almshouse populations and other institutions ministering to the indoor relief needs of indigent persons, samplings of the populations of public and private institutions caring for incorrigibles and for those who had committed offenses against the law, a sampling of school populations, and surveys of the policies of State and local education systems concerning methods for early detection of mental disease or defects and the measures employed for their amelioration." (Quotation from Williams' "The United States Public Health Service 1798-1950," page 334.)

Congress took its first formal action to initiate Federal responsibility for a mental health problem in 1929 by establishing two "United States Narcotic Farms," later renamed U.S. Public Health Service Hospitals, for the treatment of narcotic addicts. The same law created within the Public Health Service the Narcotics Division, charged with administering the two institutions, carrying out (though not supporting through grants) studies on the nature of addiction and on methods of treatment and rehabilitation, disseminating information, and assisting State and local authorities in the development of facilities for treating addicts. In 1930, Congress extended the responsibility of the Public Health Service to medical and psychiatric care in Federal penal and correctional institutions, and the Narcotics Division was renamed the Division of Mental Hygiene.

Dr. Walter L. Treadway, who had conducted pioneering field investigations on mental illness, was the division's first head. He widened its scope to include studies on the prevalence, causes, prevention, and treatment of mental illness as well as on drug addiction, although research still constituted a very small proportion of the division's work. In 1938, he was succeeded by Dr. Lawrence Kolb, Sr., who had been the first Medical Officer in Charge of the narcotic hospital at Lexington, Ky.

Kolb envisioned a national neuropsychiatric institute and mustered support among professional and volunteer organizations for its creation. World War II temporarily blocked this movement but at the same time—since many men were rejected for military service because of neuropsychiatric disorders, and many others became neuropsychiatric casualties—it brought heightened awareness of mental health problems to the Nation. Moreover, the wartime Office of Scientific Research and Development, in its Vannevar Bush report of 1945, urged the Federal Government to play a more active role in research, particularly in opening new frontiers, one of them the problem of mental illness.

When Kolb retired in 1944, he was succeeded by Dr. Robert H. Felix. Encouraged by Surgeon General Thomas Parran, Felix developed a plan for a national mental health program. His 20-page "Outline of a Comprehensive Community-Based Mental Health Program" became the working paper for the National Mental Health Act. Originally the House and Senate Bills were introduced as the "National Neuropsychiatric Institute Act," but the legislation was passed as the "National Mental Health Act." The agency authorized by this Act was called the National Institute of Mental Health to reflect a broad, positive mission to promote mental health as well as combat mental illness.

7

THE EARLY DAYS: LATE 1940'S TO MID-1950'S

Because the programs enacted in 1946 were not funded until July 1947 (i.e., fiscal year 1948), Felix, who was to become the first director of NIMH, obtained a foundation grant so that the National Advisory Mental Health Council authorized by Congress was able to begin meeting in 1946 to discuss plans for the new agency. Originally composed of six members, the council was expanded by law in 1950 to include 12 appointed members (six of whom could be lay persons) and representatives from the Veterans Administration and the Department of Defense. On April 1, 1949, the Division of Mental Hygiene was abolished, and the National Institute of Mental Health took its place.

In view of the organization's service responsibilities, it might have been feasible to attach NIMH to the Bureau of State Services. On the advice of Felix and the council, however, Congress judged that treatment of mental illness could best be furthered by stimulating research and research training and therefore the new mental health program should be placed under the National Institutes of Health (NIH). By 1952, NIMH was spending about a quarter of its budget on research and by 1954, over one-third.

The Institute created an organization with four principal branches. Three of them—Research Grants and Fellowships, Training, and Community Services—supported extramural projects. The fourth, Intramural Research, conducted studies within the Institute itself. In addition, there were three smaller staff branches: the Biometrics Branch, which became the Nation's biostatistical center for data on mental illness; the Publications and Reports Branch; and the Professional Services Branch, which had responsibility for long-range planning and for stimulating and collaborating on research in special areas of concern.

Research Grants Program

In accordance with the policy of the National Institutes of Health, NIMH gave research scientists a minimum of direction and a maximum of freedom. The Institute's advisory council took a strong interest in research policy, often holding extended discussions on research needs, methods of stimulating scientific work of high quality, and the possibility and desirability of setting research priorities. The council decided not to recommend priorities, but informal priorities did emerge. In 1952, a poll showed that NIMH advisers—present and past members of this advisory council and members of a scientific panel reviewing grant applications—favored emphasizing research on the etiology and treatment of mental illness. An analysis of the distribution of grant funds for 1948-1952 showed that those two areas were already being emphasized in the allotment of research money.

Evaluation of the grants program during those early years also disclosed that research on mental retardation, behavior disorders, psychopathy, alcoholism, and problems of the aged was being supported at a relatively low level. Research on child development and childhood mental disorders was heavily supported.

8

Research on mental illness was conducted for the most part by psychologists, sociologists, and other social scientists. Less than 15 percent of all projects were conducted by biological scientists, even though grants in neurology, including grants for research on epilepsy, cerebral palsy, and multiple sclerosis, were then handled by NIMH. Such grants were transferred to the National Institute of Neurological Diseases and Blindness after its establishment.

Grant Review Process

Applications for extramural research grants have been routed through the Division of Research Grants of NIH. This division assigns applications to the various Institutes according to a referral guide describing the parameters of research in each Institute, a process that continued even when NIMH was separated from NIH in the mid-1960's.

When a grant application reaches NIMH, it is assigned to a division and to one of the Institute's initial review groups. Known originally as study sections, these panels of consultants are largely drawn from outside Government, and the members are chosen for their prominence in a given field. The panels review in detail the grant applications for scientific merit and make recommendations to Institute staff for approval or disapproval. These recommendations, along with the summaries of the panels' reviews on all applications, are passed on to the National Advisory Mental Health Council. In early years, members of the council carefully reviewed every application again. However, as the volume of applications greatly increased, the council began reviewing in detail only those projects that raised policy issues, involved large sums of money, or on which the initial review group had submitted both a majority and a minority report. All applications must be recommended for approval by the advisory council in order to be eligible for funding by the Institute. Program managers, deciding which of the recommended projects to fund, weigh the assessments of the review groups along with such factors as availability of funds and program priorities.

In the early years of NIMH there was only one panel (aside from ad hoc advisory committees called to review special grants) to provide initial scientific review of research grant applications. But by 1957, the Mental Health Study Section had such a volume of applications that a new Behavioral Sciences Study Section was added. Since then, review committees have been created or disbanded according to increases or decreases in the volume of applications in various fields and according to program changes within the Institute.

Programed Research

The regular grants program dealt mainly with unsolicited research proposals from nongovernment scientists, and NIMH personnel soon saw a need to stimulate projects in areas of major interest where few applications were being received. The Professional Services Branch was given primary responsibility for such initiatives. In 1951, when there was great public concern about juvenile drug addiction, the branch launched studies on the nature and extent of the problem in collaboration with research institutes in New York and Chicago. The branch also undertook to develop programs in mental retardation, delinquency, alcoholism, aging, mental health in the schools, community mental health, and other areas. Special grants, reviewed at first by ad hoc panels and later by a special grants review committee, were used for supporting projects developed by the branch.

Intramural Research Program

The Intramural Research Program, authorized in 1949, did not fully get underway until 1953, when the Clinical Center was opened on the NIH campus at Bethesda, and needed laboratory space became available. However, investigations of cortical function did begin in 1949, conducted by a small unit that 4 years later was to become the Laboratory of Neurophysiology. At the start, too, the intramural program absorbed administrative responsibility for the Addiction Research Center, located at the Public Health Service Hospital at Lexington, Ky. This center, beginning in the 1930's, had been conducting studies of the abuse properties of narcotic drugs and the psychological and physiological factors in addiction.

NIMH appointed a full-time scientific director, Dr. Seymour Kety, in 1951. Shortly after he arrived it was decided that NIMH should join the new National Institute of Neurological Diseases and Blindness in setting up a joint basic research program, with Kety serving as scientific director. The programs had been combined, Kety said, because "progress in the diagnosis and treatment of nervous and mental diseases rests firmly upon a basic understanding of the nervous system through the biological and behavioral sciences." (Quotation from Brand and Sapir's "An Historical Perspective on the National Institute of Mental Health.")

Charged with establishing the best possible program for doing research on the nervous system and behavior—and, importantly, given the freedom necessary to choose how it should be done—Kety decided to establish laboratories along disciplinary lines. He chose this structure over the obvious alternative of establishing a problem-oriented program for two major reasons. First, it was his conviction that scientific discoveries are more likely to emerge when scientists choose their own research problems, that good scientists would be attracted to such a program, and that it provided for more continuity. Second, there were no powerful theories available to guide the organization of research directed at understanding such conditions as schizophrenia or mental retardation. Years later at the celebration of the NIMH's 25th anniversary, Kety recalled, "Our guidelines were excellence which can be judged, rather than relevance, which can only be guessed at—but excellence distributed over the wide range of disciplines upon which psychiatry depends."

Laboratories were opened as space became available in the new Clinical Center. Beginning in 1952, one after another was added until, by 1957, the nucleus of the Intramural Research Program was formed:

Laboratory of Socio-environmental Studies
Laboratory of Neurophysiology
Laboratory of Psychology
Laboratory of Child Research
Laboratory of Adult Psychiatry

Laboratory of Cellular Pharmacology
Laboratory of Neurochemistry
Laboratory of Clinical Science
Clinical Neuropharmacology Research Center (at St. Elizabeths Hospital)

Three of the laboratories—Neurophysiology, Cellular Pharmacology, and Neurochemistry—conducted only basic research, while the others were either partly or exclusively devoted to clinical investigations. Overseeing the latter studies was Dr. Robert A. Cohen, Director for Clinical Investigations. The term "clinical" was used to designate primarily nonlaboratory research and not, as is often inferred, to indicate applied research. Both the basic and clinical programs were directed toward understanding fundamental processes in human development and behavior. The basic research focused on processes at the level of organs, tissues, and cells, while clinical research dealt with processes at the organismic level.

In 1956, the Board of Scientific Counselors was established to advise the Institute on the content and operation of the Intramural Research Program, particularly with reference to long-range considerations. The board is made up of six members, selected for their prominence in basic and clinical sciences related to mental health; it usually meets twice a year.

Biometrics Program

Since its establishment, the Biometrics Branch has been the Nation's center for data on mental illness and has contributed in many ways to mental health research. It began modestly, taking over the already established annual census of patients in mental institutions. Later the branch expanded to include statistical surveys of psychiatric facilities—their patterns of use, their financing, staffing, and related issues; analysis of the resulting data; and research on various substantive problems, such as the epidemiology of schizophrenia and other mental disorders and the design of statistical methods for collecting and analyzing data.

Research Training Programs

Training of researchers with NIMH support began in 1948 when 19 fellowships were awarded, 17 of which had been transferred from the NIH general research fund. Research fellowships, given for periods of 1 to 3 years, have been made at three levels: predoctoral, postdoctoral, and special (meaning for the experienced investigator).

The program grew slowly at first, expanded dramatically between 1956 and 1965 (largely owing to congressional provision of additional funds), stabilized in the mid-1960's, and began to decline in the late 1960's for lack of sustained funding. Over the years, fellowships have tended to concentrate at the predoctoral level, and the majority of them have been awarded in the field of psychology.

To provide more stable support for research training and the development of research scientists, the Institute added the career investigator grant program in 1954. This afforded promising young scientists the opportunity to spend 3 to 5 years on full-time experimental work and additional research

11

training. Although the program was designed mainly to strengthen the field of clinical psychiatric research, research psychiatrists and scientists from other disciplines were also awarded support. By the end of 1960, nearly 40 scientists had been supported, all of them sponsored by medical schools or affiliated centers. At this point, the program was merged with a newly established NIH career awards program. From 1960 to 1972, this program underwent changes in structure, emphasis, and name—it is now called the Research Development Program—but its goal remained basically the same: to provide stable support for outstanding young researchers who would otherwise have difficulty pursuing research careers. The program continued to grow until 1970, when 197 researchers received awards. In 1972, 184 awards were made, totaling about $5 million.

Additional funds from Congress provided yet another training program, only partly concerned with research manpower. This was begun in 1957—not coincidentally the year the first manmade satellite was orbited by the Russians. Under this program, NIMH has awarded grants to public and private nonprofit institutions to provide financial assistance to students in behavioral sciences who are preparing for service or research in fields related to mental health. This program also underwent dramatic growth in the early 1960's but began to level off a decade later. In 1972, more than 1,500 stipends were awarded for research training at a total cost of about $13 million.

In 1973, in connection with the amended budgets of fiscal years 1973 and 1974, the Administration announced its decision to phase out Federal support for categorical professional training programs, including all research training programs in NIH/NIMH. This decision elicited strong protests from the scientific community and Congress; and, subsequently, the Administration restored a small research training program, the policies of which had not been specified when this report was written.

Prior to announcement of these phaseout policies, NIMH reexamined all of its training programs and transferred the research development program—recognized as primarily a research rather than a training program—from the training division to the extramural research division.

Overview of the Early Years

The Institute's budget and its research programs grew steadily in its first few years. Total expenditures for research programs rose from $.8 million in fiscal year 1948 to about $7.8 million in fiscal 1956, and the total Institute expenditures from approximately $8 million to $18 million. Though appreciable, this was moderate growth compared to what followed.

EXPANSION: MID-1950'S TO MID-1960'S

During the mid-1950's, there was an increasingly large backlog of good research grant applications. Although approved by the council, they could not be supported because of lack of funds.

Large budget increases for mental health research, beginning in 1957, ushered in a period of expansion. In 1957, funds appropriated for the Institute increased by more than $15 million over the previous year, including a $5 million increase for research. The Eisenhower Administration had decided to invest more money in medical research, and Congress, already sympathetic with the cause, appropriated even more than the Administration requested. Government-funded medical research had entered its prosperous years. In 1962, the NIMH research budget passed $50 million, and by 1965, had risen to over $80 million. From the mid-1950's to the mid-1960's, research support constituted from 40 to 50 percent of the total NIMH budget.

By its own wish and that of Congress, which commonly earmarked funds, the Institute applied some of the additional funds to initiate research and demonstration efforts in such problem areas as juvenile delinquency and mental retardation, and to develop certain research fields, notably psychopharmacology. The earmarking of research funds usually reflected several forces working on Congress. One was the Institute, itself, which prepared descriptions—of program areas that should be developed—in the budget sent to Congress. In addition, mental health professionals, representatives of voluntary organizations, and other persons with a special interest in mental health, including individual Congressmen, added their influence. Most research money, however, was not marked for a specific purpose.

Regular Research Grants Program

The total new and continuing research grants awarded went from about 450 in 1957 to about 1,800 in 1963. The average size of grants steadily increased, from around $16,500 in 1957 to almost $28,000 in 1963. The number dropped in 1964 but only because about 150 grants in such areas as mental retardation, aging, and basic studies of intellectual development were transferred to the new National Institute of Child Health and Human Development. However, 1964 did mark a leveling off in the growth of the research program, and several years later the grant awards began to decline in number.

The support mechanisms and programs initiated during those years of growth are described below.

Small Grants Program

Recognizing the limitations of the regular grants program, NIMH staff and advisers saw a need for a special mechanism to support promising young scientists and to respond quickly to innovative research ideas. In 1956, acting upon the recommendations of the Mental Health Study Section and the advisory council, the Institute inaugurated the small grants program to support exploratory and pilot research projects with 1-year grants not to exceed $2,000. This limit has since been raised a number of times and now stands at $5,000 to $6,000. The approximately 200 small grants awarded each year have been particularly valuable to those scientists, including a number at small institutions, who lack either the resources or the professional background to do the preliminary work required for consideration in the major grants program.

13

Psychopharmacology Program

The trend of augmented congressional support, accompanied by increased congressional direction, was particularly evident in the 1957 appropriations, when Congress earmarked $2 million in additional funds for psychopharmacology research.

The tranquilizing drugs had recently come upon the scene, generating great enthusiasm over what appeared to be a breakthrough in treating mental illness. NIMH had supported and conducted limited research on the drugs and indicated to Congress in 1955 that additional funds were needed for the Institute to launch a major effort. While NIMH was proceeding with plans for a conference on the evaluation of pharmacotherapy in mental illness, some authorities were urging that Congress provide funds for a broad-scale evaluation effort. Congress did not mandate as broad a program as some advocated, but it did add $2 million to the 1957 appropriation and earmarked it for research to evaluate the utility of tranquilizing drugs.

During 1957, the Institute established a Psychopharmacology Service Center within the Research Grants and Fellowships Branch to implement the program prescribed by Congress. The center began using a variety of mechanisms—regular grants, special grants, and contracts—to stimulate research. It also established a Scientific Information Unit to function as a clearinghouse for information on psychopharmacological research. Congressional interest and earmarking of funds continued. In 1964, this center spent about $10 million on research grants, of which about 25-35 percent were collaborative studies—research in which NIMH staff members were actively involved in the design, monitoring, and/or analysis of studies carried out by outside investigators.

Research Center and Program-Project Grants

Another innovation in the regular grants program took place in 1960 when the National Institutes of Health made $500,000 available to NIMH to establish and support clinical research centers. The money came from funds voted by Congress to expand the NIH clinical research center program in scope and content. Originally, center grants were intended solely for the support of physical resources. In 1961, however, at the insistence of the National Advisory Mental Health Council, the concept of center grants was broadened to include so-called program-project grants. These were defined as grants made to an institution, in the name of one or more principal investigators, for the support of a broadly based and often long-term research program. In 1964, $2.5 million—or about 7 percent of the grant funds awarded by the Research Grants and Fellowships Branch—went to 12 program-project grants.

International Research

In 1961, in an effort to increase the support of outstanding scientific talent outside the country, the Institute established an International Research Program Section within the Research Grants and Fellowships Branch. This action was taken in recognition that research on mental health problems should not be constrained within national boundaries and that foreign resources offered unique opportunities in a number of research areas. In 1962, the program was placed under limitations by NIH because of this country's balance-of-payments problem. Although the program has continued to be curtailed over the past several years because of this problem, a small but significant portion of the Institute's research support has gone to a variety of foreign undertakings. Activities have included research grants to investigators sponsored by foreign institutions and others to U.S. investigators sponsored by domestic institutions but which include use of foreign resources; research contracts to foreign investigators; collaborative research projects funded by U.S.-owned foreign currencies in such countries as Israel, India, Poland, and Yugoslavia; and reception in the NIMH intramural laboratories of foreign scientists under visiting and international postdoctoral programs.

Applied Research and Demonstration Programs

Like the regular research grants program, research and demonstration activities in other parts of the Institute were extended between the mid-1950's and mid-1960's. This expansion was largely due to Title V of the Health Amendments Act of 1956, which authorized NIMH to support research and demonstrations in improved methods of diagnosing, caring for, treating, and rehabilitating the mentally ill. To implement the new legislation, Congress provided $2 million in new funds for 1958. The Senate Appropriations Committee report directed that these funds be spent for studies on juvenile delinquency, drug addiction, and aging, as well as for studies on the improvement of services in mental hospitals.

Mental Health Project Grants Program

The 1956 legislation was largely carried out through the mental health project grants program, also called the Title V program, which was administered by the Community Services Branch. In the first years of the program, most grants went for demonstrations of day hospitals, aftercare programs, crisis intervention, and other services for the mentally ill. This program supported projects that were germinal in almost every important innovation in mental health care, for example, rapid and intensive residential treatment, partial hospitalization, and treatment in the community. During the early 1960's, the program increasingly supported studies in special problem areas, such as mental retardation, alcoholism, drug abuse, juvenile delinquency, aging, and suicide.

Both the scope and the budget of the program grew rapidly. Congress showed interest in its progress and provided money for its expansion. In 1964, nearly 300 grants totaling some $16 million were awarded under the Title V program. By that time, four review committees—Special Areas, Community Services, Juvenile Delinquency, and Hospital Improvement—had been established to handle the increasing volume of grant applications.

Title V research and demonstration efforts and congressional interest stimulated other activities in the parent branch, Community Services. In 1962, when it was renamed the Research Utilization Branch, it introduced a new program mechanism, the research utilization conference. Such conferences brought together researchers, practitioners, and administrators from across the country to discuss how research efforts could be used to improve operating programs. In 1964, with the establishment of sections on crime and delinquency, alcoholism and drug abuse, and mental retardation, the branch was again renamed, becoming the Community Research and Services Branch.

Special Grants in Applied Research

The collaborative research and program development activities of the Professional Services Branch were also expanding in such areas of concern as drug addiction and juvenile delinquency. Although this branch had been set up only as a staff office, by 1963 it was administering some 30 grants totaling about $2.5 million. The next year all extramural programs were placed under one associate director, and the Professional Services Branch was dissolved. Most of its grants were taken over by the Research Grants Branch.

Inhouse Applied Research and Demonstration

In his congressional testimony on the National Mental Health Act, Felix's plans for the new agency included a commitment to establish two demonstration and research outpatient clinics. The first of these was established in Prince George's County, Md., early in 1948. Later in the year a second clinic was opened on the campus of Phoenix Junior College in Phoenix, Ariz. Both were administered by the Community Services Branch.

The intent was to focus on service and community relations in the Maryland clinic and to stress research in the Arizona clinic. The Community Services Branch hoped to learn, in the Arizona setting, more about the possibilities of developing a research capability and function in the context of community service. Demographic information about the community was to be sought, as well as epidemiological data in the field of mental health.

This intent was never realized, for a variety of reasons: the unexpectedly heavy service demands encountered in the Phoenix community; the staff composition, members in general being more oriented to clinical practice than to research; and the difficulties inherent in administering a new enterprise at a distance. Accordingly, the Phoenix operation was terminated in 1955.

During this period, the Prince George's clinic did function, as intended, as a service delivery demonstration venture. At the same time, the staff developed and expanded its research function as well. These joint functions were formalized in 1954, when the clinic became the Mental Health Study Center. Since that time the center has undergone several organizational shifts. For a brief period, it was a part of the Intramural Research Program; it is now in the Division of Mental Health Service Programs. Over the years the center has developed a diversified program of community mental health research, clinical activities, consultation services, and program planning and evaluation.

16

Intramural Research Program

Unlike the extramural grants program, the Institute's Intramural Research Program grew at a steady pace, not by great increments. Resources rose from a total of about $4.8 million and 250 positions in 1957 to about $10.5 million and 400 positions in 1964.

During 1960, as a part of reorganizations in NIMH and the then National Institute of Neurological Diseases and Blindness, the laboratories in the joint basic research program were returned administratively to their respective institutes. Most of the basic laboratories were fundamentally unchanged, but NIMH reshuffled some personnel and created a new Laboratory of Neurobiology. NIMH also appointed an Associate Director for Intramural Research, Dr. John C. Eberhart. This was the first time NIMH had a combined clinical-basic intramural research program under one director. In 1961, the components of its program included:

> Nine laboratories and branches on the NIH campus
> Addiction Research Center (at Lexington, Ky.)
> Clinical Neuropharmacology Research Center (at St. Elizabeths Hospital)
> Mental Health Study Center (Prince George's County, Md.)

The character of some intramural research gradually changed. Initially much of the work had comprised single studies, but the mid-1960's saw the increasing development of more complex and integrated research on major problems of behavior. To give a few examples, work in progress included the neurological correlates of subjective experience, the biology of sleep and dreaming, and cross-cultural comparisons of personality development.

Research Information Systems

To help meet the need for ready access to information about the grants program, an elaborate coding system covering both substantive and administrative data was developed between 1959 and 1961. Since then, other grant information systems have been developed to supplement the original system and focus more on the substance of the research projects.

Because of the growing difficulties of scientific and professional communication resulting from the increased size and complexity of the mental health field, the Institute set up the National Clearinghouse for Mental Health Information in 1963. The establishment of information centers throughout the Government had been stimulated by a study of communications problems in all fields of science and medicine by the Senate Committee on Government Operations. Moreover, the House Appropriations Committee had expressed interest in seeing NIMH expand its efforts to disseminate information. The clearinghouse has the mission of maintaining a national resource for scientific information in the mental health field, whether or not the information has been produced as a result of NIMH activities. The material collected is issued in many forms to a wide variety of audiences. At the start, most of the scientific and professional information activities in the Institute, including those of the Scientific Information Unit of the Psychopharmacology Center, were transferred to the clearinghouse.

Similar clearinghouses in the areas of drug abuse and alcoholism were set up more recently.

Overview of the Expansion Period

Research flourished between 1957 and 1964, a period marked by the launching and rapid expansion of two major extramural programs—psychopharmacology and the Title V program of applied research and demonstration projects. Funds for intramural research doubled; funds for extramural research grants increased nearly eightfold.

In this period, too, came the Community Mental Health Centers Act of 1963—an event that was to change profoundly the nature of the Institute. What had been primarily a research and training Institute would also become strongly geared to services.

REORGANIZATION: MIDDLE TO LATE 1960'S

From 1964 to 1968, the growth of research support diminished, but the responsibilities of the Institute as a whole increased, and its organizational structure became more complex. NIMH was in a state of almost continuous organizational flux: Its internal structure was reshaped, and its position within the Public Health Service was changed twice in 3 years.

The most extensive reorganization of NIMH occurred during 1966. The addition of the community mental health centers program had so increased NIMH's responsibilities and budget that changes were required both within the Institute and in the Institute's relations with other agencies. The Department of Health, Education, and Welfare gave NIMH independent bureau status in the Public Health Service. This change, which was formally made on January 1, 1967, helped precipitate a reexamination of the Institute's internal structure.

Internal change was also influenced by the changing social climate. This was the era of the Great Society's attack on poverty, crime, urban problems, drug addiction, and alcoholism. President Johnson had pledged to apply scientific research to some of the Nation's social ills. NIMH had supported research and demonstration projects on the mental health aspects of numerous social problems, and now it was encouraged to sharpen its focus by creating special units or centers to deal with such problems. Among the influential persons supporting the center concept was Dr. Stanley F. Yolles, who had succeeded Felix as the Institute's director in 1964.

In the mid-1960's, centers were established to coordinate research, training, demonstration, consultation, and communication efforts in nine areas: alcoholism, drug abuse, crime and delinquency, the mental health of children and youth, suicide prevention, schizophrenia, mental health and social problems, metropolitan problems, and epidemiology.

The centers differed in size and responsibility. Some received ongoing projects and grant funds from existing programs in the Institute and, therefore, could directly support research, training, and demonstration projects in addition to their coordinating activities. These were variously referred to as "operating," "funded," "full," or "total" centers. The others were "coordinating" centers, without grant money, that stimulated and coordinated support activities throughout the Institute.

As NIMH prepared to become a bureau, several new divisions had to be created; some existing branches were designated as divisions, which were then subdivided into new branches. Altogether, the newly reorganized Institute had seven divisions: Extramural Research Programs, Manpower and Training Programs, Mental Health Service Programs, Special Mental Health Programs, Field Investigations, Special Mental Health Research, and Clinical, Behavioral, and Biological Research. In addition, at the division level, four staff offices were created to consolidate and expand certain Institute-wide management activities. The new offices were designated as Program Planning and Evaluation, Communications, Program Liaison, and Administrative Management.

The new structure involved significant administrative changes in the Institute's research programs. The major changes are described in the sections following.

General Research Grants Program

The Research Grants Branch became the Division of Extramural Research Programs (DERP), with four branches: Behavioral Sciences, Applied Research, Clinical Research, and Psychopharmacology (the old Psychopharmacology Service Center). In addition, two of the new coordinating centers were established in the division: one for schizophrenia, in the Clinical Research Branch, and one for mental health and social problems, in the Applied Research Branch.

The new structure of the research grants program reflected one especially significant new responsibility—that of applied research. With the establishment of the Applied Research Branch in DERP, the mental health project grants program (Title V) was eliminated as a unit. Projects totaling about $17 million were transferred to DERP from the former Community Research and Services Branch, which became the Division of Mental Health Service Programs.

Special Programs

The Division of Special Mental Health Programs was created to focus extramural research and training on high-priority problems of national importance and to promote the use of relevant research findings. The primary mechanism for achieving these goals was the problem area center. Five of the new centers were assigned to this division. Three of them—Alcoholism, Narcotic Addiction and Drug Abuse, and Suicide Prevention—were "operating" centers. Several million dollars worth of Title V and regular research projects in these areas formed the basis of the three centers' grant programs. The other two centers—on child and family mental health and on crime and delinquency—had the same general goals as the operating centers but were intended to achieve them through coordination with other divisions. This division was responsible also for stimulating work in other special areas, such as aging, mental health in education, and occupational mental health.

Field Investigations

A new Division of Field Investigations was created to bring together several primarily inhouse operations. These included the narcotic addiction hospitals at Lexington, Ky., and Fort Worth, Tex., which became clinical research centers; the Mental Health Study Center, which was given a new mandate to develop a model comprehensive community mental health center; a new community mental health center at St. Elizabeths Hospital, which was also to be developed as a model; and the new Center for Epidemiologic Studies, which was to conduct its own field investigations as well as provide extramural support for research and training. When all elements of the Institute's drug program were brought together in one division in 1969, as described later, the Field Investigations division was dismantled.

Mental Health Intramural Research Program

Other inhouse research laboratories, traditionally considered the Intramural Research Program, were now organized into two divisions. They were placed in an unusual organizational unit, between a division and an institute, called the Mental Health Intramural Research Program. By agreement with NIH, intramural research activities on the Bethesda campus were to remain undisturbed and to maintain administrative ties with both bureaus. These NIMH laboratories and branches became the new Division of Clinical, Behavioral, and Biological Research (a combination that lasted only until 1968, when the division was split into a primarily basic research division and a primarily clinical research division).

Intramural research laboratories not on the NIH campus and therefore not under joint NIMH-NIH administration were placed under a new Division of Special Mental Health Research. Initially it comprised the Addiction Research Center at Lexington and two laboratories, Neuropharmacology and Clinical Psychopharmacology, formed out of the old Clinical Neuropharmacology Research Center at St. Elizabeths Hospital.

Overview of the Reorganization Period

The reorganization of 1966 expanded the capacity of NIMH to handle its increasing responsibility in the areas of services and social problems. Authority for conducting and supporting research was vested in additional organizational components, including centers to spur research, training, and service programs in mental-health-related social problem areas.

THE RECENT PAST: FROM THE LATE 1960'S TO THE EARLY 1970'S

From 1968 to 1972, the Institute's budget grew by about $300 million, mainly for service programs. Funds for the general research grants program had stabilized in the mid-1960's, along with funds for many other Federal research programs. Nevertheless, the total available for NIMH research grants did increase and in 1972 was about $15 million more than in 1968. This gain was mainly due to increases for research in alcoholism and drug abuse. Major legislation had expanded the Institute's responsibilities and provided new money for research, as well as for services and training, in these areas of growing national attention.

As emphasis was placed on alcoholism and drug abuse, organizational changes paralleled changes in the levels of research support for various programs. These changes are noted in the following sections. The Institute's increased responsibility for service programs brought about another change in 1968 when NIMH became part of the new Health Services and Mental Health Administration.

General Mental Health Research Program

Since the mid-1960's, mainly because of inflation, the number of grants for general mental health research has been decreasing. In 1972, the Division of Extramural Research Programs made 993 awards, about 350 fewer than in 1968, but during the intervening period several groups of projects had been transferred. The Center for Studies of Crime and Delinquency was "funded" in 1969—that is, made an operating center—and given DERP's crime and delinquency projects. Two years later, the Center for Minority Group Mental Health Programs became operational, absorbing grants from DERP. Also in 1971, projects in services research were transferred from DERP to the Division of Mental Health Service Programs. In 1972, DERP and these other units awarded almost 200 fewer research grants than in 1968, although money involved amounted to about $1.7 million more. That year the backlog of approved but unfunded research projects, which had amounted to $1.8 million in 1969, stood at more than $4 million.

During this period, research on the major mental illnesses received increasingly focused attention. In 1969, a Depression Section was established in the Clinical Research Branch, and the staff initiated a series of collaborative projects to increase knowledge about the nature and the treatment of the depressive illnesses. The following year a Psychotherapy and Behavioral Intervention Section was established in the same branch, giving the Institute for the first time a focal point for stimulating research on the nonsomatic treatments for mental disorders. The Center for Studies of Schizophrenia, though not providing direct support for research, analyzed and coordinated Institute activities in this area and proved to be a valuable national resource for scientific information. In addition, projects were encouraged and funded in emerging areas of social and scientific interest, ranging from biofeedback to the changing role of women.

Another noteworthy change during this period was the establishment in 1968 of a Committee on Juvenile Problems in the Applied Research Branch. This committee was charged with reviewing applications for research grants in early child care, family and school mental health, and related fields, which included juvenile delinquency until the Center for Studies of Crime and Delinquency was funded a year later.

Between 1970 and 1972, DERP increased its new awards in the broad category of child mental health. In 1972, about one-third of all new awards went to child-related studies. The increased emphasis on such studies was a response to the recommendations of the Joint Commission on the Mental Health of Children, which completed its work in 1969, and a subsequent resolution by the National Advisory Mental Health Council that called for augmented research on childhood. Dr. Bertram S. Brown, who became NIMH Director in 1970, designated child mental health as the Institute's top priority, and in 1971 an internal Ad Hoc Committee on Child Mental Health reported on how to implement this priority.

Despite the many organizational changes, mechanisms for research support remained the same. DERP continued to support research through various types of grants, ranging in size from small pilot studies (of which about 200 for $1.2 million were awarded in 1972) to large interdisciplinary program-project enterprises (of which 36, totaling $7.3 million, were supported in 1972).

Division of Special Mental Health Programs

Numerous changes mark this division's history. The most significant occurred when the drug abuse and alcoholism centers were redesignated as large operating units, independent of the division—drug abuse in 1969 and alcoholism in 1971.

In other changes, one center was brought in from another division (the Center for Studies of Metropolitan Problems, transferred from the services division in 1969); one new center was created (Minority Group Mental Health Programs, in 1971). One center was eliminated: the Center for Studies of Suicide Prevention was disbanded in 1972 and the division established a more general Mental Health Emergency Section.

In 1972, three centers in the division had funds of their own: Crime and Delinquency, Metropolitan Problems, and Minority Group Mental Health Programs. The only nonfunded center in the division was the Center for Studies of Child and Family Mental Health (originally the Center for Studies of Mental Health of Children and Youth).

In 1972, the Division of Special Mental Health Programs spent $8.5 million on research grants, out of an Institute total of $82.5 million for all research grants. That same year the units concerned with drug abuse and alcoholism spent $19.5 million, more than twice that of the division they had sprung from. As a further illustration of the tremendous growth of public and governmental interest in these two problems, grants for research on drug abuse and alcoholism took 10 percent of the Institute's research grant funds in 1968 but close to 25 percent in 1972. The total of research funds, including intramural and contract work, in these two areas in 1972 was almost $37 million.

The organizational history of the Institute's efforts in these areas is traced below.

Organization of the Drug Abuse Program

Between 1966 and 1968, the Center for Studies of Narcotic Addiction and Drug Abuse began developing a national program of research, training, and services. Existing work was expanded to include not only opiates but also hallucinogens, amphetamines, barbiturates, marihuana, and other drugs. Responding to public demand for answers to questions about marihuana, the center launched a program of research on the drug's properties, usage, and effects. Other NIMH units investigating drug abuse were the Clinical Research Centers at Lexington and Fort Worth and the Narcotic Addict Rehabilitation Branch, which were all part of the Division of Field Investigations, and the Addiction Research Center, which was part of the Intramural Research Program.

In 1969, the Institute brought all these programs together in the Division of Narcotic Addiction and Drug Abuse (DNADA). This move reflected both the increasing national concern about drug abuse and the Institute's increased responsibilities, as a result of the Narcotic Addict and Rehabilitation Act of 1966, for the treatment of addicts. Legislation passed in 1970 and 1972 gave the Institute still greater responsibilities, and funds made available by White House and congressional initiatives increased resources substantially. Most of the new funds were for service activities, but they enabled DNADA to undertake or expand some major research efforts. As an example, a contract program was initiated and intramural efforts were extended to the development of nonaddicting narcotic antagonists; as another example, the intramural program at the Addiction Research Center was expanded to include studies of the abuse potential of nonnarcotic drugs. These studies were undertaken in part to meet the responsibility of DHEW, under 1970 legislation, to advise the U.S. Attorney General on the control and classification of drugs having abuse potential.

In 1972, approximately $12 million went to grants, $5 million to research contracts, and $9 million to intramural research activities including those in Lexington, Ky.—a total of about $26 million for research on drug abuse.

The Drug Abuse Office and Treatment Act of 1972 mandated establishment of a National Institute on Drug Abuse within NIMH by the end of 1974.

Organization of the Alcohol Abuse Program

The National Center for Prevention and Control of Alcoholism, established in 1966, moved rapidly to stimulate research on alcoholism by supporting university-based centers for research and training, holding conferences to focus on the problem, and developing an intramural research program at St. Elizabeths Hospital, where the primary focus was on the addictive process. The expansion in research, and in training, service, and educational activities as well, resulted in part from support of such expansion at governmental levels higher than NIMH. In 1964, DHEW formed a Secretary's Committee on Alcoholism. In 1966, President Johnson called for increased Federal efforts to meet the problem of alcoholism. Later that year the establishment of the new center, to serve as a focal point for DHEW activities in the area of alcohol abuse, became a major step in the development of a Federal alcoholism program.

In 1970, the center was upgraded to the Division of Alcohol Abuse and Alcoholism. Then, by congressional action it was made an Institute within NIMH—the National Institute on Alcohol Abuse and Alcoholism, or NIAAA. The legislation underlying this development, signed into law in December 1970, was entitled the Comprehensive Alcohol Abuse and Alcoholism Prevention, Treatment, and Rehabilitation Act. This legislation also authorized a National Advisory Council on Alcohol Abuse and Alcoholism to make recommendations to the Secretary of HEW on policy relating to the Federal alcoholism programs and to recommend approval or disapproval of alcoholism grant applications.

Within NIAAA, four divisions were created—on research, prevention, State and community assistance programs, and special treatment and rehabilitation programs. Within the Division of Research there were two major units: the Laboratory of Alcohol Research, which took over the program conducted in the existing intramural laboratory, and the Extramural Research Branch, which plans, stimulates, and provides grant support for a comprehensive program of alcoholism research and for research training.

In 1972, NIAAA expanded its extramural support. In response to the President's Health Initiative Message of 1971, the Special Programs Division awarded 31 research-demonstration grants in high-priority areas. The regular alcoholism research grants program increased its emphasis on psychosocial research. Altogether, the NIAAA awarded 156 research grants that year, which totaled over $10 million. That same year, NIAAA's Office of Program Development and Evaluation began a research contracts program to support studies that could provide relatively prompt answers to specific research questions.

Organization for Research on Services

As noted earlier, the mental health project grants, or Title V, program—which had given impetus to services research—was eliminated as a single program in the 1966 reorganization. Between 1966 and 1970, most general services research was supported by the Applied Research Branch, DERP. (Services research projects that focused on specific problems were also supported by "funded centers" in other divisions.) The staff of the Applied Research Branch worked to improve the effectiveness both of individual projects and of the whole services research program. Program administrators began to monitor and evaluate projects and to show increased concern for the development of techniques to promote the diffusion and wide use of new research findings.

In 1971, projects in mental health services research, systems research, and research utilization totaling $6.5 million were transferred from the Applied Research Branch to the Mental Health Services Development Branch, which had been established in 1969 in the Division of Mental Health Service Programs. The transfer was made in order to bring the support of services research closer to the delivery of services and thereby enhance the application of results.

Since the transfer, considerable attention has been given to research on evaluation, particularly the development of techniques for measuring the effectiveness of service delivery and determining needs for change. This kind of research is being supported within a comprehensive plan to promote the use of new knowledge by individuals and agencies delivering mental health services. In 1972, the branch awarded about 90 grants, amounting to about $8 million, for research on services.

Services research and demonstration are a responsibility also of the Mental Health Study Center, which in 1972 had a budget of approximately $743,000. As noted earlier, this unit has experienced many changes in organization since 1948. Most recently, in 1968, it was transferred to the Division of Mental Health Service Programs when the Division of Field Investigations was dismantled. Shortly afterward, the center redirected its program. Instead of continuing to develop a model community mental health center, it began to emphasize research on problems of delivering services, such as crisis intervention, and of evaluating these services.

Research on the evaluation of services is also supported by the drug and alcohol programs and in the Office of Program Planning and Evaluation, which has responsibility for the overall NIMH evaluation program.

Intramural Research Program

The period of 1968-1972 was one of increasing constraints for the intramural program, as it was for the regular research grants program. Because cutbacks were sudden, laboratory chiefs had little chance to revise plans rationally. The most severe restrictions stemmed from loss of important personnel positions. The intramural program lost nearly 15 percent of its budgeted positions, not counting positions lost when the Addiction Research Center was transferred to the Division of Narcotic Addiction and Drug Abuse. As a result, long-range plans for the use of new facilities could not be fully implemented. The sharp reduction in the number of positions available for visiting scientists, staff fellows, and clinical associates correspondingly reduced the vitalizing flow of fresh ideas and viewpoints into the organization, and the permanent staff had to function with less support.

Because of inflation, the $16.3 million allotted the program in 1972 represented an actual decrease in money for operating costs. In the intramural director's office it was necessary to discontinue a special reserve fund for launching potentially important unbudgeted pilot investigations.

In 1969, the intramural laboratories on the Bethesda campus were regrouped into two divisions—the Division of Biological and Biochemical Research (DBBR) and the Division of Clinical and Behavioral Research (DCBR). There has been some apparent expansion in both of these divisions. In 1968, a Laboratory of Cerebral Metabolism was added to the DBBR, the Laboratory of Neurochemistry in that division was expanded, and a Laboratory of Clinical Psychobiology established in the DCBR. In 1971, after 13 years of planning, the Laboratory of Brain Evolution and Behavior was set up, under the DBBR, at the NIH farm in Poolesville, Md. However, in the main these changes were made—without expanding manpower—by elevating or bringing together already existing units and by making use of newly available space, planned for in years past.

Another new laboratory—Preclinical Pharmacology—began operating during this period within the Division of Special Mental Health Research, the non-Bethesda-based part of the intramural program. Two other new laboratories—one to study memory and the other to study human behavior—and a Clinical Evaluation and Follow-up Branch were established within the same division but for lack of resources did not go into operation.

Changes in 1973

A number of recent or proposed changes affecting the Institute are programmatic and budgetary in nature. The President's budget for fiscal year 1974 (and an amended budget for 1973) reflected major Administration policy decisions about NIMH programs. These decisions had been made as part of broad Administration efforts to control Federal spending and in accordance with the Administration's New Federalism concept, under which greater reliance for social services is to be placed upon State and local governments and the private sector and less upon the Federal Government.

The proposed 1974 budget would terminate support for NIMH training programs in the categorical research and services areas, and phase out support for projects authorized under the Community Mental Health Centers Act.

Research grant programs, except for drug abuse, have suffered sizable cuts in the amended 1973 and the 1974 budgets. In 1972, $63 million was spent on general mental health research grants. The amended 1973 budget included only $56 million for such grants, and the 1974 budget included $60 million. Alcoholism research grants were also cut in the amended 1973 and the 1974 budgets. However, funds for drug abuse grants were close to $19 million in the 1974 budget, compared to $12 million spent in fiscal year 1972.

At the time of this writing, public and congressional debate continues over specific programmatic and budgetary proposals of the Administration, some of which affect NIMH.

After a policy review of its programs, DHEW decided to realign its health structure by creating several new functionally aligned agencies out of the Health Services and Mental Health Administration. The reorganization, which became effective in July 1973, temporarily transferred the Institute to NIH while organizational issues affecting NIMH were further studied. These issues included the relationship of mental health to drug abuse and alcoholism, and the relationships among research, training, and services programs. It was decided to keep all NIMH functions and programs together for the present and to create a new health agency by redesignating the Institute as the Alcohol, Drug Abuse, and Mental Health Administration (ADAMHA). Under this new organization are the National Institute on Alcohol Abuse and Alcoholism, the National Institute on Drug Abuse (formerly the Division of Narcotic Addiction and Drug Abuse), and the National Institute of Mental Health. The reorganization, which became effective in September 1973, has not been worked out in detail.

These events occurred during the final phases of the Research Task Force, so no attempt has been made to analyze them. But they provide a sense of the rapidly changing bureaucratic environment in which NIMH—and ADAMHA—participates.

SUMMING UP

In the quarter century of its existence, NIMH has supported a vast enterprise in mental health research. Much of the money and leadership for the rapid expansion of knowledge in mental health sciences came from NIMH. Its growth has been accompanied by almost continuous organizational changes, as has been sketched in this chapter.

In its earliest years, most of the Institute's grants were channeled through one branch, which was advised by one scientific review committee. In 1972, the Institute had 11 components with authority for making grants and 17 initial review groups to review research grant applications and make recommendations.

Intramural research activities, which began with the transfer to NIMH of a single laboratory, the already established Addiction Research Center, had expanded by 1972 to six divisions.

The research budget grew from less than $1 million in 1948 to more than $112 million in 1972. However, despite increases in several areas, the general research budget has remained static in recent years while costs have risen.

References

Brand, J.L., and Sapir, P. (eds). An Historical Perspective on the National Institute of Mental Health, February 1964, mimeo.

Mental Health Challenges: Past and Future. Proceedings of a Conference on the Twenty-Fifth Anniversary of the National Mental Health Act, Washington, D.C., June 1971.

Williams, R.C. The United States Public Health Service 1798-1950. Washington, D.C.: Commissioned Officers Association of the U.S. Public Health Service, 1951.

CHAPTER 3

NIMH Support of Research Activities: An Overview

INTRODUCTION

This chapter presents mainly quantitative information about the research programs of the National Institute of Mental Health. The purpose is to provide a statistical overview of the Institute's research activities; qualitative descriptions and analyses of program content are presented in subsequent chapters dealing with major segments of the Institute's research programs.

In theory, it might be possible to describe the distribution of the NIMH research program in terms of many more variables than are applied here. The data that follow were selected not only because of their relative accessibility from existing information systems, but also because they were deemed most relevant to major issues addressed in this report. Information based on a classification scheme specially developed to describe the major substantive thrusts of the NIMH research activity is also presented. Fiscal year 1972 data serve as a base, with 1973 information presented when available and 1966 data occasionally included for comparison.

Also presented is information resulting from an attempt to survey the distribution of mental health research outside NIMH. The aim was to place the Institute's research program in the context of the overall national commitment to scientific activities in the mental health field.

THE NIMH RESEARCH PORTFOLIO: A STUDY IN DIVERSITY

During 1972, NIMH spent over $112 million to support research: $82.5 million (74 percent) in research grants; $10.2 million (9 percent) in research-related contracts; and $19.7 million (17 percent) in intramural research. Within that universe of scientific activity, there is an array of projects of enormous diversity—in approach, technique, subject matter, disciplinary orientation, and purpose. Included is work that spans the entire spectrum of the behavioral sciences, from concern with single-cell function to broad social theory: studies that address problems of the malfunctioning brain, the sick family, and the unstable society; research intended to shed light on the origins, diagnosis, and teatment of mental illness, and on the nature of social ills and their consequences.

What are the mechanisms by which human and animal subjects can learn to control cardiovascular functions? How do children develop logic and other conceptual skills? Do the brain functions of autistic children differ from those of normal or brain-damaged children? How does the central nervous system respond to alcohol? Does behavior therapy induce the same outcome whether practiced by a paraprofessional or a fully trained psychotherapist? What is the nature of the neural structures that react to neurochemical transmitters? Can systems analysis techniques be used to assess the costs and the benefits of treatment in a State psychiatric hospital? What accounts for differences in achievement measures among blacks and whites?

These questions are merely a sample of those posed by investigators whose work is currently supported by NIMH. They reflect a major characteristic of the NIMH research program—its heterogeneity. The Institute's broad range of effort, and the accompanying challenges for management, have been present from the very beginning. Studies in alcoholism, drug abuse, and suicide, for example, were represented, albeit in germinal form, in the NIMH program of the 1950's.

RESEARCH GRANTS PROGRAM

In 1972, funds devoted to extramural research programs totaled $82,484,176. This sum supported 1,497 investigations through grants recommended by the 17 research review committees of the Institute, and by the National Advisory Mental Health Council and the National Advisory Council on Alcohol Abuse and Alcoholism. (The grant review process is described in the chapter "An Organizational History of NIMH Research Programs"; the review committees—called Initial Review Groups—and the Institute's awarding units most closely associated with them are listed in the appendix to this chapter.)

Units Awarding Grants

Research grants are funded and monitored by 22 organizational units within the Institute. Table 1 provides a list of these units along with the number of projects and amounts of funds administered by each during 1972 and 1973.

Types of Grants

The bulk of NIMH research grants falls into the regular grant category—grants awarded to institutions on behalf of principal investigators who will direct a specific project that has been approved through the grant review process. Several other types of grants are made: small grants, limited to $5-6,000 and 1-year grant periods; special grants, involving a high degree of initiation, development, and continuing involvement by NIMH staff; conference grants for the purpose of exchanging and disseminating information relevant to NIMH programs; and program-project grants for large-scale, long-term support of broad, multidisciplinary research programs comprising several projects sharing a common focus. Figure 1 presents the 1972 distribution of NIMH research grants in terms of these types.

Amount of Awards

Figure 2 presents a frequency distribution of research grants in 1972 by amount of award. The average amount awarded was $55,100, the median $39,642. When small grant awards are excluded, the average rises to

Table 1
Number and Amount of Research Grant Awards In 1972 and 1973, By Awarding Unit
(Amounts in thousands, rounded)

Awarding Unit	1972				1973			
	No.	%	Amount	%	No.	%	Amount	%
Division of Extramural Research Programs								
Applied Research Branch	94	6	$ 7,272	9	86	6	$ 5,534	7
Juvenile Problems Section	55	4	4,166	5	51	4	3,251	4
Social Problems Section	39	3	3,106	4	35	3	2,283	3
Behavioral Sciences Research Branch	385	26	17,469	21	373	27	16,642	20
Experimental Psychology Section	128	9	4,912	5	123	9	4,351	5
Neuropsychology Section	107	7	5,838	7	101	7	5,486	7
Personality and Cognition Section	96	6	4,878	6	98	7	4,730	6
Social Sciences Section	54	4	1,841	2	51	4	2,075	3
Clinical Research Branch	121	8	8,489	10	138	10	8,309	10
Biological Research Section	40	3	2,613	3	56	4	3,310	4
Depression Section	24	2	2,403	3	22	2	1,452	3
Psychopathology and Clinical Methods Section	35	2	2,027	2	31	2	2,028	2
Psychotherapy and Behavioral Intervention Section	22	1	1,446	2	29	2	1,519	2
Center for Epidemiologic Studies	24	2	1,501	2	28	2	1,672	2
Psychopharmacology Research Branch	177	12	10,708	13	164	12	10,287	12
Clinical Studies Section	51	3	4,217	5	55	4	5,231	6
Pharmacology Section	123	8	6,194	8	109	8	5,056	6
Special Studies Section	3	<1	297	<1	—	—	—	—
Small Grants Section	192	13	1,171	1	126	9	804	1

Subtotal, Division of Extramural Research Programs	993	66	46,610	57	915	65	43,248	52
Division of Special Mental Health Programs								
Center for Studies of Crime and Delinquency	42	3	3,605	4	33	2	2,883	3
Center for Studies of Suicide Prevention	37	2	1,650	2	—	—	—	—
Center for Studies of Metropolitan Problems	31	2	2,111	3	30	2	1,658	2
Center for Minority Group Mental Health Programs	17	1	1,097	1	27	2	2,026	2
Subtotal, Division of Special Mental Health Programs	127	8	8,463	10	90	6	6,567	8
Division of Mental Health Service Programs								
Mental Health Services Development Branch	89	6	7,968	10	81	6	7,006	8
National Institute on Alcohol Abuse and Alcoholism	123	8	7,399	9	90	6	5,344	6
Division of Narcotic Addiction and Drug Abuse	165	11	12,044	15	223	16	20,770	25
Total	1,497	100	$82,484	100	1,399	100	$82,935	100

Figure 1
NIMH Research Grants Paid in 1972 by Type of Grant Program

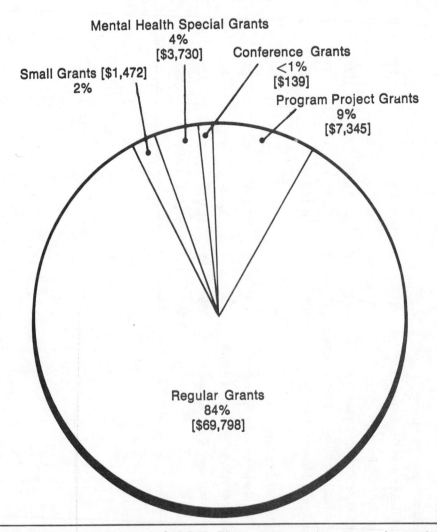

Amount—$82,484
(Amounts in thousands, rounded)

Mental Health Special Grants
4%
[$3,730]

Conference Grants
<1%
[$139]

Small Grants [$1,472]
2%

Program Project Grants
9%
[$7,345]

Regular Grants
84%
[$69,798]

$62,116 and the median to $45,746. The number and amount of awards annually since 1948 are presented in table 2, along with average (or mean) amounts for the period.

Geographic Distribution

Table 3 shows the distribution by State of the number and dollar amounts of research grants awarded in 1972. Institutions in heavily populated States—New York, California, Massachusetts, Pennsylvania, and Illinois—have received the largest number of research grants and the highest total awards.

32

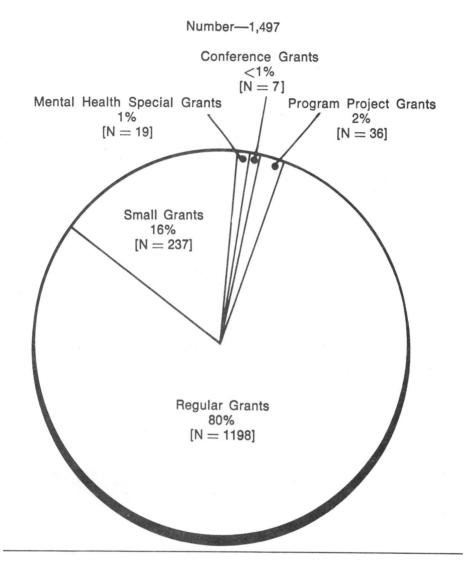

Figure 1(cont'd)
NIMH Research Grants Paid in 1972 by Type of Grant Program

Number—1,497

Conference Grants
<1%
[N = 7]

Mental Health Special Grants
1%
[N = 19]

Program Project Grants
2%
[N = 36]

Small Grants
16%
[N = 237]

Regular Grants
80%
[N = 1198]

New and Continuation Awards

An initial review group and the National Advisory Mental Health Council usually approve projects for more than 1 year of support. Typically, however, awards are actually made on a 1-year basis, with subsequent years of funding considered and approved by Institute staff; approved grants funded in this way beyond the first year are termed "noncompeting continuations." At the end of the grant period previously approved by the review group and council, the principal investigator may apply for a "competing renewal" grant—that is, a grant which permits a renewal of support for a project already underway; in such instances, the investiga-

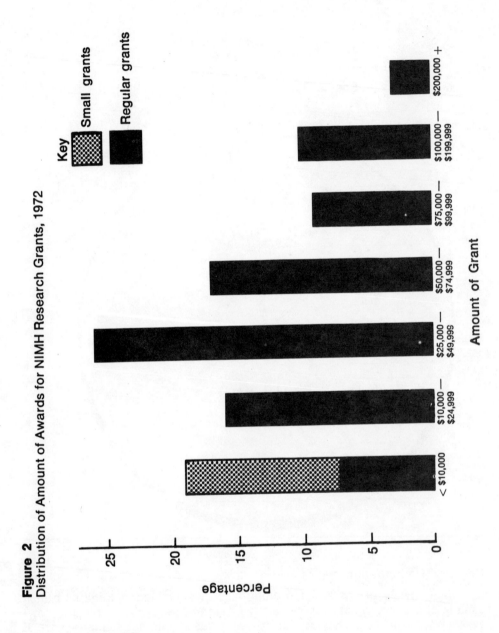

Figure 2
Distribution of Amount of Awards for NIMH Research Grants, 1972

34

Table 2
Number and Amount of NIMH Research Grants Awarded
and Mean Amount Per Year: 1948-1973

Fiscal Year	Number of Awards	Amount Awarded	Mean Award
1948	38	$ 373,221	$ 9,822
1949	45	578,695	12,860
1950	57	829,519	14,553
1951	99	1,249,024	12,616
1952	118	1,626,663	13,785
1953	118	1,698,049	14,390
1954	167	2,573,457	15,410
1955	206	3,609,166	17,520
1956 [a]	223	3,990,649	17,895
1957	440	7,326,311	16,651
1958 [b]	621	12,387,174	19,947
1959	826	17,091,297	20,692
1960	1,062	22,822,397	21,490
1961 [c]	1,286	30,492,081	23,711
1962	1,566	40,222,542	25,685
1963	1,793	49,811,007	27,781
1964	1,634	52,912,048	32,382
1965	1,632	57,227,040	35,066
1966	1,663	61,278,318	36,848
1967	1,546	61,975,811	40,088
1968	1,478	66,930,612	45,285
1969	1,505	73,008,507	48,511
1970	1,471	69,559,073	47,287
1971	1,432	73,956,861	51,646
1972	1,497	82,484,176	55,100
1973	1,399	82,935,436	59,282
Total	23,922	$878,949,134	$36,742

[a] Beginning of the small grant program
[b] Beginning of the Title V (mental health project grants) program
[c] Beginning of the program project and clinical research center program

tor's application for renewed support is reviewed once again by the appropriate review group and the council along with other applications, including those for the initiation of new projects. Since the typical project is approved for a period of only 2-3 years at a time, this process provides a vehicle for the reassessment of projects in progress. In addition to new awards, noncompeting continuations, and competing renewals, described above, investigators or staff may request a supplement to an amount awarded earlier, usually to provide funds for an unexpected contingency.

Table 4 presents the number and amounts of awards in the above categories for 1968 through 1973. The following features of research grant funding can be discerned from the data here and in figures 3 and 4.

Table 3
Number and Amount of Research Grant Awards in 1972, by State

State	No.	Amount	State	No.	Amount
California	241	$13,371,309	Iowa	11	$333,494
New York	227	15,496,226	Virginia	11	248,826
Massachusetts	116	8,214,449	Utah	9	294,094
Pennsylvania	93	5,283,687	Oklahoma	8	479,979
Illinois	75	3,407,590	Kentucky	7	309,938
Maryland	57	4,012,254	New Hampshire	7	265,074
Michigan	55	3,378,396	Rhode Island	7	224,452
Colorado	46	1,699,096	Arizona	7	216,684
New Jersey	45	3,275,841	Louisiana	6	330,027
Missouri	42	2,704,004	Vermont	6	228,378
North Carolina	42	1,981,974	Hawaii	5	232,473
Ohio	38	1,104,672	Alabama	5	141,046
Wisconsin	35	1,583,653	Mississippi	5	98,988
Connecticut	29	1,740,763	South Carolina	3	149,839
Indiana	28	1,303,534	New Mexico	3	85,729
Minnesota	26	1,656,926	North Dakota	3	75,235
Florida	26	1,160,035	Wyoming	3	56,413
Texas	26	966,856	Nebraska	2	54,959
D.C.	25	1,065,651	Arkansas	2	47,031
Kansas	25	848,451	Maine	2	27,912
Washington	19	724,656	West Virginia	2	13,289
Georgia	18	674,296	Puerto Rico	1	141,894
Tennessee	17	936,959	Nevada	1	39,312
Oregon	15	1,279,927	Idaho	1	7,552

Note: No research grant awards were made to institutions in Alaska, Delaware, Montana, and South Dakota in 1972. Fifteen awards were made to institutions in other countries.

- New grants have accounted for about one-third of the total number of grants awarded and for an average of one-fourth of all funds allocated for research grants in any given year. However, examination of new awards in the three major program areas of general mental health, alcoholism, and drug abuse reveals considerable differences. While all three areas show a decrease for 1973, new awards represented 48 percent of the total number of awards in drug abuse, as compared to 29 percent of the total number of awards in general mental health and 8 percent of the awards in alcoholism (figure 3). The same general pattern is evidenced for amount of funds (figure 4).

- Competing renewals account for approximately 10 percent of research awards and funds.

- For 1968 through 1973, noncompeting continuation awards consistently account for about half of all awards, and for close to two-thirds of all funds allocated. By program areas, these proportions vary inversely with those for new awards: The proportion of research grant

Table 4
Research Awards by Type of Award, 1968-1973
(Amounts in thousands, rounded)

	No.	%	Amount	%	No.	%	Amount	%
			1968				1969	
New Awards [a]	536	36	$15,709	23	597	40	$17,290	24
Competing Renewals	135	7	6,459	3	140	9	7,389	10
Noncompeting Renewals	710	48	43,083	64	682	45	47,028	64
Supplements	97	9	1,680	10	86	6	1,302	2
Total	1,478	100	$66,931	100	1,505	100	$73,009	100
			1970				1971	
New Awards [a]	570	39	$15,558	22	481	34	$14,755	20
Competing Renewals	129	9	7,025	10	150	10	9,400	13
Noncompeting Renewals	708	48	46,027	66	725	51	48,017	65
Supplements	64	4	949	1	76	5	1,785	2
Total	1,471	100	$69,559	100	1,432	100	$73,957	100
			1972				1973	
New Awards [a]	572	38	$23,063	28	432	31	$22,426	27
Competing Renewals	137	9	10,896	13	119	9	9,055	11
Noncompeting Renewals	707	47	46,901	57	731	52	48,558	59
Supplements	81	5	1,625	2	117	8	2,896	3
Total	1,497	100	$82,484	100	1,399	100	$82,935	100

[a] Includes small grants, which account for about 40% of the number of new awards annually, and about 8% of new award funds.

resources committed to ongoing projects increases as the proportion for new grants decreases.

Types of Institutions

Data on the types of institutions to which the awards were made are presented in table 5 for 1966 and 1972. Several significant points emerge:

- The greatest proportion of research grant awards and the greatest percentage of funds went to colleges and universities.
- Within the colleges and universities category, schools of arts and sciences received the greatest single share of the grants awarded.

Figure 3
Number of New Awards as Percentage of Total NIMH Research Programs, 1968-1973

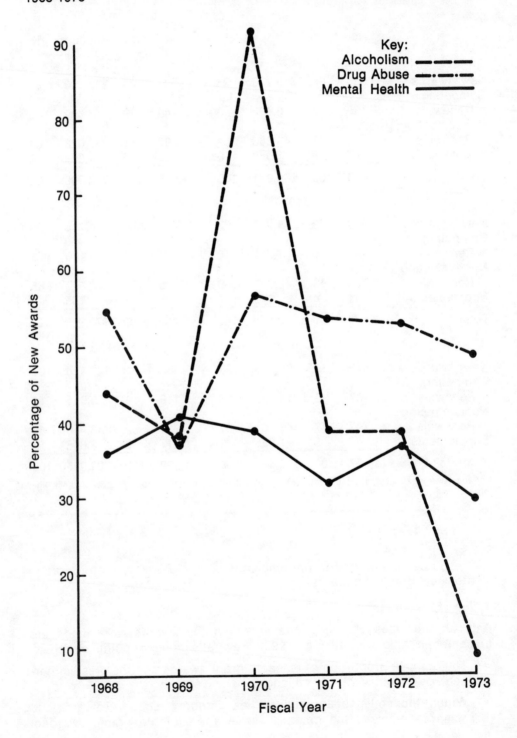

Figure 4
Amount of New Awards as Percentage of Total NIMH Research Programs, 1968-1973

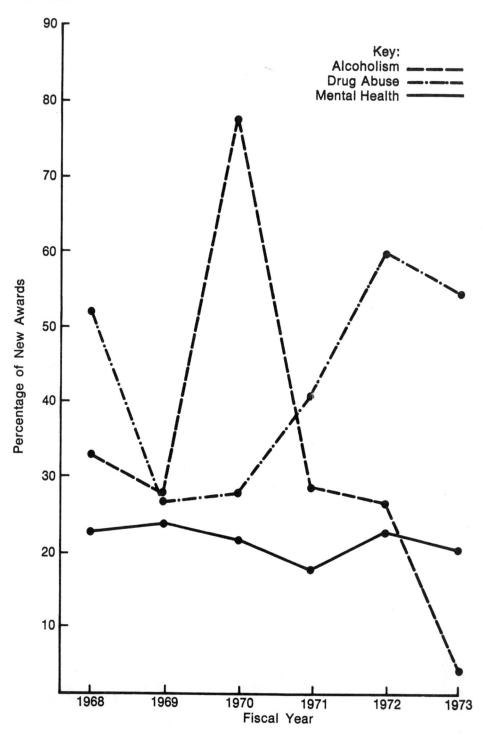

Table 5
Extramural Research Grants Awarded by Type of Sponsoring Institution
(Amounts in thousands, rounded)

	No.	%	1966 Amount	%	Mean Grant Award
Colleges and Universities	1,247	75	$ 39,163	64	$ 31,405
Schools of Arts and Sciences	701	42	16,427	27	23,433
Schools of Medicine	374	22	15,328	25	40,983
Other Schools and Components	172	10	7,408	12	43,069
Hospitals and Clinics	220	13	10,473	17	47,604
Independent Research Organizations	126	8	8,553	14	67,880
All Other Institutions [a]	70	4	3,089	5	44,128
Total	1,163	100	$ 61,278	100	$ 36,848

	No.	%	1972 Amount	%	Mean Grant Award
Colleges and Universities	1,192	80	$ 58,353	71	$ 48,953
Schools of Arts and Sciences	670	45	24,476	30	36,531
Schools of Medicine	358	24	22,839	28	63,796
Other Schools and Components	164	11	11,038	13	67,304
Hospitals and Clinics	151	10	12,639	15	83,701
Independent Research Organizations	109	7	8,754	11	80,311
All Other Institutions [a]	45	3	2,738	3	60,844
Total	1,497	100	$ 82,484	100	$ 55,100

[a] Includes schools, health and welfare departments, prisons, legal and court facilities, regional/interstate units.

Data for mean grant awards reveal, however, that these schools receive relatively low-cost grants in comparison to other institutions inside or outside the academic setting.

- Overall, although colleges and universities are the predominant recipients of NIMH research grant awards, their average award is considerably lower than that made to hospitals and clinics, or to independent research organizations, or to all other institutions.

Disciplines of Principal Investigators

The distribution of NIMH research grants and funds for 1966 and 1972, in terms of the academic disciplines of principal investigators, is portrayed in table 6. The data show that:

- Psychologists receive almost half of the Institute's resources for research. In 1972, 45 percent of research funds were awarded to investigators with degrees in psychology in contrast to 39 percent in 1966; at the same time, however, the number of grants awarded to psychologists decreased from 50 percent to 48 percent.

- The major portion of grants and funds awarded within the field of psychology are concentrated in three areas: clinical, experimental, and physiological/comparative.

- Psychiatrists comprise the second largest category of recipients of research awards and funds. However, although this group received 18 percent of the research grant funds in 1972, the proportion represents a decrease from 26 percent in 1966.

Content Overview

In terms of major programmatic as well as administrative foci, the research grant program of the Institute can be viewed within three broad areas: general mental health, alcoholism, and drug abuse. Of the total research grant funds awarded in 1972, 76 percent were in the "general mental health" category—that is, all funds awarded by units other than the National Institute on Alcohol Abuse and Alcoholism (NIAAA), and the Division of Narcotic Addiction and Drug Abuse (DNADA), now the National Institute on Drug Abuse. The proportions of total research grant funds in alcoholism and drug abuse were 9 percent and 15 percent in 1972. In 1973, the general mental health category was reduced to 69 percent and alcoholism to 6 percent, while the drug abuse proportion rose to 25 percent.

It is within these three major segments of the overall program that the distribution of research grants has been analyzed in terms of a number of content elements.

Classifying the Programs

The breadth and heterogeneity of the NIMH research program has, from the earliest program analysis efforts, posed problems for the meaningful classification and description of projects. Not only do Institute studies focus on a wide variety of mental health problems and behavioral phenomena, but a single project often involves several substantive emphases and multiple approaches to the same research question.

Table 6

Disciplines of Investigators Awarded NIMH Research Grants, 1966 and 1972
(Amounts in thousands, rounded)

Discipline	1966				1972			
	No.	%	Amount	%	No.	%	Amount	%
Psychology	835	50	$24,139	39	714	48	$37,177	45
Clinical	167	10	5,830	10	120	8	8,100	10
Developmental	65	4	2,517	4	51	3	2,755	3
Experimental	297	18	6,077	10	213	14	7,424	9
Physiological and Comparative	166	10	4,454	7	180	12	9,898	12
Psychometric	35	2	1,678	3	19	1	744	1
Social	70	4	2,239	4	79	5	5,007	6
Other [a]	35	2	1,344	2	52	3	3,250	4
Psychiatry	273	16	15,777	26	198	13	14,847	18
Other Medical Sciences [b]	138	8	5,266	9	192	13	10,773	13
Biological Sciences [c]	109	7	3,169	5	136	9	5,229	6
Social Sciences [d]	216	13	9,323	15	152	10	8,611	11
Other [e]	92	6	3,604	6	105	7	5,896	7
Total	1,663	100	$61,278	100	1,497	100	$82,484	100

[a] Includes general, counseling, educational, industrial, and personality psychology.
[b] Includes general practice, geriatrics, internal medicine, neurology, obstetrics and gynecology, pathology, pediatrics, pharmacology, preventive medicine, surgery.
[c] Includes anatomy, biology, biochemistry, embryology, genetics, neuropsychology, physiology, zoology.
[d] Includes anthropology, epidemiology, social work, sociology.
[e] Includes chemistry, ecology, education, engineering, history, language, law, library science, mathematics and biostatistics, nursing, physics, public health, speech therapy.

Consider, for example, an actual project incorporating the study of brain rhythms, electrophysiological responses of the skin, and clinical behavior both of mentally normal adults and of manic and schizophrenic patients treated either with lithium or placebo. The results of this study clearly may not only carry implications for treatment but also may improve our understanding of both the causes and diagnosis of mental illness. This example is cited to emphasize a fact sometimes overlooked when classification schemes are attempted: It is in the nature of science that the results and the implications of research cannot be foreseen at the inception of a project.

In spite of the difficulties, and in order to provide a broad overview of the content of the NIMH research program, a mutually exclusive codification scheme was developed. The codes were designed to account, in an additive way, for the entire $112 million awarded in 1972—1,497 research grants, 110 research-related contracts, and over 300 intramural projects. For purposes of the framework, a classification scheme was based on the most immediate goal or objective of each project. Five broad categories of objectives were used:

1. Diagnosis, description, epidemiology: The development of diagnostic or classification tools, epidemiological studies, and phenomenological studies intended to describe a particular behavioral phenomenon.

2. Causes and prevention: Studies designed primarily to provide an understanding of the etiology of mental illness, behavior disorders, and social problems, and of their prevention or control. Research in this area was further subdivided into two major categories:

a. Basic processes research: Studies of basic processes related to mental health that address the functioning of systems per se.

b. Problem-oriented research: Research aimed at understanding processes underlying particular psychiatric illnesses or specific mental health problems.

   In the alcohol and drug research programs, the criteria for classifying projects as "basic processes research" were modified to render the classification more analogous to that for the NIMH program as a whole. In a sense, the very fact that an investigator is studying the properties of ethanol or marihuana suggests a problem-oriented approach; however, in order to reflect more accurately the level of the research, studies focusing on the effects of alcohol or a drug of abuse on a biological or behavioral process were considered basic processes research, while investigations focusing specifically on a clinical population of alcoholics or drug abusers were regarded within the problem-oriented research category.

3. Amelioration: Studies of techniques of treatment, rehabilitation, or remediation.

4. Service delivery: Research addressing problems in the most efficient and economical delivery of therapeutic techniques to those in need of them. (Although closely related to the amelioration goal, the service delivery goal involves notions of production, systems, and organizational arrangements not included in the amelioration category.)

5. Dissemination: Research dealing with the process of communicating and utilizing research. (Relatively few research projects supported by NIMH address this as a major goal; most of the Institute's activities in the area are funded through direct operations budgets, including, for example, conferences, publications, and seminars.)

Summaries of all extramural research projects were reviewed and assigned to one of the five major goals described above. The resulting relative distribution of research resources for 1972 in the general mental health, alcohol, and drug programs is presented in table 7.

Table 7
NIMH Extramural Research Grants, 1972
(Amounts in thousands, rounded)

	General Mental Health		NIAAA		DNADA		Total	
	Amount	%	Amount	%	Amount	%	Amount	%
Diagnosis	$ 6,542	10	$ 331	4	$ 1,184	10	$ 8,057	10
Causes and Prevention (Total)	35,658	57	5,785	78	9,347	78	50,791	62
Basic Processes	22,070	35	1,054	14	4,985	41	28,109	34
Problem Oriented	13,558	22	4,732	64	4,362	36	22,682	27
Amelioration	12,420	20	1,162	16	1,353	11	14,935	18
Service Delivery	6,976	11	64	1	74	1	7,114	9
Dissemination	1,445	2	56	1	86	1	1,587	2
Total	$63,041	100	$7,399	100	$12.044	100	$82,484	100

Program Distribution

In the general mental health area (i.e., not alocholism or drug abuse) 35 percent of funds, or $22 million, were awarded for studies of basic processes research. This body of fundamental research is distributed among three major areas:

1. Biological processes—52 percent of basic processes research, including, for example, studies of the neurophysiological bases of behavior, endocrine studies, sleep, genetics, biochemistry, and mechanisms of drug action.
2. Psychological processes—34 percent of basic processes research, including studies of learning, conditioning, perception, cognition, personality, language, and communication.
3. Sociocultural processes—14 percent of basic processes research, including studies of the structure and dynamics of family and social groups, attitudes, values, interests, cross-cultural studies, and investigations of group behavior.

The remaining 65 percent, or $41 million, of general mental health research grant funds, as illustrated in figure 5, was distributed among studies focusing primarily on specific problems of mental health and mental illness. The studies encompassed all of the objectives described earlier—that is, diagnosis, causes and prevention, amelioration, service delivery, and dissemination.

Forty-three percent of the $41 million for specific mental health problems was devoted to investigations of the major psychiatric disorders: schizophrenia, depression, neurosis, psychosomatic and character disorders, and other diagnostic categories. About 11 percent of the funds for problem-focused research went into studies of learning and communication problems, including studies of hyperkinesis, dyslexia, stuttering, retardation, and school learning problems. The proportion devoted to research on mental health aspects of social problems was 19 percent, including studies of juvenile delinquency, crime, violence, poverty, and more general

Figure 5
Problem Areas Studied in Research Grants Program, 1972 [a]

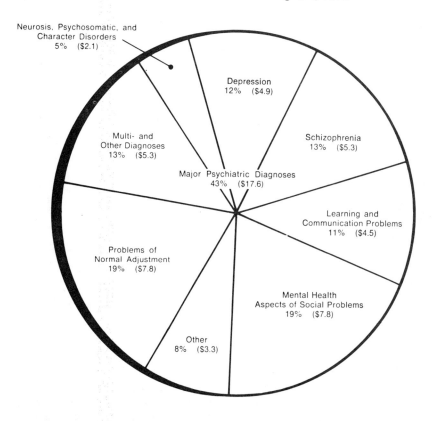

* Represents $41 million, or 65 percent of general mental health grant funds, i.e., all but basic processes research.

societal problems such as police-community relations, protest behavior, and problems related to urban living. Nineteen percent of the funds were used primarily for research on problems of normal adjustment; included here are a broad range of concerns not always definable by a diagnostic label but nonetheless involving dysfunction—for example, individual developmental and situational problems associated with adoption, adjustment to school and college, marital discord, aging, and bereavement.

RESEARCH-RELATED CONTRACTS

No formal research contract program per se exists within the Institute. Contracts require the specification of a service to be performed or an end product to be developed, and are used by program staff when appropriate in conjunction with the customary grant mechanism. In 1972, a total of $10 million was awarded for 110 contracts involving research activities. Table 8 shows how the research contract funds were distributed over the general mental health, alcohol, and drug programs, in terms of major research objectives.

Table 8
NIMH Research-Related Contracts, 1972
(Amounts in thousands, rounded)

	General Mental Health		NIAAA		DNADA		Total	
	Amount	%	Amount	%	Amount	%	Amount	%
Diagnosis	$ 538	19	$ 991	56	$ 818	15	$ 2,347	23
Causes and Prevention (Total)	709	25	253	15	1,865	33	2,827	28
Basic Processes	257	9	47	3	541	10	845	8
Problem Oriented	452	16	206	12	1,324	23	1,982	20
Amelioration	35	1	23	1	2,565	46	2,623	26
Service Delivery	1,226	43	266	15	50	1	1,542	15
Dissemination	343	12	225	13	284	5	853	8
Total	$2,851	100	$1,758	100	$5,582	100	$10,192	100

Included in general mental health are contracts let not only by the Division of Extramural Research Programs, the Division of Special Mental Health Programs, and the Division of Mental Health Service Programs but also by the Office of Program Planning and Evaluation; indeed, the Institute's evaluation program centered in OPPE is carried out exclusively through contracts. Projects under contract range from research support activities to literature reviews, preparation of handbooks, field testing of epidemiological instruments, updating of diagnostic inventories, and a variety of surveys.

Contracting is used in the field of drug abuse primarily for chemical analyses and for testing, producing, and analyzing experimental drugs, including narcotic antagonists. Other contracts are for the controlled production of cannabis and the synthesis of psychoactive materials. In addition, contracts are supported to evaluate treatment programs, to carry out information campaigns or surveys, and to sponsor conferences on important issues in the field.

The majority of research-related contracts supported in the area of alcoholism deal with the evaluation and monitoring of treatment programs. Technical studies are also included: for example, the feasibility of developing chemical agents for rapid detoxification, and the development of statistical data on alcohol-related deaths.

INTRAMURAL RESEARCH PROGRAMS

With a 1972 budget of $19,687,000—about 17 percent of all research expenditures—scientists supported directly by NIMH are actively engaged in both laboratory and clinical research spanning the entire range of the Institute's areas of concern. The largest of the several intramural components is the Mental Health Intramural Research Program. This effort is described below, followed by a discussion of the work of other Institute components responsible for the direct conduct of research.

Mental Health Intramural Research Program

Purposes and Operating Principles

The Mental Health Intramural Research Program was developed to provide talented scientists with the facilities and the working climate to conduct comprehensive, long-term, interdisciplinary research on the causes, treatment, and prevention of mental disorders and on the biological and psychosocial factors that determine human behavior and development. Unlike the extramural research grant program, which allots funds for particular projects, MHIRP supports specific investigators. These scientists conduct clinical, biological, and behavioral research on problems judged by them to be both important and ripe for fruitful attack. While the individual intramural investigator's work is subject to general scientific supervision by the laboratory or branch chief, each scientist has, within given personnel and budgetary limits, a large degree of freedom to chart his own scientific course. Projects are typically reviewed by laboratory and section chiefs for their scientific merit and overall relevance to the unit's activities. Programs are reviewed by the Board of Scientific Counselors, which ordinarily meets twice a year to discuss research issues pertinent to the various laboratories and branches. Informal as well as formal relationships among MHIRP scientists (and others) have led to many types of collaborative ventures that transcend section, laboratory, and, on occasion, Institute boundaries.

Table 9
Mental Health Intramural Research Program

	Budget		Personnel, 1973	
	1972	1973	Permanent Employees	Other Than Permanent
Mental Health Intramural Research Program	$ 720,000	$ 486,000	25	6
Office of the Director	442,000	193,000	13	6
Technical Development	278,000	293,000	12	—
Division of Clinical and Behaviorial Research	5,074,000	5,417,000	180	70
Office of the Director	490,000	145,000	8	—
Social Work	179,000	202,000	9	—
Adult Psychiatry	810,000	883,000	33	—
Child Research	407,000	381,000	21	—
Clinical Science	1,225,000	1,465,000	41	—
Clinical Psychobiology	291,000	226,000	7	—
Psychology	994,000	992,000	39	—
Socio-environmental Studies	678,000	853,000	22	—
Division of Biological and Biochemical Research	2,614,000	2,790,000	96	25
Office of the Director	71,000	63,000	2	—
Neurobiology	275,000	271,000	9	—
General and Comparative Biochemistry	495,000	558,000	20	—
Neurochemistry	454,000	458,000	15	—
Neurophysiology	401,000	477,000	16	—
Cerebral Metabolism	461,000	498,000	18	—
Brain Evolution and Behavior	457,000	465,000	16	—

Division of Special Mental Health Research	2,275,000	2,334,000	77	22
Office of the Director	367,000	372,000	17	—
Neurochemistry	—	148,000	6	—
Neuropharmacology	552,000	516,000	16	—
Clinical Psychopharmacology	731,000	749,000	23	—
Preclinical Pharmacology	621,000	549,000	15	—
Human Behavior	4,000	—	—	—
Direct Operations Total	10,683,000	11,027,000	—	—
NIH Management Fund	5,650,000	5,799,000	—	—
Total	$16,333,000	$16,826,000	378	123

Organization

Operating in laboratories at the National Institutes of Health and St. Elizabeths Hospital, and in a special facility at Poolesville, Md., MHIRP had a 1972 budget of $16.3 million, $5.6 million of which was paid to the NIH Management Fund to cover overhead and facilities maintenance. The program has three divisions divided into 18 working laboratories and branches. A breakdown of funds and personnel by division and laboratory is presented in table 9.

About 175 (or 46 percent) of the permanent staff positions are held by M.D. or Ph.D. professionals. The total includes 30 to 40 positions per year devoted to the NIH Associate Program, in which young clinicians and research associates join the staff for 2 years of service and training in their fields of interest.

Content Overview

At any one time about 300 research projects are underway throughout the intramural program. Since these projects are pursued within the overall budgetary allocation for each laboratory or branch, it is difficult to ascribe exact dollar figures to them. For purposes of classifying MHIRP research within the framework described earlier, laboratory and branch chiefs provided their best estimates of the relative emphases most applicable to the array of research within their units. Dollar figures were based on each laboratory's budget for 1972 and its proportionate share of the NIH Management Fund and other overhead costs. The interdisciplinary nature of the program and the constant interface between clinical and basic research made the classification by objectives even more difficult and forced than in the extramural categorization process. Within the causes and prevention category, the subclassification into basic process or problem-oriented research proved arbitrary and unrealistic. Thus, it is not included in the summary table. Data for MHIRP as a whole are presented in table 10 (which includes similar breakdowns for the other intramural components discussed below).

Of the research conducted in MHIRP, 81 percent is concerned primarily with increasing the understanding of processes that directly or indirectly underlie human behavior; in terms of the program analysis framework utilized, this body of work relates most closely to the objective of improving our knowledge of the causes and prevention of mental health problems. Within this broad category, the approach taken is predominantly—about 70 percent—in the biological-biochemical domain. These studies focus on the structure and functioning of virtually all aspects of the nervous system, and draw upon both animal models and clinical populations. A substantial portion of the biological studies also include psychosocial observations, and attempts are continuously made to integrate findings in a way that enhances our understanding of how biological, psychological, and social factors work together to influence behavior. Predominantly psychological approaches are taken in about 25 percent of the studies in the causes and prevention category. These include developmental studies and investigations of sensation, perception, and learning, and projects on sleep and

Table 10
NIMH Intramural Research Programs, 1972
(Amounts in thousands, rounded)

	Mental Health Intramural Research Program		ARC [a] Lexington		Other Intramural [b]		Total	
	Amount	%	Amount	%	Amount	%	Amount	%
Diagnosis	$ 49	<1	$ —	—	$ —	—	$ 49	<1
Causes and Prevention	13,272	81	1,416	80	908	57	15,596	79
Amelioration	3,012	18	355	20	425	27	3,792	19
Service Delivery	—	—	—	—	250	16	250	1
Dissemination	—	—	—	—	—	—	—	—
Total	$16,333	100	$1,771	100	$1,583	100	$19,687	100

[a] Addiction Research Center
[b] Includes intramural activities of NIAAA, Mental Health Study Center, and Overholser Division of Research and Training at St. Elizabeths Hospital.

arousal. The remaining 5 percent of the research in the causes and prevention category is primarily sociocultural in approach.

The bulk of the remaining research is in the category primarily emphasizing the amelioration objective. As in causes and prevention, the approach is most often biological and focuses on clinical and preclinical psychopharmacological investigations. Again, the integration between biological and psychosocial approaches is characteristic.

The research emphases of MHIRP differ from those of the extramural program in two ways: first, MHIRP has virtually no service delivery research; second, though MHIRP is concerned with all the other mental health problems represented in the extramural grants program, it concentrates most heavily on work related to the standard psychiatric diagnoses, with particular emphasis on schizophrenia, depression, and drug abuse.

Other Intramural Research

The National Institute on Drug Abuse maintains research operations at its facilities in Lexington, Ky., where the Addiction Research Center (1972 budget, $1,771,000) conducts studies focusing on the pharmacology, physiology, and neurology of drug dependence. Investigations also focus on the behavioral and subjective effects of a variety of drug substances. For purposes of the overview classification, ARC funds were assigned primarily (80 percent) to the causes and prevention category, and secondarily (20 percent) to the amelioration category.

Two additional research activities are located at St. Elizabeths Hospital, but they are not administratively part of the Mental Health Intramural Research Program. The National Institute on Alcohol Abuse and Alcoholism maintains an alcohol research ward at St. Elizabeths Hospital; studies there focus on biological and psychological factors in intoxication and withdrawal. Expenditures of the NIAAA unit were about $350,000 in 1972. The Overholser Division of Training and Research at St. Elizabeths focuses on psychological and cultural aspects of normal and criminal behavior; the division had a 1972 budget of approximately $500,000. The Mental Health Study Center, a unit of the Division of Mental Health Service Programs, conducts research and development on problems in service organization and delivery. The center has been long established at Adelphi, Md., in suburban Prince George's County. The 1972 budget for the Mental Health Study Center was $733,000.

SUMMARY TABLE

Table 11 provides an integration of content overview data dealing with the research grant, research contract, and intramural research programs described individually above.

Table 11
NIMH Grants, Research-Related Contracts, and Intramural Research, 1972
(Amounts in thousands, rounded)

	Total Research Grants		Total Contracts		Total Intramural		Total NIMH	
	Amount	%	Amount	%	Amount	%	Amount	%
Diagnosis	$ 8,057	10	$ 2,347	23	$ 49	1	$ 10,453	9
Causes and Prevention	50,791	62	2,827	28	15,596	79	69,214	62
Amelioration	14,935	18	2,623	26	3,792	19	21,350	19
Service Delivery	7,114	9	1,542	15	250	1	8,906	8
Dissemination	1,587	2	853	8	—	—	2,440	2
Total	$82,484	100	$10,192	100	$19,687	100	$112,363	100

MENTAL HEALTH RESEARCH IN OTHER AGENCIES

How do the Institute's research programs relate to other mental health research efforts?

The efforts of the Task Force to gather data with which to answer this important question led to an unequivocal conclusion: No useful procedures exist through which valid estimates of total national resources devoted to mental health research could be developed. Problems of definition are legion; one agency's research is another's service or demonstration program, or another's methods or system development program. For these reasons, the staff of the Task Force was frustrated in its repeated attempts to identify research programs relevant to the Institute's own research activity. The importance of describing the NIMH role in the context of the entire Federal research effort, however, led to two approaches to the issue: a broad examination of the areas of research in which other agencies are engaged, and an identification of the fields of science they support. While neither yields a firm or complete picture, both provide useful general indexes.

Program Content

The Smithsonian Science Information Exchange (SSIE) provides a central collection of research project summaries that are indexed by professional staff members. Projects funded by both public and private sources are included. Experienced research analysts at SSIE and NIMH together reviewed the SSIE data bank for projects of mental health relevance. Several important limitations of the SSIE data, however, should be made clear: The entry of projects into the SSIE system by agencies sponsoring research is not mandatory, and reporting practices vary from agency to agency; in addition, not all projects listed by SSIE are accompanied by dollar values.

Table 12, then, is based only on extramural projects listed in the SSIE files for which funding data were also available. Since there is no way to estimate reliably their dollar value, projects listed without funds are not included; substantial volumes of projects without financial data are, however, noted in the comments portion of the table. The comments section also includes information about programs of other agencies gathered through a survey.

To illustrate the need for care in evaluating the SSIE data, consider the results when a search in a specific area—alcoholism—was pursued. The total funds reported were $16,431,471; of this, NIMH research represented 41 percent ($6,692,433). However, examination of the data revealed that 51 percent of the total was contributed by nine Office of Economic Opportunity (OEO) projects, totaling $8,402,098. Summaries of these projects show them to be large-scale service-demonstration efforts, with minimal research emphasis. When the OEO funds are removed from the total, NIMH research efforts account for 83 percent of the whole.

Fields of Science Supported

A second approach to examining the commonalities of NIMH research programs and those of other agencies was to examine the fields of science in which such agencies support research. The National Science Foundation (NSF) maintains relevant data on a national basis and publishes them annually in "Federal Funds for Research, Development, and Other Scientific Activities." Table 13 shows the fields of science supported by NIMH and provides comparable data from NSF for other Federal agencies. Again, the data are useful only for a general picture of where NIMH stands vis-a-vis other agencies; for reasons cited, the statistics cannot be considered an entirely valid indicator of distribution of effort.

Table 12
1971 Extramural Projects Identified by the Smithsonian Science Information Exchange, as Relevant to NIMH Research
(Amounts in thousands, rounded)

	No.	Amount	Total 1971 Extramural Budget	Comments
National Institute of Mental Health	1,267	$73,669	$73,957	Note the close correspondence with internal NIMH figures for 1971.
National Institutes of Health (Total)	573	44,554	671,000 [a]	
National Institute of Child Health and Human Development	228	19,372	46,900	Program interests cover all human development, including population studies, pregnancy and birth, infant mortality; most pertinent to NIMH are studies in mental retardation, behavioral, cognitive, and social development, and social and intellectual aspects of aging.
National Institute of Neurological Diseases and Strokes	185	9,495	53,700	Program interests focus on neurological problems, epilepsy, cerebrovascular and muscular disorders; most pertinent to NIMH are studies of neural aspects of learning and behavior, and normal nervous system function.
National Heart and Lung Institute	25	2,794	109,800	Program interests cover cardiovascular and lung problems; most pertinent to NIMH are studies of behavioral aspects of hypertension.
National Institute of General Medical Sciences	16	2,537	77,800	Program interests center on noncategorical health research, such as biomedical technology and clinical studies of trauma, surgery, anesthesiology; most per-

54

Agency	No.	Amount	Amount	Description
National Eye Institute	51	1,970	19,200	tinent to NIMH are studies on genetics, endocrine functioning, and chemical correlates of memory. Program interests focus on visual disorders; most pertinent to NIMH are visual perception studies and pyschophysiological investigations.
National Institutes of Health (Other)	68	8,386	364,200	
Maternal and Child Health Service	23	2,156	5,735 [b]	Research program centers on applied studies aimed at improving the health of children and mothers; pertinence to NIMH research is in general developmental area. MCHS is now a component of the Health Resources Administration.
National Center for Health Services Research and Development	21	1,933	47,000 [c]	Research program focuses on health services organization, delivery, and financing, consumer education, and data systems; relevance to NIMH derives from the extent to which general health delivery studies provide models for delivery of mental health services. NCHSR &D is now a component of the Health Services Administration.
Office of Education	24	8,052	61,262 [d]	SSIE reports an additional 760 projects, without dollar values. Research focuses on the full range of educational issues, including curriculum development and testing and innovations. Most pertinent to NIMH are projects on learning disabilities. Many OE research efforts have been transferred to the National Institute of Education.
Social and Rehabilitation Service	114	7,752	31,764 [d]	Research and development activities cover all aspects of welfare and social services: administration, service

Table 12 (Continued)
1971 Extramural Projects Identified by the Smithsonian Science Information Exchange, as Relevant to NIMH Research
(Amounts in thousands, rounded)

	No.	Amount	Total 1971 Extramural Budget	Comments
Department of Defense	84	$ 5,161	$763,213 [d]	development and evaluation, quality and standards. Most pertinent to NIMH are projects on the special service needs of children, the aged, and other special groups.
USAF	17	1,318	530,377 [e]	SSIE information underestimates DOD research, since classified projects are not included. DOD research activities emphasize military technology, but some fundamental biological, and behavioral research is included. Also, there has been recent focus on drug addiction and rehabilitation studies.
USA	26	1,489	115,502 [d]	
USN	41	2,354	117,334 [d]	
Office of Economic Opportunity	46	21,366	57,187 [d]	Large-scale demonstration and evaluation programs in poverty typify research here. Studies of delivering health services to the poor are most pertinent to NIMH.
Department of Justice	16	1,096	6,033 [d]	In the Justice Department's Law Enforcement Assistance Administration, research and demonstration projects center on the reduction of crime; alleviating conditions which promote crime; intervening in criminal careers; etc. Most pertinent to NIMH are studies of the characteristics of juvenile and adult offenders, of release and probation techniques, and of drug abuse prevention. Research in the Bureau of Narcotics and Dangerous Drugs is also of relevance to NIMH.

Agency	No. of Projects			Notes
National Science Foundation	531	$13,405	$60,750 f	NSF supports a complete range of scientific endeavor in their psychology programs. The Division of Social Sciences and the Division of Biological and Medical Sciences support fundamental studies that are pertinent to NIMH research. Some projects in the international program (e.g., genetic studies of primitive populations) also are relevant to NIMH activities.
Division of Social Sciences	354	9,122	17,390	
Division of Biological and Medical Sciences	177	4,283	43,360	
Veterans Administration	—	$ —	$ —	The VA's research program is almost exclusively intramural; 5,283 research projects were conducted in VA installations in 1971. The SSIE search identified 980 studies as related to NIMH research. Projects in psychiatry, psychology, social work, and endocrine functioning are most pertinent to NIMH.
Private Nonprofit	240	20,308	—	Over 80 private nonprofit organizations supported at least one project identified as mental health related. An additional 44 projects were listed without dollar values.
State Governments	28	1,255	—	Additionally, SSIE includes 346 State government projects but has no information about costs. The National Association for Mental Health has begun and hopes to expand a project to assess State-supported mental health research more accurately.

a Source: National Institutes of Health Basic Data 1972, p. 28.
b Source: DHEW Publication No. HSM 72-5002, p. 30.
c Source: NCHSR&D Focus, p. 8.
d Source: Federal Funds for Research Development and Other Scientific Activities (NSF publication 72-317, v. XXI), Table C-10.
e Total for USAF, USA, and USN only; does not include $235,294,000 and departmentwide defense agency expenditures.
f Total for individual project support in the Division of Social Sciences and Division of Biological & Medical Sciences only; does not include $113,810,000 of individual project support in other scientific fields. Source: National Science Foundation Annual Report, 1971 (NSF publication 72-1), p. 6-7.

Table 13
Fields of Study Supported by NIMH and Other Federal Agencies, 1971
(Amounts in thousands, rounded)

Field of Study	NIMH Amount	Percent of NIMH	Comparable National Data Amount	Percentage of Total Supported by Selected Agencies						
				NIMH	NIH	Other HEW	DOD	NSF	VA	Other Federal Agencies
Psychology	$ 29,535	33	$ 115,667 [a]	25	9	19	27	8	4	8
Biological Sciences	14,385	16	845,486 [b]	2	36	3	4	7	2	46
Sociology	5,811	7	104,650 [c]	5	—	20	1	3	1	70
Anthropology	1,085	1	11,660 [c]	9	—	22	4	34	—	31
Other Social Sciences	3,336	4	189,340 [c]	2	3	42	2	10	—	41
Other Fields	35,057 [d]	39	827,837 [a]	4	68	6	8	1	4	9
Psychiatry	18,232	20	—	—	—	—	—	—	—	—
Other Medical Sciences	9,679	11								
All Other Fields	7,146	8								
Total	$89,209	100	$2,094,640	—	—	—	—	—	—	—

Note: NIMH figures include clinical medical sciences, other medical sciences, and other life sciences. Does not include fields irrelevant to NIMH.
[a] Source: Federal Funds for Research, Development, and Other Scientific Activities, Vol. XXI, ibid, Table C-17.
[b] Source: Ibid, Table C-20.
[c] Source: Ibid, Table C-27; "Other Social Sciences" includes economics, history, linguistics, political science, and unclassified social sciences. (NSF pub. 72-317), Table C-20.
[d] NSF does not support separate data on psychiatry, but includes it in a broad clinical medical category; thus, NIMH support for psychiatry, other medical sciences, and all other fields of study are combined here for rough comparison with national support for broadly comparable fields.

Initial Review Group	Most Closely Associated Awarding Unit
Juvenile Problems	Juvenile Problems Section Applied Research Branch
Social Problems	Social Problems Section Applied Research Branch
Experimental Psychology	Experimental Psychology Section Behavioral Sciences Research Branch
Neuropsychology	Neuropsychology Section Behavioral Sciences Research Branch
Personality and Cognition	Personality and Cognition Section Behavioral Sciences Research Branch
Social Sciences	Social Sciences Section Behavioral Sciences Research Branch
Clinical Projects	Clinical Research Branch
Clinical Program Projects	Clinical Research Branch
Epidemiologic Studies	Center for Epidemiologic Studies
Clinical Psychopharmacology	Psychopharmacology Research Branch
Preclinical Psychopharmacology	Psychopharmacology Research Branch
Mental Health Small Grant	Small Grants Section, Office of the Director, Division of Extramural Research Programs
Mental Health Services	Mental Health Services Development Branch
Crime and Delinquency	Center for Studies of Crime and Delinquency
Metropolitan Mental Health Problems	Center for Studies of Metropolitan Problems
Narcotic Addiction and Drug Abuse	Center for Studies of Narcotic and Drug Abuse
Alcohol and Alcohol Problems	National Institute on Alcohol Abuse and Alcoholism

CHAPTER 4

Basic Research: I. Advances in Knowledge of the Biological Processes Underlying Behavior

This chapter begins the account of progress in mental health research since the founding of the Institute. Here and in the two chapters immediately following, discoveries in three broad scientific areas—biology, psychology, and sociology and related disciplines will be summarized. Upon the advances of basic research research in these areas depend in large part our expectation for solutions to mental health problems.

These chapters on basic research do not pretend to be encyclopedic. They aim simply to note a number of the major accomplishments, to show by example how separate threads of scientific inquiry converge to produce essential advances, and to identify where, in the opinion of expert reviewers, the future challenges lie. This chapter on biological research, for instance, opens with highlights of the work—in which hundreds of investigators representing half a dozen scientific disciplines participated over a long period—that has dispelled a critical part of the mystery surrounding depression, one of the most serious and prevalent of mental illnesses. As the account illustrates, landmark discoveries in mental health often rest on the progress of many investigators working in many fields. The pathway to a discovery and its practical use can be traced in retrospect but rarely can be laid out in advance. Succeeding chapters describe advances in the psychological and sociocultural sciences. Other chapters then summarize our better understanding of mental illness today and our vastly more effective ways of dealing with it. Except for the fruits of basic research, those accounts could not have been written.

A CASE STUDY: THE PSYCHOBIOLOGY OF DEPRESSION

Twenty-five years ago, our understanding of the causes of mental illness was vague and speculative. During the preceding 50 years, however, research had supplied considerable information essential to improving that understanding—information about the organization and functioning of the central nervous system. Only in this century has it been recognized that the central nervous system is made up of billions of individual nerve cells or neurons that connect with one another across tiny spaces called synapses. Until these synapses were described by anatomists, classical dogma held that the nervous system was a syncytium—one continuous network much like the blood vessels of the circulatory system.

The knowledge that there were gaps and spaces between the individual elements of the nervous system posed an important question for neuroscientists, namely, how it is that messages get transmitted from one neuron to another. Twenty-five years ago, there was considerable discussion as to the nature of nervous transmission: did nerve cells communicate by transmitting electrical or chemical signals? Research employing electrical recording techniques with capability for resolving the activity of individual nerve cells was needed to resolve the issue. Even before such techniques could be applied, however, it was necessary to overcome the seemingly monumental obstacle of "unraveling" and isolating for investigation the fragile neurons that are intertwined with such labyrinthine complexity. Scientists approached this problem of accessibility of nervous tissue by studying simpler organisms like the squid, whose "giant" nerve cells have permitted neurophysiologists to stimulate and record from individual neurons that could be directly visualized. Other approaches were to study the peripheral nervous system with its clusters of neurons, like the sympathetic ganglia that lie alongside the spinal cord and brain proper. Still other lines of inquiry concentrated on the neuromuscular junction, since the way in which nerves excite muscle turns out to be very similar to the way in which neurons excite each other. Through these and a variety of other approaches, it became clear that the transmission of information in the nervous system is achieved through the release of chemical substances—called neurotransmitters—at nerve terminals. The chemical enters the synaptic space and changes the permeability of the next cell's membrane. This change produces an electrical impulse that leads to the release of a neurotransmitter at the next synapse, starting the process all over again. In this fashion, electrical messages are propagated for long distances along thousands of brain cells without loss of signal. Instead of causing cells to fire, the chemical message may heighten their readiness to fire or may inhibit them from firing. Man's actions and behavior, his emotional state, and his thinking are regulated through the sum total of activity at the synapse.

At the same time that neurophysiologists and neuroanatomists in many laboratories were piecing together this information on the nervous system, other scientists, chiefly chemists and biochemists, were developing concepts and methods for analyzing the metabolism of chemical substances in the organs and tissues of the body. These methods and concepts were to provide the foundation for understanding the biochemistry of the brain and for a revolutionary improvement in our knowledge of the major psychoses.

The next major problem was to identify the chemicals released at the nerve endings and to map their location in the central nervous system; here, the NIMH Laboratory of Clinical Science has had an outstanding role. As a notable example, one scientist, who later received a Nobel Prize, found that certain nerves transmit their messages to the muscle fibers of the heart by releasing norepinephrine at their terminals. This is a biogenic amine classified chemically as a catecholamine. It is the precursor of epinephrine, more familiarly known as adrenaline, the hormone that helps the body respond to stress. Other investigators later found that norepinephrine is the transmitting agent throughout most of the sympathetic nervous system, which permeates virtually every tissue of the body. And strong evidence now has accumulated that it is present as a neurotransmitter in the central nervous system.

NIMH laboratories made another crucial advance. In order for the synapse to be cleared after one message so that it can be ready for the next one, the transmitter substance must be removed. In the case of norepinephrine, Institute scientists have shown that this is done primarily by rapid reuptake into the terminal of the transmitting nerve. There, some of the norepinephrine is destroyed by an enzyme, monoamineoxidase (MAO); the rest of it is stored in protective granules for further use.

To arrive at and elaborate upon these significant discoveries, scientists have used several principal methods. Delicate chemical analyses enable them to detect and measure the compounds present in a given portion of an animal's brain under given conditions. Radioactive tracer techniques enable them to study what happens when radioactively tagged samples of substances under investigation are injected into experimental animals. Histochemical fluorescence, introduced by Swedish investigators in the early 1960's, enables them to actually see cells carrying certain compounds because under fluorescent light these glow in different shades. These are only a few examples of the sophisticated methodologies being used and developed in NIMH-supported laboratories and elsewhere for study of the brain's chemistry.

Action of Antidepressants

The discovery of new facts about the brain's communication system coincided with the discovery that drugs found to be chemically effective in treating depressions fell into two classes. These are the monoamine oxidase inhibitors, such as phenelzine, and the so-called tricyclic antidepressants, of which imipramine is the best known. The MAO inhibitors were derived from a compound, iproniazid, that had been developed in 1951 to combat the tubercule bacillus. It proved to be a powerful antituberculosis drug but also to have unexpected side effects, including euphoria and hyperactivity, which led some psychiatrists to try it as a tranquilizer and others, later, as an antidepressant, which it proved to be. Clinical tests of imipramine were made in the early 1950's because of the hopeful reports on chlorpromazine, a closely related drug, as an agent against schizophrenia. Imipramine was found to be effective not against schizophrenia but depression.

Researchers at NIMH and elsewhere discovered that both types of drug have a common effect on the brain: they facilitate the action of norepinephrine as a transmitter at the synapse. The MAO inhibitors accomplish this by checking the enzyme that normally destroys norepinephrine. The tricyclic antidepressants accomplish it by blocking the reuptake of norepinephrine into the nerve terminals.

Before the discovery of the antidepressant drugs, the only effective treatment for severe depression was electroconvulsive shock. However, the effect of electroconvulsive shock on neuronal function was not understood. Now it has been found, in the laboratory of an Institute-supported investigator, that such treatment increases the rate at which the brain synthesizes norepinephrine. Thus, superficially disparate therapies such as electroshock and drugs turn out to have a common outcome because they have a common effect on the norepinephrine supply.

A different line of evidence comes from research with the major tranquilizer, reserpine. This drug induces behavioral depression in certain types of patients. The effect of reserpine on norepinephrine has now been found to be opposite from that of the treatments that make depressed patients better. It has been found to deplete the supply of norepenephrine by releasing the neurotransmitter from its protective granules in the neuron and laying it open to destruction by the MAO enzyme.

Another strand of the story comes from still another direction. An investigator supported by an NIMH grant was studying the psychological factors that could produce lesions in the stomachs of rats. To control for the strength of the electric shocks that he used as a stress, he wired electrodes on the tails of pairs of animals in series so that each partner received exactly the same shock. One animal of each pair, however, had some control over the situation: by making a certain response, it could turn the shock off. The other was helpless. The rat that could do something about this stressful situation, it turned out, had far fewer lesions in its stomach than the helpless partner.

The condition of being helpless to do anything about a misfortune, like the loss of a loved one, is known to produce a temporary "situational depression," with clinical symptoms similar to those of the psychotic depression. Knowledge of this fact, coupled with an awareness of the norepinephrine-deficiency hypothesis for depression, led the investigator and his collaborators to the discovery that the level of norepinephrine in the brains of the helpless rats was much lower than that in the brains of those who could do something about the situation.

Convergence of Disciplines

Such advances in our understanding of the depressive illnesses depended on the synthesis of concepts and techniques from a wide range of scientific disciplines—physiology, psychology, chemistry, anatomy, and pharmacology. The research was facilitated also by the interest in psychoactive drugs aroused when chlorpromazine was used successfully to treat schizophrenia—a story that will be touched upon in the chapter on NIMH's basic research activities. From the diversity of basic research, coupled with clinical science when the time was ripe, many lines of inquiry—including work on the heart and the stomach as well as on the brain—have converged to enlarge our understanding of the nature of and treatment for a major and pervasive mental illness.

Despite impressive progress in this field, in the Institute's laboratories and in other laboratories around the world, much remains to be learned. For example, the antidepressant drugs generally do not provide relief of symptoms until several weeks after treatment starts, and the reason for this delayed effectiveness is not yet completely understood. Further, norepinephrine is just one neurotransmitter. The neurotransmitters released in the great majority—close to 90 percent—of the brain's synapses have yet to be identified. The effects of hormones and their cyclic variations on the release and synthesis of transmitters remain to be worked out. Two substances closely related to norepinephrine—dopamine and serotonin—are affected by some of the same psychoactive drugs and may also be involved in depression. And the relationship between mania, on the one hand, and depression on the other, and the issue of whether they are chemically similar or opposite conditions still need to be resolved. Further, experiential factors enter into the effectiveness of drug treatment in mental disorder. NIMH-supported investigators have shown that the effectiveness of drugs can be potentiated when patients are also receiving appropriate psychosocial treatment.

The study of these variables and their interactions is a challenge for future research. A better understanding of how the brain works and how the environment impinges on brain processes should provide a firmer foundation for understanding normal behavior and for the more effective use of drugs and other treatments in the prevention and cure of mental illness.

The rest of this chapter reports upon other major developments in brain research during the past quarter century. Though treated in less detail than the accomplishments cited above, to which a number of them contributed, some of these are likely to prove of even greater importance.

GENETIC INFLUENCES ON THE BRAIN AND BEHAVIOR

A wealth of evidence has accumulated during the past two decades showing that genes play an important role in the regulation of normal and abnormal behavior. As a result, a new interdisciplinary field has emerged—behavioral genetics. It assumes that human variability is attributable to both genetic and environmental sources. Research has shown that a wide range of abilities, personality traits, and perceptual processes are under some degree of genetic control. More recent investigations have found the same to be true for a variety of behavioral disorders, headed by schizophrenia and including the depressive psychoses, developmental dyslexia or reading disability, alcoholism, and some forms of mental retardation. This section presents recent evidence on the genetic factor in the psychoses and reports advances in explaining the mechanisms by which genetic factors affect behavior in some forms of mental retardation and of certain abnormal behavior in animals. Findings on biochemical processes that may be under genetic control in schizophrenia and depression are presented in other sections.

Heritability of Schizophrenia and Depression

By studying pairs of identical and nonidentical twins in which one twin became schizophrenic, researchers in the U.S., Norway, England, and Denmark—some supported by NIMH—have garnered ample evidence that heredity plays an important, though not exclusive, role in determining susceptibility to schizophrenic breakdown. This finding has been confirmed and advanced by investigations of schizophrenics and their families carried out since the early 1960's, notably by intramural and other NIMH-supported scientists. The adoptive parents of children who later became schizophrenic, it was found, had no higher incidence of schizophrenia than the adoptive parents of normal children. However, the biological parents of adopted children who later became schizophrenic did have a high rate of schizophrenia themselves. Schizophrenic parents also had more schizophrenic children, even when these were raised by normal adoptive parents.

Among the questions still to be answered are what the inherited susceptibility to schizophrenia consists of, what triggers the actual breakdown, how various kinds of schizophrenia may differ biologically, and why, if one identical twin has schizophrenia, the likelihood that the other twin will become schizophrenic runs from 25 to 40 percent, and not 100 percent. One likely answer to the last question has been offered by a study of identical twins, conducted by Institute scientists. The schizophrenic twin weighed less at birth, the investigators found, was perceived by his parents as vulnerable, was always the focus of more worry and attention than his cotwin, and had difficulty in achieving any degree of autonomy and separateness. This persistent pattern resulted in part from what the investigators call "rigidly imprinted role expectation, initiated at birth, determined by the constitutional differences and subsequently reinforced by minor differences in development." (In several cases it was the larger twin who became schizophrenic, but in each case this twin had undergone accident or illness in earlier childhood and had become the weaker of the pair.) To the twin who became schizophrenic, the world always appeared more threatening, and its stresses mounted as he grew into adolescence and early adulthood.

Early results from an Institute-funded longitudinal study of the children of schizophrenic mothers fit in with the findings of the intramural group. A clear correlation is shown between the development of schizophrenia and the kind of pregnancy and birth difficulties that might have caused damage to the patient's central nervous system either before or during birth. Where there is a genetic predisposition to schizophrenia, such prenatal and perinatal damage may trigger the disease.

In the case of manic-depressive psychosis, the concordance rate in identical twins has been found to be higher than in schizophrenics, ranging from 50 to 100 percent. In fraternal twins it runs as high as 40 percent. Among first-degree relatives of manic-depressives, the incidence of this psychosis ranges from 8 to 11 percent; in the general population it has been estimated at 0.7 percent. Other studies indicate that in at least some cases a susceptibility to manic-depressive psychosis is transmitted from mother to son and that it is linked to the loci for red-green color blindness on the X-chromosome. Adoption studies have not been completed.

Heredity in Some Forms of Mental Retardation

Genes transmit heredity's message through alterations in enzymes or other proteins. What these alterations are in the case of an inherited susceptibility to schizophrenia or manic-depressive psychosis remains to be learned, though research has suggested they may involve the production or control of neurotransmitters in the brain. In the case of certain types of mental retardation, however, research has shown not only the heritability of the conditions but also the nature of the biochemical defect inherited. Such work is among the outstanding achievements in recent decades of brain and behavior research.

The most notable example is phenylketonuria (PKU), a rare condition afflicting one out of every 20,000 newborns, in whom, if untreated, it produces severe mental retardation and other defects. PKU results from the body's inability to convert the amino acid phenylalanine to tyrosine, and this inability results from the lack of a single enzyme, whose production is controlled by a single gene. Major contributions to understanding the biochemical defect in PKU have been made by investigators in the NIMH intramural program.

In the early 1950's researchers reported the first instances of successful treatment, with a diet low in phenylalanine. The diet had to be started as soon as possible after birth, however, because the PKU baby, though born mentally normal, lost about 5 IQ points for every 10 weeks that the treatment was delayed. With a urine test, used originally, the condition could not be diagnosed until the infant was several weeks old, but development of a blood test in 1960 made it possible to detect the disease soon after birth. With this test and the special diet, thousands of children have been spared phenylketonuria's grave symptoms.

About 85 other genetic diseases of metabolism, each with an enzyme defect, have been identified. For reasons that are not clear, almost half of the known genetic abnormalities involving an enzyme defect lead to central nervous system damage and mental retardation. Perhaps the developing brain is exquisitely sensitive to alterations in the normal steady-state levels of amino acids.

As studies of such diseases have progressed, it has become apparent that heritability is far from synonymous with incurability. On the contrary, knowledge about hereditary susceptibility to various kinds of mental—and other—disorders can lead to precise forms of intervention and to effective prevention or treatment. In many genetic diseases, the organism tolerates a deficiency of more than 90 percent of the affected enzyme, so therapy that reaches the modest goal of restoring even a small proportion of normal activity can prove extremely valuable.

Other types of mental retardation involve chromosomal abnormalities—for example, mongolism or Down's syndrome, also called trisomy-21 because of the extra chromosome found in its victims. And some chromosomal abnormalities that do not produce severe retardation are associated with maladaptive behavior; for instance, the XYY condition has been associated with aggressive and violent behavior in some male prisoners and in some mentally retarded patients. The techniques and methods available for the study of such chromosomal anomalies have been developed only within the past few years. Current studies of how such anomalies are caused have produced some evidence that infectious agents of various kinds may be responsible.

Investigations in Laboratory Animals

Studies of behavioral genetics in man have been complemented significantly by experimental investigations in laboratory animals. One widely used approach involves the production and comparison of inbred strains. Investigators using this methodology have described strain, and hence genetic, differences in learning ability, activity levels, sexual behavior, aggressive behavior, sensitivity to the effects of alcohol, and other factors. Similar results have been obtained through selective breeding.

Another powerful approach to the analysis of genetic determinants of behavior is the study of mutations. Investigators have found conditions in laboratory animals, many of them involving locomotor dysfunction, caused by mutations of a single gene.

After the behavioral effects of genetypic differences have been identified, the search turns toward uncovering the mechanisms responsible for the behavior. One line of research, supported in part by NIMH, has investigated strains of mice subject to abnormal behavior that, like some types of abnormal behavior in human beings, is triggered by stress. In this case the abnormal behavior is epileptic-like convulsions, and the stress that induces them is sound—the ringing of a bell. Extensive research has shown that mice susceptible to these audiogenic seizures have remarkably low brain levels of two of the neurotransmitters, norepinephrine and serotonin.

Another important development is the discovery of the nature and genesis of inherited cerebral defects in a variety of Bar Harbor mice strains. In a number of these mutants, it appears that a single gene mutation affects critical early interactions of neurons and, therefore, the structural organization of the cerebral cortex and cerebellum.

Analysis of how genetic information is translated into the specific structures of the nervous system in animals provides a basis for understanding genetic anomalies and genetically influenced behavioral traits in man, and may open the way to either treatment or prevention.

BIOLOGICAL BASIS OF BRAIN DEVELOPMENT

How the Brain Develops

Because the embryo is almost inaccessible to some forms of study, researchers who have tried to enlarge our understanding of the normal or abnormal development of the brain have generally concentrated on the postnatal period. However, the thalidomide episode—in which a drug taken during pregnancy led to malformation of the offspring—underlined that the embryo, rather than being completely sheltered in the uterus, is extraordinarily vulnerable. Further research in this field has shown that such vulnerability is highly specific as to time and place.

In the formation of the nervous system, a sequence of precisely timed events occurs, such that the consequences of harmful effects on the embryonic nervous system vary widely according to the phase of development involved. The basic sequence includes cell divisions, cell migrations, cell differentiation, cell death—presumably to modulate cell number—and synaptogenesis, or the formation of nerve cell interconnections. It occurs at different times in different parts of the nervous system. In each region of the brain there is a critical period for each of the sequential events of development.

Research on imprinting has illustrated the interplay of the genetically determined imprinting mechanism and the environmental condition that enables the action to be expressed. For example, the mechanism makes newborn ducklings follow the most prominent object they see, whether this be the mother duck or the researcher. When the environmental condition fails to occur at the proper time—for example, if the duckling sees nothing or nobody during the crucial hours—imprinting does not take place, even though the proper stimulus is presented later. This work eventually led to a Nobel Prize.

Researchers, a number of them supported by NIMH, have amassed considerable evidence that early experience can modify many other basic inherited components of behavior. Frequent handling early in life, for instance, will make genetically aggressive mice more docile. Monkeys reared without normal peer relationships become socially and sexually abnormal. Following extreme sensory deprivation, or after environmental enrichment in the early postnatal period, the brains of experimental animals reveal significant changes in the dendritic branching of their nerve cells and in the density of dendritic spines in their cerebral cortex. In rats that had lived in an enriched environment, providing both the need and the opportunity for exercising the brain, as well as the body, the cortex grew larger in relation to both the rest of the brain and to the cortex of impoverished rats. These rats demonstrated an enhanced problem-solving ability.

Just as noxious chemicals or viruses can do especially severe harm to an embryo, while leaving adults unharmed, the lack of certain necessary food substances such as protein can also be most devastating early in life. The developing nervous system appears to be exceptionally sensitive to early and severe malnutrition. Recent studies have shown an irreversible reduction in the number of brain cells in the brains of mice that had been malnourished during the prenatal and neonatal periods, when cell division is at a peak. The earlier the malnutrition occurs, and the longer it lasts, the greater the permanent deficit. Both anatomical effects (brain weight at birth, cell number, cell size, myelin formation) and biochemical effects (changes in RNA and DNA—ribonucleic acid and deoxyribonucleic acid—proteins, and activity of enzymes and neurotransmitters) have been documented. These changes are accompanied by apathy, exaggerated reactions to frightening situations, and impaired learning.

Recently the vulnerability of different regions of the brain has been studied as a function of the time at which each region matures. However, very little is yet known about such timetables or about the genetic program according to which certain genes may be turned off or on at different times in development.

Hormonal Effects on Nervous System Development

Foremost among the internal factors believed to play an important role in regulating the development of the nervous system are the hormones. Research in the 1950's demonstrated that the female offspring of guinea pigs subjected to treatment with the male hormone during sensitive periods of development will be less likely to show typical female sexual responses and more likely to show male-typical behavior when treated with appropriate hormones at maturity. Other work showed that in the absence of exposure to the male hormone, subsequent behavior in the adult male animal is female in character. These and other studies, including some in man, suggest that early interaction between hormones and neurons somehow determines how the brain develops in order to produce characteristic adult behavior.

Our information about the hormonal control of motivated behavior has numerous gaps, including a lack of specification of (1) what the active chemical may be—the hormone itself or some metabolite and, if metabolite, which one; (2) how cellular function is changed by hormonal action; and (3) what areas of the brain are involved. Further, the field of behavioral endocrinology has been dominated thus far by interest in gonadal hormones and sexual behavior. But gonadal hormones also influence nonsexual behaviors, and other hormones, such as the thyroid and glucocorticoid, are equally important in the development of behavior. Thyroid hormone, for example, affects numerous aspects of neuronal maturation, including postnatal cell formation, protein synthesis, cell size, cell number, packing density of neurons, dendritic morphology, synaptogenesis, and electrical activity. Some of these findings were developed in NIMH's intramural laboratories. Substances like cortisol and thyroxin, which can be used to change the rate of certain aspects of neuronal development, may have enormous potential for the experimental analysis of relationships between structure and function.

Neural Plasticity

Studies concerned with the effects of stimulation and of stimulus deprivation on the developing organism are all concerned in one way or another with the plasticity of the nervous system as it relates to information processing. Another kind of plasticity that characterizes the developing organism is its remarkable capacity for recovery of function following brain injury. For example, in the mature animal the prefrontal cortex is necessary for spatial-mnemonic abilities, the precentral cortex for voluntary motor activity, the inferotemporal cortex for visual discrimination. Removal of these cortical regions in the adult results in corresponding deficits in these functions. However, if the removals are made in the immature animal these functions are spared to varying degrees. Also, as discussed later, a certain type of brain injury in human beings has more serious effects when it occurs in adulthood than in infancy.

One of the most exciting new leads in the quest for an understanding of the mechanisms involved in recovery has been the discovery of collateral sprouting. Neural structures deprived of their normal input because of damage to axons with which they would normally be connected, have been shown to acquire new contacts from undamaged axons in the vicinity. (Axons are the long nerve fibers that carry a neuron's electrical impulse to the synaptic gap linking it to another neuron.) These remaining normal axons sprout collaterals much as a plant might sprout new branches, and these collaterals appear to occupy the sites formerly occupied by the injured axons. It is imperative now to determine if these new synaptic junctions are functional and if they can mediate behavior. Recent research with newborn rats and hamsters suggests that the answers may be affirmative. Findings in this area could have major implications for facilitating recovery of function following brain injury of all sorts, from asphyxia at birth to atherosclerosis in the elderly.

Regeneration of Neurons

Collateral sprouting refers to the capacity of uninjured neurons to develop new collaterals. What about the capacity of injured neurons to regenerate? The belief through most of this century has been that while the spinal cord of fishes and amphibians could be reconstituted after surgical transection, that of reptiles, birds, and mammals could not. Experiments in the last 25 years, however, have challenged this view. Evidence now indicates that certain neurons of the mammalian central nervous system and spinal cord are indeed capable of regenerating their severed processes. But effective contacts are aborted by certain unfavorable conditions, such as formation of scar tissue. Further research should help to reveal the factors limiting effective regeneration.

PHYSIOLOGY AND CHEMISTRY OF BRAIN CELLS

As noted earlier, the human brain is composed of some 10 billion neurons—electrically active cells linked through junctions, or synapses, which are formed at the contact points between the receptive surfaces of one cell and the transmitting surfaces of other cells. The brain also has glia cells, ten times as many as neurons, which are electrically inactive. Their function is almost completely unknown, but presumably, important.

Studies over the period under review have produced important fundamental knowledge about the neurons. The work has shown, for example, that neurons are specialized by location, shape, and cellular metabolism and by the population of other nerve cells with which they can directly communicate. They are specialized also for the synthesis and secretion of transmitting molecules—neurotransmitters—capable of affecting the behavior of cells with which synapses are formed.

Researchers recently have been placing new emphasis on the study of cell membranes. Each membrane has certain "recognition sites" to which the axons of specific neurons are drawn. These sites may hold the answer to what Bernard Katz, Nobel Laureate, has called one of the most challenging questions in biology: "What are the guiding forces that cause the axons of developing or regenerating nerve cells to grow, to travel long distances to their specific terminal stations, and among millions of cells, to make contact with only a selected few?" A technique has now been developed to isolate pure membranes in order to analyze their components and determine their function, but this area of research is still in its earliest stages.

Each neuron also has receptors for specific hormones and neurotransmitters. These receptors, too, have become a focus of study. The first demonstration that an abnormality in a receptor can lead to a specific disease was recently made in the case of the insulin receptor in the obese hyperglycemic mouse. It is a relatively safe prediction that some human diseases will be shown to be caused by defects in receptor structure and function.

By analyzing the structure of brain cells at the highest possible level of resolution, examining their chemical composition, and detecting their function, which differs according to their location, much other basic information essential to the continued unraveling of the operations of the brain has been produced during the period under study.

MECHANISM OF ACTION OF THERAPEUTIC DRUGS

A number of independent lines of investigation have converged upon the functions in the brain of norepinephrine and dopamine, members of the chemical family of catecholamines, and of serotonin, an indoleamine. As noted earlier in this chapter, there is strong evidence that norepinephrine is a neurotransmitter in certain portions of the brain, and treatments for depressive psychosis appear to have a common biochemical effect: by one means or another they facilitate the action of norepinephrine at the synapses. Dopamine and serotonin, among other compounds, have also been identified as putative neurotransmitters. Dopamine is the precursor of norepinephrine.

Dopamine and Schizophrenia

When chlorpromazine was introduced in 1952 for the treatment of schizophrenia, little was known about the drug's action besides its clinical usefulness. It appeared to have simply a calming effect. But soon studies sponsored by the Institute and the Veterans Administration showed that chlorpromazine and other phenothiazines appeared to act not merely on symptoms of schizophrenia but on biochemical mechanisms involved in that disorder.

Meanwhile, another line of research was turning up information about what seemed an entirely related condition, Parkinsonism or Parkinson's disease. It was found that the corpus striatum, a brain region which regulates body movements, normally has a very high level of dopamine. The brains of patients with Parkinson's disease, however, had markedly diminished levels of dopamine in this region. Dopamine itself could not be used to treat these patients because it does not cross the blood-brain barrier. But its precursor, L-dopa, does cross the barrier, and its use frequently produced dramatic improvement.

At the same time, physicians were noting that schizophrenics who received large doses of the phenothiazines often developed tremors that closely resembled the symptoms of Parkinsonism. Studies of the effects of these drugs upon dopamine turnover in the brain made it seem very likely that the phenothiazines were acting upon synapses that contained dopamine, lowering the level of that neurotransmitter. Biochemically, schizophrenia thus appeared to be a sort of reverse Parkinson's disease.

Further evidence came from studies of amphetamine psychosis, a condition nearly indistinguishable from paranoid schizophrenia. There is evidence that this psychosis may be induced by the action of amphetamine at certain synapses. The drug causes more dopamine to be released by some cells and also blocks cellular efforts to take it up again.

Thus arose the hypothesis that, in the treatment and perhaps the prevention of schizophrenia, dopamine is the agent that must be blocked. This remains a promising lead even though all antischizophrenic compounds are now known to block the action of both dopamine and norepinephrine to varying degrees.

Three Generations of Psychopharmacology

During the first generation of psychopharmacology, roughly the 1950's, psychotropic drugs appeared in large numbers. Clinicians throughout Europe and the U.S. essentially founded the field by dint of adventurous, courageous, and lucky explorations of drug influences upon psychiatric patients. Most of their studies were informal, uncontrolled, and seemingly without solid rationale.

The past decade has seen a second generation of development, during which researchers have been concerned with developing techniques to monitor precisely the therapeutic action of drugs and to study the physiological and psychological processes that they affect. This work might be called the beginning of truly scientific clinical psychopharmacology. The drugs are now seen to exert their effect through some sort of interaction with synaptic mechanisms in particular brain structures.

There is hope that a third generation will witness new drugs developed according to rational principles based on more nearly complete information about synaptic dynamics. The study of body fluids, an important area of research today, may lead to methods of classifying different subtypes of mental disorders according to specific biochemical criteria. If so, it may become possible to predict accurately which subtype will respond to which form of psychopharmacological treatment.

Recent developments in this area include a gas liquid chromatographic method for determining a breakdown product of norepinephrine, a chemical called 3-methoxy-4-hydroxyphenylethylene glycol (MHPG), in blood, urine, and cerebrospinal fluid. Previous research was slowed by the fact that the blood-brain barrier works both ways, not only preventing most body substances from entering the brain but also preventing brain substances from entering the body unaltered, thus interfering with convenient study of these substances. Because of the new technique, however, it is now known that in dogs, MHPG in the urine represents the major metabolite of brain norepinephrine; in manic-depressive patients the urinary excretion of MHPG has been shown to vary with changes in their affective state.

Such studies may provide ways of discriminating among the many different types of depressive disorders, and they may lead to the development of specific and rapidly acting drugs with sustained antidepressant effects.

BRAIN CORRELATES OF LEARNING AND MEMORY

It has been recognized at least since the time of Plato that learning and memory must have a structural basis; that, in order for an experience to influence subsequent behavior, the experience must induce some enduring change within the organism. But until recently there were almost no clues as to the nature of that change. Now the clues are both electrophysiological and chemical, and over the past decade they have spurred a remarkable expansion of interest in the search for neural events underlying learning and memory.

Researchers who concentrate on the electrophysiological aspects of memory have generally worked with the simplest possible systems—for example, with small groups of giant cells of the sea slug nervous system. Among other subjects, the investigators have been concerned with habituation, which has been called the simplest form of learning; it is the process by which organisms stop responding to stimuli that are not important to them. If, as many scientists believe, the brain is completely prewired, how do cells learn to stop responding? How do they know the stimuli are unimportant? Recent work suggests that habituation results in part from the activity of interneurons, which are neurons that intervene between sensory and motor neurons. When a stimulus repeatedly appears uninteresting or harmless, there is a decrease in the efficacy of the synapses between these interneurons and the motor neurons that drive the actual muscles involved. Habituation is further discussed in the chapter on the psychological processes underlying behavior.

Much other work of the past decade has concentrated on neurochemical aspects of memory and learning. One level of research has established that the presence or absence of synaptic transmitters in brain tissue can affect the behavior of the intact organism. Evidence from other studies suggests that the converse may also be true, that the concentration of such transmitters in brain tissue is higher in animals that have learned a response than in animals that have not. While much is left to be desired in the methods used in some of these studies, the results do encourage the hypothesis that specified levels of neural transmitters may have behavioral correlates.

In another line of research, investigators have been trying to elucidate the neurochemical basis of memory by finding out how to block it. The work is done with animals that have learned to make a certain response. Of particular significance is the recent finding that antibiotics, like puromycin and acetoxycyclohexamide, which are known to interfere with the synthesis of protein, interfere with memory also. For example, Institute-supported researchers have found that when puromycin is injected into the brains of mice that have been trained to take a particular turn in a maze, the animals forget the appropriate responses and must be retrained. Perhaps what has been blocked is the assembling of amino acids into a "memory protein'; at any rate, the blocking occurs only when the dose of antibiotic is large enough to vastly reduce the normal rate of protein synthesis. It is not yet certain, however, whether what has been blocked is the storage of information, or its retrieval. Research has also shown that memory is not a unitary phenomenon: short-term memory processes, for example, can be distinguished from long-term memory processes.

Sites of Learning and Memory Processes

While those studies have been examining the physiological processes of learning and memory, others have been concerned with determining where in the brain these processes occur. One of the most challenging problems is to establish animal models for the study of certain human afflictions, such as Korsakoff's syndrome and cases of herpes simplex encephalitis, that result in brain damage. In trying to do so, investigators have demonstrated repeatedly that the hippocampus is concerned with certain types of learning and with at least some aspects of memory. They have shown, for example, that changes in electrical activity in the hippocampus reflect the process of learning a habit and that memories can be disrupted by manipulating the hippocampus electrically, chemically, or surgically. The way in which the hippocampus is involved in learning and memory, though, is still poorly understood.

However, other parts of the temporal lobe, as studied in NIMH intramural laboratories and elsewhere, have been definitely implicated in visual learning and visual memory. And it is now clear that the frontal lobes interconnect with all other cortical areas and, also, with many subcortical areas such as the basal ganglia, thalamus, and hypothalamus. Indeed, the prefrontal cortex is the only cortical area that interacts intimately both with the sensory and motor regions of the brain and with the limbic system structures implicated in emotions and motivation. The frontal lobes are thus in a unique position to integrate and regulate behavior in terms of information derived from both the external and internal environments. Research over the past 25 years has also shown that the cortex of the frontal lobes, once thought to be an undifferentiated structure and the repository for general memories, can be separated into several subareas, anatomically and functionally. Each of these subareas serves different classes of behavior; for example, it has been demonstrated that the cortex on the ventral aspect of the monkey's frontal lobes is involved in the inhibition of behavior while the cortex on the dorsal surface affects the organization of spatially-oriented behavior.

The Hemispheres

The last 25 years, too, have brought an increased awareness of the importance of the right cerebral hemisphere and the general acceptance of the idea that the two halves of man's brain show a complementary specialization with respect to cognitive processes. The classical view of right hemisphere functions was a restricted one: the right hemisphere could be the site of speech in left-handers, and it could take over the function of speech after damage to the left hemisphere in children. However, a substantial body of evidence now indicates that the right hemisphere is concerned with important nonverbal functions and that right cortical damage produces nonverbal perceptual and memory disorders differing in kind from the deficits seen after corresponding damage to the left hemisphere. Electroencephalographic evidence by NIMH-supported investigators corroborates clinical and surgical evidence that the left hemisphere tends to dominate during language activities, while the right hemisphere predominates during spatial and what might be called intuitional kinds of thinking. Such findings raise the possibility that special educational techniques can eventually be devised to help people who may find their reliance upon one hemisphere or the other a hindrance—for example, people who have difficulty learning verbal skills.

Research findings on the effects of early brain damage in nonhuman primates have helped stimulate interest in (a) how cerebral organization develops from infancy onwards in normal and in brain-damaged children and (b) whether and by what mechanisms children with brain damage sustained in infancy recover more function more rapidly than adults with similar injuries. A prime example of cortical plasticity is the discovery that children sustaining injury to the left hemisphere in infancy do not develop the severe aphasias, or language disorders, characteristic of such injury in the adult. There is evidence that in children the right hemisphere can take over the language functions of the left hemisphere. Efforts are under way, and are likely to be increased, to understand the conditions under which this transfer of function occurs.

Twenty-five years ago there was a general feeling of skepticism regarding the possibility of relating brain mechanisms to such higher functions as learning and memory. The area was looked upon as almost a deadend. The great advances made since then illustrate the riskiness of making judgments regarding the future developments in any area.

BIOLOGICAL BASES OF MOTIVATION AND AROUSAL

Hunger, of course, motivates animal or man to seek food; thirst, to seek water. But what are the biochemical bases of this behavior and of other motivated behavior? And, a related question, what biological mechanisms regulate an individual's state of arousal, which ranges from the deepest sleep to the highest readiness for action? The past quarter century has seen important strides toward answering such questions.

Part way through the period under review, researchers began delineating those brain areas, in the hypothalamus, critically involved in the control of hunger and thirst. Though the studies failed to elucidate the mechanism of such control, they paved the way for recent and current research that promises to reach the goal. Two other developments have advanced this work: (1) techniques that have made it possible to inject minute amounts of chemicals directly into the brain and thereby modify motivated behavior, and (2) as earlier sections have indicated, an increased understanding both of the biochemical pathways in the brain and of the anatomical distributions of the catecholamines. Thus, there has been a convergence of biochemical and anatomical knowledge.

It has long seemed likely that the relatively slow changes involved in shifts in motivational state must involve shifts in chemical activity because such chemical shifts, too, are relatively slow; it now seems certain that we are on the verge of a fine-grained analysis of the physiological mechanisms that underlie motivated behavior.

Reward Systems

In the type of learning known as operant conditioning and the type of treatment known as behavior therapy, as discussed in the chapter on psychological processes, reinforcement or reward has a critical role. Scientists, spurred by the finding that brief periods of electrical stimulation delivered to certain portions of the brain can be reinforcing, have been trying to find by what mechanisms and in what parts of the brain the effect of reinforcement or reward is controlled. Both electrical and chemical stimulation have been used to make a start toward mapping the so-called reward systems of the brain. It has become clear that norepinephrine, discussed earlier as a neurotransmitter, is critically involved and is present in those systems shown by stimulation and ablation techniques to be crucial for the maintenance of motivated behavior.

A similar analysis of systems that control the effects of punishment, rather than reward, and of the importance of another possible neurotransmitter, serotonin, in the functioning of these systems seems likely to lead to a better understanding, and therefore treatment, of both pain and pathological anxiety. Also, attempts are under way to understand both schizophrenia and depression in terms of inadequately functioning reward and punishment systems of the brain.

Pain

Another system of vital importance to normal behavior is the one controlling pain. According to the traditional view, taught in most medical schools until fairly recently, pain was controlled by a specific sensory system, with specialized pain receptors and fibers that projected through a specific pain pathway to a pain center in the brain. In the late 1950's and early 1960's, however, clinical observations of such conditions as phantom limb pain, the burning sensation of causalgia, and the intense pain of the neuralgias, none of which could be cured by conventional neurosurgical approaches, indicated the need for new concepts. In addition, psychologists observed that pain thresholds varied as a function of culture, early experience, attention, the meaning of the situation, and other variables. Such findings indicated that psychological factors play a powerful role in determining the presence or absence of pain, or the level of perceived pain in given situations.

A new theory of pain, formulated in 1965, has gained increasing recognition. The theory proposes that a gate-like mechanism exists in the somatic transmission system so that pain signals can be modulated before they evoke perception and response. The gate can be opened or closed by variable amounts, depending on factors such as the relative activity in large and small peripheral nerve fibers and on various psychological processes such as attention and the effect of prior experience. The theory has led to new techniques to control pain.

Many problems remain. Though investigators have done much to reveal spinal cord mechanisms, little information is available about the anatomical structures that receive pain signals in the brainstem, thalamus, and cortex, and about the changes and interactions such signals must undergo.

Sleep

Of the numerous circadian rhythms pervading the existence of all living things, the daily sleep-wakefulness cycle is the most obvious and intriguing, since normally over one-third of our lives is spent in sleep. Disorders of sleep and arousal have been repeatedly implicated in various kinds of psychopathology.

A new era of sleep research was opened during the past 25 years by (1) the demonstration of measurable gradations and periodicities in the EEG correlates of sleep; (2) the finding that periods of rapid-eye-movement (REM) during sleep correspond with periods of dreaming; (3) the discovery of the brain's reticular formation and the subsequent identification of two loci, in the diencephalic and caudal brainstem, in which electrical stimulation may induce sleep and in which lesions may induce chronic insomnia culminating in death; and (4) the discovery that these two loci are biochemically distinct.

In the field of sleep research, as is generally the case in science, knowledge accumulated through a continual interaction among scientists working in many laboratories on problems that intrigued them. It could not have been foreseen in 1949 that one experiment, demonstrating that destruction of the brainstem reticular activating system led to coma, would in one way or another provide the basis for unparalleled advances in the understanding of such phenomena as emotion, sleep, attention, learning, and memory. No one could have designed that experiment with its ultimate significance in mind.

NEURAL BASES OF SENSORY AND MOTOR PROCESSES

The subjects of sensation and sensory-motor processes have been of central concern throughout the history of brain and behavior research. The senses of particular interest have been the distance senses, vision and audition, which localize and identify objects in space. Among other problems, the questions of how light and sound are transduced by the receptors to yield a nerve impulse, and upon what paths in the central nervous system the impulse travels to reach the motor neuron are major ones for both neurophysiology and neuroanatomy. So the fields of sensation and motor control have constituted a meeting ground for physiology, anatomy, and psychology.

Sensory Processes

In 1946, research on the central mechanisms of vision and audition was strongly influenced by simplistic notions of the mechanisms of stimulus processing in the nervous system. It was widely believed that pitch discrimination would be abolished by removal of auditory cortex, that the subcortical visual pathway consisted merely of relays or reflex centers. It was assumed that nothing of great psychological significance occurred until the sensory impulse reached the appropriate area of the cerebral cortex, at which point the perception of the sensory event occurred. However, presently available evidence suggests that subcortical structures like the superior colliculus and inferior colliculus, instead of being mere reflex centers, play an important role in attention, learning, and perception. Thus, 'higher processes" are not necessarily limited to the association cortex, and not even to cortex.

Investigators seem to be at the threshold of major discoveries in the physiology of such complex visual processes as attention, depth perception, and binocular vision. Moreover, recent studies have provided new insights into the neurophysiological basis of shape perception and some startling discoveries about how vision develops in young animals.

The modern concept of a visual receptive field rests upon studies in the early 1950's on the retinal ganglion cells in the cat. These studies, using techniques for isolating and recording the activity of single cells in the nervous system, found that receptive fields of cat retinal ganglion cells are small, roughly circular, and organized in a concentric fashion. There is a circular area within which light will either excite or inhibit a given cell; just outside that region there is an annular, or surrounding, area in which light has the opposite effect. The findings led to psychophysical theories that account for many properties of human spatial vision on the basis of inhibitory input to retinal ganglion cells.

Recent research has forced investigators to question whether or not the organization of the receptive field is inborn. This work has shown that if kittens are reared so that each eye is exposed only to horizontal or vertical lines, the orientation of receptive fields of cells in the cortex is profoundly affected. Each eye connects to cells whose receptive fields are oriented in the same way as the lines—vertical or horizontal—to which the eye was exposed. There are no obliquely oriented receptive fields. The question then arises: If receptive fields in the cortex are indeed determined by visual experience, is there a critical period for their normal development? In an attempt to answer this question, kittens have been exposed to visual patterns for short periods of time at various ages. Exposure for as little as 1 hour on the 28th day of life seems sufficient to determine cortical receptive field orientations. How durable these effects are remains to be established.

Such studies of the functional development of the brain may be expected to have important implications for the understanding and treatment of certain ophthalmological problems, among them severe astigmatism.

Studies of the anatomy and functions of the visual system, in which intramural laboratories have had an important role, have recently been extended to provide insights into the pathways and mechanisms involved in the processing of visual information in the primate brain. The research has added considerably to our understanding of how certain defects in learning can arise, and of how the temporal lobe of the brain is organized.

As with vision and audition, research on the chemical senses—taste and olfaction—and of somatic sensation has advanced markedly in the past 25 years. The Institute has supported some of it. From studies of the mechanism of taste has come evidence for a pattern theory of information-processing. This holds that different kinds of information do not necessarily arise from different receptor sites. Instead, they may arise from the same sites and are differentially transmitted through variations in the amplitude and frequency of signals.

Motor Processes

The current era of research on cerebral control of movement began 100 years ago with the discovery that muscular contraction could be elicited by electrically stimulating a region of the cerebral cortex that is now called the motor cortex. The early neurophysiologists developed the technique of electrical stimulation to a point where it could be used to study how the cerebrum controlled movement, but they recognized that movements produced by electrical stimulation are nonvolitional and abnormal in pattern. Technical obstacles caused a 50-year delay in the application of the single-unit recording approach to an understanding of motor function.

Observations on neuronal activity in animals trained in the performance of motor skills have now been carried out for a number of brain structures: the cerebral cortex, cerebellum, and basal ganglia. According to classical views, the activity of neurons in the sensory or motor areas of the brain changes only in relation to sensory stimulation or motor activity. However, recent studies in an intramural laboratory have shown that the activity of motor cortex neurons can be "preset" by the animal's expectation of what is to come, even though there is no overt behavioral response.

Research on the patterns of neuronal activity associated with movement in animals with experimentally produced models of human motor disturbances seems an especially promising research area. Though abnormalities in limb movement would appear to be chiefly of neurological interest, they also relate to more general patterns of behavioral abnormality. For example, although the mannerisms of schizophrenics and autistic children and the manifestations of chorea have no comprehensible explanation at present, other than "release of automatic behavior," these abnormalities may be the direct result of specific malfunctions of the motor system.

A related area of interest has been concerned with the degree to which sensory-motor coordination in the infant and effective adaptation to sensory distortion in the adult take place only when the individual has the opportunity to make appropriate adjustments to his own movements. One group of NIMH-supported studies, using kittens that were deprived of the opportunity to correlate visual experiences with self-initiated movements, provided evidence that sensory feedback was essential for the proper development of visual-motor coordination. On the other hand, the results of another group of NIMH-supported studies, which used infant animals surgically deprived of somatosensory feedback, indicated that such feedback was apparently not necessary for many aspects of motor development. The issue of the sensory control of movement thus remains unresolved.

NEURAL BASES OF SOCIAL BEHAVIOR

Animals, including man, can be induced to attack, flee in fear, desert their young, court a mate, and engage in sexual behavior by altering the brain. Although these facts had been demonstrated earlier, it remained for investigators of the last 25 years to make more explicit the neuroanatomical substrate for these behaviors.

For example, early studies on attack behavior, using electric stimulation of various parts of the brain, implicated the anterior lateral hypothalamic area; more recent studies have shown that the critical region is more extensive, extending through most of the hypothalamus and even posteriorly into the brainstem. In the case of sexual behavior, too, more brain structures appear to be involved than the early studies indicated. Most dramatic is the research in this area demonstrating that anomalies of adult sexual behavior can originate in prenatal and neonatal aberrations in hormone balance. It appears that the brain is organized or differentiated for sexual behavior (and most probably other behaviors) at an early period in development. The discovery of the neuroanatomical, neurophysiological, neuroendocrinological, and neurochemical bases of these mechanisms is an important task for future research.

In animals, at least, hormone levels also affect behavior in the group. Studies of groups of monkeys have demonstrated that dominance rank correlates with the individual's testosterone level, and exposure to defeat in encounters correlates with decreased testosterone levels. Environmental stresses appear to affect gonadal activity, presumably through the mediation of cells in the hypothalamus that respond to hormones. However, the introduction of male or female hormones does not reliably shift the relative levels of aggressive-submissive activity.

The effects of brain damage on social behavior have been clarified by other studies of monkey groups. It has been found, for example, that when medial temporal or orbital frontal parts of the brain of dominant monkeys are removed, the animals become the most submissive members of the group. Indeed, if monkeys living in the wild lose these areas of the brain, they no longer respond adequately to social stimuli and ultimately wander off from the group and perish.

Perhaps the most significant findings about the brain's regulation of social behavior come from Institute-financed research on monkeys that have been isolated from their social group early in development. As an adult, such an animal will display autistic-like behavior when unprovoked and panic-like behavior when excited. Moreover, it will not engage in either play or normal sexual behavior. It is a nonsocial individual. Electrophysiological studies have indicated several abnormalities in the brains of such animals. Thus, a unique research model for studying the neural basis of aberrations in social and other behavior, and of possible means of treatment, now exists, but its potential has not yet been realized. This research is described further in the following chapter.

In comparison with various forms of agonistic behavior, parental and other forms of altruistic and affectional behavior have received surprisingly little attention by neuropsychologists. Even more neglected has been play behavior, so characteristic of the developing organism and so disastrously affected in autistic children and those with minimal brain damage.

References

Aghajanian, G.K. LSD and CNS transmission. Annual Review of Pharmacology, 12:157-168, 1972.

Aghajanian, G.K., Foote, W.E., and Sheard, W.M.H. Action of psychotomimetic drugs on single midbrain raphe neurons. Journal of Pharmacology and Experimental Therapeutics, 171:178-187, 1970.

Agranoff, B.W. Protein synthesis and memory formation. In: Lajtha, A. (ed). Protein Metabolism of the Nervous System. New York: Plenum, 1970.

Anton-Tay, F., and Wurtman, R.J. Brain monoamines and the control of anterior pituitary function. In: Martini, L., and Ganong, W.F. (eds). Frontiers in Neuroendocrinology. New York: Oxford University Press, 1971.

Axelrod, J. Noradrenaline: Fate and control of its biosynthesis. Science, 173:598-606, 1971.

Baastrup, P.C., and Schou, M. Lithium as a prophylactic agent. Its effect against recurrent depressions and manic-depressive psychosis. Archives of General Psychiatry, 16:162-172, 1967.

Baylor, D.A., and Nicholls, J.G. Receptive fields, synaptic connections and regeneration patterns of sensory neurons in the central nervous system of the leech. In: Carlson, F.D. (ed). Physiological and Biochemical Aspects of Neural Integration. Englewood Cliffs, N.J.: Prentice-Hall, 1968.

Benzer, S. From the gene to behavior. Journal of the American Medical Association, 218:1015-1022, 1971.

Bernstein, J.J., and Bernstein, M.E. Neuronal alteration and reinnervation following axonal regeneration and sprouting in mammalian spinal cord. Brain, Behavior and Evolution, 8:135-161, 1973.

Bloom, F.E. Localization of neurotransmitters by electron microscopy. Research Publications of the Association for Research in Nervous and Mental Diseases, 50:25-57, 1972.

Bloom, F.E. The gains in brain are mainly in the stain. In: Worden, F., Adelman, G., and Swazen, J. (eds). The Neurosciences: Paths of Discovery. Cambridge, Mass.: MIT Press. In press.

Bloom, F.E., Iversen, L.L., and Schmitt, F.O. Macromolecules in Synaptic Function. Neurosciences Research Program. New York: Rockefeller University Press, Vol. 8, 1970.

Bodian, D. Neurons, circuits and neuroglia. In: Schmitt, F.O., Quarton, G.C., and Melnechuk, T. (eds). The Neurosciences—A Study Program. New York: Rockefeller University Press, 1967.

Brady, R.O. Cerebral lipidoses. Annual Review of Medicine, 21:317-334, 1970.

Broadhurst, P.L., Fulker, D.W., and Wilcock, J. Behavioral genetics. Annual Review of Psychology, 25:389-415, 1974.

Bullock, T.H., and Horridge, G.A. (eds). Structure and Function in the Nervous System of Invertebrates. San Francisco: Freeman, 1965.

Bunney, W.E., and Davis, J.M. Norepinephrine in depressive reaction. Archives of General Psychiatry, 13:483-494, 1965.

Butter, C.M., Snyder, D.R., and MacDonald, J.A. Effects of orbital frontal lesions on aversive and aggressive behavior in rhesus monkeys. Journal of Comparative and Physiological Psychology, 72:132-144, 1970.

Chow, K.L., and Leiman, A.L. The structural and functional organization of the neocortex. Neurosciences Research Program Bulletin, Vol. 8, 1970.

Cowan, M. Anterograde and retrograde transneuronal degeneration in the central and peripheral nervous system. In: Nauta, W.J.H., and Ebbesson, S.O.E. (eds). Contemporary Research Methods in Neuroanatomy. New York: Springer-Verlag, 1970.

Dahlstrom, A., and Fuxe, K. Evidence for the existence of monoamine-containing neurons in the central nervous system. I. Demonstration of monoamines in the cell bodies on brain stem neurons. Acta Physiologica Scandinavica, 62:Suppl. 232:1-55, 1964.

Delgado, J.M.R. Radio stimulation of the brain in primates and in man. Anesthesia Analgesia, 48:529-543, 1969.

Demolina, A.F., and Hunsperger, R.W. Organization of the subcortical system governing defense and flight reactions in the cat. Journal of Physiology, 160:200-213, 1962.

DeRobertis, E. Molecular biology of synaptic receptors. Science, 171:963-971, 1971.

De Wied, D. Effects of peptide hormones on behavior. In: Ganong, W.F., and Martini, L. (eds). Frontiers in Neuroendocrinology. New York: Oxford University Press, 1969.

Douglas, W.W. Stimulus-secretion coupling: The concept and clues from chromaffin and other cells. British Journal of Pharmacology, 34:453-474, 1968.

Dunbar, F. Emotions and Bodily Changes. New York: Columbia University Press, 1954.

Eccles, J.C. The Physiology of Synapses. New York: Academic Press, 1964.

Edholm, D.G., and Bacharach, A.L. The Physiology of Survival. New York: Academic Press, 1965.

Ehram, L., Omenn, G.S., and Caspari, E. (eds). Genetics, Environment, and Behavior: Implications for Educational Policy. New York: Academic Press, 1974.

Euler, U.S. von, and Eliasson, R. Prostaglandins. New York: Academic Press, 1967.

Evarts, E.V., Bizzi, E., Burke, R.E., DeLong, M., and Thach, W.T., Jr. (eds). Central Control of Movement. Neurosciences Research Program Bulletin, Vol. 9, 1971.

Finger, S., Walbran, B., and Stein, D.G. Brain damage and behavioral recovery: Serial lesion phenomena. Brain Research, 63:1-18, 1973.

Fischbach, G.D., and Dichter, M.A. Electrophysiologic and morphologic properties of neurons in dissociated chick spinal cord cultures. Developmental Biology, 37:100-116, 1974.

Fonberg, E. Control of emotional behavior through the hypothalamus and the amygdaloid complex. In: Physiology, Emotion, and Psychosomatic Illness. Ciba Foundation Symposium 8. Amsterdam: Elsevier, 1972.

Frigyesi, T.L., Rinvik, E., and Yahr, M.D. Corticothalamic Projections and Sensorimotor Activities. New York: Raven Press, 1972.

Garattini, S., Shore, P.A., Costa, E., and Sandler, M. Biological role of indolealkylamine derivatives. Advances in Pharmacology, 1968.

Glassman, E. The biochemistry of learning. An evaluation of the role of RNA and protein. Annual Review of Biochemistry, 38:605-646, 1969.

Goldman, P.S. Functional development of the prefrontal cortex in early life and the problem of neuronal plasticity. Experimental Neurology, 32:366-387, 1971.

Gottschalk, L.A., Knapp, P.H., Resiser, M.F., Sapira, J.D., and Shapiro, A.P. (eds). Psychosomatic Classics. Basel: S. Karger, 1972.

Grafstein, B. Axonal transport: Communication between soma and synapse. Advances in Biochemical Psychopharmacology, 1:11-25, 1969.

Groves, P.M., and Thompson, R.F. Habituation: A dual process theory. Psychological Review, 77:419-450, 1970.

Guth, L. Trophic influences of nerve and muscle. Physiological Reviews, 48:645-687, 1968.

Guth, L., and Windle, W.F. The enigma of central nervous regeneration. Experimental Neurology, 5:1-43, 1970.

Harlow, H.F., and Harlow, M.K. Social deprivation in monkeys. Scientific American, 207:136-146, 1962.

Harris, G.W. Sex hormones, brain development and brain function. Endocrinology, 75:627-648, 1964.

Heston, L.L. The genetics of schizophrenia and schizoid disease. Science, 167:249-256, 1970.

Hirsch, H.V., and Spinelli, D.N. Modification of the distribution of receptive field orientation in cats by selective visual exposure during development. Experimental Brain Research, 13:509-527, 1971.

Hirsch, J. (ed). Behavior—Genetic Analysis. New York: Mcgraw-Hill, 1967.

Hodgkin, A.L. The Conduction of the Nervous Impulse. Springfield, Ill.: Charles C Thomas, 1964.

Hubel, D.H., and Wiesel, T.N. Receptive fields, binocular interaction and functional architecture in the cat's visual cortex. Journal of Physiology, 160:106-154, 1962.

Iverson, K. Epidemic wave of thyrotoxicosis in Denmark during World War II. American Journal of Medical Science, 217:121-129, 1949.

Jouvet, M. The role of monoamines and acetylcholine-containing neurons in the regulation of the sleep-waking cycle. Ergebnisse der Physiologie, Biologischen Chemie und Experimentellen Pharmakologie, 64:166-307, 1972.

Kandel, E.R., and Kupfermann, I. The functional organization of invertebrate ganglia. Annual Review of Physiology, 32:193-258, 1970.

Katz, B. Nerve, Muscle, and Synapse. New York: McGraw-Hill, 1966.

Katz, B., and Mildei, R. The release of acetylcholine from nerve endings by graded electrical pulses. Proceedings of the Royal Society (Biol.), 167:23-38, 1967.

Kennedy, D., Selverston, A.I., and Remler, M.P. Analysis of restricted neural networks. Science, 164:1488-1496, 1969.

Kety, S.S., and Schmidt, C.F. The nitrous oxide method for the quantitative determination of cerebral blood flow in man: Theory, procedure and normal values. Journal of Clinical Investigation, 27:476-483, 1948.

Kety, S.S. Current biochemical approaches to schizophrenia. New England Journal of Medicine, 276:325-331, 1967.

Kety, S.S., Javoy, F., Thierry, A.M., Julou, L., and Glowinski, J. A sustained effect of electroconvulsive shock on the turnover of norepinephrine in the central nervous system of the rat. Proceedings of the National Academy of Sciences, 58:1249-1254, 1967.

Kopin, I.J. False adrenergic transmitters. Annual Review of Pharmacology, 8:377-394, 1968.

Kuffler, S.W., and Nicholls, J.G. The physiology of neuroglial cells. Ergebnisse der Physiologie, Biologischen Chemie und Experimentellen Pharmakologie, 57:1-90, 1966.

Levi-Montalcini, R. Growth control of nerve cells by a protein factor and its antiserum. Science, 143:105-110, 1964.

McClearn, G.E., and DeFries, J.C. Introduction to Behavioral Genetics. San Francisco: Freeman, 1973.

McGaugh, J.L., Zornetzer, S.F., Gold, P.E., and Landfield, P.W. Modification of memory systems: Some neurobiological aspects. Quarterly Reviews of Biophysics, 5:163-168, 1972.

MacDonnell, M. F., and Flynn, J.P. Control of sensory fields by stimulation of the hypothalamus. Science, 152:1406-1408, 1962.

Manosevitz, M., Lindzey, G., and Thiessen, D.D. Behavioral Genetics: Method and Research. New York: Appleton-Century-Crofts, 1969.

Maynard, D.M. Organization of neuropil. American Zoology, 2:79-96, 1962.

Melnechuk, T., and Schmitt, F.O. (eds). The Neurosciences. New York: Rockefeller University Press, 1967.

Newman, J.D., and Wollberg, Z. Multiple coding of species-specific vocalizations on the discharge of auditory cortex of squirrel monkeys. Brain Research, 54:287-304, 1973.

Noel, G.L., Suh, H.K., Stone, J.G., and France, A.G. Human prolactin and growth hormone release during surgery and other conditions of stress. Journal of Clinical Endocrinology and Metabolism, 35:840-851, 1972.

Olds, M.E., and Olds, J. Approach-avoidance analysis of rat diencephalon. Journal of Comparative Neurology, 120:259-296, 1963.

Penfield, W. The Excitable Cortex in Conscious Man. Springfield, Ill.: Charles C Thomas, 1958.

Penfield, W., and Roberts, L. Speech and Brain-Mechanisms. Princeton: Princeton University Press, 1959.

Raisman, G. Neuronal plasticity in the septal nuclei of the adult rat. Brain Research, 14:25-48, 1969.

Raisman, G., and Field, P.M. Sexual dimorphism in the neuropil of the preoptic area of the rat and its dependence on neonatal androgen. Brain Research, 54:1-29, 1973.

Rakic, P. Guidance of neurons migrating to the fetal monkey neocortex. Brain Research, 33:471-476, 1971.

Robinson, B.W. Forebrain alimentary responses: Some organizational principles. In: Wayner, M. (ed). Thirst. New York: Pergamon Press, 1964.

Rosenthal, D. Genetic Theory and Abnormal Behavior. New York: McGraw-Hill, 1970.

Rosenthal, D., and Kety, S.S. (eds). The Transmission of Schizophrenia. London: Pergamon Press, 1968.

Rosvold, H.E., Mirsky, A.F., and Pribram, K.H. Influence of amygdalectomy on social behavior in monkeys. Journal of Comparative and Physiological Psychology, 47:173-178, 1954.

Scheibel, M.E., and Scheibel, A.B. Organization of spinal motoneuron dendrites in bundles. Experimental Neurology, 28:106-112, 1970.

Schildkraut, J.J. The catecholamine hypothesis of affective disorders. American Journal of Psychiatry, 122:509-522, 1965.

Schildkraut, J.J. Neuropharmacology of the affective disorders. Annual Review of Pharmacology, 13:427-454, 1973.

Schildkraut, J.J. and Kety, S.S. Biogenic amines and emotion. Science, 156:21-30, 1967.

Schneider, G.E. Early lesions of superior colliculus: Factors affecting the formation of abnormal retinal projections. Brain, Behavior and Evolution, 8:73-109, 1973.

Schmitt, F.O. (ed). The Neurosciences: Second Study Program. New York: Rockefeller University Press, 1970.

Selye, H. The Physiology and Pathology of Exposure to Stress; A Treatise Based on the Concepts of the General Adaptation Syndrome and the Diseases of Adaptation. Montreal: Acta, 1950.

Slotnick, B.M., and Nigrosh, B.S. Maternal behavior or mice with cingulate cortical, amygdala, or septal lesions. Journal of Comparative and Physiological Psychology, 1974. In Press.

Snyder, S.H. Madness and the Brain. New York: McGraw-Hill, 1974.

Sokoloff, L. Cerebral circulation and behavior in man: Strategy and findings. In: Mandell, A.J., and Mandell, M.P. (eds). Psychochemical Research in Man. New York: Academic Press, 1969.

Somjen, G. Sensory Coding in the Mammalian Nervous System. New York: Appleton-Century-Crofts, 1972.

Sperry, R.W. Selective communication in nerve nets: Impulse specificity vs. connection specificity. Neurosciences Research Program Bulletin, Vol. 3, 1965.

Stanbury, J.B., Wyngaarden, J.B., and Fredrickson, D.S. (eds). The Metabolic Basis of Inherited Disease. New York: McGraw-Hill, 1972.

Stenevi, U., Bjorkland, A., and Moore, R.Y. Morphological plasticity of central adrenergic neurons. Brain, Behavior and Evolution, 8:110-134, 1973.

Steward, O., Cotman, C.W., and Lynch, G.S. Re-establishment of electrophysiologically functional entorhinal cortical input to the dentate gyrus deafferented by ipsilateral entorhinal lesions: Innervation by the contralateral entorhinal cortex. Experimental Brain Research, 18:396-414, 1973.

Stretton, A.O.W., and Kravitz, E.A. Neuronal geometry: Determination with a technique of intracellular dye injection. Science, 162:132-134, 1968.

Sutherland, E.W. Studies on the mechanism of hormone action. Science, 177:401-408, 1972.

Thoenen, H., and Tranzer, J.P. The pharmacology of 6-hydroxydopamine. Annual Review of PHarmacology, 13:169-180, 1973.

Usdin, E., and Snyder, S.H. Frontiers in Catecholamine Research. Proceedings of the Third International Catecholamine Symposium. New York: Pergamon Press, 1973.

Wald, G. Molecular basis of visual excitation. Science, 162:230-239, 1968.

Weiner, N. Regulation of norepinephrine biosynthesis. Annual Review of Pharmacology, 10:273-290, 1970.

Werman, R. CNS cellular level: membranes. Annual Review of Physiology, 34:337-374, 1972.

Wiesel, T.N., and Hubel, D.H. Single cell responses in striate cortex of kittens deprived of vision in one eye. Journal of Neurophysiology, 26:1003-1017, 1963.

Worden, F.G., and Galambos, R. Auditory processing of biologically significant sounds. Neurosciences Research Program Bulletin, Vol. 10, 1972.

Worden, F.G., and Schmitt, F.O. (eds). The Neurosciences: Third Study Program. Cambridge: MIT Press, 1974.

Wurtman, R.J. Neuroendocrine transducer cells in mammals. In: Schmitt, F.O. (ed). The Neurosciences: Second Study Program. New York: Rockefeller University Press, 1970.

Wurtman, R.J., Axelrod, J., and Kelly, D.E. The Pineal. New York: Academic Press, 1968.

Yates, F.E. Physiological control of adrenal cortical hormone secretion. In: Eisenstein, A.B. (ed). The Adrenal Cortex. Boston: Little, Brown, 1967.

CHAPTER 5

Basic Research: II. Advances in Knowledge of the Psychological Processes Underlying Behavior

Basic research in psychology involves inquiry into the processes of perceiving one's environment, of responding to stimuli, of learning, remembering, and thinking, and into the development of emotions, motivations, aspirations, and values. Like basic biological research, studies of the psychological bases of behavior seek new knowledge of man. The growth of this knowledge leads to practical application.

The sections that follow reflect the current organization of fields within psychological research, namely, conditioning and learning, memory and language, personality, perception, developmental psychology, aging, and social psychology. Each section opens with a brief overall orientation to the field and NIMH's role in supporting it. Research on specific areas within the field is then described and evaluated. The sections end with examples of the application of basic research findings to the solution of practical problems.

CONDITIONING AND LEARNING

The historical sources of conditioning are the Russian physiologist, I. P. Pavlov, and the American psychologist, E. L. Thorndike. Almost simultaneously at the turn of the century, these men established the principal features of modern conditioning theory, or, as it is sometimes called, "behavior theory," or "learning theory." Pavlov was concerned with glandular and smooth muscle responses innervated largely by the autonomic nervous system. Thorndike, on the other hand, was concerned with motor responses of striate skeletal muscle innervated largely by the central nervous system. Pavlov's procedure was regarded as a stimulus substitution operation in which the stimulus for one reflex is attached to the response of another—that is, a new reflex is acquired. Thorndike's procedure, later known as operant conditioning or reinforcement theory, involved the presentation of "reinforcement"—or reward—following a motor response, and was conceived as a matter of strengthening the response by the "contingent" intervention of an appropriate stimulus that had reinforcing properties. This alleged paradigmatic difference has survived to the present, and still supplies behavior theory with one of its most fundamental and least questioned principles. However, there are signs that behavior theory is about to enter a new phase. Information has accumulated over the last three-quarters of a century that current theory finds difficult to accommodate; a reconsideration of old theoretical positions is imperative if progress in behavior theory is to continue.

In the years between 1925 and 1950, behavior theory made its largest advances in the United States. During the 1950's many ingenious experiments testing the dominant behavior theories were conducted. Operant conditioning has emerged as the most frequently used concept, with theoretical and laboratory work followed up by a large number of researchers. This work has made a deep impression upon thinkers and disciplines outside of psychology itself.

In the recent past, theory development in classical or Pavlovian conditioning has been moderately active with the appearance of a mathematically oriented model and a new theoretical system for classical conditioning considered extremely potent by scholars in the field—as well as rather specialized theories based on specific experimental situations (e.g., theory of persistent behavior, theory of aversive control).

The importance of cognitive processes in learning is seen by some researchers as a revived and pervasive theme. Several other venerable problems have been revived. For example, the investigation of memory in nonhuman organisms was one of the earliest successful applications of behavioristic techniques to the solution of cognitive questions. Recently there has been a return to this classical problem, with new behavioral methods providing a degree of control not previously possible.

Finally, the considerable influence of ethological concepts must be recognized. Early in the 25-year period under discussion, experimental psychology focused its attention on two species: the normal adult human and the highly inbred laboratory rat. A broadening influence on behavioral scientists has come from a recognition of the power of some of the methods and concepts developed by ethologically trained investigators. As a result, recent years have seen increasing awareness of the fact that species is an important consideration, that all stimuli are not potentially equal in the control of behavior, and that the analysis of naturally occurring situations can provide new insights into the nature of the environmental-organismic interaction.

NIMH has become an increasingly important source of funds for research in conditioning and learning. Although relatively few grants were made early in the Institute's history, by 1956 support had been provided to the major investigators in several fields. From this point on the Institute supported a broad range of research, touching upon all aspects of conditioning, animal learning, memory, motivation, circadian rhythms, ethology, and related topics.

The NIMH intramural program has been active in certain aspects of the field, particularly in the study of learning and memory in nonhuman primates, the relationship of early learning and motivation to behavioral development, and developmental aspects of the learning process. In the Laboratory of Operant Behavior at St. Elizabeths Hospital, the Institute supports a program of basic research related to behavior modification; the studies involve both normal and mentally ill subjects.

Operant Conditioning

From the research and discussions in the period from 1925 to 1950 a form of reinforcement theory grew up that postulated two types of learning—operant conditioning, the one used by this theory, and Pavlovian or classical conditioning. This version of reinforcement theory sprang essentially from the work of the psychologist, B.F. Skinner, whose early research was with animals. The prominence of Skinnerian reinforcement theory was based largely upon the success of operant conditioning rather than the rational defense that Skinner was able to rally for two types of conditioning. The theoretical reexamination of that duality is in progress in many quarters today, and there is reason to hope that simplification of behavior theory through reduction to a single underlying type of behavior process is not far off.

The success of operant conditioning is, obviously, a matter apart from whether conditioning theory should be of dual or single type. What Skinner accomplished was the dramatic demonstration that voluntary behavior—with which Thorndike, too, had been concerned—could be placed under at least as sharp and precise control as any other response in an organism's repertoire, including the Pavlovian kind of response. Research on operant conditioning is now probably the single most widespread field in all of learning, particularly if the applications to problems in everyday living are included. NIMH has provided relatively extensive support for operant conditioning research.

The most active topic of research within operant conditioning is probably "schedules of reinforcement," or how delivery of the reinforcements should be timed. For example, even very brief intervals between the response and the onset of the reinforcing stimulus will reduce markedly the effectiveness of the conditioning; the overall effectiveness is inversely proportional to the length of the delay interval. However, though it is clear that brief delays in the reinforcement retard the association of stimuli and responses, it is less clear how delays influence persistence of the reinforced response when reinforcement is discontinued (extinction) or when the arrangements governing the delivery of reinforcement are altered (as in discrimination reversals).

Interestingly, laboratory investigations have shown that responses which are reinforced only on some occasions are more likely to persist in the face of nonreinforcement than responses that are always reinforced. Extensive investigations of the relations between reinforced and nonreinforced occurrences have led to the development of a behavior technology in which schedules of reinforcement play an important role.

The effect on motivation of omitting reinforcers has received increasing attention in recent years. In certain situations, motivational increments associated with the omission of reinforcers can be demonstrated. Some of the effects of omitting reinforcers can come under the control of previously neutral stimuli, a fact that has been incorporated into so-called frustration theory, which has been applied to a wide range of problems. However, the conditions under which stimuli associated with omission of reinforcers increase response strength and the conditions under which they decrease it are not well understood.

Implications of the discoveries concerning temporal factors in reinforcement seem to be these: Where specific skills (handwriting, for example) or nonverbalized responses (emotional reactions or sphincter control, for example) are to be trained, immediacy of reinforcement is essential. Thus, much of the training that goes on in the early years of life (as well as much of the retraining that goes on in clinical settings) requires the utmost attention to the design of situations that minimize delay of reinforcement. But as work in training the more cognitive aspects of education is undertaken, delayed reinforcement may be more effective.

Classical Conditioning

Extensive research over the last 25 years has dealt also with problems in classical conditioning. One area that has received considerable attention is the study of conditioned fear. Under natural conditions most organisms behave in ways that minimize contact with noxious stimuli, but occasionally animals and men show a curious inability to behave in this adaptive way. One interesting laboratory analog of maladaptive or neurotic behavior is generally spoken of as "learned helplessness." This appears after laboratory animals have been subjected to punishment—electric shock, for example—that they can neither predict nor control. After a time, they do not try to avoid the punishment even when, in the second phase of the experiment, they have been given the means to do so; they are in a state of helplessness and chronic fear, much like that in some forms of depression. Eventually, however, with repeated exposure to the second situation, the animals do come to learn that they are in control, to the extent that by doing something they stop the pain. These results, from research supported by NIMH, may have implications for the treatment of certain neurotic behaviors.

Other important problems are escape and avoidance behavior. In general, escape learning follows the general rules applying to operant conditioning. Avoidance behavior continues to be a classic psychological problem; no single theory of avoidance is without difficulties. The usual interpretation of avoidance behavior assumes that two different processes are occurring. Though such theories have considerable generality, a number of problems exist, suggesting the need for alternative ways of viewing the situation. NIMH programs on these problems and on conditioned fear have produced experimental and methodological innovations and detailed and valuable data; they have also developed a cadre of younger investigators, significant figures in the field.

The responses elicited by noxious stimuli sometimes include aggressive behavior. For example, if two laboratory animals are confined in a chamber where mild electric shocks are delivered to them, attacks of one upon the other are frequently seen. Such aggressive behavior has been compared to the competitive and combative behavior of men and animals in natural situations; however, careful distinctions are required when such comparisons are made. It has been shown also that in laboratory situations such aggressive behavior occurs when food reinforcement is omitted, testifying to the aversive character of stimuli associated with extinction.

A moderate amount of recent activity relates to cognitive (or awareness) processes in classical conditioning. One investigator has identified situations in which verbal instructions modify conditioned emotional responses, has shown how preparation for a painful stimulus can reduce the emotional response, and how "relaxation" procedures can reduce conditioned responses to painful stimuli. Another investigator has found that in a conditioned autonomic response, cognitive factors seem to influence the process of conditioning, since subjects who had correct information about the goals of an experiment became conditioned but subjects who had incorrect information did not. Still another line of work has attempted to determine the influence of personality factors on the speed and extent of conditioning.

Autonomic Conditioning

In recent years evidence has accumulated from many investigators that functions mediated by the autonomic nervous system—activities previously considered to be beyond voluntary control—can in fact be brought under control through operant conditioning. These activities include heart rate and brain waves. Such findings may lead to important applications in medicine and psychiatry, through the technique of biofeedback, and they seem likely to bring about a revision of behavior theory that will recognize not two but a single underlying type of behavior process. Much of this work has had NIMH support.

Habituation

As stated in the chapter on biological processes, habituation is the process by which organisms stop responding to stimuli that are not important to them; it may be one of the simplest forms of learning. Suggested as a "model system" for the study of the neurophysiological basis of learning, habituation is involved in fundamental reactions such as the orienting response. Accordingly, one finds habituation being studied in a wide variety of situations with organisms from sea snails to Homo sapiens.

Habituation of the orienting response is a valuable tool for investigating memory processes in infants. For example, an infant may be exposed to a visual or auditory stimulus, the intensity of which is positively correlated with the intensity of sucking on a pacifier; with continued exposure to the stimulus, the infant's sucking begins to wane (which can be taken as evidence of short-term recognition of the stimulus as unchanging) while a change in the stimulus may result in an increase in the intensity of sucking (which can be taken as evidence that the stimulus change was detected). By such techniques, one recent study has examined detection of linguistic features of auditory stimuli by infants. Presumably other problems in infant perception and memory could be studied by such methods.

Biological and Behavioral Rhythms

Many biological systems show orderly cyclic changes. Although some of these rhythms are highly correlated with changes in the external environment, others seem to occur in the absence of outside influences. Such independence of external changes suggests the existence of mechanisms called biological clocks.

The behavior of animals and of human beings is influenced by these biological rhythms. For example, early research found that peaks in general activity in rats occur about every 24 hours. Because such cycles only approximate the 24-hour period, they are called "circadian" (from the Latin for "about a day").

Many physiological functions undergo large fluctuations throughout the day, and these circadian rhythms affect responses to the environment in many ways. For example, a dose of amphetamine might be fatal at one time of day and merely cause discomfort at another. Or a pilot might fall unconscious from lack of oxygen at 4 p.m. and be much less affected at 4 a.m. Evidence suggests that even the outcome of psychotherapy is influenced by its timing. The relation of circadian rhythms to human variability in learning, job performance, and other activities is being examined.

No single nervous system structure that modulates the various changes on the circadian cycle has been found. There is considerable interest in the possible role of the neurotransmitters, which are discussed in the preceding chapter.

NIMH has supported some of the leading research in this field.

Applications of Research in Conditioning and Learning

Because they make it possible to obtain sensitive behavioral baselines, the techniques of operant conditioning have provided the main avenue for evaluating the effects of drugs upon behavior, considered apart from physiology. Among the behaviors that may be examined, for example, are motor skills, memory, sexual and emotional reactions, eating, and drinking.

Programed instruction has been almost entirely a contribution of operant conditioning. Programing consists of arranging the material to fit the needs of an individual learner, taking account of the steps of learning, and making provision for the acquisition of one step before undertaking the next. Mechanical devices for presenting material to be learned and for recording pupil responses continue to be invented. For economic reasons alone, the future of popular mass education may depend upon adequate research in this area.

Behavior modification is essentially an extension of the technology of teaching to such problems as mental retardation, reading disabilities, and stuttering and stammering. The entire range of normal learning may be included in this general category of behavior modification.

Behavior therapy (a term sometimes used synonymously with "behavior modification" and sometimes restricted to psychiatrically deviant behavior) is now widely pursued in psychiatry and clinical psychology. It involves the application of reinforcement principles and the technology of teaching to patients with behavior disorders. It is discussed further in the chapter on research treatment techniques.

Systematic desensitization treatment procedure represents an application of Pavlovian or classical conditioning, parallel to the therapeutic applications of operant conditioning.

As noted earlier, habituation techniques for the study of the orienting response have been applied to the study of memory and perceptual processes in infants.

MEMORY AND LANGUAGE

The study of man's memory and linguistic capabilities, which are closely intertwined, is central to the understanding of the human mind. The ways in which memory processes are conceptualized and how they are studied are influenced by attitudes concerning psychological inquiry. In the period from about 1920 to about 1960, the study of memory was under the sway of associationistic and objectivist doctrines that led to abandonment of the term "memory" in favor of the term "verbal learning." With this orientation, memory was conceived largely in terms of specific associations between stimuli and internal representations of experience called "traces" (or sometimes habits), and verbal learning research concentrated on the acquisition of associations, their retention, transfer, or forgetting, and the various conditions governing acquisition and forgetting rates.

Beginning in the mid-1950's the verbal learning orientation waned, and it is again legitimate to speak of and to study memory. A significant factor in this change has been the conception of man as an information-processing system. When studies showed that man's apprehension of his environment is selective and is subject to severe limitations on the amount of information he can take in and process, interest began to focus on coding processes, temporary and more permanent storage mechanisms, organization and chunking in memory storage, and the importance of retrieval cues to effective recall. Memory came to be viewed as a structured, organized, and dynamic system. The information-processing approach required the integration of such separate fields as perception, verbal learning, memory, cognition, and the use of language (psycholinguistics). The change in conceptions of memory has been paralleled by developments in linguistics and psycholinguistics; an emphasis on cognitive factors in language processing has attended a revolution in linguistic theory.

NIMH, principally through its extramural research programs, has been active in the development of these fields. Increasing proportions of research funds from 1961 to 1971 were allotted for work on human memory and language development. Roughly 12 percent of the 1971 support for psychological processes went for studies of human memory and psycholinguistics.

Information Processing

Research in the 1950's indicated that information overload is a real possibility for the human operator and that the operator, faced with more information than he can handle, filters out some of the input and attends to the rest. These findings made clear the limited capacity of the human operator. On the other hand, an investigation in 1966 showed that memory capacity is much greater than a limited capacity view of performance would predict. The human operator, according to this research, is able to "chunk" information into units containing a great deal of information. Other words for "chunk" are "code" or "recode." These findings are compatible with a limited capacity because the number of chunks can remain small. At the same time, a hierarchical arrangement of chunks can increase the amount of information retained, because a hierarchy is essentially the "chunking of chunks." It has been proposed that the memory capacity is approximately seven chunks, but the information packed into the chunks or into a hierarchy of chunks would vastly exceed seven units.

Memory Stores

These information-processing notions pertain primarily to permanent memory or long-term "store." As noted in the chapter on biological processes, researchers have found evidence for other kinds of memories as well. Apparently, memory stores may be classed as very short-term, short-term, and long-term, with possibly other states in between.

Studies of patients in whom bilateral hippocampectomies have been performed to relieve intractable cases of epilepsy have supported a distinction between long- and short-term stores. In these patients, short-term memory is intact, but the capacity to transfer material into long-term memory seems to be lost. Other research has shown somewhat different results, but there seems to be no doubt that the concept of memory stores and the methods used to differentiate and to study them are useful in the analysis of memory deficits in older people and in patients with brain damage.

Organization and Retrieval Processes

Investigations of clustering and of subjective organization in the recall of lists of related and unrelated words seem in general to fit into the concept of chunking or recoding. Mnemonic systems and imagery have been used as organizing procedures, sometimes with dramatic results in terms of the adequacy and accuracy of recall. Presentation systems for verbal materials that highlight and point out the organizational structure of the materials have produced high levels of recall.

There is an increasing tendency to regard the contents of long-term memory as permanent and failure of remembering as failure of retrieval rather than failure to have the information in storage. As evidence, under appropriate conditions use of retrieval cues significantly augments recall over what it would be without the cues.

It is generally believed that information enters the system at the very short-term memory, where it is subject to loss and transformation. What is left then enters the short-term store, a store of limited capacity, where various processes take place, such as rehearsal, recoding of the material, transfer to long-term memory, and loss. The long-term store is thought to have unlimited capacity. Before material that is stored in long-term memory can be used, it must be transferred to the short-term memory, assumed to be a working memory.

Other recent research has demonstrated that memory can be generative. That is, we can answer questions to which answers have not been learned by consulting our memories for bits and pieces of pertinent information that can then be integrated or related in ways called for by the new question. Long-term memory is, therefore, not a repository of static elements but an active, integrating, constructive mechanism.

Since the early sixties 20 NIMH-supported investigators have been working on such problems—retention in memory storage systems and the processes of retrieval of information from them. Their investigations address such questions as what strategies or organizing procedures facilitate retention and retrieval, what makes recall more difficult than recognition memory, and what are the most effective learning procedures.

Psycholinguistics

When psycholinguistics developed in the early fifties it had a good deal in common with work in verbal learning, though its focus of interest differed. However, the revolution in linguistic views concerning language, instigated in 1957 by Noam Chomsky, made the old theoretical basis of psycholinguistics untenable. Hence, psycholinguistics was reborn, about 1962, and began to attract the interest of many young investigators. Chomsky gave formal proof that associationistic and information theory approaches to language could not account for the knowledge people have of their language or for their ability to use language productively. He argued effectively that the sentence must be the unit of linguistic analysis and that the description of sentences and of the ways they are understood involves an underlying or deep structure from which, by a set of transformations, the surface structure (what we hear and say) is derived. The effect of this revolution on psycholinguistics was to make it a form of cognitive psychology.

Over the past years key laboratories of psycholinguistics and language development have received consistent NIMH support. The emphasis has been more on adult and developmental psycholinguistics than on speech perception, biological factors, and semantics.

Many studies of the comprehension of and memory for sentences have been carried out in the effort to see whether Chomsky's linguistic model (and the units of linguistic analysis generally) can be used also as a model of the speaker-hearer. Although some support for the model has been found, the evidence for it is less than clear-cut. Hence, the orientation has shifted to the study of strategies that people use to discern the underlying structures of sentences and the cues in the surface structure that point to the underlying grammatical relations.

Higher Mental Processes

The return of psychologists from exclusive preoccupation with very simple behaviors to research on complex cognitive processes—such as problem solving, concept attainment, language behavior—has been made possible not only by new ways of conceptualizing these processes but also by new laboratory and theoretical tools for studying them.

The tape recorder permits human speech to be captured in laboratory settings for subsequent systematic analysis. Video tape provides the same capability for recording physical movements. The eye-movement camera takes a record of the successive foci of attention of a subject engaged in a laboratory task. The digital computer can be used to generate stimuli, to record behavior, and to build theoretical models, or simulations, of the information processes that people use in performing complex tasks. These new tools have revolutionized the study of complex cognitive processes.

The tools, and particularly the computer simulation tools, build an effective bridge, also, from the complex behaviors to the phenomena of memory. For example, subjects carrying out mental multiplications in a laboratory experiment must hold a variety of information in their memory, including intermediate products they have calculated. Computer technology allows the investigator to simulate the subjects' processes, and to build into the simulation assumptions about memory capacities and speeds of memory processes that have been suggested by research on simpler memory tasks. In this way, theories about the simple mechanisms can be tested in the context of more complex performances, while theories of complex processes can be expressed in terms of organizations of the simpler mechanisms. Thus, the new techniques provide a powerful means for bringing our new knowledge of man as an information-processing system to bear on the kinds of complex tasks that man must perform in his everyday life.

The computer simulation techniques have had their widest application in the study of problem solving. NIMH-sponsored research has shown that a general model can be built of the processes that subjects use to discover the solution to some particular kind of problem. Moreover, the studies have shown that by constructing variants of the model, the causes of individual differences in problem-solving behavior can be explored and explained. For example, in one application of this technique, it was discovered that students solving algebra problems differed widely in the respective reliance they placed upon syntactic and semantic clues.

Out of these studies of problem solving have come not only a general theory of problem-solving processes, in terms of information processing, but also a method for approaching the notion of "cognitive style." To the extent that researchers can characterize accurately and in detail the cognitive styles of particular individuals, the researchers have a tool for diagnosing difficulties the individuals may be encountering in thinking or learning. An understanding of differences in cognitive styles may also help us to understand more deeply the organizations of cognitive processes that characterize various forms of paranoia and schizophrenia.

Cognitive simulation is also beginning to be used as a principal tool for exploring the organization and semantic content of long-term memory. In a system of this complexity, it is difficult to predict behaviors by means of verbal or simple mathematical models. Simulation techniques permit the investigator to represent in some detail a variety of interrelations in memory among semantic elements, and to infer the consequences of these interrelations for behavior.

The research on complex cognitive processes, a substantial part of it supported by the Institute, is closely related to work generally labeled "artificial intelligence."

Applications of Memory and Language Research

Recent work has shown that optimal strategies for instruction in reading or for learning words in a foreign language can be based on relatively simple models of the learning process. While such theories are still inadequate, they do provide alternative ways in which instruction can be carried out and can predict which one will be best; tests support the predictions. Further development of the models may well increase our ability to optimize instruction.

Past prediction of learning has not been effective, one authority points out, because the variables used were not related to learning processes or to educational techniques but only to outcomes. Individual differences should be conceptualized in terms of the processes postulated in contemporary theories of learning, development, and human performance. Effective strategies for learning probably can be taught, once we have a better idea of what processes are involved in various tasks. Adjustment problems such as drug use, delinquency, and inadequate development of ordinary skills like reading often accompany school failure and dropping out of school. More effective instructional procedures could have the benefit of reducing the frequency of dropping out. Only an occasional grant has been awarded for work directly pointed at new instructional methods or strategies. At present, however, a few projects are aimed quite specifically at problems of reading acquisition, reading disorders, and children's language learning skills.

Research in this area also bears upon the adjustment problems of old age. An important question, for instance, is whether the changes in memory associated with normal aging are caused by deficits in cognition or in performance. Research has focused on speed of response in learning-memory performance, and the results make older persons look poorer than their cognitive abilities alone would indicate. Noncognitive dimensions of performance probably should be investigated—in particular the effects of strangeness and discomfort in experimental contexts. Also, means of helping elderly persons in memory performance should be investigated further. These include learning and recall strategies in which the material to be remembered is specially organized with the use of associational or mediational techniques.

Research on memory and language has clinical application, too. For example, its findings and techniques can be used to help diagnose patients with various kinds of memory loss and thus to influence decisions on treatment. Work on effective instructional methods may have value in ameliorating aphasia and language disorders. The use of bilateral hippocampectomy to treat severe cases of epilepsy was greatly reduced by the finding—through the application of laboratory techniques for research on memory—that this operation interfered seriously with memory. Psycholinguistic research may be important to understanding schizophrenic language and language problems in autistic children.

MOTIVATION

Motivation is a central concept in psychology, since it is considered to be the source of the energetic aspect of behavior as well as an important factor in decision and choice. It figured prominently in the psychology of the 19th century in treatments of the will and volition, of intention and choice, and of conation and striving notions that have a rational and conscious character. The mainstream of psychological accounts of motivation in the early 20th century, however, did not use these concepts but instead—reflecting the influence of the theory of evolution and of psychoanalytic theory—"instinct" and, later, "drive."

The emphasis under instinctive and drive doctrines was on the impulsive character of motivation, coupled with the assumption of irrationality and the unconscious. Although cognitive controls over the irrational motive factors were recognized—and in a sense psychoanalysis can be characterized as a means of making the unconscious conscious—the underlying mechanisms of motivation were conceived to be automatic and inexorable. Drive theory was predicated on the existence of biological sources, such as hunger, thirst, and sex, which seemed to motivate animal behavior; it was extended to human beings mainly through the concept of acquired drive. Acquired drives, motives, or needs were thought to be established through learning.

Research on motivation from the 1920's until recently was mainly oriented to the study of biological drives in animals, although some studies were made of humans under semistarvation conditions and with reference to their sexual behavior. Conflict of drives was investigated with both animals and humans. Acquired drive studies dealt largely with animals and, except for studies of fear, were largely unsuccessful. Extensive studies have been made of the arousal, measurement, and effects of such human motives as anxiety, achievement, affiliation, approval, aggression (e.g., the frustration-aggression hypothesis), power, and dependency, and attention has been accorded to the possibility that some apparent motives (affiliation, for example) may actually be based on anxiety rather than on the motive named.

In its early years NIMH provided much of the support for studies of human motives. Starting with a few studies on fear and anxiety, the effects of stress on motivation and personality, and children's test anxiety, the grant programs by 1966 were funding numerous investigations of achievement motivation, aggressive behavior, expression and reduction of hostility, and motivational processes in abnormal populations, including retardates as well as psychotics. Long-term support was provided for work on the diagnostic significance of the Thematic Apperception Test. Other investigations focused on the effects of anxiety upon learning.

The intramural program supported a number of projects concerning human motivation and values, test anxiety, achievement need and defensiveness in children, as well as studies of parent-child interaction in relation to achievement behavior and moral behavior. Motivational factors in chronic schizophrenics, too, were studied in some detail, the interest being in affiliation behavior, effects of censure and praise, and arousal and performance.

It has become clear that motivation is a more complex matter than the model of unconscious, automatic, inexorable drive implies. The drive model is a deficit model, i.e., drive arises when bodily tissues are depleted of needed substances, as in hunger and thirst, and intake of these substances reduces the drive. But there also is evidence for motivation of the kind seen in exploration, manipulation, and curiosity. This kind of evidence controverts a deficit model and suggests that there may be an optimal state of arousal that animals seek and prefer to a tension-free state.

Another indication of the drive model's inadequacy is seen in the fact that measurements of human motives, such as achievement, do not predict actual behavior very well. To improve prediction it is necessary to take account of two other factors: the value an individual attaches to an outcome or an incentive and his judgment of the likelihood that he will actually be able to achieve the outcome. It therefore becomes important to study choice, decision, and value as involved in human motivation.

Only a few NIMH grantees have worked on problems of choice, decision, and value in human motivation. A few others, in work somewhat relevant to the area, have dealt with determinants of human judgment in a variety of situations. Here emphasis is placed not so much on motives as on values or incentives and the cognitive factors that enter into decision. One project has shown how eating behavior in obese people is heavily responsive to external cues—for example, the sight of food—while in normal people it is more responsive to internal stimuli. Another has shown that behavioral and emotional changes induced by drugs or the receipt of false information are more persistent when the individuals attribute the changes to themselves rather than to an external agent. Another NIMH-supported study demonstrates the impact of cognitive factors on pain perception. It shows that a person's pain tolerance is significantly increased when he controls (or thinks he controls) the administration of the painful test stimuli. In similar experiments several investigators are examining the effects of cognitive control on aggression.

Applications of Research on Motivation

An emphasis on values and goals represents a change in orientation to the problems of motivation. The change carries important possibilities for the application of research findings.

How does an individual develop goals and values? What are they at a given point in time? What factors govern whether or not he will see a situation, line of work, or career as a means of attaining his goals and realizing his values? How do long-term in contrast to short-term goals and values enter into immediate decisions? How far into the future can goals be projected? Is it necessary to have subgoals on the way to some ultimate goal? How and when do goals and values change, and why?

Answers to such questions are significant to understanding behavior patterns not merely of individuals but also of various socioeconomic and cultural groups. The values of contemporary society do not seem to be incorporated equally by all subgroups. Greater knowledge of values, goals, intentions, and similar factors bearing upon decisionmaking is critical to understanding this phenomenon.

There is a relationship between the matters just discussed and the view that behavior is determined by reinforcement. According to that view, one does not need to know about motives but only about reinforcers, because it is reinforcers that control behavior. Much can be said in favor of this stand, particularly on the basis of work in schools, hospitals, and institutions. However, reinforcers may be only another name for goals and values so that the reinforcement approach may be compatible with the reorientation concerning human motivation summarized here. Reinforcers as used in token economies and similar procedures are either fairly obvious and concrete (e.g., candy, cigarettes, privileges, recess time in school) or have to be discovered by observation of people in order to determine their preferences and valued activities and objects. Further research into goals, incentives, and values may enable more subtle and less tangible outcomes to be employed in programs in which reinforcement is the major technique employed.

PERSONALITY

Individual differences in behavioral patterns, along with the seeming consistency in a person's behavior, typically lead to the conclusion that people behave differently because they have different personalities. Personality traditionally has been thought to relate to the socially or individually defined adequacy of coping patterns. Knowledge of personality variables and relationships to other aspects of human functioning therefore should be directly relevant to understanding mental illness. Indeed, many of the theories and concepts of personality originated in the study of emotionally or mentally disturbed persons and have been generalized to the description or explanation of more normal behaviors and individuals.

Investigators conducting research on personality have used clinical, experimental, quantitative, developmental, and cross-cultural methods. Although earlier research relied heavily on clinical approaches, recent studies have stressed experimental and manipulative procedures or have used differential correlational techniques. Published clinical and naturalistic observational studies have been relatively infrequent but the latter are increasing.

The different methodologies appear to relate to several different perspectives or traditions that provide varying goals in personality research. Researchers and theorists differ in whether (a) they view a person as being like all other persons and seek therefore to determine the general laws of personality development and functioning that hold over the range of all individuals; (b) they perceive an individual as similar to some other individuals and hold therefore that personality is most fruitfully conceived and studied by identifying different types of subjects; or (c) they consider a subject unique, unlike any other person in his organization of psychological processes and his behavioral patterns. These approaches can be viewed as complementary, in that personality processes cannot be understood unless seen from these several vantage points. Yet the necessary integration of findings has not occurred, and the field is characterized by diffuseness, diversity of techniques, noncumulativeness of findings, and little consensus in theory.

A relatively high percentage of grants and funding in the early NIMH years was devoted to personality research. The prevailing theoretical orientation was psychoanalytic and most of these projects were psychodynamically oriented. With the expansion of NIMH programs, the proportion of personality grants fell. In the decade of the 1960's, which was one of rapid growth of NIMH programs, the proportionate number of grants and the amount of support for study of personality hit a plateau in spite of a large increase in absolute dollar funding. A more drastic change is evident in recent years. From proportional stability over most of the previous decade, a precipitous drop occurred between 1968 and 1971.

In the intramural program most personality research has been carried out within four units: the Personality Development Section of the Adult Psychiatry Branch; the Personality Section of the Laboratory of Psychology; the Personality and Environment Section along with the Personality and Stress Section within the Laboratory of Socio-environmental Studies; and the Child Research Branch. A number of studies also were initiated by the Mental Health Study Center.

Psychodynamic Formulations

The major conceptualizations and research in the study of personality during the first half of the century derived from theories of Freud and his followers, which depicted behavior as impelled by inner forces in the form of needs, drives, and impulses, often operating below the level of consciousness. A gradual change in psychoanalytic formulations has occurred, leading to an increased concern about human relations and how motives, motivational conflicts, and adaptational behavior patterns center about experience with significant persons in one's life. Psychodynamic concern also has shifted to an interest in ego functions—those aspects of the personality responsible for organizing behavior with respect to the realities of one's environment.

An alternative psychodynamic orientation to personality, less deterministically tinged, has stressed the self concept as the core of personality and the individual's behavior. In reaction both to psychoanalytic emphasis on unconscious motivations and conflicts and to definitions of behavior based on stimulus-response learning theory, some theories and research have emphasized a holistic, idiographic, integrated approach to personality and behavior, concern with the person's subjective world, his concept of self, and the dependence of behavior on the person's interpretation of environmental stimuli. The notions of self-consistency and the need for self-actualization have loomed large in these conceptions.

Trait Formulations

Another major way of viewing personality stems from consideration of psychological traits. Intuitive categories propounded by early theorists stimulated efforts to measure and describe persons through the proposed taxonomies. These have been supplemented during the last few decades by empirical trait-system frameworks developed by psychometricians. The approach has been dependent on a variety of statistical methods that aim to derive dimensions or factors to explain or describe individual variability on trait or attribute measures. It has been directed primarily toward the specification and measurement of separate personality dimensions, such as manifest anxiety, field independence, repression-sensitization, and locus of control. Such research and the tests or scales on which it depends have not been integrated or related in a coherent way. Indeed, many personality variables in recent years have been fractionated into smaller constructs. For example, social extraversion, derived as one of three components from the original introversion/extraversion dimension, has itself been divided into five components. One component is dominance, which itself has recently been fractionated into as many as 30 to 40 aspects.

The evidence for assuming that personality comprises broad underlying dispositions—whether conceived as basic factors, pervasive dynamic motives, or particular lifestyles—has been questioned in recent years. Particularly critical have been neobehaviorists and proponents of the newest paradigm in the personality area—social learning theory—which is discussed below. Because of problems in operationally defining major inner determinants of psychodynamic theories, these theories have resisted experimental verification or refutation. Their facility in interpreting past events is beguiling, but their efficiency in predicting and modifying behavior is questionable.

The notion of consistency in personality functions and the unitary holistic view of the self concept have also been challenged, particularly when personality is studied by other than self-report methods. The evidence on which the challenges have been based has been interpreted by some as the result of methodological inadequacies of tests and measures, poor sampling, and the limitations of the particular raters or clinical judges. Furthermore, it has been argued that even if overt behavior is not highly consistent, it is useful to postulate enduring genotypic personality dispositions.

Social Learning and Behavior Formulations

Perhaps the most important development of the last decade for personality research has been the advance in formulations of behavior theory and, especially, in the applications of the theory to the modification of complex human behavior—as discussed earlier in this chapter. The progress of behavioral approaches, from the animal laboratory to the clinic, has been accompanied by an expansion of social learning concepts concerning the processes of observational learning, vicarious reinforcement, and self-regulatory behavior, or self-control. Behavioristic and social learning proponents conceptualize the phenomena of personality in terms of basic learning, cognitive, and perceptual principles. The study of personality has been incorporated by them within the larger framework of the study of behavior, more specifically, the study of complex human social behavior.

Learning theories that involved translations of psychodynamic formulations had little impact on explanations of complex human behavior. Developments in behavior theory in the mid-1950's, however, shifted attention to detailed examination of the conditions under which given psychological phenomena occur and the mechanisms through which changes are effected. Social behavior was analyzed in terms of antecedent conditions that evoke it and reinforcing consequences that maintain it. Researchers were able to demonstrate that, by systematically altering external controlling variables, many response patterns could be induced, eliminated, and reinstated.

This kind of research has emphasized the importance of rigorous experimentation and theoretical progress and thus has depended on methodological advances to permit controlled studies of significant interpersonal phenomena in real life or lifelike settings. Progress has been especially notable in experimental studies, with children, of the role of modeling cues in "identificatory" or observational learning, and in studies of aggression and self-control.

Recent Developments

As indicated earlier, the influence of social learning and of cognitive theories of behavior have been accompanied by a decline in activities linked with psychodynamically oriented theories. This has been correlated with a substantial decrease in animal research intended as analogs for personality processes and on global motivational states that assumed too great a situation generality.

Another major shift has been away from the construction and validation of personality scales designed to measure single motivational dispositions. However, more cognitive dispositions are attracting interest, as seen in the measurement of expectancies regarding internal versus external control of reinforcement ("locus of control"). This construct has had widespread utility in areas as divergent as psychophysiology, clinical, learning, personality, and social psychology because it appears to be a critical cognitive link between stimulus and response in instrumental learning (or operant conditioning). Unless the individual comes to believe that there is a causal connection between his own behavior and an outcome event, he is unlikely to modify that behavior to increase the probability of occurrence of that event.

Among the promising research areas is self-regulation. If behavior is the result of interactions between the individual and the conditions of his life, how can the individual achieve greater control over his actions and states? How can he modify his environment in order to achieve his most important—and difficult—goals? Questions of this sort have been asked for ages, but they are now being posed in ways that make them subject to research, with the ultimate promise of enabling the individual to gain substantially in self-control. Recent work includes studies on the role of covert and overt self-instruction, training and self-management, response-reinforcement contingencies, delay of gratification, and self-reinforcement (which calls for the setting both of a standard and of a self-reward contingent upon achieving a performance matching the standard).

Another promising and important area is the nature and management of aggression. Research has begun to clarify the conditions that encourage and sustain violence. One of these is exposure to violent models, particularly if their aggressiveness is sanctioned and rewarded.

The organization of personality continues to defy available methodologies. The limitations of traditional correlational and factor analytic strategies for studying personality structure and organization have been widely recognized, but adequate replacements are not yet at hand.

Personality Assessment

Personality assessment refers to the description of the personalities of individuals. In the basic form of assessment, one person makes statements about the personality of another on the basis of observations made in a particular context. In all the diverse kinds of assessment, there are four components: (a) the target or the subject being described; (b) the context or the situation in which observations are made and the conditions under which the description is produced; (c) the observations of an observer-reporter; and (d) the executive assigning the final scores or measurements. The chief advance in recent years has been the identification of these components and the recognition that each may introduce biases or distortions.

The history of personality assessment has been one of fads and fashions. Enthusiasm typically is generated for what seems to be a promising new methodology, test, or topic, only to fade away in the light of accumulated negative findings. In assessment, more is known about what is not true than what is true. While much is known about methodology and measuring techniques, there are no established laws of personality to integrate and explain empirical findings.

A wide variety of assessment techniques and instruments have been developed. At one extreme are relatively unobtrusive measures, including behavior observations and sociometric techniques; at the other, highly structured tests, scales, and inventories. Falling between are clinical procedures such as the interview and projective techniques. One important trend has been a shift in emphasis away from the middle and toward the two extremes of this continuum. During the decade following World War II, the field of personality assessment was largely dominated by a single orientation, psychoanalytic theory, and by its methodological offshoot, projective techniques, such as the Rorschach and Thematic Apperception Tests. Over the past decade, psychoanalytic thinking has begun to be replaced by social learning and other forms of behavior theory, and research involving projective techniques has dwindled drastically. Naturalistic behavior relatively unconstrained by interventions of the investigator has received increased attention, while, at the other extreme, a rapid proliferation of research on structured scales and inventories has occurred.

Typically, instruments and methods are fairly adequate in terms of some technical psychometric criteria, e.g., reliability. But exactly what such instruments measure is uncertain. This problem is partly a matter of instrument format and content, but recent developments show that more basic influences come from the observer and the situation.

When the observer is in the role of interpreter or synthesizer of protocols, he is doing what a person does in everyday life, though presumably in a more sophisticated way. There have been two major developments in this area. First, research has shown that the clinician or other judge, given data about a person, cannot assess the person's personality and behavior better than quantitative objective methods, and often does not do so well. Work on how clinical judgments are made shows that a quantitative model can be formulated to represent the weightings a judge gives the several kinds of information available to him, and that the quantitative formula will predict better than the clinician himself. The conclusion is that human judgment should be used only when objective methods cannot be.

In the second major development, research has shown that the human mind tends to develop the belief that two unrelated variables are correlated. Untrained observers, after experience with protocols lacking any association between diagnosis and diagnostic signs, came to believe that particular associations were indeed present. More disturbing, these beliefs often coincide with those of expert, experienced clinicians.

The major developments in assessment seem therefore to have originated in conceptual theoretical work rather than from empirically oriented investigations. The most significant empirical studies have been those that tested concepts and furthered understanding of the assessment process. Needed now are the development of better conceptual formulations and definitive measures for assessing them and, above all, integration of existing knowledge into systematic theory.

Applications of Personality Research

Research on personality has led to a rethinking of concepts regarding the nature, causes, and modification of personality disturbances. The theoretical focus on behavior has been accompanied by efforts to analyze social learning and cultural conditions that seem to be its determinants, and to modify behavior directly by changing the relevant psychosocial conditions. There is growing recognition that behavior deficits (such as lack of cognitive, intellectual, and interpersonal skills), disadvantageous life situations, and inappropriate models and reinforcement systems all may have major parts in the development and maintenance of personality disorders, which may be viewed as arising from problems of living rather than as signs of intrapsychic disease.

PERCEPTION

Research on perception is an integral part of psychology and represents a well-established subdiscipline within experimental psychology. Moreover, considerations of the nature of perception play some role within essentially every subdiscipline of the behavioral sciences.

Although perception has not been a major focus of Institute activity, NIMH from the beginning has stimulated and supported important research areas in this field. Also, since 1959 a few intramural scientists have conducted research on perceptual processes, both in normal individuals and in psychiatric patients. Specific foci of investigation have been perceptual adaptation, individual differences in normal perceptual function, drug effects, perceptual and cognitive style, and perceptual functions in psychiatric patients and their families.

Neurophysiology

Perhaps the outstanding achievement of perceptual research since the start of Federal support has been the success in correlating behavioral measures with neurophysiological events. Sensory and perceptual phenomena have been differentiated by the fact that physiological mechanisms underlying sensory events could be identified, but those for perception could not. Such a distinction persisted only because the correlations could not be established. Significant progress in bridging this gap has been made. Studies of retinal interaction in invertebrates have led to the identification of inhibitory mechanisms that account for contour formation at all levels of the phylogenetic scale. Progress in anatomical and photochemical studies of the retina and in neurophysiological investigation of the retina and higher centers has done more to resolve the enigmas of color vision than was achieved in the entire previous history of this field. Identification of feature detectors in the cortex has provided an entirely new framework for understanding complex perceptual events and, perhaps most importantly, has provided a methodology for studying the development, plasticity, and the effects of deprivation on the nervous system. Much of this significant work fell outside the purview of NIMH.

Studies of the effects of motion produced either by moving stimuli or by eye movements have begun to elucidate the neurophysiological mechanisms contributing to the processing of information. NIMH-supported investigators have contributed to the work in this area.

Research on differentiation of hemispheric function, in both normal and brain-damaged persons, has produced generalizations on how language is processed in the nervous system and how complex stimuli such as faces are recognized. NIMH has supported investigations on a range of topics, such as behavioral effects of brain injury, effects of brain damage on perceptual and attentional functions, neurophysiological aspects of visual discrimination, psychophysiological processing of sensory information, and neuropsychological basis of visual recognition and perception.

Methodology

Progress in science is tied to advances in methodology. This is particularly true for perception during the last two decades.

Several lines of investigation have been concerned with improving the accuracy of results obtained in experiments with human beings. One has been the development of the theory of signal detection, which is concerned with the behavior of subjects who are making sensory judgments. In terms of this theory, responses are a joint product of the sensory process and the subjective criterion of the observer. This criterion can contaminate the estimates of sensory threshold. For example, in pain perception, a given physical stimulus or bodily condition may or may not be called painful, or may even go unnoticed, depending upon such factors as the social situation and the observer's attitude, anxieties, and personality. Signal detection theory provides a quantitative technique for differentiating sensory from subjective effects.

A second important methodological development recognizes that the experimental subject may play an active role and that the experimental situation itself can subtly influence the subject's behavior. This finding can be illustrated by research on hypnosis. Until recently, it was assumed that the hypnotic trance produces a unique state with sensory and perceptual alterations such as paresthesia and anesthesia, as well as the classical hypnotic phenomena of posthypnotic suggestion, age regression, etc. Recent research has demonstrated that most of the phenomena associated with hypnosis can be attributed to the motivation of the subject to play a role, to conform to the implicit wishes and desires of the experimenter, or to contribute to science. The term "demand characteristics" has been used to describe the totality of these effects on the behavior of hypnotized subjects. The effect of demand characteristics on data obtained in hypnotic experiments is so profound that one theorist has argued that the concept of hypnotic trance is neither viable nor essential, and that the phenomena of hypnosis can be explained by more common, less esoteric concepts. Most other theorists agree with the general thrust of this position, while maintaining that hypnosis does produce some unique changes, probably an altered state of consciousness.

The significance of this research is not confined to hypnosis. It has been demonstrated that the same subtle influences occur in a wide variety of situations, including potentially every experiment with human beings. It must now be asked to what extent the verbal reports of subjects taking projective tests, the responses of an observer in a psychophysical experiment, and the description of symptoms in the clinic, to name a few, are influenced by this phenomenon. Also, to what extent are the symptoms reported by a mental patient determined by demand characteristics and mediated by cultural influences? Fortunately, the development of new experimental techniques, such as the use of simulator groups, task-motivation instructions, and suggestibility scales, essential to hypnosis research, have relevance to any experimental or clinical situation. NIMH grants have supported much of this significant work.

The principal implications of these advances are (a) an awareness that the subject is by no means a passive responder to stimuli and (b) an increased sensitivity to the influence of variables previously ignored, but which can have a profound influence on the results of experimental studies with human beings. It is true that many perceptual phenomena are so robust that their identification or interpretation would not be altered by these methodological considerations. On the other hand, much perceptual research is concerned with more subtle effects whose existence and nature may be studied only under conditions for which methodological considerations are critical. These include studies of perception ranging from investigation of sensory thresholds of perception in psychosurgery to personality analysis of normal persons by projective tests.

A case in point is the investigation of critical flicker fusion frequency (CFF). In the late 1940's a battery of psychological and physiological tests was used to evaluate the effects of psychosurgery. Of these tests, administered to patients before and after the operation, the CFF was outstanding in its ability to predict success in ameliorating psychotic symptoms. This finding led to hundreds of studies of the effects of psychological and physiological phenomena on CFF. Since the actual change in the sensory threshold is small, the subsequent demonstration that subjective factors have an effect on CFF has called into question the value of this vast effort. Similar questions could be raised for many experimental investigations in human perception, particularly those involving patients.

In the last 20 years, the assumed involvement of perception per se in phenomena associated with personality structure, dynamics, and motivational state has been eliminated. In effect, the underlying mechanisms have been found to be operating on the response side rather than the perceptual. A large number of sophisticated experiments have demonstrated that the differences in the way people respond to a situation cannot be attributed to fundamental differences in their perception of the visual world.

Progress has been made, particularly within the last 5 years, with respect to our understanding of the initial events in perception. Previous research focused on photochemical and neurophysiological mechanisms; recent efforts are better classified in terms of an information analysis approach. The work has been directed toward breaking down and elucidating the subprocesses that previously had been lumped together. Research has investigated the degree of independence among channels within the visual system and has been able to distinguish such subprocesses as iconic representation, scanning, and encoding that occur as substages in perception. This work has formed a bridge between the findings of earlier physiological studies and such processes as reading, short-term memory, and reaction time. One result may be an increase in our ability to present information effectively. If we fully understand the intricate processes that take place between the stimulation of the sense organs and the encoding of this information by the attentional and memory systems, we may be in a position to improve the efficiency of information processing. Use of a language—analogous to that of symbolic logic—capitalizing upon the natural way the brain works may increase our ability to deal with conceptual problems. The Institute has supported a number of investigators in this field.

Significant advances have also been made with regard to our understanding of binocular vision and depth perception, a process that represents one of the highest achievements of evolution and that is temporarily or permanently impaired in a large percentage of the population. NIMH supports several long-term studies on problems of space and perception, the visual illusions, perception of movement, and maintenance of visual orientation.

Much has been learned about the processing of electrophysiological signals from the intact human brain. The techniques used, involving the electronic separation of signal from noise, enable investigators to study how the brain responds to stimuli elsewhere in the organism. The response is termed an evoked potential. The present state of the art is heuristic, the problem being the extent to which the brain's responses to complex stimuli can be identified and recorded. At present, the sharpness of contours can be so easily identified as to permit refraction of the eye with evoked potentials. Further development may have a profound effect on future studies of perception.

Applications of Perceptual Research

Since perceptual processes are involved in the acquisition and processing of knowledge, many theorists have long attempted to understand the altered mental states in psychopathology as either the result of, or as reflecting, disorders of perception. Perhaps the most familiar example has been the effort to evaluate motivation and personality with projective tests. Other work included studies of perceptual "defense" and "subliminal" perception. The investigators' interest in perception as related to personality and to mental states stemmed from the assumption that perceptual indicators were less subject to contamination by defense mechanisms and thus more accurately reflected fundamental dynamic processes.

As noted earlier in this chapter, improvements in methodology have shown that assumption to be incorrect. Differences in the way individuals respond to a situation are not caused by differences in the way they physically perceive it. This conclusion, reached with the help of NIMH support, has freed investigators for work in other areas.

Findings of research on perception have had clinical application as well. A prime example is the use of perceptual indicators in the evaluation of the information-processing capacity of the visual field, a process that is an essential part of neurophysiological examinations.

Animal research in psychophysics has provided information that underlies many clinical applications. Findings relevant to human welfare include the nature of hearing losses caused by certain drugs and by intense noise, and the effects of analgesic drugs.

DEVELOPMENTAL PSYCHOLOGY

This field is concerned with changes over time in psychological functions and processes—both the fine-grained changes within age periods and the broad changes and continuities between major periods of development throughout the life cycle. It has cohesiveness as a distinct field within psychology by virtue of its developmental core. At the same time it draws upon and contributes to most other areas of psychology. When their developmental aspects are considered, basic psychological processes such as learning, memory, perception, motivation, and major fields of research such as psycholinguistics, behavior disorders, and group behavior are part of the domain of developmental psychology. Similarly, psychological theories and technologies, whether from a psychoanalytic, cognitive, or operant reinforcement background, are in debt to the developing young of the species for the material of the science.

In 1948, the first year of NIMH research grants, developmental studies constituted more than a third of the total support. Grants were given for a wide range of topics: early personality development, emotional disorders of childhood, effects of social crises (wartime experiences) on child development, and studies of psychological ecology. This was a strong beginning in a field of psychology that at that time was not in the mainstream of academic psychology.

NIMH support, in the intramural and extramural programs, was well in advance of the popularity curve in developmental psychology that came into psychology in the late fifties. Developmental psychology was strongly represented in the initial program plans of the intramural program. The clinical orientation in the program and the influence of psychoanalytic theory gave developmental issues a priority consideration. Scientists brought to NIMH in the developmental area represented, however, a range of theoretical backgrounds and research interests. The increased availability of NIMH research grants quickly augmented the research force, bringing a meteoric rise in the amount of research on developmental problems during the late 1950's, the 1960's, and the 1970's. Contributing significantly to the growth of the field has been the work in the developmental aspects of learning, cognition, and perception.

Infancy

In recent years, research on infancy—an age period that was neglected after the work during the 1930's—sharply increased and greatly changed our understanding of the organism and the conditions that contribute to its development. It had been believed that what mattered with infants was only provision for their physical needs. Infants were not understood as psychological organisms reacting to and also acting upon their physical and social environments. Now studies of infants' sensory equipment, perceptions, attention, and ability to learn and be conditioned in the first few days and weeks of life have changed the image of the infant. Likewise, investigation of infant-caretaker interactions has demonstrated how each triggers and shapes the behavior of the other. The development of knowledge concerning the complexity of infant capacities, the plasticity and vulnerability of the infant, the responsivity of the infant to variable physical and social stimuli has not only elucidated the nature of infancy but also laid the necessary groundwork for understanding continuities from early to later characteristics in the individual and the effects of early experiences on later healthy or pathological outcomes.

Significant to this research has been the work on nonhuman infants. For example, through NIMH-supported longitudinal studies of monkeys, it has been possible to pin down the influences of disturbed infant-mother relationships not only as they affect the infant but also as they influence later peer relationships and the ability to carry on normal adult sexual relationships and parenting. Investigators have demonstrated abnormalities in infant monkey behavior (states remarkably similar to human depression) that are the consequences of long periods of total or partial social isolation, or of maternal separation. Work underway seeks to determine the biochemical correlates of induced depression-like behavior in animal subjects, and to relate these correlates to the biochemical data from human subjects and to the theoretical model of the biochemistry of depression described in the preceding chapter. Other work with monkeys has investigated conditions that may be useful in undoing some of the crippling consequences of earlier deprivation.

Studies of human infants, like those of monkey infants, have included research on infant attachment behavior, separation anxiety, interaction of infant and caretaker, environmental deprivation and stimulation, conditions giving rise to behavioral disorders, and techniques of rehabilitation. A line of animal research that has lost some of its attraction in human research is the hypothesis of the critical period, or imprinting. That hypothesis seemed to possess great explanatory power at one time, but it has proved too simple to account for the behavior of the human child.

The many apparently disparate topics of infant research converge in providing a body of knowledge that is being utilized by society. It is now possible to detect early signs of disability and pathology in infants and to intervene with specific kinds of remedial treatment. Research has also provided the knowledge enabling us to establish good infant care environments and to train caretakers to give to infants the kinds of care that are adapted to infant needs and capacities and that will help to equip them for a chance at psychologically healthy development.

Work on infancy is far from finished. There is solid evidence that the first several years have great importance for subsequent development, but there are many unknowns regarding the specifics and the mechanisms involved. The knowledge is applicable to policies and methods of child care—in the family, in the group care of infants and young children, and in the decisions of courts and social agencies.

Cognitive Processes in Children

The early research on intellective processes stressed the measurement of intelligence; the study of thought processes was virtually nonexistent in American research. In the past decade and a half there has been a surge of research interest and work in the nature of children's thinking. Greatly influenced by the Swiss psychologist, Jean Piaget, researchers have mapped children's mental models of their worlds at successive stages and have demonstrated a developmental patterning in how the child regards reality, in both the physical and social world, how he understands causal relations, and the kinds of conceptualizations and abstractions of which he is capable. Much of this research has stressed the normative developmental aspects; some has dealt with the effects of environmental input on the nature of the child's thought.

Language Development

Developmental psycholinguistics has been a highly active area. Prior views about language acquisition, such as imitation and reinforcement have been rejected; the important role of linguistic universals in the development of language has been indicated. Research findings demonstrate the commonalities in language development in children of different cultures. Research in this area is directed to understanding how children use the language they hear in learning speech and to understanding and characterizing their degree of linguistic knowledge at various stages of development. A recent view is that language is a manifestation of general cognitive development in the child, the careful study of which will have implications not only for language development but also for school learning and the remediation of speech and school problems.

Perceptual Development

The development of perception was little understood 25 years ago. While few believed that the perceptual world of the infant was as unorganized as implied by William James' "booming, buzzing confusion" rhetoric, no method for experimentally investigating perception among nonverbal infants and children was available. In effect, the period during which the most rapid changes take place in nervous organization was inaccessible to experimental investigation. Yet the importance of early development was evident from studies of adults, blind from birth or early childhood, for whom sight was restored by surgery, and of the neurological and behavioral effects of early sensory isolation in experimental animals. The remarkable plasticity of the perceptual system, particularly its dependence on and interaction with motor development, as demonstrated by perceptual "rearrangement" studies, further underscored the critical importance of early development to understanding perception.

Fortunately, two advances have overcome that deficiency. By analyzing eye movements with the aid of corneal reflection, it is possible to make inferences regarding the sensory capacities and visual organization of newborn infants. And, by using conditioning techniques, it is possible to study subjects of all ages. For example, operant conditioning techniques in which the infant is rewarded for making simple responses such as head-turning, sucking, and eye-movements are yielding, in many cases, our first real information about what infants see and hear. Such information is critical not only to perceptual theory but also to a broad range of clinical problems—from identifying the nature of congenital defects to tracing the pattern of normal development. It is also important to the understanding and treatment of sensory-perceptual disorders such as reading and learning disabilities, both of which are significant educational and public health problems.

Children's Learning

Although the advances in learning theory and research are described in the section on conditioning and learning, some comment is relevant here concerning changing trends and emphases in research on children's learning. Studies of children have both reflected the experimental research on animal and adult learning and influenced it. In the relatively simple laboratory designs characteristic of the 1950's, researchers repeatedly demonstrated that simple response patterns in children could be induced, eliminated, and reinstated by systematically altering external controlling variables. These impressive findings have led to many applications in work with deviant children. Operant conditioning procedures, as noted earlier, have been put to use in programed teaching, in training retarded children, and in modifying aberrant behavior.

Not surprisingly, the advances in behavior theory have been accompanied by a substantial decline in child research from the point of view of psychodynamically oriented learning theories. However, with notable vigor, social learning theory approaches have entered the learning field. The scientific confirmation of the influence of modeling, and the discovery of the conditions under which it is most effective, has probably provided one of the brightest spots in behavioral dynamics since Freud's contributions to an understanding of both development and defense mechanisms. Research has confirmed that much learning occurs on a vicarious basis through observation of other people's behavior and of its consequences for them. Modeling principles have not only enhanced the explanatory power of behavior theory but also have provided a base for developing additional therapeutic procedures for use with children. This research is further discussed in the Treatment of Mental Disorders chapter, in the section on modeling.

Another new direction in research on children's social learning is the investigation of reciprocal child and adult influences on each other. The child is no passive bystander, waiting to be modified by environmental events, but instead is himself an active agent who modifies these events. Research has begun to attack the two-way causal process.

Social and Personality Development

The advances in knowledge of the processes of perception, cognition, and learning have opened the way to fruitful reexamination of old, substantive problems in human development, such as child-rearing influences, sex typing, and the development of prosocial and antisocial behaviors, of goals and values.

Earlier research on the influences of child-rearing conditions typically used interviews and correlational studies involving broad parent and child characteristics. Because the yield of stable and clear findings from these studies was low, investigators lost interest. This area of research has again become active but with changed emphases and approaches. Experimental studies of social learning (reinforcement theories and observational learning) have brought new conceptualizations as well as new methodology to investigations of adult influences on child behavior. At the same time, advances in techniques of observing have reopened interest in naturalistic studies.

Conceptualizations of rearing influences, which traditionally have been in the framework of psychoanalytic theory and mother-child relations, are becoming more varied and broader. However, information on how Americans rear their children and how values and principles of rearing develop is still sparse. Relatively little can be said about the stability or change in rearing practices, in various sectors of the population, over the past several generations. What are the emergent forms of family and of child rearing in our society, and what are their influences on children's development? Did the parental practices under which present-day adults and adolescents were reared have any influence on their current behavior and values—and if so, what and how? More attention needs to be given, also, to socialization factors from outside the family—such as the school, the mass media, the organization of cities, and social problems.

Current research on sex differences and sex typing is attempting to sort out biological, environmental, and cultural bases for the psychological similarities and differences between boys and girls. The findings will have a bearing on an extraordinary number of issues in the sciences and in social policy.

In the study of social behavior, children's aggressions and transgressions, their anxieties and guilts have long been in the researchers' repertoire of variables. Recently, increasing interest has been shown in children's social competence—their altruistic and cooperative tendencies, striving for independence, development of responsibility, self-esteem, and ability to cope with stress. Research in these areas needs to be encouraged.

Research on the deeper meanings of differences in the behavior of different groups—racial, national, cultural, subcultural—has not been carried far enough. Greater attention is needed in this realm. At the same time, individual differences within subpopulations should be investigated so that universally significant variables are not attributed to transient differences among subpopulations.

Methodology

In child research, attempts are being made to lessen discontinuity between experimentation and naturalistic observation. The controlled conditions of the laboratory setting are becoming much more natural. Also, experimenters have been taking to the field—for example, through the planned manipulation of social reinforcement in natural settings. Research depends heavily on direct observation of behavior, yet the human observer presents many problems as a research tool. Methodological studies are needed to improve observational procedures and to permit more adequate study of complex ecological and social influences on individual behavior.

Applications of Developmental Research

Because basic researchers in developmental psychology have emphasized underlying processes, there has been and continues to be an impressive array of applications to society. For example:

- Research on the development of levels of aspiration, along with studies on the effects of success and failure and of praise and reproof on performance, has had the cumulative effect of changing the attitudes and methods of educators with regard to motivating children. Although derogation has not disappeared, there is little question that the dissemination of research findings indicating the deleterious effects of creating feelings of failure and loss of self-esteem has led to modifications in educational practice.

- Likewise, studies of gifted children have changed a cultural value system and a set of stereotypes picturing the genius as weak and eccentric and have led to a new image of the gifted child.

- Studies of the effects of institutionalization on children have led to radical reforms in the care of children without parents. Foster home placement has, to a large extent, replaced institutionalization.

- Observational studies of young children, along with clinical findings, have shown that long and unpredictable separations from primary caretakers or frequent disruptions in the caretaking can have serious and long-lasting consequences.

- Research on cognitive and language development has contributed vitally to changes in the educational system, particularly the adaptation of curricular structures to the capacities of the children.

- TV programs such as Sesame Street use knowledge obtained from research in developmental psychology.

- Laboratory research on operant conditioning, begun with animals, has led to behavior modification techniques that now have many practical applications in school and clinic and in parent education.

- Research on learning from the observation of models has led to new therapeutic approaches, applied successfully to a wide variety of problems—intractable fears and inhibitions, aggressive behaviors, delinquent patterns, sexual dysfunctions, psychosomatic disorders, self-injurious behaviors, speech disorders, and behavioral deficits.

112

Not all of the applications are pure successes, of course. Intervention or enrichment programs such as Head Start, for example, have had complex histories. They show that success is not easily won; also that there are problems in defining success and failure. The various intervention programs demonstrate, too, that it is easier to show the deleterious effects of environments than to discover and implement optimal environments for children of varying individual attributes and from various social surroundings. The intricacies and difficulties in moving from research findings based on laboratory work and limited research samples to generalizations and applications in real-life circumstances must not be ignored. Nevertheless, the list of examples is evidence of the tremendous resource for understanding human behavior that is inherent in developmental research.

Developmental psychology has accumulated knowledge about how children think and learn, how they are influenced by punishments, incentives, knowledge, and how environmental conditions influence their motives, values, and achievement. This knowledge is directly relevant and applicable to family living, education, psychiatry, institutional management, manufacture of toys, writing of children's books, city planning, and understanding of intercultural conflicts.

Although this knowledge has had wide effect, glaring gaps exist between what is known and what is utilized. As one example, more is known about the psychology of learning than is practiced in education. Thousands of elementary school teachers are turned out of colleges each year, teachers whose prime concern will be the learning process yet who have never had courses in learning or cognitive theory. Similarly, many judges and lawyers who are daily deciding the fates of children—deciding on parents for them, punishments, rehabilitation—have never had training in developmental psychology.

Human Aging

Historically, in the subject matter or theories of academic psychology there was little about aging. Research began with a practical emphasis on problems and deficits associated with aging (e.g., retirement, institutionalization, physical incapabilities, deterioration in memory and thinking, and psychoses). Since the field was outside the interests of academic psychology—and, to a considerable degree, still is—little support for research or training was forthcoming. In the 1950's, a few investigators began basic inquiry into psychological processes inherent in, or closely associated in this culture, with aging. In the early 1960's, when developmental considerations entered into investigations of cognitive and learning processes, and at a time when developmental psychology involving children had become an active area of research, gerontological issues as developmental issues gained more recognition. During this time, there also were strong social and political pressures for increased consideration of older persons.

The history of the Institute's role is given in the Mental Illness and Behavior Disorders chapter, along with a report on research on aging that falls outside the area of basic psychological processes.

Although gerontological research is now a viable field, there still are large gaps in our understanding of human aging. The cultural bias against the elderly has been evident as much within science as in society at large. Only now is there a core of trained and sophisticated investigators coming into the field. Because the field is still young, there is not a large body of consolidated findings.

Cognitive Functioning

Research has been done on thought processes, particularly in terms of measurement of intellectual functioning. The finding from earlier cross-sectional studies of a decline in reasoning ability with age has not been confirmed by more careful research when disease processes are ruled out. The large individual differences in intellectual performance among the aged raise questions regarding the causes for age-related decline, and indicate the need for investigation of the relation of mental impairment not only to disease processes but also to earlier environmental experiences and education and current environmental conditions and stimulation. Relevant to these questions is a landmark interdisciplinary study carried out by the NIMH intramural laboratories, in which normal, healthy, aged men were studied over a period of 12 years. The data showed that in many aspects of cerebral physiology, as well as of cognitive and behavioral functioning, these men had much less deficit than was usually reported in subjects from institutional or general populations.

Perception and Learning

One important change that occurs with age is some slowness in reacting to signals in the environment. The intake of information and the performance of even well-learned tasks require more of the organism's efforts. Furthermore, compared with younger groups, older age groups have difficulty in storing information so that it can be readily retrieved when needed.

Although there is descriptive evidence of memory changes in old age (early memories are presumed to be well retained, while recent memories are not), there are no acceptable explanations for these phenomena, and the methodological problems in undertaking good studies are of considerable magnitude.

Research designs on learning and perception have concentrated on comparing performance of two groups, 20-year-olds and 65-year-olds, and have provided almost no information on performance in intervening years.

Personality and Social Psychology

Much of the past work on personality of aged persons has dealt with major psychiatric disabilities. A trait approach to personality characteristics has been used in a number of studies comparing young people with old.

The data are far from clear with regard to changes with age in characteristics such as psychological rigidity, introversion, and passivity. These are critical dimensions, bearing on practical issues of trainability or retrainability in later years.

Relatively little research has been done on the stability of the self concept through the years. Whether or not older people disengage from social roles and find satisfaction or dissatisfaction from this kind of disengagement is an open issue.

A number of studies have indicated behavioral impairment related to isolation, loneliness, and "uselessness" associated with retirement, physical disabilities, and institutionalization—findings that raise serious questions for many social policies and practices. There is need for ecological and ideological studies of American society to ascertain the nature of societally fostered stresses on the older, and increasingly growing, proportion of the population.

Studies of attitudes in this culture have generally indicated many negative stereotypes about the aged. In sum, the aged are not valued; the values of youth predominate.

Attitudes of persons in middle and later life are an area of uncertainty. There is some evidence that aged persons are less open to change and more desirous of retaining the status quo. Research in this area needs to be updated, since there appear to be generational changes; that is, one generation and the next generation of older people do not appear to be identical.

The aging person exists in a context of high risk—from the physical and social environment and his own health. There is little so far in basic research to indicate how the individual will cope with and defend against these stresses. This whole area needs clarification and sophistication in the development of research designs and methods.

Biological, Psychological, and Sociocultural Interrelations

In the last few years, there has been increasing collaboration between researchers in the health fields and those in psychology and sociology, with increasing interest in the interaction between genetic predisposition and environmental factors in aging, health, and behavior.

SOCIAL PSYCHOLOGY

The fact that man's behavior, intellect, and personality are fundamentally shaped by his social environment has been recognized since the dawn of intellectual history. Yet the scientific study of social psychology was not undertaken until the second quarter of the 20th century. The foundations of modern social psychology were laid in the period between the two world wars. Four developments were of greatest importance: (1) the establishment of procedures for measuring attitudes and assessing public opinion; (2) the invention of objective methods for observing and recording social interaction and interpersonal relations; (3) the demonstration that important social phenomena, such as leadership, group problem solving, social norms, and interpersonal influence, could be brought into the laboratory and investigated by use of the experimental method; (4) the advances in statistics that made possible the estimation of the parameters of large populations from small samples, the analysis of complex data, and the efficient use of multivariate experimental designs.

With America's entry into World War II, social psychologists were mobilized to employ their newly developed expertise toward the solution of problems of national survival. Facilities for conducting survey research were set up in the Federal Government, and research was undertaken to assess civilian morale, motivation of industrial workers, and public reactions to governmental programs. Social psychologists assisted in the development of programs designed to heighten the performance and morale of military personnel. And toward the end of the war, social psychologists played a major role in the effort to assess the effects of strategic bombing on enemy morale. These experiences served as a dramatic demonstration of the practical value of social psychology and provided a major impetus to its rapid postwar growth.

Proportionately but not in terms of actual funds, NIMH support for social psychological research was highest in the 1950's (about 4.5 percent of all NIMH grant funds) and dropped sharply in the middle 1960's (1.15 percent of grant funds but much higher in actual dollars than during the 1950's). It had increased by 1971.

In the intramural research program the level of support over the past 5 to 10 years has been relatively stable. The research has included such areas as children's interpersonal perception and behavior; perceptions and responses to physical illness; the effects of social structure on socialization, stress, and creativity; social factors in self-esteem; the study of the family as a small group.

In terms of substantive accomplishments NIMH has played an important but not a major role in social psychological research. In areas such as social learning and aggression it has supported the outstanding investigators and can be said to have played the key support role. In other areas, such as social cognition, social perception, attitudes and social influence, conformity, cooperation and competition, leadership and group problem solving, NIMH supported important research, but the major research was supported by other agencies. Even in areas where there was more than token NIMH support—for example, group dynamics, attitude change, social perception—NIMH support tended to develop only after those fields had become well-established research areas.

Social Influence and Attitude Change

Most research and theory development in this field in the past 25 years has been on social influence and attitude change. During World War II, several studies on propaganda and persuasive communications were conducted for the U.S. Armed Forces. These studies raised many theoretical and empirical issues on the extent to which communications persuade people to change their attitudes and opinions.

The theories and methodologies developed in this early work were applied in a project supported by NIMH. This research first measured the opinions and attitudes of the public and the mass media toward mental illness and then studied methods for producing changes in these attitudes and opinions. Another application of the early work on attitude change concerned attitudes and behaviors related to various aspects of health and illness, as, for example, dental health and disease, smoking and cancer, and auto safety and accidents. Studies are underway on such problems as the psychological and emotional preparation of patients for surgery and the preparation of women for the emotional stresses of childbirth.

A second major line of research had its origins in work on the effects of cognitive inconsistency, or cognitive dissonance, on attitude change. A number of studies have considered how certain factors and situations—including expectations, social support, forced compliance, exposure to and avoidance of information—work to produce greater or lesser change in attitudes.

Another area of research contributed a different perspective. This is the work characterized as the functional approach to attitudes and attitude change, or the study of the functions that attitudes serve for the individual. Investigators have divided the study of antecedents and consequences of attitude change produced by communication into a number of subtopics: source characteristics, message characteristics, channel characteristics, receiver characteristics, and destination characteristics. Research typically examines some aspect of one or more of these to learn if attitude change is produced and if so, what kind and to what extent. The work has focused on important social issues—for example, methods for changing racial prejudice.

Social Perception and Cognition

How human beings perceive others and themselves has been of interest to psychologists for many years. Sociological theorists of the early 20th century were much concerned with such concepts as "the generalized other" and "taking the role of the other" in analyzing the nature of social behavior. Later, personality theorists were concerned with how human beings perceive one another and how this affects their behavior and experience.

Studies in the late 1940's and the 1950's of how impressions are formed demonstrated that certain perceived characteristics of people influence social behavior toward them. One focus of research in the 1950's and early 1960's was on the accuracy of such perception and its relation to attitudes and behavior. The work was based partly on the assumption that accuracy was a prerequisite to social effectiveness and that empathy was important to social adjustment and mental health. Methodological problems were numerous. By the early 1960's it began to be clear that the focus on accuracy and empathy oversimplified the problem. Attention was then shifted to an examination of the processes involved and away from a concern with the accuracy of their perception.

A more recent development is the work on "perceived freedom." People often believe they enjoy freedom, and this belief seems to affect their behaviors in a wide variety of situations. "Outcome freedom" (the person feels that he has a high probability of obtaining desired outcomes) is differentiated from "decision freedom" (belief that he, rather than others, selects the outcomes he will seek and the way he will seek them). The concepts of rewards, costs, and payoffs are used to analyze perceived freedom situations and how perceived freedom relates to social behavior.

Social Interactions and Group Processes

During the last 25 years, a great deal has been learned about the immediate antecedents of aggression and the internal emotional states that facilitate or inhibit its occurrence. Considerable progress has also been made in identifying the processes by which aggressive behavior is learned. NIMH has provided important support to research in this area. One significant product has been evidence showing the importance of "observational learning," or imitation, in the acquisition of aggressive behavior. It is now well established that the observation of violence can affect not only the likelihood that an individual will engage in such behavior but also his choice of targets. A good beginning has been made toward understanding how the viewing of violence on television affects the incidence and nature of aggressive behavior.

A different line of investigation has concentrated on the cognitive determinants of aggression. Conceptions of what behaviors constitute violence and what situations justify aggressive behavior differ greatly among different segments of the population. There is evidence that an individual's readiness to engage in aggressive behavior and his choice of targets are both influenced by the way he attributes responsibility for experienced frustrations and injustices. Much research has been done on how stereotypes influence the choice of targets and provide psychological justification for aggression. Several investigators have documented the cognitive processes by which an individual justifies his behavior after he has harmed another person, and although more research is needed, it appears that these processes—defense mechanisms—may reduce inhibitions against further aggression.

The threat to society posed by human aggression has directed attention away from the fact that man also engages in altruistic behaviors, such as cooperation, sharing, helping, nurturing, and sacrificing for the welfare of others. It is clear, however, that a balanced view of human nature must recognize its prosocial as well as its antisocial components, and social psychology has been concerned with both.

In recent years there has been a marked tendency to view both aggressive and altruistic behavior as being shaped by essentially the same underlying psychological processes. This trend is most evident in research on social learning, which has shown that an individual's readiness to engage in either aggressive or altruistic behavior can be heightened by exposure to a suitable model. Other research has shown that social interaction tends to be governed by a principle of reciprocity whereby either aggressive or altruistic behavior is responded to in kind. And a good deal has been learned about the ways in which the incentive structure of the social environment, or its "schedules of reinforcement," affect the incidence of both sorts of behavior.

In the last few years, a growing number of social psychologists—some with NIMH support—have become involved in research on specific kinds of prosocial behavior. Progress has been made toward an understanding of the processes underlying interpersonal attraction and the formation of social bonds. Though it is too soon to evaluate the ultimate significance of these investigations, they are concerned with important social phenomena.

118

One of the more active research areas during the last decade deals with what may be called responsible social behavior. This research has investigated situations in which an individual is presented with a conflict between behaving in his own immediate self-interest or in the interest of a larger group of people. In the experimental situations, the social good requires that individuals not attempt to maximize their own immediate gains. Such social problems as littering, pollution, and cheating on the payment of taxes derive from this kind of conflict of interest. The research has thrown considerable light on determinants of cooperative or responsible behavior but has been criticized for relying heavily on "artificial" situations involving rather trivial payoffs and restricted to two-person interactions. Recent work indicates that it can be extended to situations involving more people.

Immediately after World War II, many social psychologists turned their attention to the processes by which a group influences the beliefs, attitudes, and behavior of its members. The ensuing research documented the pressures to uniformity that are generated within a group. It was shown that groups tend to develop norms, or standards of conduct, to which members are expected to conform and that these norms exert a profound influence in such diverse realms as industrial productivity, politics, academic achievement, health practices, juvenile delinquency, the use of alcohol or drugs, group therapy, and intergroup relations. By 1960 "conformity theory" had become so well established that most social psychologists turned to other research topics. However, many problems in this area remain unsolved.

As research has proceeded, it has become evident that groups can have a profound effect on the psychological adjustment and mental health of their members. The effects of broken homes and marital conflict on the social well-being of children are well known, though not well understood. The sociometric position of an individual within a group is now known to influence the likelihood that he will engage in various forms of antisocial behavior. Other research has found that the incidence of mental and physical illness differs substantially among different positions in social systems such as business and industrial organizations. Research has only begun to clarify the mechanisms that bring about these effects, and further support of work in this general area should produce useful results.

Applications of Social Psychological Research

The topics of social psychological research—group cohesion, group productivity, trust and suspicion, attitude change, social pressures and conformity, the resolution of conflict, aggression, prosocial behavior—reflect many concerns and major problems of living. Research on the determinants of antisocial behavior is related to such problems as aggression and violence, delinquency, intergroup hostility, and exploitation. Research on prosocial behavior is relevant to the field of mental health in terms of what it can tell us about helping, cooperation, and the formation of social bonds, such as friendship and marriage. The study of withdrawing behaviors is especially relevant to such issues as alienation, dependency, alcoholism, and drug abuse.

In one form of social psychological research, social problems are taken into the laboratory and simulated. In this tradition are studies on prosocial and altruistic behavior; on effects of television, urban stress, imprisonment; and on aggression, obesity, smoking, and crowding. In another form the laboratory in effect is taken into the field, and research conducted on social institutions. Whether in laboratory or field settings, the study of basic social psychological processes can contribute substantially to our understanding of human adjustment, mental health, and mental illness.

References

Appley, M.H. Derived motives. Annual Review of Psychology, 21:485-518, 1970.

Atkinson, J.W., and Birch, D. The Dynamics of Action. New York: Wiley, 1970.

Bandura, A. Vicarious processes: A case of no-trial learning. In: Berkowitz, L. (ed). Advances in Experimental Social Psychology, Vol. 2. New York: Academic Press, 1970.

Berkowitz, L. Social norms, feelings, and other factors affecting helping and altruism. In: Berkowitz, L. (ed). Advances in Experimental Social Psychology, Vol. 6. New York: Academic Press, 1972.

Bindra, D. A motivational view of learning, performance, and behavior modification. Psychological Review, 81:199-213, 1974.

Bolles, R.C., and Moot, S.A. Derived motives. Annual Review of Psychology, 23:51-72, 1972.

Botwinick, J. Geropsychology. Annual Review of Psychology, 21:239-272, 1970.

Caldwell, B., and Ricciuti, H. (eds). Review of Child Development Research, Vol. 3. Chicago: University of Chicago, 1973.

Cartwright, D. Influence, leadership, control. In: March, J.G. (ed). Handbook of Organizations. Chicago: Rand-McNally, 1965.

Cofer, C.N. Motivation and Emotion. Glenview, Ill.: Scott, Foresman, 1972.

D'Amato, M.R. Derived motives. Annual Review of Psychology, 25:83-106, 1974.

Elkind, D. and Sameroff, A. Developmental psychology. Annual Review of Psychology, 21:191-238, 1970.

Fillenbaum, S. Psycholinguistics. Annual Review of Psychology, 22:251-308, 1971.

Fodor, J.A., Bever, T.G., and Garrett, M.F. The Psychology of Language: An Introduction to Psycholinguistics and Generative Grammar. New York: McGraw-Hill, 1974.

Gallin, E.S. and Moody, M. Developmental psychology. Annual Review of Psychology, 24:1-52, 1973.

Green, R.G. Aggression. Morristown, N.J.: General Learning Press, 1972.

Greene, J. Psycholinguistics: Chomsky and Psychology. Hammondsworth, England: Penguin, 1972.

Harris, A.H., and Brady, J.V. Animal learning—visceral and autonomic conditioning. Annual Review of Psychology, 25:107-133, 1974.

Hartup, W.W. and Yonas, A. Developmental psychology. Annual Review of Psychology, 22:337-392, 1971.

Herrnstein, R.J. Formal properties of the matching law. Journal of the Experimental Analysis of Behavior, 21:159-164, 1974.

Hinde, R.A., and Stevenson-Hinde, J. Constraints on Learning. London: Academic Press, 1973.

Hoffman, H.S., and Ratner, A.M. A reinforcement model of imprinting. Psychological Review, 80:527-544, 1973.

Hoffman, H.S., and Solomon, R.L. An opponent-process theory of motivation: III. Some affective dynamics in imprinting. Learning and Motivation, 5:149-164, 1974.

Hoffman, M., and Hoffman, L. (eds). Review of Child Development Research: Vols. 1 and 2. New York: Russell Sage Foundation, 1964, 1966.

Irwin, F.W. Intentional Behavior and Motivation: A Cognitive Theory. Philadelphia: Lippincott, 1971.

Jenkins, H.M. Effects of stimulus-reinforcer relation on selected and unselected responses. In: Hinde, R.A., and Stevenson-Hinde, J. Constraints on Learning. London: Academic Press, 1973.

Johnson-Laird, P.N. Experimental psycholinguistics. Annual Review of Psychology, 25:135-160, 1974.

Jones, E.E., Kanouse, D.E., Kelley, H.H., Nisbett, R.E., Valins, S., and Weiner, B. Attribution: Perceiving the Causes of Behavior. Morristown, N.J.: General Learning Press, 1972.

Latane, B., and Darley, J.M. The Unresponsive Bystander: Why Doesn't He Help? New York: Appleton, 1970.

Leventhal, H. Findings and theory in the study of fear communications. In: Berkowitz, L. (ed). Advances in Experimental Social Psychology, Vol. 5. New York: Academic Press, 1970.

Lindsay, P.H., and Norman, D.A. Human Information Processing: An Introduction to Psychology. New York: Academic Press, 1972.

Lippsett, L., and Reese, H. (eds). Advances in Child Behavior, Vols. 1-4. New York: Academic Press, 1963-1973.

McGuire, W.J. Attitude change: The information-processing paradigm. In: McClintock, C. (ed). Experimental Social Psychology. New York: Holt, Rinehart and Winston, 1972.

Miner, J.B., and Dachler, H.P. Personnel attitudes and motivation. Annual Review of Psychology, 24:378-402, 1973.

Moore, B.R. The role of directed Pavlovian reactions in simple instrumental learning in the pigeon. In: Hinde, R.A., and Stevenson-Hinde, J. Constraints on Learning. London: Academic Press, 1973.

Moray, N. Listening and Attention. Hammondsworth, England: Penguin, 1969.

Murdock, B.F., Jr. Human Memory. New York: General Learning Corporation, 1971.

Mussen, P. (ed). Carmichael's Manual of Child Psychology, Vols. 1 and 2. New York: Wiley, 1970.

Neisser, U. Cognitive Psychology. New York: Appleton-Century-Crofts, 1967.

Norman, D.A. Memory and Attention: An Introduction to Human Information Processing. New York: Wiley, 1969.

Ryan, T.A. Intentional Behavior: An Approach to Human Motivation. New York: Ronald, 1970.

Slobin, D.I. Psycholinguistics. Glenview, Ill.: Scott, Foresman, 1971.

Steiner, I.D. Group Processes and Productivity. New York: Academic Press, 1972.

Tulving, E., and Donaldson, W. (eds). Organization of Memory. New York: Academic Press, 1972.

Tulving, E., and Madigan, S.A. Memory and verbal learning. Annual Review of Psychology, 21:437-484, 1970.

Weiner, B. Theories of Motivation: From Mechanism to Cognition. Chicago: Rand-McNally, 1972.

CHAPTER 6

Basic Research: III. Advances in Knowledge of the Sociocultural Processes Underlying Behavior

INTRODUCTION

The systematic study of the interrelationships between man's behavior and the society and culture in which he lives is represented by the work of social psychologists, sociologists, and cultural anthropologists. Each discipline approaches the problem in a somewhat different manner and with somewhat different methods, but the goals are similar: to define the behavior in question and to determine the processes by which it is induced, maintained, or altered by sociocultural variables.

In this chapter, no attempt has been made to cover all the important developments during the last quarter century in the fields of sociology, anthropology, and social psychology. Instead, the chapter first describes one body of research illustrative of the work in these fields. Next it discusses four selected social science areas, citing one or two examples of research to indicate the type of work going on in each. Then it provides an overview of certain research approaches that are gaining increasing prominence in social science. The chapter concludes with a statement of recommended research priorities.

SOCIOLOGY OF THE SELF CONCEPT: AN EXAMPLE OF SOCIAL SCIENCE RESEARCH

Inasmuch as social science progress has been made along a broad front, no development with the possible exception of improvements in methodology, stands out above all others. Hence, this chapter opens with a report on a fairly typical body of social science research. This work, much of it conducted as part of the NIMH Intramural Research Program, deals with social determination of self-esteem, an essential component of mental health. This research helped uncover new information about the self concept of members of minority groups and about factors that influence self-esteem in all children.

The first large-scale systematic study of the social determinants of self-esteem in children was conducted among juniors and seniors in 10 randomly selected high schools in New York State in 1960. Some 5,000 adolescents, representing a variety of social classes, national backgrounds, races, and religious groups were studied. The significance of self-esteem for mental health was soon apparent. The investigator's self-esteem scale showed that people who rated low on self-esteem were both more likely to strike other people as depressed and more likely to express feelings of unhappiness and discouragement. Moreover, the lower a person's self-esteem, the more likely he was to have numerous psychosomatic symptoms of anxiety.

The investigator also found that adolescents from higher social classes tended to have higher self-esteem than those from lower social classes. Contrary to expectation, however, this was not because the former had higher social prestige in the community but because of differences in family relationships. Overall, fathers in the higher classes had warmer relationships with their adolescent children, particularly with their sons, than did fathers of lower social class position, and these warm relationships accounted for their sons' higher self-esteem.

If social class prestige as such does little to affect the self-esteem of children, neither does the prestige of religious, ethnic, and racial groups in the society. This finding flatly contradicts an enormous amount of theoretical and popular writing in this area. For example, since 1927 a number of investigators have studied the social prestige of various religious, racial, and ethnic groups in the United States. Usually they found that such groups as the English, Welsh, and Scottish headed the rankings, with the blacks near the bottom and other groups in between. Fourteen such groups were represented among the high school students in the New York State study. The results showed that the correlation between the social prestige of the group and the self concept of the adolescent members was almost zero.

Among children, then, it appears that ascribed statuses—that is, social statuses accorded the individual at birth or based on the accomplishments of parents—have weak effects on their self-esteem. The children's own achievements, though—how well they do in school work, how popular and successful they are with other children—have decidedly stronger effects. It should not seem paradoxical, then, that among adults social status (i.e., the result of the adult's individual achievement) does tend to be associated with self-esteem.

The immediate social context of the child's life is another important contributor to self-esteem. As evidence, Jewish children raised in predominantly gentile neighborhoods were found to have somewhat lower self-esteem and more psychosomatic evidence of anxiety than Jewish children raised in Jewish neighborhoods. Similarly, Protestants raised in Catholic or Jewish neighborhoods had somewhat lower self-regard than those raised in neighborhoods inhabited chiefly by coreligionists; and the same held true for Catholics. In general, the relationship between the characteristics of an individual and those of his immediate environment has an important bearing upon his feeling of self-worth.

Further evidence has come from research on self concept among blacks and whites. In the New York study, the self concept of the average black adolescent was found to be only slightly lower than that of his white counterpart. This finding ran contrary to most views current at the time. It has since been substantiated by at least a dozen other studies that showed no systematic difference in the self-esteem of black and white children. However, black children in dissonant contexts (predominantly white schools) scored lower than black children in consonant contexts (predominantly black schools), partly because the former were more likely than the latter to have experienced racial discrimination directly. It should be noted, however, that black children in predominantly white schools got somewhat better grades than blacks in predominantly black schools. If greater success in school leads to greater success as working adults, their self-esteem can be expected to rise. Some data on adults do show that economically more successful blacks tend to have higher self-esteem than less successful ones.

Children, it is now clear, tend to compare themselves with others in their immediate environments rather than with some broad social average. Thus, a child who is poor will have lower self-esteem only if those around him are wealthier than he. A child from a broken family is more likely to have low self-esteem if he finds himself in an environment in which this family structure is stigmatized and unusual; if broken families are common and less stigmatized, his self-esteem will not be lowered. In general, children's reference groups are the immediate environments of which they are a part—their schools, neighborhoods, peer groups, and families.

Also strongly related to a child's self-esteem is his perception of his parents' attitudes toward him, particularly his mother's. Positive attitude does not mean unbridled permissiveness or total devotion; children whose parents are excessively lenient appear to have lower self-esteem than those whose parents impose reasonable restraints and who punish the child when justified. Of critical concern is parental interest in the child. Children whose parents punish them in some way when they perform poorly in school have higher self-esteem than those whose parents pay no attention. Indifference to the child appears more devastating than punishment.

Siblings, of course, also constitute an important part of the child's world. One study of adolescents found that a particular sibling structure, namely, younger boys with mostly older sisters, was associated with high self-esteem. These "younger minority-sex" boys, however, appear to have a particular type of self-esteem, namely, an unconditional self-acceptance. Rather than being more successful than others, they turn out to be actually less successful. Their marks in school, for example, are significantly lower than the school marks of other boys. The chief difference, however, is that while other boys who do well in school tend to have high self-esteem and those who do poorly tend to have low self-esteem, for these "younger minority-sex" boys, school marks make no difference; their self-esteem is high whether their academic achievement is good or bad. The same turns out to be true for their social success. The love and acceptance of the younger boy by father, mother, and older sisters appear to establish a firm feeling of self-worth.

Research on the social determination of the self concept has refuted many, if not most, of the preconceptions of both lay persons and social scientists. In some cases the preconceptions turned out to have been wrong, as in the assumption that minority group members have lower self-esteem; in other cases, they have proved to have been excessively simple. For example, it is often supposed that a family breakup adversely affects the self-esteem of the child. Sometimes it does, but research indicates that the frequency depends on certain conditions. If the mother was very young at the time of the rupture, for instance, the likelihood of a clear, negative effect on the child is greater than if she was older. Further, it turns out that children from broken families whose mothers remarry, tend to have a lower self-regard than those whose mothers do not remarry, and this negative effect is particularly strong among older children. Finally the effect is influenced by the cultural value system of the group or the neighborhood. Only where divorce or other type of family rupture is strongly stigmatized is the child of a broken family especially likely to have low self-esteem. Social science has moved increasingly toward the specification of conditions under which generalizations hold, thereby adding concreteness to the understanding of social phenomena.

Such findings are but a sample of the results emerging in this area of research. Work underway includes research on the social factors that bring about change in the self concept, on coping mechanisms adopted by individuals to protect their self-esteem, and on determinants of adult self concepts. Systematic research has shown that many popular conceptions of self-esteem determinants are myths, and that the operation of social forces in this area is far more subtle than is ordinarily assumed.

ILLUSTRATIVE DEVELOPMENTS IN FOUR AREAS

Since the number of specialized substantive areas in sociology, anthropology, and social psychology are too numerous to be adequately treated here, the chapter addresses only four of them: social stratification and psychological functioning; social factors in the development and treatment of mental disorder; demographic trends and mental health; and social problems. The discussions of these areas exemplify types of research and findings in the social sciences; they do not begin to cover the chosen areas, let alone all of social science.

Social Stratification and Psychological Functioning

It is a universal feature of social life, true of all known societies whatever their level of development, that individuals acquire differential status, honor, and power—that societies, in other words, are stratified. This finding from earlier studies has given rise to important questions for social scientists, among them: (1) How similar are the nature and bases of stratification in various societies? (2) How does the individual's location in the stratification system bear upon his psychological functioning—his personality, attitudes, emotions, values, orientations, mental health? (3) If stratification does have psychological effects, why is this so—what is there about the class experience that is the critical element? This section reports answers to these questions contributed by research over the last two to three decades.

Stratification in Diverse Societies

One of the most important and general findings in stratification research is the relative invariance of people's ratings of occupational prestige, regardless of which country is studied. This finding is basic to the measurement of social class position and thus to all research in social stratification. It is also of great theoretical importance in its implication that the stratification system is much the same across all—or, at least all industrialized—societies.

Here, as in most other basic research, a finding is the result of a long series of studies by many investigators. The first major work in this area was the National Opinion Research Center study of 1946. The American population at that time agreed to a remarkably high degree on the relative prestige of various occupations. Regardless of which segment of the population was examined, and regardless of people's own occupational levels, most Americans ranked occupations similarly, in a regular and nearly invariant hierarchy from physician to bootblack. Later studies showed that this relatively invariant pattern continued to hold over the next quarter century and that it applied to various special subpopulations, even to children as young as 9 years of age and to seriously disadvantaged people.

Another major step in this process of discovery was a 1956 reanalysis of studies of occupational prestige in six industrial societies: The United States, Great Britain, Japan, New Zealand, the Union of Soviet Socialist Republics, and West Germany. Again, extremely high intercorrelations (mainly in the .90's) were discovered among these countries despite their cultural differences and despite the inclusion in the analysis of a major noncapitalist state. At least in industrialized countries, the stratification system is much the same everywhere.

More recent studies have extended this finding to many other countries, several of them non-Western, several of them noncapitalist, and some of them nonindustrialized or only partially so. The evidence for universality or near-universality in occupationally based stratification systems is thus considerable. The fact that the same occupations are accorded essentially the same level of respect in such diverse societies suggests that fundamental social forces influence men's regard for one another.

Social Class and Psychological Functioning

Over the last several decades evidence has accumulated that the individual's location in the stratification system bears strongly on his thoughts, feelings, and behavior. This finding is by no means restricted to our society. Research reveals similar relationships of class to perceptions, attitudes, and values in all industrialized countries. In support of this thesis, evidence from a great diversity of sources and countries has been gathered. For example, in the United States, Italy, West Germany, Norway, the Soviet Union, and Sweden, occupational position is consistently related to job satisfaction, with highly placed men always more satisfied. In the United States, Italy, West Germany, Norway, England, France, Australia, Mexico, and the Netherlands, there are fairly consistent relationships between class position and feelings of happiness or psychic well-being: The "better off" are in all instances happier. In eight of eleven countries for which data on parental values exist, the lowest class (of those studied) is the most likely to value obedience. And in seven countries, class position is positively related to men's belief in the possibility of change in human nature, a belief that has been taken as an indication of confidence

126

that man can master his environment. Location in the stratification system seems to have remarkably similar psychological effects everywhere in the industrialized world.

In addition, a nationwide survey of employed men was able to specify precisely a number of psychological effects of class. The higher men's social class position, regardless of such factors as their race, region of residence, and religion: (1) the more likely they are to value self-direction rather than conformity to external authority; (2) the more self-confidence and less self-deprecation they express; (3) the greater their sense of being in control of the forces that affect their lives; (4) the more open-minded, nonauthoritarian their views of others and of social institutions; (5) the more personally responsible (less literalistic) their conceptions of morality; (6) the more trustful they are; (7) the more receptive they are to innovation and change; and (8) the greater their intellectual flexibility.

Specification of Critical Elements

The bridges that have thus far been established between social stratification and psychological functioning consist mainly of correlations, which are statistical indications that two sets of phenomena are somehow related to one another. Crucially lacking is an explanation of the mechanisms that bring them about. Without such an understanding, there can be no firm, rational basis for the design of interventions to enhance individual functioning.

Promising beginnings have been made, nevertheless, toward identifying the mechanisms that underlie the correlations. One such attempt, an intramural project, began almost two decades ago with a study in Washington, D.C. It was addressed to confirming earlier reports about class differences in child-rearing practices and to discovering if these differences in parental practices could be traced to class differences in what parents value for their children. When parents were asked what qualities they considered most important in their children, striking class differences appeared. Middle-class parents were more likely to value self-direction; working-class parents were more likely to value conformity to external authority. The former stressed internal standards for behavior; the latter, conformity to externally imposed rules. Moreover, these class differences in parental values were related to class differences in child-rearing practices, not only for disciplinary practices but also for the division of responsibility.

In middle-class families, fathers are likely to take on considerably greater responsibility for providing emotional support to their children, particularly to their sons. In working-class families, fathers' roles are more likely to be limited to imposing constraints.

A second study, in Turin, Italy, showed that social class position had essentially the same effects on parental values, despite the very different cultural and economic circumstances of Turin. This study also indicated that class differences in fathers' values—and, to a lesser but still substantial degree, their wives' values—could be interpreted largely in terms of class-related differences in men's occupational conditions, particularly in the opportunity to exercise self-direction in work. Of primary importance in determining men's opportunities for occupational self-direction are closeness of supervision, routinization, and the substantive complexity of the work.

A third study—this one based on a cross-section of all men employed in civilian occupations throughout the United States—made it possible to extend these findings in several important respects. First, these data demonstrated a remarkable generality to the relationship between class and paternal values: The relationship exists and is of approximately equal strength in all segments of American society. Second, these data show social class to be more strongly related to paternal values than is any other major line of social demarcation, more strongly in fact than all other major lines of social demarcation combined. Third, the importance of occupational conditions for explaining the relationship between social class and paternal values is much more firmly established by these data than by those from Turin. And finally, these data show that class and occupation are related not only to parents' values for their children, but also, and in exactly the same way, to their values for themselves, to their self-conceptions, and to their social orientations.

These findings establish a prima facie case that men's social class position affects their values and orientations, at least in substantial part, because of class-related conditions in their occupational lives. The actual concrete work that males in different classes tend to do—especially the substantive complexity of their work with things, data, and with people—has major effects on how they think, feel, and act. This explanation, of course, assumes that the interrelationship of class, occupation, and values is not just a function of what types of men go into what types of jobs. Further analysis has shown that the job does affect the man and, in fact, that the effects of job on man are stronger than are the reciprocal effects of selective recruitment and job-molding.

Class stratification, of course, is not the only dimension of social structure that affects people's thoughts and feelings, and statistical techniques are not the social scientist's only methods. For example, black males in the lowest socioeconomic levels were studied by an anthropologist on the NIMH staff. This study concluded that the typical black streetcorner man wanted to follow the values and life styles of the country's major culture, but found it impossible to hold a steady job because he knew that society looked down on menial work and therefore on him.

> The streetcorner man wants to be a person in his own right, to be noticed, to be taken account of, but in this respect, as well as in meeting his money needs, his job fails him. The job and the man are even. The job fails the man and the man fails the job.

> Furthermore, the man does not have any reasonable expectation that, however bad it is, his job will lead to better things. Menial jobs are not, by and large, the starting point of a track system which leads to even better jobs for those who are able and willing to do them. The busboy or dishwasher in a restaurant is not on a job track which, if negotiated skillfully, leads to chef or manager of the restaurant. The busboy or dishwasher who works hard becomes, simply, a hardworking busboy or dishwasher. . . .

Thus, the job is not a stepping stone to something better. It is a dead end. It promises to deliver no more tomorrow, next month or next year than it does today. (Quotation from Elliot Liebow's "Tally's Corner. A Study of Negro Streetcorner Men," published by Little, Brown in 1967.)

The streetcorner man failed at marriage because basically he could not support his family. He took to the streetcorner to make friends and regain some feeling of self-worth.

Social Factors in Etiology and Treatment of Mental Disorder

Sociocultural factors probably play a more important role in mental disorder than in any other type of disease and are inextricably interwoven with every phase and aspect of mental health. Who becomes a mental patient, what treatment is provided, and the nature and success of that treatment depend to some degree on sociocultural variables.

A major early interest in research on the social epidemiology of mental disorder was the hypothesis that mental disorders in general, and schizophrenia in particular, are products of civilization, or of urban life, or of a highly complex social structure. The results of a number of important studies, which have attempted to test this hypothesis by examining rates of schizophrenia in presumably less complex societies, seem to indicate that the magnitude of mental disorder in these societies is of roughly the same order as that in highly urbanized, Western societies. These data are hardly precise enough to demonstrate that there are no differences in rates of schizophrenia among societies, but they have led investigators to turn their attention to the examination of intrasocietal variations, where there is evidence of much larger, consistent differences in rates of disorder. Of all the many social variables that have been studied, social class has proved to be by far the most important.

Class and Schizophrenia

Numerous studies, more than 50 at last count, some of them either undertaken or supported by NIMH, consistently indicate that schizophrenia occurs most frequently at the lowest social class levels of urban society. The evidence comes from research completed in Canada, Denmark, Finland, Great Britain, Norway, Sweden, Taiwan, and the United States—an unusually large number of countries and cultures for establishing the generality of any relationship in social science. Moreover, the exceptions are few and partial: they occur in small cities and rural areas or in special subpopulations of larger cities; none contradicts the larger generalization that an especially high rate of schizophrenia occurs at the lowest social class levels of urban populations.

A number of studies have examined the possibility that the statistical relationship between social class and rates of schizophrenia is only artifactual, the result of methodological error. The principal issues are the adequacy of indices, the completeness of the search procedures used, and the relative merits and defects of incidence and prevalence as appropriate statistical measures. Although these issues are not entirely resolved, the very fact that many studies using many different research methods have all come to the same conclusion argues strongly that the class-schizophrenia relationship is not just a statistical artifact.

The question of whether or not social class is related to schizophrenia is essentially no longer in dispute; the question now is why. A large body of research has been undertaken to clarify this issue. While evidence has accumulated in support of a number of highly reasonable competing interpretations, a definitive answer still eludes us. Several studies have examined the proposition that the class-schizophrenia relationship is essentially due to the downward social mobility of those suffering from mental disorder. Other investigators have advanced the view that it is not so much a matter of real differences in mental disability between the classes as a question of whether or not members of different social classes are differentially perceived or defined as mentally ill.

Evidence has been presented that psychiatric authorities, police, and employers come to label as mentally disordered certain lower class behavior that is merely socially deviant. The result is alleged to be either direct commitment to a hospital or the setting in motion of complex changes in social expectation and self conception that sometimes eventuate in hospitalization. A rather large number of studies have taken still another approach. They have argued that it is not social class as such but certain associated social processes that are responsible. Thus, the class-schizophrenia relationship has been explained in terms of social isolation, social integration, aspiration-achievement discrepancies, and minority position in the community. These interpretations are plausible and for the most part consistent with the existing data. But there is no evidence to favor them over the most straightforward interpretation of all: that social class is related to schizophrenia primarily because the conditions of life built into lower social class position are conducive to this disorder.

Several possible hypotheses about how class-related conditions of life might contribute to schizophrenia are solidly based in research on the psychological concomitants of class but are as yet untested in research on schizophrenia. One is that lower class people, who are exposed to more stressful conditions of life, have fewer institutional resources either for escaping stressful situations or for mitigating the consequences of stress. Another is that lower class conditions of life limit people's internal resources for dealing with stressful or problematic situations. These, of course, are not incompatible interpretations. The latter is particularly appealing, because it is based on the fundamental fact of the social psychology of class: that members of different social classes, by virtue of enjoying (or suffering) different conditions of life, come to see the world differently—to develop different conceptions of social reality, different aspirations and hopes and fears, different conceptions of the desirable. Class differences in orientation may be an important bridge between social conditions and mental disorder.

Stress and Schizophrenia

The evidence for stress playing a role in the etiology of schizophrenia is much less certain than that for social class, but it is sufficient to establish a prima facie case. Although a definitive study remains to be done, the pertinent studies, taken altogether, do indicate that stress is associated with the occurrence of schizophrenia. Moreoever, one important study shows that the relationship between stress and schizophrenia does not simply reflect the high levels of stress prevalent in the lower social classes. This investigation, involving schizophrenics and matched controls in the lowest social class of San Juan, Puerto Rico, reports that during the year before the onset of symptoms, the schizophrenics experienced notably greater stress than did the controls. Even when judged by the harsh standards of life of the San Juan slums, the stresses that preceded the onset of schizophrenia were unusually severe.

The Interaction of Genetics, Stress, and Social Class

The evidence briefly summarized above indicates that both social class and stress are probably involved in the etiology of schizophrenia. It is clear, though, that neither alone provides a sufficient explanation of the disorder. The incidence of schizophrenia in the lowest social class, though higher than in other social classes, is probably not over 10 percent; and the incidence of schizophrenia among people subjected to even the most heavy bombardment of stress under normal life conditions is, again by absolute standards, probably not very high. Thus, although any interpretation of the etiology of schizophrenia must take these social factors into account, it is not possible to explain schizophrenia in terms of these variables alone.

Exactly the same can be said for the only nonsocial variable that has been firmly linked to schizophrenia: genetics. The evidence for genetics playing a role in the etiology of schizophrenia is well-established. Yet genetics alone cannot explain the occurrence of schizophrenia. As noted in the chapter on the biological processes underlying behavior, the concordance rate for monozygotic twins of schizophrenics, though higher than that for dizygotic twins and for siblings, is, in the more carefully executed studies, a good deal less than 100 percent; it falls in the range of 25 to 40 percent.

These facts argue that the explanation of schizophrenia lies in the interaction—the joint occurrence—of genetic predisposition, social stress, other conditions of life associated with social class position, and, undoubtedly, other factors as well. In line with this conception, one prominent investigator has advanced the hypothesis that the constricted conditions of life experienced by people of lower social class position foster conceptions of social reality so limited and so rigid as to impair people's ability to deal resourcefully with the problematic and the stressful. Such impairment would be unfortunate for all who suffer it, but would not in itself result in schizophrenia. In conjunction with a genetic vulnerability to schizophrenia and the experience of great stress, however, such impairment could well be disabling.

Whether or not this particular view will prove to be the key to the puzzle, the hypothesis does nicely illustrate a type of interpretive model more adequate to the complexities of the present and rapidly cumulating evidence than the earlier interpretive models. These tried, unsuccessfully, to see schizophrenia as resulting entirely from genetics or family relationships or social class or stress or some other single variable. An interactive model can deal with the reality that no one factor explains schizophrenia, that some combination of relevant conditions must be present for schizophrenia to result.

It should be noted that testing any theoretical model based on the hypothesis of interactive relationships among causal variables requires a different mode of research from that ordinarily employed in epidemiological studies of schizophrenia. It is essential that genetic, psychological, and social factors be studied together, in the same research, rather than in separate studies.

The class-schizophrenia association also highlights the intimate relationship between "basic" research on social process and "applied" research on mental disorder. The initial discovery of class differences in rates of schizophrenia was a byproduct of a program of fundamental research on the social ecology of Chicago, in which mental disorder was but one of a host of dependent variables. Findings on the social patterning of rates of schizophrenia, in turn, have stimulated much important research on such fundamental issues as the relationship of social class to values and orientation. And these studies, in turn, become the source material to which we must turn for hypotheses for the future research that will explore alternative interpretations of the strong and consistent relationship between social class and schizophrenia.

Social Factors in Treatment

Even the manifestations of illness may take different forms in the several social classes. A number of studies have demonstrated that people from varying social backgrounds who come for treatment are likely to have different presenting symptoms. In the middle class, the presenting symptoms are likely to be psychological, in the working class, organic. In the case of milder disorders, in fact, whether or not the individual obtains treatment frequently depends more on social, cultural, and interpersonal factors than on the nature of the disorder. Thus, even with regard to the elementary issue of obtaining medical care, cultural, structural, and social psychological factors play an important role.

Once the individual enters into treatment, social and sociopsychological factors play a role in the type of treatment he receives. The medical model, of course, assumes that the treatment is suitable to the ailment. But certainly this is not always the case with regard to mental illness. Particularly before the advent of psychoactive drugs, studies clearly demonstrated the strong relationship of social class to type of treatment. Even within mental hospitals, patients with middle-class backgrounds were more likely to receive psychoanalytic, psychotherapeutic, or group therapy treatment; working-class patients or lower-class patients were far more likely to receive somatic treatment or custodial care. The patient's race also affects the nature of the treatment. A recent study of 320 schizophrenic patients in a Philadelphia mental hospital concluded that white therapists tend to have different expectations of, and therefore respond differently to, Negro and white patients. This study found that blacks were much more likely to be treated with drugs and were much less likely to receive psychotherapy than white patients. White patients, furthermore, stayed in the hospital about 50 percent longer than blacks. Finally, white patients tended to receive treatments that differed according to their symptoms and social class, while black patients were treated more homogeneously—that is, given drugs—whatever the symptoms.

Since treatment is carried on in particular social settings, the social scientist is interested in the organizational structure and relationships of the mental hospital, as well as those of other institutions. The concept of the hospital as a therapeutic community has been under very active sociological study during the past quarter century. It has helped to generate such approaches as milieu therapy and group therapy as alternatives or adjuncts to individual psychotherapy. A number of the most important early studies leading to the widespread adoption of milieu therapy were undertaken by social scientists who were on the staff of the Institute or held NIMH grants. These studies showed how cultural patterns tended to develop on wards and the effect they had on individuals, and how factors of communication, power, and organizational structure influenced the kind of treatment that patients obtained during "the other 23 hours." Current thinking is that the effects of milieu therapy and of psychoactive drugs—both came into widespread use at about the same time—interact and are jointly responsible for the striking decline in mental hospital populations since the mid-1950's.

Demographic Trends and Mental Health

While many social scientists examine cultural and structural conditions that generate psychological stress or social problems, a number of others engage in population studies to uncover likely sources of future stress. Some, for example, investigate trends in populations known to be vulnerable to stress or trends in population conditions known to generate characteristic stresses. Illustrative of this approach is demographic research on widowhood and on urbanization.

Widowhood

Research on age and marital status shows that major structural changes are taking place. For example, the birthrate in the male population is higher than in the female. Yet the male population grows more slowly than the female because the male death rate is higher, and the lower birthrate among females is more than made up by their lower mortality. As a result, the female population grows more rapidly than the male, and the sex ratio becomes more female. In the native white population the number of males per 100 females dropped from 103 in 1900 to 97 in 1960.

The excess gain in female population was made mostly at the older ages, with the result that in these ages the population is predominantly female. In 1960, among the native white population of the United States, there were 13 percent fewer males than females in the 60- to 69-year age range and 23 percent fewer at ages 70 to 79. This excess of females makes the usual pair arrangement impossible for a substantial minority.

When marital behavior is also considered, the imbalance proves worse. Men generally marry women younger than themselves, and the gap widens at older ages. Divorced and widowed women at older ages thus find it difficult to remarry. In 1960 only 39 percent of white females at age 60 and over were in the usual pair situation.

The society can thus anticipate a large and increasing proportion of aged widows, whose long-accustomed role has been terminated and to whom society assigns no alternative role or function. What are the mental health consequences for this large group and, indirectly, for their children and grandchildren? How do they respond to aging, loneliness, and status ambiguity? What are the psychological consequences of segregation in retirement communities compared to those of residence in an extended family structure? By pointing to such questions, demographic research calls attention now to research that may be needed to deal with problems of the future.

Urbanism

Certain of the characteristics attributed to urban life—size, density, heterogeneity, segmentation of roles, and weak normative controls, for example—have been held responsible for a variety of social stresses and are associated with the rise in certain social problems. The multiplicity of urban characteristics makes it difficult to specify which particular urban element is having which specific effect, but there is little doubt that certain conditions are in fact stressful and do generate distinctive social problems.

The 20 years from 1950 to 1970 witnessed the highest rate of world population growth ever known, and the last century has seen a gigantic shift in the geographic distribution of people. By 1970 about 864 million people—24 percent of the world's population—lived in 1,777 cities of more than 100,000 inhabitants. By the end of the present century, if no major catastrophe intervenes, the population in such places is expected to rise to 2.5 billion, or three times the 1970 figure. By then about 40 percent of the human race will live in cities of 100,000 or more and around 25 percent in cities of a million or more. Thus, the world as a whole will reach in a quarter century the stage that the advanced countries have already reached. (These predictions were made by Kingsley Davis in chapter 6 of "World Urbanization," 1950-1970, Vol. II, published in 1972 by the Institute of International Studies, Berkeley, California.)

With respect to number of individuals, human communities are becoming more like termite mounds than like mammalian groups. Since human beings, unlike termites, are ill-fitted for life in dense aggregations, they must use their technology to adapt to city living. The very expansion of cities shows that their effort to do so has been successful. Life expectancy in cities has been so improved that in advanced countries it almost equals, and in less advanced countries exceeds, that of the countryside. On the other hand, there are signs—including the exodus to the suburbs and high rates of crime, drug abuse, and mental illness—that the adaptation of man to cities and vice versa is more successful at the physical than at the social and psychological level, and that as cities increase in size the adaptation becomes more difficult. Environmental pollution of varied kinds creates hazards that require perpetual effort to detect and overcome. As time goes by, an ever greater proportion of our advanced technology is used simply to overcome the deleterious effects of advanced technology.

In the light of the trends revealed by demographic analysis, research dealing with the social problems and psychological stresses associated with urbanization becomes urgent.

Social Problems

The main social science research developments in the fields of intergroup relations, sex roles, crime and delinquency, and poverty are reviewed in the chapter on social problems. This section discusses some broad theoretical considerations applicable to the field of social problems as a whole and describes some research illustrative of work in this field.

Most of the issues classified as social problems are subsumed under the heading of what sociologists term "deviant behavior." Deviant behavior, of course, is defined in terms of the norms and values of a particular society; hence, behavior that represents conformity in one society may represent deviance in another. Deviant behavior is behavior that violates institutionalized norms—that is, expectations that are shared and recognized as legitimate within a social system. Crime, delinquency, alcoholism, drug taking, suicide, job absenteeism, prostitution, and so on are deviant because they violate the rules or disrupt the functions of society. This is not to say, of course, that psychopathology may not be responsible for certain forms of deviant behavior, but psychopathology is not its defining quality; psychopathology may underlie conformity as well.

Since the early research on crime and delinquency, it has become strikingly clear that these activities take place within a particular social environment and by virtue of identification with certain reference groups. Among youth, most crime is essentially a group activity. Among adults, this may be less the case, but it is largely sanctioned within a certain social environment. Hence, research on groups, group structure, and group formation, as well as research on reference groups, is relevant to this problem.

Social norms also govern patterns of drug consumption, drug addiction, and alcoholism. Drug-taking as a cultural phenomenon is clearly illustrated by the spread of marihuana on college campuses: It is a group phenomenon characterized by social contagion and cultural diffusion. Similarly, student outbursts on college campuses are far less a reflection of the mental health problems of the participants than of the social contagion by which values and ideas are transmitted from some people to others.

The case of alcoholism illustrates the significance of social norms for social problems. Most research in this area has focused on biological and psychiatric issues, to the relative neglect of sociological issues. Yet it is obvious that drinking is a social phenomenon. As one authority observes:

> Drinking patterns appear to vary in terms of the beverage used, the circumstances under which drinking takes place, the time, the amount, and the individual's own attitude and those of others toward his drinking. All drinking patterns are learned just as any other behavior is learned.... There are no universal drinking patterns for John, the average citizen. In any event, John will not drink like a Zulu, or an Austrian, or a Japanese; in fact, he will not drink like a New Yorker, or a Californian, or a ditch digger, or a

135

Yale man, or a Kentucky mountaineer, unless he is or has been in socially significant contact with such a group. (This observation was made by Marshall B. Clinard on page 288 of "Sociology of Deviant Behavior" published in 1957 by Holt, Rinehart and Winston.)

To understand various forms of deviance, then, we must understand more about such underlying factors as social processes, the nature of groups, the coerciveness of group norms, patterns of communication and transmission of ideas and values, and social and psychological determinants of attitudes, opinions, and values.

Although the social scientist generally seeks to examine the general social processes underlying specific social problems, he may also be involved in direct factfinding or immediate policy-related research. One example is the attempt to determine the true rate of crime in American society. The issue is of enormous importance. To answer it correctly is a necessary prelude to our understanding of criminal activity, as well as to effective efforts to control it. To answer it incorrectly may be very damaging. When a police department in a given community reports a rapid increase in serious crime, this increase may simply reflect changes in law enforcement practices or the increased willingness of citizens to report crime, or even changes in the definition of serious crime. Such reports, therefore, may not reflect a change in the actual rate of crime in the community.

When people themselves were asked, in a survey sponsored by the President's Commission on Law Enforcement and Administration, about their experiences at the hands of criminals, they reported vastly more crime than the official figures showed. For example, actual burglaries were three times, and forcible rape more than three-and-one-half times, the official rates. This information, of immense value to police departments and the general public everywhere, was obtained through the use of survey sample techniques developed by sociologists over the last quarter century.

Other examples of research on social problems appear in the chapter dealing with them. Two points should be noted here: that the scientific underpinnings for research on these problems derive from basic theoretical and methodological developments in social science, and that one cannot understand social disorganization without first understanding social organization.

METHODOLOGICAL DEVELOPMENTS IN SOCIAL SCIENCE RESEARCH

In the process of contributing to knowledge in various substantive areas and establishing certain general propositions of social life, social science has been developing a number of distinctive new approaches in recent years. They represent not knowledge per se but, of even more importance, modes of acquiring knowledge.

The past decade or so has been one of the most active and fruitful periods in the development of sociological methodology, in terms both of innovations that have become standard practice and of ideas that are in the burgeoning stage. The forties and fifties were chiefly devoted to the development of methods for data collection; the period since then has focused on methods for data analysis. One reason has been the increase in the number of mathematically trained and mathematically oriented scientists who have entered sociology and have brought their expertise to bear on its problems. An even more important reason has been the introduction and widespread use of the computer. No factor has been more important in transforming sociological methodology than the availability of computers and the development of packaged programs, which have made it possible for substantively oriented researchers to employ the newly available statistical techniques in their research.

Because of these developments, sociologists in the 1960's began to use multiple regression analysis on a wide scale. Among other benefits, this technique enabled investigators to control simultaneously a large number of variables when examining the effect of any one variable on a dependent variable, and to obtain explicit coefficients measuring the size of the effect. Other techniques such as multivariate analysis of variance, canonical correlation, factor analysis, and multiple discriminant analysis are today commonplace in social research. In general, these methods are much stronger than the old cell-by-cell comparisons that were characteristic of quantitative analysis in sociology 10 years ago.

Sociometry

The increasing sophistication of social scientists in their use of quantitative methods is nowhere better represented than in the application of sociometric measures and their derivatives. Sociometric measurement itself has changed considerably since the term "sociometry" was introduced to describe quantitative techniques for studying interpersonal relations in small groups. In the past, such data have generally been presented graphically and descriptively; today, quantitative indices are common. The application of this approach to group differences and prejudice has resulted in a great volume of meaningful data.

Secondary Analysis

Increasing interest in the secondary analysis of data is another important development of the last decade. As a result of the computer-generated revolution in quantitative data analysis, it is possible to store microlevel data on computer tapes, making them easily accessible either through remote terminals or physical transmission. A second stimulus for this development is the increasing cost of data collection, making it likely that future researchers will turn increasingly to data already available for the examination of their propositions. Moreover, the 1960's witnessed a substantial increase in the number, scope, and quality of data archives, in which studies focusing around a central theme are stored in one location. These archives still leave much to be desired, but they are likely to expand and to be increasingly utilized in the coming years. Finally, an increasing growth can be expected in awareness of the limitations of general propositions enunciated on the basis of a particular study. Ultimately, general propositions, which are the aim of all science, must be demonstrated in a variety of periods and circumstances, even if the studies involve different measures of the same concept. Although secondary analysis has drawbacks and is not intended to substitute for primary data collection, it has been insufficiently exploited and represents one of the most promising areas for future development.

Social Indicators and Policy Research

During the last decade significant work has been done, too, in the area of social indicators. Through the development and use of such indicators, it may eventually be possible to keep tabs on major social trends in the same way that economic trends can now be monitored. At the present, conceptual issues are still being worked out, and the appropriate dimensions for social accounting are still under consideration. A few economists have begun work in social accounting, which traces the movement of persons in the educational system, in the health system, and in the occupational system. Thus, the methodology for social accounting has begun but is presently in its infancy.

Still another important development has been in methods of policy-related research. Evaluation has become a major tool of Federal policy. Under Government requirements many evaluations have been carried out, a very large proportion of them very poorly. Even newer than evaluative methods are methods for social experimentation. Several major sets of social experiments—in income maintenance and housing, for example—have been carried out or planned. This work, too, is in its infancy.

Computer Simulation

The advent of the computer has induced social scientists to engage in computer simulation of social processes in order to show the consequences of certain processes. Unfortunately, the available information does not meet the model's needs; it has not been possible to put together sufficiently rich and sufficiently precise data so that the system on the computer actually simulates the real system.

Systems Analysis

Instead of examining the relationship between an independent and a dependent variable, or even simultaneously considering a number of presumed causal and consequence variables, systems analysts have recently been examining organizational or institutional structures (families, factories, mental hospitals, educational institutions) in terms of circular or feedback relationships. Advanced statistical techniques and computer technology have made it possible for investigators to unravel the complexity of such structures.

Larger Units of Analysis

Although most quantitative sociological research has been conducted with individuals as subjects, social scientists have recently turned attention to larger units of analysis, called "collectives." The term "collective" is now used to refer to any combination of individuals, whether small informal groups, formal organizations, cities, or nations. These collectives can be characterized in terms of various dimensions, just as individuals can be characterized, and multivariate analyses of the data can be conducted. Thus, one can speak of the wealth of an individual or the wealth of a city, even if the latter is determined by aggregating discrete individual characteristics. Social scientists are now conducting multivariate analysis of samples of schools, factories, hospitals, societies, and so on. With such analyses, a new and higher level of generality has been reached.

Contextual Analysis

In this type of investigation, the focus shifts from the individual or collective to the environment within which it exists. For example, current studies of families of psychiatric patients view psychopathology in the individual person as a product of family process rather than of a process within the individual himself. Also, some scientists have become interested in the relationship between the characteristics of individuals and those predominant in their environments—their dissonance or consonance. The focus on the environment of groups reflects the same approach. While earlier anthropologists might study the village itself, some more recent workers would focus on the relationship of this village to the larger society.

Studies of Social Change

For many years social scientists have been concerned with the evolution and development of social systems. However, in the last 25 years this concern has become differentiated and greatly expanded. Theories and methods have been especially elaborated to monitor social change, to determine some of the influences leading to particular changes, and to determine the impact of change.

Such change has been studied at different levels. At one level is the study of individual changes. For example, samples of selected populations have been studied before and after mass education campaigns. As another example, psychological depression was evaluated before and after the Cuban missile crisis. Sociological interest has usually been on naturally occurring events affecting populations of substantial size rather than on controlled interventions with convenient subjects.

At another level, investigators are interested in the evolution and development of small social groups. To some extent this research parallels on the social level studies of individual growth, development, and senescence. One group of studies concerns the development of training and therapy groups; another is interested in developmental processes in ad hoc laboratory groups; a third is concerned with phases of family development.

Finally, at a third level, there is increasing interest in change in large-scale social systems and structures. Numerous studies have attempted to assess the effects of modernization on social systems and in doing so have been helpful in measuring the impact of social change on individuals.

RESEARCH PRIORITIES

It is extremely difficult to establish priorities in any basic research field because the course of scientific development is often unpredictable, and any effort to direct science strictly within predetermined channels is likely to lead to aridity. The judgments in this chapter are not meant to exclude excellent research in other social science areas.

Research focused on fundamental scientific issues in the area of social and cultural processes and research on questions more immediately relevant to mental health and social problems are both essential. Program priorities arising from a clear recognition of immediate problems rightly deserve a prominent place; yet in reacting to needs of the moment, NIMH should not lose sight of the necessity to be equipped to approach the future in other than a reactive fashion. The Institute's strategic goals can best be met, perhaps can only be met, if considerable effort is directed toward building up theory, methods, and substantive knowledge that will provide the means for meeting both the known and the unknown challenges that lie ahead.

Persons concerned with research priorities and the allocation of research support should be equipped with suitable decisionmaking glasses—bifocals that permit them to avoid the pitfalls both of research myopia (with its failure to see beyond near-term goals) and of research hyperopia (with its neglect of possible near-term applications). There is no standard prescription for these lenses: The Nation's circumstances vary from time to time, and the scientific disciplines concerned are not at a uniform stage of development. But the need for such glasses is crucial.

The substantive research recommendations that follow have been selected on the basis of several different considerations: (a) work of special importance or centrality to scientific progress; (b) work with strong implications for, or having a direct bearing on, mental health; and (c) new, neglected, or underdeveloped areas that show promise of fruitfulness. The order in which the recommendations are presented does not correspond to degree of priority.

Social Research Methodology

All science is heavily dependent on its methodology, and methodological work at present constitutes one of the most active and creative areas of social science. Such work should be strongly encouraged. The following areas in particular deserve support:

1. Multivariate methodology:

a. Further development of multivariate measures for use with attribute data;
b. Efforts to bring computer packages for multivariate analysis of attribute data to the same level of availability as that for continuous variables;
c. Continued development and assessment of statistical approaches to causal modeling.

2. Analysis of change through time:

a. Further developments in panel analysis, with particular stress on causation;
b. Methods for analysis of life histories and similar longitudinal data, including use of graphical techniques, lagged regression, and stochastic models;
c. Support on developing the interface of history and the more quantitative social sciences.

3. Social experimentation: A newly developing area of social research with important practical implications, since large-scale Government programs adopted and continued in the absence of knowledge concerning differential effectiveness can lead to costly partial successes

140

and even more costly failures. A number of methodological problems demand solution.

4. Causal analysis: In which one of the most prominent techniques introduced in recent years is "path analysis"; refinements and improvements are being introduced and should be encouraged.

Although the above probably represent the most active areas of methodological interest in recent years, many other areas require methodological development. These include: (1) development of techniques for studying interactions; (2) increased development and use of secondary analysis; (3) increased focus on the methodology for studying unplanned events, such as disasters and riots; (4) improvements in ethnography and participant observation; and (5) certain other promising methods, such as computer simulation, use of game theory, and use of unobtrusive measures.

Social Structure, Social Interaction, and Psychological Functioning

This topic is of central significance to the mission of the Institute. How society is organized and how the individual fits into that organization importantly shape the individual's personality, behavior, attitudes, beliefs, values, and life experiences. The importance of the major aspects of social identity—class, race, sex, religion, age, marital status—for personality formation and individual functioning has been abundantly documented. What is currently lacking is an adequate specification of the component and intervening variables that lead from social structural position to individual functioning.

Mechanisms Linking Social Structure and Individual Functioning

Although there is ample empirical documentation of the association between location in the social structure and various aspects of thought and behavior, the social structural variables tend to be rather broad and remote factors reflecting a complex diversity of experience. The higher rates of schizophrenia in the lower class have appeared in study after study, but the debate still rages regarding what it is about being lower class that is responsible for the statistical association. The same principle applies to other findings regarding social structure, on the one hand, and thought and behavior, on the other. Are the relationships spurious? Can component, intervening, or suppressor variables be discovered? Can the causal sequence involved be spelled out? These issues have important scientific and practical significance.

Status, Role, and Individual Functioning at the Organizational and Small Group Level

It is in our participation in formal organizations such as community organizations, churches, and work places, in small groups such as families, friendship groups, and clubs, and in other forms of organizational and group life that such factors as social class, race, sex, and age concretely influence the way we think and act. Through microanalysis of small group social interaction and process, social scientists have sought to discover laws that explain the observable interactions in all small groups. Further research in this area is strongly recommended, for many of these small groups are primary sources of affection, respect, and protection as well as primary sources of strain, conflict, and frustration; their implications for the mental health of the individual are self-evident. Larger organizations are also important: Two social scientists have noted that in American society preschool children and nonworking housewives are the only large group of persons whose behavior is not substantially "organizational." An increased focus is recommended on the impact of certain aspects of organizational structure, such as formalization and alleged impersonalization of relationships, and on the mental health and well-being of the individuals immersed in these formal organizations.

Social Structure and Psychological Processes

In speaking of the consequences of social structure, such elementary psychological processes as memory, learning, perception, concept formation, and cognition should not be neglected. Continued active support of research in attitudes, opinions, and values is also recommended. It is important to know more about how social structure and personality affect them, how to measure them, and how to change them. Another important area is "social perception." The individual's location in the social structure influences the way he perceives his world; hence, the objective realities of the social world are not necessarily identical with the individual's perception of them. Research should seek to account for discrepancies between objective events and subjective interpretations of them, to identify factors predictive of individual variations in such perceptions, and to examine how subjective perceptions may change the objective environment.

Structural Sources of Individual Stress

Research on how patterned social experience generates anxiety, insecurity, malaise, alienation, and the like—responses that may influence mental health—warrants priority. A great many social structural factors at one time or another have been suggested as inducing stress. They include role conflict, such as a father's conflicting obligations to his family and to his work; role ambiguity, such as uncertainty about how to treat the adolescent—as a child or as an adult—and current uncertainty about women's roles; a value system that encourages exalted aspirations and a structure that frustrates these aspirations for many; social instability and turmoil, challenging accepted values and beliefs in a wide variety of areas and threatening the individual's stable structure of beliefs; rapid and widespread geographical mobility, sundering established interpersonal relationships; the boredom, alienation, insecurity, and pressures of either technologically or bureaucratically structured places of work; and various other problems of modern living.

Although there is strong reason to think that such problems induce disagreeable emotional states, there is very little compelling empirical evidence that this is true; on the contrary, the evidence is often flatly contradictory. Evidently certain coping mechanisms and certain contextual factors can free the individual from potential stressors. This phenomenon in particular demands investigation.

Social and Cultural Factors Immediately Related to Mental Health

Studies by sociologists, anthropologists, social psychologists, and psychiatrists on social factors directly bearing on mental health should have high priority. One major problem is mental health measurement and classification. Is mental disorder a single type of disability or a number of distinct discrete entities? Is it a continuous variable, or attribute, or a multidimensional typology? How can we improve the selection of indicators and the formation of indices, both of mental disability and of positive mental health? These issues—further discussed in the chapters on mental illness and on mental health services—demand investigation.

Information is also needed on how psychological symptoms are identified in the population, how people differentially located in the social structure construe symptoms, and how social factors influence who gets what kind of treatment. We also need to know more about certain innovative treatment settings, such as halfway houses, day mental hospitals, community mental health centers, and home treatment programs. These settings involve social interaction within the treatment environment and between the patient and the community, and thus require careful studies of social contexts.

As discussed further in the chapter on treatment, a number of new "lay therapies" have emerged in recent years—encounter groups, sensitivity movements, marathon sessions, etc.—and these deserve analysis and evaluation. Because group structure and social interaction are such important elements in these therapies, the theories and methodological procedures of social science can be brought to bear in their evaluation.

Studies of the relationship of large-scale social structure to the pathogenesis of mental disorder should continue but should focus more directly on intervening variables, of which the family is perhaps the most important. Further knowledge is needed regarding the family's role in the development of mental illness. Studies dealing with the structure and evaluation of psychiatric institutions are needed, too, as are further studies of medical and psychiatric education and of the mental health professions as organized social structures.

Anthropological work on the effects of culture change, acculturation, and migration on mental illness should be supported. Also needed are studies of the efficacy of forms of psychotherapy in other than Western cultures.

Ethnography of Exotic and Modern Societies

The ethnography of exotic societies, meaning those radically different from our own, is the sole source of scientific knowledge about the full variety of cultural forms worked out by human societies. Such knowledge is vital for the study of many of the relations among cultural, psychological, environmental, biological, and historical variables; thus it is vital for understanding human behavior.

Such societies are vanishing at an alarming rate. As a result of rapid social and cultural change, caused by westernization in general and the encroachment of communications systems in particular, the results of millenia of human experience in social life are being rapidly inundated. If the

143

information is not obtained soon, it will be lost for good, at great cost to social science and mankind. Support of such research is thus essential.

Ethnographic studies of advanced societies also merit support. Though anthropologists have studied certain aspects of American society, they have frequently focused on the deviant, the problematic, the bizarre. Many important aspects of social process tend to be ignored simply because they are part of commonplace social functioning and are taken for granted. Yet, if social and psychological functioning is to be understood, it is imperative to study the settings in which people actually spend their lives. Similarly, research should be undertaken on the conforming and powerful, and not only the deviant and powerless, segments of society.

Comparative Research in Sociology

All social science is comparative, whether it is the anthropological comparison of exotic cultures with one another or with modern cultures, the sociological comparison of different groups, statuses, or social categories, or the social psychological comparison of experimental and control groups. Unfortunately, anthropologists tend to ignore the differences among status groups within a culture and sociologists fail to compare their own societies to others. Both fields have been impoverished as a consequence.

One limitation of American sociology is that, with few exceptions, it studies only America. Sociology is concerned with establishing general propositions based on the relationships among variables, but if one wants to study the relationship between X and Y, one cannot do so on the basis of one case. Furthermore, if one establishes a relationship between X and Y within a society, the question remains whether the same relationship would obtain in a comparable one. Only when one can show that the same types of relationships among variables appear in other societies—perhaps with different cultural, political, and technological development—can one hope to establish general propositions about societies. One striking example is the study cited earlier showing a remarkable similarity in occupational prestige ranking in a large number of societies, some with radically different political and cultural traditions.

There are many methodological problems involved in comparative studies, such as the problem of phenomenal identity and conceptual equivalence. Some progress is being made toward their solution, but there is much to be done. Unfortunately, such comparative work is often costly, and it will be necessary to select carefully those research proposals meriting support.

Although the sociologist can study a given aspect of social structure and can ascertain some of the mental health or social problem consequences, he can rarely change that structure or deliberately create alternatives. There are those, of course, who advocate certain alternative structures—familial, religious, economic, technological—in order to overcome the disadvantages of existing institutional arrangements. Such claims cannot readily be assessed. But the sociologist can study "natural experiments," institutional structures already to be found somewhere in the society or in other societies, in an attempt to assess their consequences and to compare them to those dominant in our society. Research on such social and cultural alternatives should receive high priority.

References

Barber, B. Social Stratification: A Comparative Analysis of Structure and Process. New York: Harcourt Brace, 1957.

Berelson, B., and Steiner, G.A. Human Behavior: An Inventory of Scientific Findings. New York: Harcourt Brace, 1964.

Blalock, H., Jr. Causal Inferences in Nonexperimental Research. Chapel Hill: University of North Carolina Press, 1964.

Blau, P.M. Structural effects. American Sociological Review, 25:178-193, 1960.

Blau, P.M., and Duncan, O.D. The American Occupational Structure. New York: Wiley, 1967.

Clinard, M.B. Sociology of Deviant Behavior. New York: Holt, Rinehart and Winston, 1957.

Coleman, J.S. Equality of Educational Opportunity. U.S. Office of Education. Washington, D.C.: U.S. Govt. Print. Off., 1966.

Davis, Kingsley. World Urbanization, 1950-1970, Vol. 11. Berkeley: Institute of International Studies, 1972.

Duncan, O.D. Path analysis: Sociological examples. American Journal of Sociology, 72:1-16, 1966.

Goffman, E. Asylums: Essays on the Social Situation of Mental Patients and Other Inmates. Garden City, N.Y.: Anchor Books, Doubleday, 1961.

Hauser, P., and Duncan, O.D. (eds). The Study of Populations: An Inventory and Appraisal. Chicago: University of Chicago Press, 1959.

Inkeles, A. Industrial man: The relation of status to experience, perception, and value. American Journal of Sociology, 66:1-31, 1960.

Inkeles, A., and Rossi, P. National Comparisons of Occupational Prestige. American Journal of Sociology, 61:329-339,1956.

Kendall, P.L., and Lazarsfeld, P.F. Problems of survey analysis. In: Merton, R.K. (ed). Continuities in Social Research: Studies in the Scope and Method of "The American Soldier." Glencoe, Ill.: Free Press, 1950.

Kohn, M.L. Class and Conformity: A Study of Values. Homewood, Ill.: Dorsey Press, 1969.

Kohn, M.L. Special class and schizophrenia: A critical review and a reformulation. Schizophrenia Bulletin, 7:60-79, 1973.

Lazarsfeld, P.F., and Rosenberg, M. (eds). The Language of Social Research: A Reader in the Methodology of Social Research. Glencoe, Ill.: Free Press, 1955.

Liebow, E. Tally's Corner: A Study of Negro Streetcorner Men. Boston: Little, Brown, 1967.

Lindzey, G., and Aronson, E. The Handbook of Social Psychology, Vol. 1. Reading, Mass.: Addison-Wesley, 1968.

Merton, R.K. Social Theory and Social Structure. Glencoe, Ill: Free Press, 1957.

Merton, R.K., Broom, L., and Cottrell, S., Jr. Sociology Today: Problems and Prospects. New York: Basic Books, 1959.

National Academy of Sciences. Rapid Population Growth: Consequences and Policy Implication, Vol. 1. Baltimore, Md.: Johns Hopkins Press, 1971.

Pearlin, L.T. Class Context and Family Relations: A Cross-National Study. Boston: Little, Brown, 1971.

Pettigrew, T. A Profile of the Negro American. Princeton, N.J.: Van Nostrand Reinhold, 1964.

Rosenberg, M. Society and the Adolescent Self-Image. Princeton, N.J.: Princeton University Press, 1965.

Rosenberg, M., and Simmons, R.G. Black and White Self-Esteem: The Urban School Child. Rose Monograph Series, No. 3. Washington, D.C.: American Sociological Association, 1972.

Skinner, B.F. Beyond Freedom and Dignity. New York: Knopf, 1971.

Stanton, A., and Schwartz, M. The Mental Hospital: A Study of Institutional Participation in Psychiatric Illness and Treatment. New York: Basic Books, 1954.

Taeuber, I., and Taeuber, C. People of the United States in the 20th Century. Census Monograph. Washington, D.C.: U.S. Govt. Print. Off., 1971.

Wechsler, H., Solomon, L., and Kramer, B.M. (eds). Social Psychology and Mental Health. New York: Holt, Rinehart and Winston, 1970.

Williams, R.M. American Society: A Sociological Interpretation. New York: Knopf, 1960.

Yarrow, M.R., Campbell, J.D., and Burton, R.V. Child Rearing: An Inquiry into Research and Methods. San Francisco: Jossey-Bass, 1968.

CHAPTER 7

The Basic Research Activities of the National Institute of Mental Health

INTRODUCTION

The three preceding chapters have described the major themes, outcomes, and directions of basic research in the fields of biology, psychology, and the social sciences. This chapter reviews the research practices and implicit policies of the Institute in its past and current support of basic research, offers recommendations for future directions of NIMH basic research efforts, and discusses improvements in organizational and administrative arrangements for assuring support of needed basic research.

DEFINITION OF TERMS

Numerous attempts have been made over the years to define the nature of basic research and to contrast it with so-called applied research. The task is laced with difficulty since neither type of research is inherently more scientific than the other or uses different methods or techniques; moreover, neither type can be argued to have a greater stake in fulfilling the mission of a health research agency.

Despite the hazards inherent in artificial categorization, there continues to be a practical need in the health context to differentiate basic research from research more readily categorized in relation to a specific problem area. The work of some researchers is manifestly aimed at the direct solution of clinical and categorical problems, while the work of others moves toward the same goal through a different route—by increasing our understanding of fundamental processes. For purposes of this report, then, "basic" refers to the study of underlying processes and mechanisms; "applied" refers both to the application of information on processes and mechanisms and to the clinical study of particular disorders and their prevention and treatment.

It is this distinction that has been used by the Task Force in analyzing the basic and categorical research programs of the Institute; the criteria have been further elaborated in the chapter on NIMH support of research activities, where they formed the basis for describing the overall research activities of the Institute.

DISCREPANT VIEWS OF THE ROLE OF BASIC RESEARCH

Among scientists, basic or applied, there is no question that research on fundamental processes has made, is making, and will continue to make valuable contributions to the mission of NIMH. But it is increasingly apparent that the scientists' conviction is no longer enthusiastically, or even tolerantly, shared by some sectors of society. The use of nonprogrammatic, nontargeted research as one of the approaches to the solution of practical problems meets with frank impatience. Many believe that the process of discovery could be accelerated by the adoption of a more focused, directed, coordinated research program. The nonscientist finds it difficult to understand the investigator's insistence on studying mechanisms and processes, some of which may appear to be remote from or tangential to problems identified by laymen as requiring urgent attention.

Such an understanding can often best be conveyed through a case history of research progress. The utility of investigator-initiated, nonprogrammatic basic research in contributing to NIMH goals can be illustrated, for example, by reviewing the history of a major discovery in the field of mental health. The story of one such discovery—the value of chlorpromazine in the treatment of schizophrenia—is recounted below.

LESSONS FROM A MAJOR DISCOVERY

The Committee on Brain Sciences of the National Research Council, supported financially by NIMH, undertook in 1969 to sponsor several historical inquiries into the nature of scientific discovery and its application. The project's intent was to describe in detail the events and processes leading to a landmark discovery and its application "in the hope that this would help to clarify not only what took place but also how one or another type of intervention might have affected the chain of events." Because the introduction of chlorpromazine for the treatment of schizophrenia was judged to have been the outstanding single practical contribution to psychiatry in several decades, it was chosen as the subject of the first study.

Now completed, Judith P. Swazey's study of the history of chlorpromazine begins with an account of the rise of the synthetic dye industry more than a century ago, and specifically with the discovery and synthesis by a German research chemist in 1883 of chlorpromazine's progenitor, phenothiazine. The new-found compound was a basic ingredient of one of the first coal tar dyes, methylene blue, and it had immediate uses in the dye industry. Much later, drugs of the phenothiazine family were tested for a number of medical uses, particularly during the second quarter of the 20th century. But chlorpromazine itself, a phenothiazine amine, was not synthesized and tested until 1950, by a research chemist working in the laboratories of a French pharmaceutical house.

In a foreword to the history, Dr. Seymour S. Kety, of the sponsoring committee, sums up some of the lessons to be drawn.

> There were many crucial discoveries, along numerous devious pathways, in ways that could not have been anticipated, to the synthesis of chlorpromazine . . . and its application in psychiatry. Those crucial contributions came from basic research and applied research, organic chemistry, biochemistry, physiology, pharmacology, surgery, experimental psychology, and eventually psychiatry. . . . The logic of a master plan was completely lacking; in its stead were a multitude of smaller plans, creative and logical

but none having as its goal a treatment of mental illness. . . . One conclusion, immediately apparent and rather surprising, is that none of the crucial findings or pathways that led, over a century, to the ultimate discovery of chlorpromazine and was essential to it would have been called relevant to the treatment of mental illness even by the most sophisticated judge.

If an attempt had been made to target research toward the treatment of schizophrenia, which of the crucial discoveries and pathways could have been supported as relevant?

Hardly the synthesis of phenothiazine by a chemist interested in methylene blue; not the study of anaphylaxis in guinea pigs (which is more clearly related to asthma); not the identification of histamine and its pharmacology (a substance that was not known to occur in the brain until many years later and whose role there is still obscure); . . . not the search for antihistaminic drugs; . . . not studies on operant conditioning in animals, and not the search by an anesthesiologist for an antihistaminic-sympatholytic drug that might be useful in mitigating surgical shock.

Not until 1949, Kety points out, after phenothiazine amines had been synthesized in the search for better antihistamines and after one of them, promethazine, had been used in the management of surgical shock, would a committee to plan and direct research toward a treatment for schizophrenia have found "an observation that it might have recognized as relevant to its goal: an unwanted and unsearched for sedation, but a kind of sedation different from that which was known to occur with the barbiturates—a 'euphoric quietude'."

And if in 1949 such a committee had acted upon this clue with all possible speed, "It is highly doubtful that the goal would have been achieved more rapidly than it actually was . . . ." Chlorpromazine was synthesized the following year, 1950; the first clinical trials began in 1951; a full-scale clinical test began in 1952; and chlorpromazine use spread beyond France, the country of its origin, in 1953.

Why did the crucial steps in the synthesis and application of chlorpromazine take so long? "Some of the time was used in carrying out necessary experiments and in publishing," Kety answers, "but the bulk of the time was spent in awaiting a collision between an item of knowledge and a creative and appropriately trained mind."

The foregoing account of chlorpromazine and its application in medicine is not an isolated example of the process by which a free system of scientific inquiry has resulted in contributions of salutary significance to society. Indeed, there are few 20th century advances that are not indebted in this way to basic scientific research. Moreover, the story of chlorpromazine underscores the view, expressed by all those concerned with the Task Force review, of the basic research activities of the Institute: that the scientific process is threatened when research must fit preconceived notions of what is relevant, and that basic research cannot be programed or planned in the manner of more applied research.

NIMH SUPPORT OF BASIC AND APPLIED RESEARCH

The intramural and extramural programs, as described in the chapter on NIMH support of research activities, represent two independent but complementary approaches to the NIMH research mission. While both are dedicated to supporting high-quality research, they differ with regard to scope and emphasis placed on basic research.

Table 1 presents a summary of the distribution of basic and applied program research within the intramural and extramural components of the Institute. As indicated in the table, the intramural program accounts for $16.3 million or about 20 percent of the total NIMH research expenditures, while the extramural program represents $63 million or roughly 80 percent of the total NIMH research budget. Considering both programs together, the overall support of basic research in 1972 amounted to 44 percent of the total $79.4 million research budget. However, the distribution of resources differed markedly in the two programs. In the intramural program, 81 percent of the budget was devoted to basic studies; in the extramural program, 35 percent.

TREND TOWARD APPLIED RESEARCH

In spite of the near balance achieved in 1972 in the basic and applied research programs of the Institute as a whole, recent years have witnessed an increasing polarization between proponents of organized, staff-initiated, large-scale research efforts in categorical (or applied or problem-oriented) areas on the one hand, and of decentralized, investigator-initiated research, selected for support solely through a process of peer review, on the other.

In federally financed health research during the past few years, increasing emphasis has been placed on studies specifically targeted toward problem areas. The trend is mirrored in the extramural research programs of the National Institute of Mental Health. Various approaches to analyzing the extramural programs in mental health research today all indicate, as does table 1, that 30-35 percent can be viewed as noncategorical or basic, while the remaining two-thirds involves categorical research. This ratio is precisely the reverse of that which obtained in the extramural programs a dozen years ago.

Another measure of the Institute's support for extramural basic research can be obtained by considering the percentages of approved grants funded over the 3-year period from 1971 through 1973 as recommended by the initial review groups concerned most directly with basic research. Table 2 contains these percentages, together with comparable figures for initial review groups in all other elements of the research program.

As table 2 indicates, in 1971, 64 percent of approved projects in the basic areas were paid as compared to 82 percent of all other approved research. In 1973, the corresponding percentages dropped to 37 percent for basic areas and 57 percent for the others. The 1973 funding rate for projects in basic areas shows a decrease of 42 percent from its 1971 level, while projects in other areas show a decrease of 30 percent. Not only was the funding rate for basic projects lower to begin with, but it has declined more rapidly.

Table 1

Distribution of Research Funds for Basic and Applied Studies in the Intramural and Extramural Programs, 1972
(Amounts in thousands, rounded)

	Intramural		Extramural		Total	
	Amount	%	Amount	%	Amount	%
Basic	$13,272	81	$22,070	35	$35,342	44
Applied	3,061	19	40,971	65	44,032	56
Total	$16,333 [a]	100	$63,041 [b]	100	$79,374	100

[a] These figures include $5.6 million contributed to the NIH Management Fund for administrative costs, maintenance of facilities, and patient-care functions but exclude the expenditures of the National Institute on Alcohol Abuse and Alcoholism; Mental Health Study Center; Addiction Research Center, Lexington; and the Overholser Division of Research and Training at St. Elizabeths Hospital.
[b] Excludes alcohol and drug abuse research expenditures.

Table 2

Paid Projects as a Percentage of All Approved Projects, CY 1971-1973 [a]

	CY 71	CY 72	CY 73
Basic [b]	64%	57%	37%
All Other [c]	82%	83%	57%

[a] CY—Council Year; e.g., CY 71 projects are those reviewed at the National Advisory Mental Health Council meetings of June 1970, November 1970, and March 1971.
[b] Basic—Projects reviewed by the experimental psychology, neuropsychology, personality and cognition, social sciences, and preclinical psychopharmacology review groups.
[c] All Other—Projects reviewed by all other review groups; see Appendix A, chapter 3 for complete list.

Table 3

Number of Positions in Intramural Research Program, NIMH

1966	1968	1970	1972	1974
481 [a]	452 [a]	401	378	378 (est.)

[a] Does not include positions for Addiction Research Center, part of the intramural program through 1968.

The trend away from support of basic research is mirrored also in the intramural program. A reflection of this trend is given in table 3, which contains the number of full-time permanent positions (scientific and supporting staff) in the intramural program from 1966 through 1974. Over the 9-year period, there has been roughly a 20 percent reduction in force in the intramural program, and a significant decrease, therefore, in support of its research activities.

THE INSTITUTE'S SUPPORT AND DISTRIBUTION OF BASIC RESEARCH EFFORT

It is difficult to consider relative priorities among areas of research against the current backdrop of either fixed funding patterns or shrinking levels of support for basic scientific investigations. But it is both possible and important to analyze the Institute's current basic research effort from the standpoint of the distribution of the effort (a) among the basic sciences and (b) within each basic science. This subject has received considerable attention and discussion by the Task Force participants. Reflected here are only some of the major considerations that have emerged; others are noted in various contexts throughout the report.

Analyses of the overall research are provided in the chapter on NIMH support of research activities; this section will focus on the two major research programs in the general mental health category: the extramural grants program ($63.0 millon in 1972) and the Mental Health Intramural Research Program ($16.3 million in 1972). Excluded from the analyses that follow are other intramural activities in general mental health (e.g., Mental Health Study Center) and all research activities of the alcohol and drug abuse programs.

Distribution Among Major Disciplines

Table 4 presents a breakdown of the Institute's research programs along major disciplinary lines.

The table shows that for the total Institute biological research accounts for 39 percent, psychological research for 38 percent, and social science

---

Table 4
Extramural and Intramural Programs in General Mental Health, 1972
(Amounts in thousands, rounded)

Research Approach [a]	Basic Amount	%	Type of Research Applied Amount	%	Total Amount	%
Biological [b]	$21,640	61	$ 9,474	22	$31,114	39
Psychological [c]	10,017	27	19,750	45	29,767	38
Social Science [d]	2,404	8	9,569	22	11,973	15
Other [e]	1,281	4	5,239	11	6,520	9
Total	$35,342	100	$44,032	100	$79,374	100

[a] Intramural research breakdown based on the major focus of each laboratory or branch. Extramural research analysis based on the discipline of the principal investigator modified by research area.

[b] Includes psychopharmacology, mechanisms of drug action, physiological psychology, biological psychiatry, neurology, anatomy, neuroanatomy, biology, biochemistry, genetics, neurophysiology, physiology, zoology, and chemistry.

[c] Includes experimental, child and developmental, clinical, personality, educational personality, general and psychometric psychology, and social psychiatry.

[d] Includes social psychology, anthropology, sociology, and epidemiology.

[e] Includes all other disciplines, such as medical specialties, education, and public health.

---

research for 15 percent of the overall research budget. The distribution of resources across these three major categories differs considerably, depending upon whether the research is basic or applied. For example, in applied areas, the amount of money devoted to psychological research is the same as that given to biological and social science research combined. In the basic areas though, biological research accounts for one and one-half times as much as all other areas of basic research.

The distribution of resources differs also depending on whether the research is conducted in the intramural program or through extramural auspices. A summary of intramural/extramural substantive emphases appears in table 5.

In the intramural program, the predominant emphasis is on biological approaches (biological, 70 percent; nonbiological, 30 percent). The reverse obtains in the extramural program, where the predominant emphasis is nonbiological (nonbiological, 69 percent; biological, 31 percent).

Table 5
Extramural and Intramural Programs in General Mental Health, 1972
(Amounts in thousands, rounded)

| | Research Component | | | | | |
| | Extramural | | Intramural | | Total | |
Research Approach	Amount	%	Amount	%	Amount	%
Biological	$19,659	31	$11,455	70	$31,114	39
Psychological	25,461	41	4,306	26	29,767	38
Social Science	11,401	18	572	4	11,973	15
Other	6,520	10	—	—	6,520	8
Total	$63,041	100	$16,333	100	$79,374	100

Distribution Within the Major Disciplines

This section presents a brief analysis of the distribution of resources within each of the major disciplinary areas of basic research covered by the Task Force review. The data contained in tables 6, 7, and 8 are based on a more detailed analysis of the findings presented in the two preceding tables. Again, only the major considerations that have emerged will be discussed.

Within Biology

Table 6 provides a picture of the distribution of funds in 1972 for major substantive areas within biology.

An analysis of the approximately $21.6 million devoted to the support of basic studies in the biological sciences in 1972 shows that two areas, psychopharmacology and mechanisms of drug action and physiological psychology, together account for 59 percent of all funds devoted to basic

Table 6
Basic Research: Biological Approaches, 1972
(Amounts in thousands, rounded)

Subdisciplines	Extramural		Intramural		Total	
	Amount	%	Amount	%	Amount	%
Psychopharmacology [a] and Mechanisms of Drug Action	$ 3,609	31	$ 3,658	36	$ 7,267	34
Biological Psychiatry	830	7	—	—	830	4
Physiological Psychology	4,997	44	506	5	5,503	25
Other Biological Sciences [b]	2,035	18	6,005	59	8,040	37
Total	$11,471	100	$10,169	100	$21,640	100

[a] Includes pharmacology and psychopharmacological research by psychiatrists.
[b] Includes neurology, anatomy, neuroanatomy, biology, genetics, biochemistry (exclusive of mechanisms of drug action), neurophysiology, physiology, zoology.

biological investigations, or almost 50 percent more than all other areas of biology combined. In the extramural program, 75 percent of research grants go to studies in these two fields; only 25 percent of extramural money is distributed among all other areas of biology.

Within Psychology

Table 7 provides a distribution of major disciplinary areas represented in the basic psychological research efforts supported through NIMH grants and intramural funds.

Over half of the $10 million research budget devoted to basic psychological studies is in the area of experimental psychology, with the remainder of the funds distributed among all other areas. (An analysis of categorical or applied research programs shows that in those programs the reverse is the case: Over $20 million is channeled to clinical, personality, and child development researchers, with only $1.6 million going to experimental psychologists.) It should be noted that experimental research encompasses a wide variety of topics which interdigitate with the other categories; for example, developmental studies may be supported under this rubric though they are not carried out by developmental psychologists.

Within Social Sciences

Table 8 gives the distribution of basic research funds within social science disciplines. Social psychologists receive almost half of the funds allocated to social science research, while anthropologists and sociologists together account for almost all of the remainder.

Table 7
Basic Research: Psychological Approaches, 1972
(Amounts in thousands, rounded)

	Extramural		Intramural		Total	
	Amount	%	Amount	%	Amount	%
Experimental	$ 4,603	62	$ 653	26	$ 5,256	52
Child & Development	572	8	1,878	74	2,450	24
Personality	481	6	—	—	481	5
Clinical	661	9	—	—	661	7
Other [a]	776	10	—	—	776	8
Social Psychiatry	393	5	—	—	393	4
Total	$ 7,486	100	$ 2,531	100	$10,017	100

[a] Includes counseling, education, psychometrics and statistics, and industrial and general psychology.

Table 8
Basic Research: Social Science Approaches, 1972
(Amounts in thousands, rounded)

	Extramural		Intramural		Total	
Subdisciplines	Amount	%	Amount	%	Amount	%
Social Psychology	$ 346	46	$229	40	$1,057	45
Anthropology	586	32	—	—	586	24
Sociology	333	18	343	60	676	28
Other	67	4	—	—	67	3
Total	$1,832	100	$572	100	$2,404	100

As noted in table 4, the social science disciplines receive 8 percent of the Institute's total support for basic research. The low funding levels for basic social science research can be contrasted with support afforded social scientists in applied research. Of the $12 million devoted to social science research in 1972, more than $9.5 million went to support applied research projects.

RECOMMENDATIONS

The issue of setting priorities for research has been a central concern of the Task Force. The issue as it applies to the entire research program of the Institute and as it relates specifically to basic research is also discussed in the chapter on administration and organization. Regarding basic research, it is essential that an active program be maintained at a healthy productive level at both the biological and psychosocial ends of the life science continuum. This is so because the very nature of the basic research process is exploration of the unknown. If anyone knew in advance what knowledge would be found and how to find it, there would be no need for this kind of research.

The Institute's Targeted Priorities

The single most dominant issue in discussions and work sessions of the Task Force has been the role of basic research within the context of a mission-oriented Government agency and, more specifically, the question of whether the basic research activities of the Institute can be targeted or programed. In the final analysis, the notion of strengthening the tie between basic research activities and the overall program priorities received little support from Task Force participants. Instead, there was overwhelming agreement that setting specific institutionally determined priorities for basic research is inappropriate.

Substantive Recommendations

The optimal strategy for solution of the Nation's mental health problems depends upon keeping open a broad front of scientific inquiry—short, of course, of supporting any and all research disciplines. There was wide agreement that the Institute should focus its support on those fields reviewed in the three preceding chapters. Many domains of biology, psychology, and the social sciences have been excluded even though it is conceivable that findings from these fields might ultimately have relevance to NIMH concerns. Excluded because they lack sufficient criteria of relevance are, for example, all or most studies in the fields of enzymology, immunology, virology, physical chemistry, reproductive physiology, personnel psychology, sensorimotor research in the use of instruments, advertising psychology, public opinion research, and physical anthropology.

Support for Basic Research

Criteria for determining the amount of basic research that should be supported in connection with health and other social goals are difficult to establish. Indeed, there exists no coherent set of principles nor underlying theory that could be drawn upon to determine, for example, what proportion of all Federal funds should go into research on problems that are capable of being solved or ameliorated by scientific means; what proportion of these research funds should go into biomedical research as compared to, say, energy research; or, within biomedical programs, how should the funds allocated for research compare to those for training and services.

Criteria for determining the amount of the total NIMH research budget that should be given to the support of basic research are no less difficult to establish. Many argue that each mission-oriented agency should assume the responsibility for supporting basic science at a level which bears some fixed relation to the size of the applied science budget. There is an implication in some cases of an immutable and universal percentage beyond which support of basic research should not be increased. The Task Force view, in contrast, is that, in the absence of a priori principles, the allocation of resources to basic research should be based on the record of accomplishments of such research. The record in the field of mental health is set forth in this report, particularly in the accounts provided in the three preceding chapters. The record of accomplishments for biomedical research in general can be found in such documents as "Biology and the Future of Man," a comprehensive review undertaken by the National Academy of Sciences, in "The Behavioral and Social Sciences: Outlook and Needs," and in the aforementioned recent NIMH-supported retrospective study of chlorpromazine conducted by the National Academy of Sciences.

These and other analyses of scientific achievement indicate that the source of future knowledge resides, in large measure, in basic research. Because progress in the solution of the Nation's biomedical and social problems is contingent on the development of new knowledge and new ideas, the Task Force recommends that basic research be regarded as of central importance to achieving the Institute's mission. Such research should be considered as valid and critical as other means, including other research means, used to reach NIMH goals.

Recommendations for Distribution of Basic Research Within Areas

Analysis of the basic research programs supported by the Institute's grant mechanisms shows that the range of studies on the psychological bases of behavior is somewhat broader than that of studies on the biological and sociocultural bases. There is some evidence that support for research in biology and social science is being sought more actively from sources other than NIMH. Eminent social scientists have commented that leading investigators in their field have begun to perceive NIMH as having reduced its interest in basic social science research. Among many biologists, NIMH was rarely seen as an important source of support. Even though the view may be overstated, the result for NIMH may be a loss of high caliber work in areas essential to its mission.

Biological Research

Within biology, approximately 59 percent of the funds is devoted to studies on the mechanisms of drug action, biogenic amines, and physiological psychology. It is regarded as entirely appropriate that the Institute continue to provide strong support in these areas. The Institute should, however, find ways to increase its support of other pertinent areas of neurobiology—neuroanatomy, neurophysiology, behavioral and biochemical genetics, and neuroendocrinology. Ultimately, contributions from all of these areas will be necessary to understand fully even the simplest behavioral act, or to prevent behavioral or mental disorders of any type. Knowledge of the biochemical factors in psychopathology provides an opening into the incredibly complex puzzle of mental illness. For complete understanding of the mental disorders, it is necessary to know if selective areas of the brain are involved, what physiological functions are disturbed, how hormonal factors affect neurotransmitter function, and how these processes and their normal development are regulated by genes. It is recommended, therefore, that the Institute support a broader range of biological investigations, without, however, diminishing support for the research in neurochemistry or psychopharmacology.

Psychological Research

In contrast with biology, psychology represents a field of scientific endeavor in which current levels of support would appear to reflect major trends in the field. The Institute's strong emphasis on experimental psychology in the extramural program and child developmental psychology, in the intramural program primarily, is in keeping with the demonstrated abilities of these subdisciplines to contribute substantially to the understanding of behavior and its development. Because of the relevance of psychological research to the understanding of normal and abnormal behavior and to the promotion of psychological adjustment, NIMH must continue to regard such research as central to its concerns. It is advisable also that the Institute continue to interpret the domain of its inquiry broadly, supporting research on mechanisms of learning and memory as well as studies aimed at the assessment of personality and avenues of individual adjustment.

As shown earlier, table 4, the Institute supports applied psychological research twice as heavily as psychological research on basic processes. Further, as shown in table 2, the proportion of approved projects that is actually funded is higher for applied studies than for basic studies. Efforts should be made to achieve a better balance between support for basic and support for applied psychological research.

Social Science Research

The Institute devotes about 15 percent of its research funds to studies by social scientists. However, only about one-fifth of the money for the social sciences supports basic research. As with other areas of knowledge, the solution of social problems and of problems related to the social aspects of mental health relies heavily on the transfer and application of theories, methods, and findings from basic research. Funds for basic studies should be increased and a more reasonable balance between basic and applied programs should be established. This recommendation is congruent with the ends sought by the Task Force Study Group on Social Problems; its review of the Institute's programs directed toward social problems indicates that these were lacking in cohesion and basic conceptual underpinnings.

The recommendations to support a broader range of biological research and to increase support of social science research is consonant with the general principle that broad and free-ranging inquiry is the optimal strategy for basic research. It may be argued that other Federal agencies, such as the National Science Foundation and the National Institutes of Health, provide adequate support for basic biological investigations. The difficulty is that bureaucratically defined boundaries are not always consonant with considerations of scientific relevance. Thus, when basic research is supported by an agency that has a specified mission, the investigators are more alert to possibilities that lead in the direction of the goals of that mission. Though guided by the logic of scientific research, and given choice points with approximately equal scientific promise, scientists are more likely to go in the direction of the mission. This is well illustrated in the case of Dr. Julius Axelrod, Nobel Laureate, whose work on biogenic amines was encouraged by his transfer from the National Heart Institute to the National Institute of Mental Health. Certainly it is not desirable to define the subject matter of interest to NIMH in terms of what other Institutes exclude, but rather in terms of what NIMH will likely need to understand in order to pursue solutions to the Nation's mental health problems. Incidentally, scientists from the academic community wish to apply for grant support from Institutes whose stated goals are most consonant with their own. The current procedure, under which management decides which grant applications should go to which Institute, creates an unnecessary step in the administrative process.

Creation of Neurobiology Initial Review Group

The Institute's extramural research division supports basic research through a peer review system of initial review groups. Presently, the Behavioral Sciences Research Branch of the Division of Extramural Research Programs provides for much of the support of basic research through its review groups in experimental psychology, neuropsychology, personality and cognition, and social sciences. Basic studies in biological research (other than neuropsychological investigations) are supported mainly by the Pharmacology Section of the Psychopharmacology Research Branch. No review group composed of neurobiologists, other than the preclinical psychopharmacology committee, considers grant applications in basic biological studies. The Task Force recommendations for substantive emphases within biology would involve creation of a new initial review group in neurobiology.

Criteria for Selection of Projects Within and Across Areas

The most frequently enunciated criterion, both within the Task Force and outside, for the support of basic research projects and programs is that of excellence. No one committed to the development of valid information based on scientific inquiry would argue with the notion that excellence must be the abiding criterion for the commitment of funds to research. Indeed, there is little purpose in restricting this standard to basic research or applying it more rigorously to basic than to applied or categorical efforts. To do so would raise the untenable possibility that the Institute should under some conditions wittingly support poor research.

The peer review system has been developed as a mechanism for assigning priorities to grant proposals on the basis of scientific merit. One of the virtues of this mechanism is that it is empiric rather than dogmatic, thus assuring that there will be a close correspondence between important developments in the scientific field and the research supported by NIMH. In addition, the peer review system provides a means of assessing "ripeness" or researchability of scientific problems. A recent NIH response to an OMB paper on the peer review system argued that:

> Readiness of a research area is not scalable with any degree of accuracy by field/discipline/specialty over the whole range of NIH

responsibilities. In the vast domains of inquiry, where the lack of knowledge is greatest, a priori identification and quantitative scaling of "ripe" areas is fraught with such hazards and uncertainty that a different sort of approach, operational in character, has been developed. Against well-known desiderata—preventing or curing cancer, diabetes, gout, etc.—proposals from scientists are evaluated by their peers in terms of technical and program priority. Scientists can only work where there is a problem they can "get a handle on." If a project application achieves a high technical merit rating, the specific problem it addresses is "ready" or "ripe" for exploration. Limiting support to proposals of high quality automatically insures that resource application matches readiness.

The same conclusions apply where NIMH programs are concerned. Finally the peer review system is a vehicle for considerations of relevance—not on a wholesale dogmatic basis but on a project-by-project basis. It would be unrealistic to assume that estimates of scientific merit do not implicitly entail judgments of ultimate significance and mission relevance. Projects of high technical merit but of apparent trivial import could not reasonably be given high-priority ratings by scientific experts.

The peer review system, in the view of the Task Force and its consultants, is the appropriate mechanism for arriving at research priorities for the Institute. As such, it must be protected and strengthened. A number of suggestions and recommendations for maintaining the high quality of this system are given elsewhere in this report, mainly in the administration and organization chapter. The Task Force study groups on basic research endorse in particular the suggestions for modifying the procedures for appointing new members. The suggested modifications, it is believed, would protect more effectively against the criticism that individuals perpetuate their scientific biases by advising on the selection of their own replacements.

The most important step the Institute can take in relation to the initial review groups is action to maintain uniformly high standards of excellence for all of its review groups, no matter in what research area. In addition, steps should be taken to insure that high quality proposals will not go unfunded in some areas, while projects of lesser merit are funded in others. Moreover, a more uniform emphasis on quality may serve to increase the fluidity of funds across the review process, with funds for projects not deemed worthy of support in one area made available for funding highly regarded projects in another.

Relationship Between the Intramural and Extramural Research Programs

Independence of Programs

The Task Force participants have repeatedly emphasized that basic process research, unlike applied-categorical research, is not enhanced by attempts at central planning imposed on the investigator. Since the intramural organization is primarily concerned with basic research, central planning of its work is inappropriate.

Substantive Emphasis

The intramural program of NIMH, like the intramural programs of the National Institutes of Health, has proved to be a setting conducive to high-quality research. Continued support of this program is highly recommended. Because of the limited size of the intramural program, and the necessary restraints on its growth and turnover, the intramural program cannot mirror the extramural program in breadth of substantive coverage. Indeed, no specific guidelines emerged from the Task Force's review specifically addressing the issue of program balance in the intramural program. There is, however, general agreement that a reconsideration of substantive emphases is necessary in the light of shrinking budgets—with the view toward strengthening those segments of the intramural research program that do not now enjoy sufficient support. Analyses of the relative support afforded major subfields discussed earlier should be considered in this priority-setting process. With due consideration for the uniqueness of the intramural research programs, the process should be accomplished where possible with the aid also of peer review.

Collaboration

Collaboration between intramural and extramural programs should continue to be on an informal rather than a formal basis.

1. Extramural researchers who wish to work in the intramural laboratories should be allowed to continue to work out such arrangements with appropriate intramural investigators, provided that facilities are available.

2. Intramural investigators should continue to be invited to participate in extramural activities, such as site visits, conferences, and initial review group activities, on a regular ad hoc basis.

3. Sabbatical and work assignment exchanges for limited periods should be encouraged.

The Research Environment

Basic research is most effectively conducted in an environment conducive to and supportive of the scientific enterprise—that is, an environment in which fundamental research is seen as the foundation of the entire program. It is recommended, therefore, that advocacy and support for research be strengthened and institutionalized at the highest levels of the NIMH organization.

SUMMARY OF MAJOR CONCLUSIONS

In the last decade there has been an increasing trend in NIMH toward emphasizing categorical or targeted research and deemphasizing basic research. Because basic research generates new knowledge about the myriad of complex processes constituting human normal and abnormal behavior, knowledge necessary for alleviating mental illness and strengthening mental health, the trend toward reducing the support of basic research should be halted and reversed.

With an increase in support of basic research, funds for currently under-supported areas of basic research in the fields of biology and the social sciences could be increased, while strong support of psychological studies is maintained.

Basic research on biological, psychological, and sociocultural processes cannot be planned to nearly the extent possible for targeted and applied research.

The criterion for funding of all research—basic and targeted—is and should be scientific excellence, a criterion that inherently includes considerations of relevance and the likelihood of advancing knowledge.

References

The Behavioral and Social Sciences: Outlook and Needs. Englewood Cliffs, N.J.: Prentice Hall, 1969.

Handler, P. (ed). Biology and the Future of Man. London: Oxford University Press, 1970.

"Peer Review." Commentary on an OMB paper prepared by the Office of the Director, NIH, April 11, 1973.

The Research Grant Program of the NIMH: A Source Book of Descriptive Data—Fiscal Year 1961. March 15, 1962.

Swazey, J.P. Chlorpromazine: Innovation and Revolution in the Drug Treatment of Mental Disease States. Boston: Massachusetts Institute of Technology Press, in press.

CHAPTER 8

Research on Mental Illness and Behavior Disorders

INTRODUCTION

Mental illness and behavior disorders today are among the Nation's most severe public health problems. In terms of morbidity rather than mortality and in terms of human suffering and economic loss, these disorders rival heart disease and cancer. A survey published in 1968 showed that nearly half of all hospital beds in this country were occupied by patients with mental syndromes. Data from the National Health Survey prepared in 1970 by the National Center for Health Statistics indicate that an estimated 20 million adults have had mental health problems.

It has been estimated that 10 percent of the United State's population suffers from some mental illness, with approximately one-seventh of these actually receiving psychiatric treatment. If rates of first admission into a broad spectrum of psychiatric facilities are applied to a life table, the results would predict that 1 in 20 of all United States children who survive beyond age 15 will develop schizophrenia sometime during their lives. One study reported that approximately 80 percent of the urban population in its survey, in the age group 15-59 years, had varying degrees of symptoms of mental pathology that affected performance of daily life roles. About 24 percent of the sample were classified "impaired," that is, had marked or severe symptom formation or were incapacitated.

The national costs of these disorders are immense. Apart from the incalculable price extracted in human misery and suffering, and without attempting to identify in the costs of other illnesses that amount linked to psychological factors—for example, the role of psychological tension in causing ulcers and hypertension—recent estimates of cost to the Nation approach $20 billion per year.

The pervasiveness and serious national costs of mental disorders were recognized in the original establishment of the National Institute of Mental Health within the National Institutes of Health. Studies of mental illness and behavior disorders were the main focus of the early NIMH research effort and, with research on treatment, constituted over 65 percent of extramural grant support. Since then, the relative emphasis NIMH has placed on research directly concerned with mental illness and behavior disorders has changed substantially. This is reflected in the distribution over time of extramural grant funds. In NIMH's first 25 years, there has been an increase in absolute dollars devoted to all mental illness research but a substantial decrease in the relative emphasis devoted to direct research—that

162

is, categorized, or clinical, or targeted research—on the mental disorders. This relative decline, computed over all extramural grants, is from approximately 65 to 15 percent. Further, within the broad category of direct research on mental disorders, there has been an increasing trend to channel mental illness research predominantly into studies of the most severe of the mental disorders—the functional psychoses, namely, schizophrenia and affective disorders. Correspondingly, the proportion of research resources going to all other areas has dropped. Thus, in 1971, more than 60 percent of all extramural grants for direct research on the mental disorders was expended on functional psychosis research, more than three times the combined total of research expenditures on psychosomatic illnesses, psychoneuroses and personality disorders, and organic psychoses. This distribution is not consistent with relative incidence and prevalence data. It does reflect, however, the relative social cost and human suffering involved, and critical scientific considerations; i.e., that more severely ill patients are hospitalized and therefore available for study and that the roots of mental disorder are more likely to be discovered when studied in the most severe forms.

The relative decrease in a primary research focus upon mental illness and behavior disorders stems from numerous factors. Foremost among these are legislative pressures to focus research on emerging social concerns, such as alcoholism and drug abuse; a broadening concept of mental disorder that includes such social problems as crime and delinquency; and an increasing emphasis by scientists on basic biological and psychological studies in seeking the causes of mental illness.

PROBLEM DEFINITION

DSM II, the Diagnostic and Statistical Manual of Mental Disorders (3rd edition), published by the American Psychiatric Association, is the current national standard for psychiatric diagnosis. It identifies 148 different mental disorders, grouped into 10 major categories (see table 1). (One of these major categories—mental retardation—is not surveyed in this report because it is currently the responsibility of health research components outside NIMH.) The bulk of the Task Force's attention was addressed to the following conditions which, from both clinical and research perspectives, were determined to be of primary importance: schizophrenia, affective or depressive disorders, organic brain disorders, psychoneuroses, psychosomatic disorders, childhood mental illness, and mental health problems of aging. The Study Group on Mental Illness and Behavior Disorders approached the task from two perspectives: developments in the overall scientific approach to these problems, and developments in research directly relevant to the specific disorders.

MAJOR RESEARCH TRENDS

Despite the dwindling proportion, over the last 25 years, of NIMH research funds devoted strictly to research on mental illness as traditionally conceived, the increase in absolute terms has been considerable. The expanded body of research activity has been marked by a number of trends that have yielded significant advances in knowledge. The trends have included:

Table 1
List of DSM-II Diagnoses and Code Numbers †

(Reproduced with permission of the American Psychiatric Association)

I   MENTAL RETARDATION

310.	Borderline
311.	Mild
312.	Moderate
313.	Severe
314.	Profound
315.	Unspecified

With each: Following or associated with

.0	Infection or intoxication
.1	Trauma or physical agent
.2	Disorders of metabolism, growth or nutrition
.3	Gross train disease (postnatal)·
.4	Unknown prenatal influence
.5	Chromosomal abnormality
.6	Prematurity
+ .7	Major psychiatric disorder
+ .8	Psycho-social (environmental) deprivation
.9	Other condition

II   ORGANIC BRAIN SYNDROMES (OBS)
A   PSYCHOSES

Senile and pre-senile demantia

290.0	Senile dementia
290.1	Pre-senile dementia

Alcoholic psychosis

+ 291.0	Delirium tremens
+ 291.1	Korsakov's psychosis
+ 291.2	Other alcoholic hallucinosis
+ 291.3	Alcohol paranoid state
+ 291.4*	Acute alcohol intoxication*
+ 291.5*	Alcoholic deterioration*
+ 291.6*	Pathological intoxication*
291.9	Other alcoholic psychosis

Psychosis associated with intracranial infection

292.0	General paralysis
292.1	Syphilis of CNS
292.2	Epidemic encephalitis
292.3	Other and unspecified encephalitis
292.9	Other intracranial infection

Psychosis associated with other cerebral condition

293.0	Cerebral arteriosclerosis
293.1	Other cerebrovascular disturbance
293.2	Epilepsy
293.3	Intracranial neoplasm
293.4	Degenerative disease of the CNS
293.5	Brain trauma
293.9	Other cerebral condition

Psychosis associated with other physical condition

294.0	Endocrine disorder
294.1	Metabolic and nutritional disorder
294.2	Systemic infection
294.3	Drug or poison intoxication (other than alcohol)
+ 294.4	Childbirth
294.8	Other and unspecified physical condition

B   NON-PSYCHOTIC OBS

309.0	Intracranial infection
+ 309.13*	Alcohol* (simple drunkenness)
+ 309.14*	Other drug, poison or systemic intoxication*
309.2	Brain trauma
309.3	Circulatory disturbance
309.4	Epilepsy
309.5	Disturbance of metabolism, growth, or nutrition
309.6	Senile or pre-senile brain disease
309.7	Intracranial neoplasm
309.8	Degenerative disease of the CNS
309.9	Other physical condition

III   PSYCHOSES NOT ATTRIBUTED TO PHYSICAL CONDITIONS LISTED PREVIOUSLY

Schizophrenia

295.0	Simple
295.1	Hebephrenic
295.2	Catatonic
+ 295.23*	Catatonic type, excited*
+ 295.24*	Catatonic type, withdrawn*
295.3	Paranoid
+ 295.4	Acute schizophrenic episode
+ 295.5	Latent
295.6	Residual
295.7	Schizo-affective
+ 295.73*	Schizo-affective, excited*
+ 295.74*	Schizo-affective, depressed*
295.8*	Childhood*
295.90*	Chronic undifferentiated*
295.99*	Other schizophrenia*

Major affective disorders

296.0	Involutional melancholia
296.1	Manic-depressive illness, manic
296.2	Manic-depressive illness, depressed
296.3	Manic-depressive illness, circular
+ 296.33*	Manic-depressive, circular, manic*
+ 296.34*	Manic-depressive, circular, depressed*
296.8	Other major affective disorder

Paranoid states

297.0	Paranoia
+ 297.1	Involutional paranoid state
297.9	Other paranoid state

Other psychoses

298.0	Psychotic depressive reaction

IV   NEUROSES

300.0	Anxiety
300.1	Hysterical
+ 300.13*	Hysterical, conversion type*
+ 300.14*	Hysterical, dissociative type*
300.2	Phobic
300.3	Obsessive compulsive
300.4	Depressive
+ 300.5	Neurasthenic
+ 300.6	Depersonalization
+ 300.7	Hypochondriacal
300.8	Other neurosis

Table 1 (Continued)

V   PERSONALITY DISORDERS AND CERTAIN OTHER NON-PSYCHOTIC MENTAL DISORDERS

Personality disorders

	301.0	Paranoid
	301.1	Cyclothymic
	301.2	Schizoid
+	301.3	Explosive
	301.4	Obsessive compulsive
+	301.5	Hysterical
+	301.6	Asthenic
	301.7	Antisocial
	301.81*	Passive-aggressive*
	301.82*	Inadequate*
	301.89*	Other specified types*

Sexual deviation

+	302.0	Homosexuality
+	302.1	Fetishism
+	302.2	Pedophilia
+	302.3	Transvestitism
+	302.4	Exhibitionism
+	302.5*	Voyeurism*
+	302.6*	Sadism*
+	302.7*	Masochism*
	302.8	Other sexual deviation

Alcoholism

+	303.0	Episodic excessive drinking
+	303.1	Habitual excessive drinking
+	303.2	Alcohol addiction
	303.9	Other alcoholism

Drug dependence

+	304.0	Opium, opium alkaloids and their derivatives
+	304.1	Synthetic analgesics with morphine-like effects
+	304.2	Barbiturates
+	304.3	Other hypnotics and sedatives or "tranquilizers"
+	304.4	Cocaine
+	304.5	Cannabis sativa (hashish, marihuana)
+	304.6	Other psycho-stimulants
+	304.7	Hallucinogens
	304.8	Other drug dependence

VI   PSYCHOPHYSIOLOGIC DISORDERS

305.0	Skin
305.1	Musculoskeletal
305.2	Respiratory
305.3	Cardiovascular
305.4	Hemic and lymphatic
305.5	Gastro-intestinal
305.6	Genito-urinary
306.7	Endocrine
305.8	Organ of special sense
305.9	Other type

VII   SPECIAL SYMPTOMS

	306.0	Speech disturbance
	306.1	Specific learning disturbance
+	306.2	Tic
+	306.3	Other psychomotor disorder
+	306.4	Disorders of sleep
+	306.5	Feeding disturbance
	306.6	Enuresis
+	306.7	Encopresis
+	306.8	Cephalalgia
	306.9	Other special symptom

VIII   TRANSIENT SITUATIONAL DISTURBANCES

307.0*	Adjustment reaction of infancy*
307.1*	Adjustment reaction of childhood*
307.2*	Adjustment reaction of adolescence*
307.3*	Adjustment reaction of adult life*
307.4*	Adjustment reaction of late life*

IX   BEHAVIOR DISORDERS OF CHILDHOOD AND ADOLESCENCE

+	308.0*	Hyperkinetic reaction*
+	308.1*	Withdrawing reaction*
+	308.2*	Overanxious reaction*
+	308.3*	Runaway reaction*
+	308.4*	Unsocialized aggressive reaction*
+	308.5*	Group delinquent reaction*
	308.9*	Other reaction*

X   CONDITIONS WITHOUT MANIFEST PSYCHIATRIC DISORDER AND NON-SPECIFIC CONDITIONS

Social maladjustment without manifest psychiatric disorder

+	316.0*	Marital maladjustment*
+	316.1*	Social maladjustment*
+	316.2*	Occupational maladjustment*
	316.3*	Dyssocial behavior*
+	316.9*	Other social maladjustment*

Non-specific conditions

+	317*	Non-specific conditions*

No Mental Disorder

+	318*	No mental disorder*

XI   NON-DIAGNOSTIC TERMS FOR ADMINISTRATIVE USE

319.0*	Diagnosis deferred*
319.1*	Boarder*
319.2*	Experiment only*
319.3*	Other*

† Many of the titles here are listed in abbreviated form.
+ These are new diagnoses, that do not appear in DSM-I.
* These diagnoses are for use in the U.S. only and do not appear in ICD-8.

Focus on Interaction

Results of the last 25 years of research have brought into much sharper focus the importance of interaction of biological, psychological, and social factors in the development of mental illness and behavioral disorders. This has resulted in a shift away from the oversimplified purely biological or purely psychological theory about etiology. (See, for example, the discussion in the chapter on sociocultural processes of the possible interaction of genetics, stress, and social class in the development of schizophrenia.) These developments can be illustrated by the growth of interdisciplinary societies such as the American College of Neuropsychopharmacology where the focus is on the relationship of biology and behavior and by the growth of studies that look simultaneously at biochemical and sociocultural factors in a given individual's mental disorder.

Developments in Biology

A major recent development is the emergence of exciting hypotheses about the biological factors involved in the interaction noted above. Three lines of psychobiological evidence have been used to help generate these new hypotheses:

1. There is evidence that genetic factors play an important role in schizophrenia and depressive illness. These genetic factors must express themselves through as yet unidentified changes in RNA and DNA.

2. Chemical agents are currently known that can exacerbate both schizophrenia and depression and that can markedly decrease the symptomatology in acute schizophrenia and in manic-depressive and depressive illness.

3. It is known that most of the drugs that affect the monoamine neurotransmitters—norepinephrine, dopamine, and serotonin—change mood and cognition in man, functions that are disturbed in most mental illnesses. These drugs act by affecting metabolic processes, at least some of which may represent a biological defect or dysfunction in these illnesses. Drugs that exacerbate or decrease symptomatology in the two major functional psychoses affect neurotransmission. Although other biological systems may well be involved, the drugs' effects on neurotransmission may be critical to their mode of action. Thus, a promising and powerful avenue of research has involved study of the role of neurotransmitters in schizophrenia and depressive illness; the search for protein defects, some of which may be genetically transmitted; and the elucidation of the specific therapeutic modes of action of psychopharmacological agents in these disorders.

Coming together as they do, the data from research in genetics, recent work on the neurotransmitters, and pharmacology offer an important opportunity for future advances in understanding the biological factors involved in mental illness.

166

Major Changes in Psychological and Sociocultural Research

Research on psychological and sociocultural approaches has over the last 25 years sought new avenues and shown some marked shifts in direction. Global or simplistic explanations (e.g., the schizophrenogenic mother) have received decreasing attention, while less dramatic but potentially much more productive methodological and conceptual initiatives have been fostered. These include:

1. Methodological advances in quantifying observations and judgments of symptoms, nonverbal behavior, affective states, and social behavior. These advances have made possible extensive research on problems critical to the understanding and management of clinical disorders. For example, investigators have been:

a. Seeking relationships among biological and behavioral factors in specified mental disorders, e.g., in depression;

b. Attempting to establish the symptoms and behavioral "dimensions" of psychosis, thus leading to new typologies and new classification systems for the mental disorders;

c. Devising methods for identifying psychiatric cases in the community;

d. Comparing two or more treatments in a given clincial condition, e.g., the comparative efficacy of psychosocial therapies and tranquilizing drugs in treating chronic schizophrenia;

e. Predicting response to specified treatment, e.g., to antidepressant and tranquilizing drugs;

f. Charting the symptomatic and behavioral course of a clinical condition;

g. Establishing the major components of personal, social, and clinical adjustment in the community.

2. Firm demonstration, as noted in the chapter on sociocultural processes, that the prevalence of schizophrenia is highest in the lowest social classes of urban communities. A definitive explanation awaits further research. Investigations of the possibly more pertinent variables have demonstrated significant class-linked differences in parental values, parenting techniques, and ability to cope with stress.

3. An increasing focus on long-term developmental problems in the study of normal and abnormal growth of personality: Out of this trend have come longitudinal, prospective research strategies for studying such issues as etiology and vulnerability to various psychiatric disorders. The high risk design is a method for determining a wide range of factors that contribute to the development of disorders, and makes possible prospective, rather than retrospective, analyses of contributing events. This strategy has successfully provided new leverage in the study of schizophrenia and can be applied in the study of other major mental disorders.

4. The capacity to quantify patterns of normal social behavior and psychopathology: This has made possible new studies estimating the

influence of culture on the nature and shape of psychoses in various ethnic and national groups. Three such major studies have been the WHO International Pilot Study of Schizophrenia, the U.S.-U.K. Cross-National Project, and the Hawaii Study of Ethnic Variations in Psychopathology and Normality. These studies provide new evidence on what may be common in psychosis and what aspects of psychosis vary across cultures. We are now in a position to evaluate the influence of this major environmental consideration—a position that has grown out of careful and sound methodological developments over the past 15-20 years.

5. Other significant developments in the psychosocial area include: (a) an increased capacity to measure nonverbal expressions of behavior; (b) the development and application of new multivariate statistical procedures to the analysis of factors from the psychological and biological spheres; (c) new approaches to studying the dynamics of family interaction and the role of the family in fostering and shaping psychoses in one or more of its members; and (d) progress in behavior theory, which has made major contributions to our understanding and treatment of neurotic and psychotic disorders.

New Evidence About the Genetics of Mental Illness

The observation that mental illness tends to run in families has been made for centuries. The clustering of illness in close relatives has been documented clearly for the schizophrenic disorders, the affective disorders, and alcoholism, and less clearly for sociopathy and childhood behavior disorders. But the critical issue was whether this clustering represents the effect of social or of genetic transmission. After a decade of genetic studies, it has become quite clear that both factors are involved. The focus now is on how these sets of factors interact.

Historically, European psychiatrists tended to interpret the available data as supporting biological transmission, while American psychiatrists favored psychosocial transmission. Until recently, the research data could be interpreted either way. Mental illness among the parents of mental patients could be viewed to indicate either that the parents had the same genetic abnormality, or that they had transmitted the illness to their children through their upbringing. But a series of studies launched in the early 1960's has begun to shed some light on this question. Several new strategies are employed: (1) various types of adoption studies such as those in which the children of mental patients are raised in normal adoptive families; (2) discordant identical twin studies, in which genetic factors are common to series of paired sick and healthy twins, thus allowing a focus on environmental factors; (3) heredity-environment interaction studies; and (4) genetic marker studies.

Adoption studies have now been conducted with schizophrenics, sociopaths, and alcoholics and are presently underway in the field of affective disorders. As noted earlier, twin studies carried out within the NIMH intramural research program have helped to specify variables in a child's environment that are associated with the development or the absence of schizophrenia in monozygotic (identical) twins discordant for the illness.

The first phase of a study to estimate the relative contributions of heredity, environment, and heredity-environment interactions has been carried out in Israel. Together, these projects have led to a much greater acceptance of genetic factors as one set of determinants in mental illness. Simultaneously, however, they show that nongenetic factors are also important.

There continue to be significant differences of opinion between widely respected investigators on the question of just how substantial the genetic factors really are. Wtih respect to schizophrenia, for instance, one group (the Biological Sciences Subcommittee of the Mental Illness and Behavior Disorders Study Group) states that "a genetic form of schizophrenia definitely exists. The offspring of schizophrenics raised in normal adoptive homes manifest process schizophrenia and, in addition, a variety of other psychiatric diseases. Inspection of the data does not document that deviant rearing aggravates the manifestations of schizophrenia, nor does it document that rearing in normal familial settings can attenuate the appearance of schizophrenia." A second group (the Subcommittee on Psychological and Sociocultural Sciences) however, points out that the concordance rate for schizophrenia in monozygotic twins is only 25 to 40 percent; this constitutes the most compelling evidence for the operation of environmental factors in the production of schizophrenia. In addition, they contend that data from a recent NIMH-supported adoption study can be interpreted as indicating an attenuating effect on the appearance of schizophrenia when the children of schizophrenics are reared in normal adoptive homes: That is, 7 percent of adopted-away offspring of a schizophrenic parent were diagnosed as schizophrenic from an intensive clinical research interview. However, based on hospital record diagnoses, only 2 percent of the subjects were labeled schizophrenic. Other studies, also utilizing hospital record diagnoses, have found 10-15 percent of the offspring of one schizophrenic parent to be schizophrenic. Thus, they assert that the 2 percent rate of hospital-diagnosed schizophrenia in these adopted-away subjects is evidence for attenuation of the disorder's occurrence. Despite the still existing differences of opinion, few researchers today—as compared with the situation a few decades ago—rely on either heredity or environment exclusively for an explanation of the development of schizophrenia.

Though adoption studies have not been completed for the affective disorders, researchers have found that first-degree relatives of manic-depressives have much higher rates of manic-depressive psychosis than the general population (8-11 percent, as compared to .7 percent). Similarly, monozygotic twins are reported to have a concordance rate of 50 to 100 percent for the disorder, while dizygotic twins have a concordance rate ranging from 0 to 40 percent. These data are of the same order of magnitude as those found in other illnesses in which a genetic etiology is generally accepted, such as diabetes, cleft palate, and cleft lip.

Further evidence of a genetic factor in (bipolar) manic-depressive disease comes from studies indicating that at least in some cases, the illness is transmitted from mother to son, and that it is linked to the loci for red-green color blindness on the X-chromosome. No such genetic marker has thus far been found with respect to unipolar depressive disease (depression only, without episodes of mania), and no evidence of a specific kind of transmission has been presented. Nevertheless, other indications of a genetic factor in depressive illness—for example, higher concordance rates in monozygotic than dizygotic twins—are present.

The presence of genetic factors in schizophrenia and the affective disorders may imply the existence of a genetically transmitted protein defect. The only way that genes can transmit their message is through alterations in enzymes and other proteins. Alternatively, if the genetic influence is nonspecific and polygenic, the nature of its effect may resemble the way in which genes affect intelligence and height.

Focus on the Family

Over the last two decades there has been a sharp increase, a leveling off, and then a decrease of resources going into studies of intrafamilial factors that contribute to pathogenesis of mental disorders. Initially, viewing the patient as part of a family and of a larger social network rather than attempting to explain the pathology in isolation led to a series of exciting hypotheses and apparent breakthroughs. However, the complexity of the studies and a lack of appropriate methodologies have led to major difficulties in efforts to substantiate the concepts. As a result, there has been some decrease of work in this area of research.

Studies on the family, however, have progressed from clinical descriptions of psychopathology in family members to a focus on pathological relationships, and then to a concentration on communication patterns. More appropriate techniques and new research strategies designed to overcome some of the many difficulties in mounting and conducting this type of study have recently been devised. Some of the more promising developments in this area will be described in the section on schizophrenia.

Development of High Risk Studies

Research on mental illness has long been plagued by a major methodological problem: how to establish with certainty whether differences between normal and psychotic people are the cause or the result of illness. To get around this problem, one needs to study people before they become ill. In 1963, a joint U.S.-Danish team began to study children of schizophrenic mothers—children who were at high risk of becoming psychotic. Since then, many additional prospective studies have begun, and offer hope that it will be possible to determine which preillness characteristics are linked to the development of schizophrenia. For example, early and as yet unreplicated findings from that first study suggest a relationship between stress during pregnancy, early loss of the mother figure without an adequate substitute, and the presence of serious psychopathology in the father, on the one hand, and, on the other hand, the likelihood of serious psychopathology developing among the children of schizophrenic mothers.

After a decade of experience with these studies a new sense of both their potential value and limitations is beginning to emerge. For example, the acquisition of appropriately composed samples has proved more difficult than expected. Also, measures used with children of one age group are not always applicable to a different age group. This of course leads to serious problems in attempting to study the same variable across a wide age span. Finally, investigators are realizing the need to settle for "intermediate" outcomes, because going through the schizophrenia risk period may take children 20 years or more.

Development of Reliable and Standardized Psychological Measurements

Since the early fifties, researchers have significantly advanced their ability to describe psychopathological phenomena in objective terms. In order to disentangle the influence of environment and genetics in mental disorder, ways must be found to describe and measure various kinds of social behavior, of mood, of social performance, and of adjustment in the community. These measurements must not only be reliable but also sufficiently standardized to serve researchers across the country in such varied settings as a clinical interview, a hospital ward, or a community mental health center.

Furthermore, rating scales must be applicable to many specific conditions, such as schizophrenia, depression, or anxiety states. The new techniques are not confined to global measures of severity or improvement. Rather, they attempt to provide quantifiable measures of specific symptoms, as well as a standardized profile of the major dimensions of behavioral psychopathology. Several new scales have been designed to analyze the behavior of patients during clinical interviews. Other instruments have been developed specifically to analyze behavior on the ward and social behavior in the community.

To improve the reliability of such measures, researchers have tried to standardize the clinical interview itself by developing a standard situation in which the data are collected and the behavior judged. They have also attempted to take advantage of the varying strengths and perspectives of a wide range of observers. With the new techniques, the patient's behavior may be assessed not only by clinicans but also by adjunct clinical personnel, such as nurses and ward attendants, and by lay relatives.

Since the introduction of quantification and the standard interview procedure, it has become possible to put many elements of psychiatric diagnosis into computers—a development that will become increasingly important in years to come. The new techniques have also made it possible to study the diagnostic process itself. For example, the influence on diagnosis of such diverse factors as the psychiatrist's ethnic background and the length of his experience can now be measured.

An improved ability to objectify these behavioral characteristics has made it possible to explain many puzzling discrepancies in mental health statistics reported by different nations. Using standardized interview and diagnostic procedures, investigators on the U.S.-U.K. Diagnostic Study demonstrated that differences observed in official statistics for first-admission rates to British and American mental hospitals for schizophrenia and affective disorders were a result, primarily, of differences in diagnostic practice between British and American psychiatrists. The standardized diagnostic procedures essentially eliminated these differences. Using the new methodology, the WHO International Pilot Study of Schizophrenia has obtained preliminary findings indicating that the core symptoms of schizophrenia can apparently be found everywhere, whether patients are diagnosed in Denmark or in Nigeria. On the other hand, studies in Hawaii using the same techniques have shown marked differences in the ways in which behavior and emotion are expressed in similarly severe psychoses.

Despite these improvements, psychological scales are not sensitive enough to measure changes in clinical states and reliably distinguish between such diagnostically critical emotional facets as depression and apathy. The deliberate pace of development in psychosocial research on mental illness can be attributed partly to this lack of precise technique in clinical evaluation. Thus, while new hypotheses and findings in basic biological and psychological research on mental disorder have been increasing rapidly, techniques for measuring behavioral aspects have moved ahead less effectively, making it difficult to test the critical hypotheses. Extremely important questions such as, "Is depression (in which a certain type of biochemical abnormality is found) the same in New York as the same depression in California (in which no such abnormality has been noted)?" have not been satisfactorily answered. Although researchers are increasingly capable of assessing biological abnormalities, their ability to measure behavioral traits with precision and on this basis to group patient populations into homogeneous subgroups is still extremely limited. Consequently, it is often difficult to compare findings reported by different investigators despite use of the same diagnostic terms. The lack of really sensitive measures also makes it difficult to study with accuracy the course of an illness in any group of patients.

Study of Neurotransmitters

A large and growing body of data suggests that the biogenic amines may play a key role in emotional disorders, both in the development of mental disease and in its alleviation or prevention through drugs. The evidence is particularly forceful with respect to depression and schizophrenia.

The biogenic amines—chemicals derived from some of the essential amino acids—include at least two types of putative neurotransmitters: the catecholamines and the indoleamines. Both may transmit messages in areas of the brain that have to do with drives and their relation to higher order intellectual functions. Many mood-changing drugs may act by modifying the metabolism of the neurotransmitters. This finding has spurred research on the relationship among specific drugs, specific transmitters, and specific behavioral effects.

Emphasis is now being placed on further clarifying the action of neurotransmitters, and identifying other, unknown kinds of transmitters. The transmitters that can be studied today are only a small fraction of those acting in the brain. However, as noted in the chapter on biological processes, altering the two currently most studied neurotransmitters seems to "turn on" and "turn off" some symptoms of the two major psychoses. The work of the past 10 years has already shed much light on how neurotransmitters are produced and broken down, and how they provide the central nervous system with great flexibility in terms of gradations of stimulation and response.

In clinical settings, breakdown products of brain transactions used to be measured in urine, but several metabolites do not pass the blood-brain barrier. Recent breakthroughs in biochemical methodology have allowed researchers to study critical metabolites in cerebrospinal fluid and in CNS tissue obtained from simple surgical procedures or autopsy materials, and to tag metabolites both in urine and cerebrospinal fluid.

The original hypotheses about the role of biogenic amines in mental disease may turn out to be greatly oversimplified, but the study of these transmitters continues to offer enormous promise.

Study of Sleep

Mental illness frequently involves disturbed patterns of sleep. Researchers, using new techniques of electroencephalographic recording and analysis, have been able to document some differences between the sleep of psychotic and nonpsychotic persons, and to develop valuable hypotheses. They have found abnormal reactions to rapid-eye-movement (REM) deprivation among several kinds of patients. (REM sleep is sleep accompanied by recurrent periods of fast brain waves, quickened heart rate, erections, irregular breathing, and dreaming.)

Nearly all mood-changing drugs, particularly amphetamines and barbiturates, radically reduce the amount of REM sleep. When people who take such drugs try to do without them, they feel rebound effects from repressed REM—sometimes with terrifying nightmares or even seizures. This REM rebound is so disturbing that they may reach for another pill to fall asleep, and the cycle continues.

Schizophrenics sometimes do not show a rebound after REM deprivation. The relationship between REM sleep and depression is more complicated. Depressed patients typically suffer sleep disorders, some of them awakening abnormally early, others having their entire night punctuated by awakenings. As characterized by sleep patterns, there appear to be two kinds of depression. Longitudinal studies of sleep in psychotic depression have shown that the most disturbed phases of illness are marked by conspicuous reduction of total sleep, virtual absence of the deeper stages of sleep, and, generally, the lowest percentages of REM. Other research has defined a subgroup of depressives who show an increase, rather than a decrease, in their percentage of REM sleep during illness. One group of antidepressant drugs totally eliminates REM sleep. As research continues, the study of sleep may yield a quantifiable measure of differences among types of depression, as well as a measure of intensity of inner distress.

SCHIZOPHRENIA

Many investigators and clinicians believe that the syndrome "schizophrenia" includes several different related mental illnesses. The symptoms include withdrawal; autism; disturbed patterns of interpersonal relationships, learning, and performance; decreased motivation or apathy; distorted sensory acuity and perception; disturbed conceptual processes; and distorted interpretations of reality. Unfortunately, the diagnosis is still based on descriptions of behavior, supplemented by detailed case histories. There are still no objective or organic tests of schizophrenia, analogous to X-ray or blood count.

Improving the Means of Diagnosis

Wide differences in diagnostic concepts and practices continue to impede substantially the understanding of schizophrenia. Efforts have been made to classify patients according to such criteria as past history or prognosis rather than presenting symptoms. Some investigators believe that basic psychological, neurological, metabolic, or genetic indices will become the most useful ways of classifying the schizophrenias. As yet, there is no universally accepted way of integrating the concepts of past history, prognosis, symptomatology, and neurobiological groupings into one diagnostic system. Recently, investigators have attempted to combine at least two such approaches—for example, combining the results of reaction time experiments (which showed that schizophrenics took longer to shift attention from light to sound stimuli) with the measures from a systematic structured interview. Together, although such measures may produce much more homogeneous subgroups for research, and, possibly, a better selection of treatments, followup studies have not yet proved their worth.

The current American Psychiatric Association typologies for schizophrenia do not predict treatment outcome as well as some newer typologies; one, for example, distinguishes between "process" schizophrenia, with its slow, insidious onset and poor prognosis, and "reactive" schizophrenia, which occurs after a more normal childhood and definable precipitating circumstances. Some researchers have hypothesized that the "process" type is likely to involve a more prominent biological component, while the "reactive" type, which is marked by more acute onset and flamboyant symptoms, may have a more heavily psychological etiology. Although imperfect, the new typologies have been more useful in predicting response to drug treatment, generating new research leads.

As part of the WHO International Pilot Study of Schizophrenia, the investigative team from the United States, one of nine countries participating, is attempting to standardize and revise prevailing diagnostic classifications. It has also compared different diagnostic systems from the standpoint of the accuracy with which they predict outcome. It appears that symptoms alone are not good outcome predictors. As noted previously, early findings from NIMH-supported cross-cultural studies suggest that the central features of schizophrenia may be universal, although there is still some question whether or not this is true in preindustrial societies.

When the research of different investigators can be carried out on similar or comparable subjects, using similar criteria and clinical descriptions, computer technology will make it possible to advance understanding of schizophrenia as a whole rather than in part.

Unraveling the Genetic Factor

In the 1940's, scientists believed that if one identical twin became schizophrenic, his cotwin was likely to develop the same disorder in 80 percent of the cases. Though the concordance rate reported in more precise recent studies has decreased substantially to 25-40 percent, some genetic factors clearly seem to be involved. Supporting evidence appears in studies that have found a correlation between the degree of consanguinity and the likelihood that a relative of a schizophrenic will also become schizophrenic. While only 1 percent of selected nonschizophrenic populations can expect to become schizophrenic, the risk for second-degree relatives of a schizophrenic is 2-3 percent; for first-degree relatives, about 10 percent; and for twins, and the children of two schizophrenic patients, higher yet. Recent adoption studies show that the offspring of schizophrenics have a higher percentage of schizophrenia (7 percent) and "borderline" or "schizophrenia-spectrum" disorders (28 percent), than do adopted-away children of normal parents, 18 percent of whom were affected. These studies, while not yet definitive, hold great promise for an eventual unraveling of the differential effects of nature and nurture in schizophrenia.

Much more needs to be known about specific mechanisms which underlie genetic factors in schizophrenia.

Biochemical and Physiological Factors

In search of an abnormal substance that might be causally linked to schizophrenia, investigators have studied most anatomical structures and a very large number of biochemical systems and substances. To date, no anatomical or biochemical abnormalities have been associated consistently and exclusively with schizophrenia. The search continues, however, and a number of highly promising biochemical hypotheses are being actively explored.

The Dopamine Hypothesis

The "dopamine hypothesis" arises from findings that most drugs useful in treating schizophrenia block the effects of dopamine and dopamine-like compounds in the brain. Very high doses of antipsychotic drugs can produce symptoms similar to Parkinsonism in up to 90 percent of all patients. Parkinson's disease has been found to stem from a deficiency of dopamine; L-dopa treats Parkinsonism by increasing the level of dopamine. When L-dopa has been tried to treat the Parkinson-like tremors of schizophrenics, it has often exacerbated their psychosis. It has also precipitated psychotic-like symptoms in patients who took it for other reasons, suggesting that abnormal levels of dopamine and/or other catecholamines may help to produce the symptoms of schizophrenia.

Additional evidence comes from the fact that amphetamine psychosis, which resembles paranoid schizophrenia, may be produced by a hyperactive dopamine system. Drugs that are effective against amphetamine psychosis, such as chlorpromazine, are also effective against schizophrenia. Reports of abnormalities in brain levels of dopamine-related enzymes, in the brains of schizophrenics, remain to be confirmed.

The Transmethylation Hypothesis

A structural similarity has been detected between certain hallucinogens, such as mescaline, and some of the catecholamines. This finding led certain scientists to theorize that schizophrenia might be caused by abnormal, methylated amines that act as hallucinogens and thus produce psychotic symptoms. This hypothesis was stimulated when NIMH scientists and other researchers found that large quantities of methionine, the amino acid that supplies the methyl group, exacerbate some symptoms of schizophrenia in a number of patients. If an abnormal substance of this sort does exist, it is very likely related to an abnormal enzyme. One strategically placed enzyme for the transmethylation hypothesis is monoamine oxidase (MAO). A deficiency in MAO activity has been reported in the blood platelets of some schizophrenic patients, but this remains to be confirmed.

Abnormal Proteins

Many reports have linked abnormal large-molecule proteins, or other biochemical or physiological findings, to the etiology of schizophrenia, but they have not been replicated. However, there is continuing work related to reports of possible abnormal globulin in some schizophrenics.

Psychological and Sociocultural Factors

Relationship Between Social Class and Schizophrenia

One of the most consistently replicated findings in schizophrenia research is that high rates of mental disorder, and particularly schizophrenia, are concentrated in the lowest status occupations and the poorest areas of large cities.

A major problem has been to determine whether these high rates are a cause or an effect of the disorder. The latter possibility is suggested by the "drift" hypothesis, which maintains that as a result of the debilitating effects of their illness, schizophrenics tend to drift into lower status areas of the city, and from higher to lower status jobs. Studies that have tried to trace the social mobility of schizophrenics indicate that although such downward "drift" may well occur, it probably does not fully explain the relationship between schizophrenia and lower social class origins. Although many methodological issues remain, it would seem that social class is one of the factors interacting in the causal sequence that leads to schizophrenia. The possible interaction involved is discussed in the chapter on sociocultural processes.

Experimental Psychological Studies

The importance of examining interactions is also emphasized by the history of experimental psychological studies of schizophrenia. Taken in total, these studies indicate that, compared with normal individuals, schizophrenics:

1. Have a greater tendency toward stimulus avoidance;

2. Show a greater inability to maintain attention and set;

3. Show a deficit in the appropriateness of their categorizations and generalizations;

4. Are harder to involve in experimental tasks. This reluctance to taking part may be paralleled by a general lack of motivation outside experimental settings. Schizophrenics seem relatively more motivated in situations where good performance results in escape from noxious stimuli;

5. Show disturbances in autonomic functioning, the most consistent of which is that they are psychophysiologically less flexible in responding to tasks confronting them. Their arousal level is not so directly related to the demands of the situations in which they find themselves as is that of normals;

6. Are more socially withdrawn and perform more poorly in tasks involving social stimuli as compared to neutral stimuli.

Although the existence of each of these deficits is demonstrated by a wide variety of experiments, the etiological significance of the findings is problematic. It is possible that any one deficit or any combination of deficits causes the others.

Thus, despite the substantial advances that the experimental study of the psychology of schizophrenia has made in identifying the psychological deficits that distinguish schizophrenically ill from psychologically normal human beings, major questions remain. These questions center around the variability, reliability, and etiological significance of the findings. Underlying each of these questions is the problem of interactions—the possibility that one variable's effect might be different for different conditions of a second variable (e.g., the effect of level of intellectual functioning on the schizophrenic's willingness to become involved with another person is different in men than in women).

Such interactions may occur both among variables that measure different aspects of psychological functioning, and between such variables and different types of subjects. The investigation of both types of interaction is important for the understanding of the great variability in response found in experimental studies of schizophrenics. It seems likely that such an emphasis on the study of interactions would help clarify the etiological significance of much of the research already done. Even if, as is extremely unlikely, schizophrenia is completely determined genetically, the individual's development does not take place in vacuo but in interaction with his environment—be it intrautero, intrafamilial, or social. In order to understand such interactions, we have to develop not only genetic markers for differentiating relevant genetic predispositions, but also means of differentiating and describing environmental factors with which they interact.

Role of the Family

Early work with families focused on the content of the family members' relationship; more recent research has concentrated not on what is said but how it is said. For example, one team of investigators has analyzed communication styles in a broad array of psychopathological families. The investigators have been able to distinguish families (with 95 percent accuracy and little overlap between groups) with schizophrenic offspring not only from those whose offspring are normal but also from those whose offspring are neurotic or have character disorders. They also report that the frequency of communication deviations manifested by parents, such as peculiar language, overexactness, or blurred meanings is highly predictive of the severity of illness in offspring. Their major findings have been replicated in several other settings.

These studies have led to new hypotheses about the possible etiologic role of the family in the development of schizophrenia; its role in the development of language and thought in general; and its possible interaction with genetic and stress factors in the occurrence and perpetuation of the disorder.

Although disturbances of family processes may be secondary to the illness, rather than a cause, continued definition, clarification, and specification of interactional and communication styles may, at a minimum, provide us with clues to improved interventions. The need to determine which came first—the illness or the disturbed family processes—is one important reason for the present emphasis on prospective studies of children at high risk to schizophrenia. This problem has also led to the development of other innovative methodologies such as simulation techniques and experimental family studies. In experimental family studies, the interaction of parents of a normal child is studied when they are with a young schizophrenic. Conversely, their "normal" child is studied in interaction with parents who have a schizophrenic offspring. Although it is a complex matter to interpret the results, one rather unexpected finding does clearly emerge: Normal parents had a normalizing influence on the schizophrenics, in that the latters' problem-solving abilities (measured pre- and postinteraction) were enhanced following the session.

This novel strategy overcomes many of the difficulties in other family study designs as well as many inherent in prospective studies of children at high risk. The design for the experimental family studies evolved out of and built upon the important developments in the area over the last 25 years. Without that background, this level of sophistication would not be possible today.

There is need for expanded support for the study of the family's and the schizophrenic's effects on one another and how these relate to their ability to work, relate, and gain satisfaction from their lives. For example, there is now reasonably good evidence that schizophrenics living with negatively overinvolved families are more frequently rehospitalized. Yet, little is known of the determinants and interaction sequence of the process that leads to symptom exacerbation and rehospitalization. Only when this process is more precisely defined will effective intervention become possible.

RECOMMENDATIONS FOR FURTHER RESEARCH ON SCHIZOPHRENIA

1. Given the exciting hypotheses about the biochemical aspects of schizophrenia, NIMH's research effort should strongly support clinical investigation of biological factors. The investigation of the dopamine hypothesis deserves special attention at this time. In addition, basic neurobiological and neuropharmacological research efforts are absolutely essential. As in the rest of science, clinical researchers in mental illness can only apply the findings of scientists working at more basic levels.

2. There is a need for further adoptive discordant twin and other studies that can disentangle the genetic components of schizophrenia from the psychosocial components. Studies should concentrate also on the families and life history experience of high risk groups.

3. It is essential that appropriate balance be maintained in NIMH research support of biologically oriented as contrasted with sociopsychological studies of schizophrenia. The evidence available to date strongly suggests that nonbiological, psychosocial factors play a major pathogenic role in the development of schizophrenia. The need for study of psychosocial factors in adjustment is especially important because of the changing treatment context of present-day psychiatry; that is, because most schizophrenic patients today are treated and maintained in the community, the study of factors that affect community adjustment is critical for the eventual development of specific treatment interventions, either alone or in conjunction with drugs. New approaches that aim to study these factors more systematically and reliably should be encouraged.

The above three recommendations may seem to have emphasized the separate study of the relevant biological, genetic, and sociopsychological factors in schizophrenia. However, real progress can only be made when the interaction of these three sets of factors is understood.

4. Such studies should go hand-in-hand with further standardization of procedures to characterize schizophrenic subjects and the development of better diagnostic techniques. These will probably require the simultaneous measurement of biological and psychological functions. They may also require using video, computer, and other new technologies.

5. At this time studies of sleep in schizophrenia should probably receive relatively low priority, since they seem to have made their contributions.

AFFECTIVE DISORDERS

The affective disorders comprise a heterogeneous group of emotional disturbances that range from transient periods of mild dejection to incapacitating illnesses that may terminate in suicide. They constitute perhaps the most severe group of mental disorders in the United States in terms of prevalence, economic cost, and even mortality. Of the 20,000 suicide deaths recorded in the United States each year, more than 80 percent are believed to be precipitated by depressive illness. In this country, between 3 and 8 million persons suffer from depression at any given time; roughly 15 percent of all adults have recognizable symptoms.

Fortunately, the affective disorders also are one of the most currently promising and dynamic areas of research in the mental health field. A vast amount of new biological and psychological data about the disorders has accumulated in the past decade, much of it through NIMH-supported research. Diagnostic categories and criteria, which are becoming increasingly more precise, differentiate between unipolar depression—a condition of recurring episodes of depression—and bipolar depression—a condition of recurring episodes of both depression and mania. Marked progress also has been made in therapy. In addition to treatment with electric shock and antidepressant drugs, unipolar and bipolar patients can now be treated with lithium carbonate, use of which may become as significant a development as use of insulin for diabetes. Collectively, existing treatments are effective for approximately 80 percent of the patients experiencing depressive psychoses.

Developing a More Accurate Diagnosis

The concept of unipolar and bipolar affective illness represents a major advance. Whereas most previously proposed diagnostic categories were rather unsystematic and had no demonstrated etiological significance (except for the recently developed primary-secondary system of diagnosis), the current unipolar-bipolar differentiation is supported by a variety of factors. These include: (a) genetic studies, which show that the relatives of manic-depressive patients have an increased incidence of manic illness while the relatives of depressive patients have a lower incidence of manic illness; (b) a difference in the characteristic time of onset—the age at onset of bipolar illness peaks at 26 years, while that of unipolar illness peaks at 45; (c) a difference in the response to lithium. Consequently, more homogeneous sample populations are available for research. Nevertheless, accurate distinction among various types of unipolar illness and between "normal" and clinical depression remains difficult, and further work is required in this area.

During the last few years, new standard diagnostic methods have been developed through the Institute's Collaborative Program on the Psychobiology of the Depressive Disorders that will help to make possible definitive comparative research on diagnostic systems. Such research is now being developed.

As a further refinement in diagnosis, two general types of unipolar depressions have been hypothesized: "pure depressive disease" and "depression spectrum disease." The typical patient with pure depressive disease is a male whose illness starts after the age of 40, and in whose family are equal numbers of male and female relatives who also suffer from depression. The typical patient with depression spectrum disease is a female whose illness developed before the age of 40, and in whose family more depression is seen in female relatives than in males. However, the males in her family show increased levels of alcoholism and sociopathy.

Depression appears to be an important factor in triggering many physical illnesses as well as in determining their outcome. "Giving up" or "having given up" may lead to death. Evidence suggests that patients who suffer from a depressive illness after a heart attack, for instance, develop a large number of physical complications during the ensuing recovery period that not only prolong convalescence but increase the likelihood of a fatal outcome. Other research has revealed that, despite a high incidence of severe depression among patients hospitalized for medical illnesses, these depressions are mainly unrecognized—and thus left untreated—by the attending medical personnel.

Additional evidence of underdiagnosis emerged in recent cross-national study of diagnostic practices in the United States and England, which pointed up differences in patient sampling, methods of diagnosis, and concepts of depression and schizophrenia between the two countries.

Unraveling the Genetic Factor

Research is providing increasing evidence that certain affective disorders have a significant genetic basis. The risk of developing bipolar illness is .7 percent in the general population; it rises to 8, 9, and 11 percent for first-degree relatives—parents, siblings, and children, respectively—of manic-depressives. Twin studies have reported monozygotic concordance rates that range between 50 and 100 percent, and dizygotic rates of 0 to 40 percent. As noted earlier, these figures are approximately similar to those determined for illnesses such as diabetes, congenital pyloric stenosis, and cleft palate, in which a genetic etiology is generally accepted. However, the findings do not preclude the possibility that the disease is transmitted in whole or in part, in some subjects, through upbringing. This question can be resolved only through adoptive and other appropriate studies. Ongoing genetic studies are attempting to demonstrate a specific mode of transmission and/or linkage with a known genetic marker.

In one study, patients who for the most part had two generations of affective illness in their families were considered to be a homogeneous group; the findings suggested a predominant X-linked transmission, since manic-depression appeared to be transmitted from mother to son. The data indicated that the locus for manic-depressive illness is linked to the loci for red-green color blindness on the X chromosome. Possible linkage with the Xga blood group on the same chromosome was also indicated.

Biochemical and Physiological Factors

The two prevailing theories about the psychobiology of depression include the "catecholamine" and the "serotonin" hypotheses. At present, the former is more widely accepted and is the focal point of more studies.

The Catecholamine Hypothesis

Historically, American experimenters have concentrated largely on the role of the catecholamines, while European and British studies have dealt primarily with the indoleamines, such as serotonin. According to the catecholamine theory of affective disorders, depression results from a functional deficit of the transmitters norepinephrine and/or dopamine at brain synapses, while mania results from an oversupply of these transmitters. This theory originated with evidence that reserpine—which was sometimes prescribed in large doses for hypertension and which was known to decrease the amount of catecholamines in the brain—was often associated with severe depression. Furthermore, the two groups of effective antidepressant compounds both increase functional brain catecholamines, though by different mechanisms: the tricyclic compounds inhibit the reuptake of catecholamines into the presynaptic nerve endings; the monoamine oxidase inhibitors reduce the activity of the enzyme which is involved in the degradation of catecholamines, thus making more catecholamines available. The data that implicate the catecholamines in triggering manic episodes are particularly convincing, since they are supported by studies of transmitter metabolites in the urine and cerebrospinal fluid of manic patients, as well as by studies of the effects of lithium.

The Serotonin Hypothesis

Here again, the association of reserpine with depression led researchers to suggest that this might be caused by a decrease in functional brain serotonin, since reserpine decreases the amount of serotonin (an indoleamine) available at brain synapses, as well as the amount of catecholamines. According to this theory, depression is associated with a deficit of serotonin, and mania by an excess. The evidence is somewhat more convincing for depression, since some precursors of serotonin have been reported to relieve depression in some patients. Furthermore, there have been suspiciously low levels of 5-hydroxyindoleacetic acid (5-HIAA), the major breakdown product of serotonin, in the cerebrospinal fluid of depressed patients, as well as in the brain tissue of patients who committed suicide.

Electrolyte Studies

Possible changes in water and electrolyte metabolism have been reported during mood disturbances. The uptake of biogenic amines into the cell is dependent on the sodium and potassium gradients across the cell membranes. This, plus the fact that lithium influences mood disorders, suggests that electrolyte phenomena may be related to affective illness.

Sleep Studies

Depressed people suffer from insomnia and other sleep disturbances. Their sleep problems can even serve as a measure of their illness. Psychotic patients suffer from two to three times the sleep reduction of nonpsychotic depressed patients. The acute phase of illness is marked by the most conspicuous abbreviation of total sleep, reduction of deeper stages of sleep, and the lowest percentage of REM sleep. Researchers are now trying to find out whether patients who suffer recurrent episodes of depression or manic-depression have any abnormalities in their sleep patterns before the manifestations of their recurring illness.

Longitudinal Studies of Individual Patients

Because it is so difficult to find truly homogeneous subgroups in the affective diseases, researchers have learned to study individuals and use them as their own controls through different stages of their sickness and health, both with and without medication. The establishment of adequately staffed metabolic research wards in various settings has allowed investigators to observe individual patients more closely, and to correlate their behavior with a wide variety of biochemical changes.

Developing New Psychological Models of Depression

New experimental and theoretical models have evolved in the field of psychology that show great promise in unraveling the causes and nature of depression. These models, discussed below, together with the traditional psychopathological and psychodynamic models, have broadened research in the whole area.

Behavioral and Cognitive Models

Many psychologists are currently less interested in what the patient says and thinks, and more in how he behaves and how the environment reinforces or negates this behavior. This movement is in accord with the strong behavioristic trend and also with findings of research on learning and conditioning. It has led to several new models that try to explain and define the various states of depression. Moreover, by adopting a naturalistic approach to the problem of depression, patients can be studied in their day-to-day relations in the community.

Other research has centered on the "cognitive" aspects of depression. One investigator holds that patients experience sadness, loss of motivation, and suicidal wishes because their thinking is disturbed, and not vice versa, as most psychologists traditionally have believed. In depression, he believes, a "negative set" takes command of the organism. Both in their dreams and in their waking fantasies, depressed people have a negative view of their self, of the outside world, and of the future. Depression is a cognitive disorder, this investigator says, and, therefore, any experience of success that boosts the patients' unrealistically low self concept should lift their depressed mood.

Animal Models

Other researchers believe that some of the circumstances in which depressions arise can be reproduced in animals. Even if it proves impossible to develop an animal model for schizophrenia or thought disorder, they hold, it may be possible to develop one for depression, since mood alterations could have developed very early on the phylogenetic scale. Investigators supported by NIMH have attempted to produce depression in monkeys by separating infants from their mothers; others have used drugs that deplete brain catecholamines. Pioneer work by various investigators have produced animals who seem uninterested in their environment, who have the appearance of being depressed, and who behave in a manner that could be interpreted as depressed. The complexity of the problem, however, is reflected in the fact that there are clear species differences. Recently, one researcher has developed an animal model of depression based on the concept of "learned helplessness." The model suggests that early experience with persistent and uncontrollable trauma leads to the development of a passive, helpless approach to dealing with frustration in later life.

RECOMMENDATIONS FOR FURTHER RESEARCH ON THE AFFECTIVE DISORDERS

1. NIMH's research effort should give great emphasis to a continuing clinical investigation of the biological factors involved in affective illness in view of the evidence that the affective disorders are caused, at least in part, by a genetically transmitted biochemical defect. Basic neurobiological and neuropharmacological research are absolutely fundamental for this. As in the rest of medicine, clinical researchers in mental illness rely on scientists working at more basic levels. Other areas needing emphasis include: (a) the role of neurotransmitters and

of brain metabolism in affective illness; (b) the biochemical, endocrinological, and environmental factors involved in triggering such illness; and (c) the mode of action of drugs which alter affective illness.

2. Adoptive studies are needed to disentangle the genetic components of affective illness from the psychosocial components. Genetic studies, both clinical and basic, should also be broadened extensively.

3. Depression is a condition of the whole organism—the psychosocial as well as the biological. In less severe depressions, which constitute about 75 percent of the patient population, psychological and situational factors appear to play the major roles and are currently poorly understood. We are, for example, only beginning to understand the role of personality predisposition and behavioral reinforcement principles in these cases. Research in affective illness must show an adequate balance between biological and psychosocial approaches, and not swing too far in either direction because of a current upsurge in productivity in part of a field.

4. It is imperative to standardize the procedures used to characterize depression and to develop better diagnostic techniques. Development of such techniques will involve simultaneous measurement of many aspects of psychological and biological functioning in depressed patients. The effort also will require long-term studies of patients' reactions to treatment and of the progress of their disorders; needed too will be descriptions of patients during well periods. Few links now exist between the psychological phenomena of affective illness and biochemical abnormalities. A more nearly complete understanding of the biological bases of affective illness requires more adequate techniques for measuring psychological and clinical aspects of depression.

5. Promising psychosocial research must be encouraged. Such research includes work on the behavioral analysis of depression, further development of animal models, the concept of the "depression-prone" personality, the new approaches to treatment, and the cultural meaning and manifestations of the depressed psychological state.

6. In 1970, NIMH inaugurated the Clinical Research Branch Collaborative Study of Psychobiology of the Depressive Disorders to encourage a series of coordinated research projects in many parts of the country in an effort to find out how various biological, psychological, and environmental forces combine to create the depressive state. This program should be expanded during the coming years.

ORGANIC PSYCHOSIS

Of all mental illnesses, organic psychosis has been the most severely neglected by researchers. Yet patients with organic psychosis (sometimes called organic brain syndrome) fill about one-fourth of the total mental hospital beds in the country.

Organic psychosis is the term for a diverse group of disorders that result from diffuse impairment of brain tissue function. These include: presenile and senile dementia; alcoholic psychosis; and impairments associated with infections, vascular disease, tumors, traumas, degenerative disease, endocrine or nutritional disorders, drugs, and childbirth. Some of them are acute and may be reversible; others are chronic.

Patients with senile dementia alone make up roughly 15 percent of all mental hospital admissions in the State of New York. It has been estimated that one million Americans would fall into the "certifiable" category because of senile mental disorders. Only a small proportion of them are in mental hospitals, however. Most are in nursing homes or with their families. On the other hand, many of the aged who are in mental hospitals are actually not mentally ill—they are sent there because there is no other place for them to go. Unfortunately, there are, at present, no effective organic therapies for most senile and presenile psychoses. To what extent the paucity of available therapies is due to extremely little research activity is an important question.

The little research being carried out on organic psychosis is generally performed outside the mental health field, by workers in other areas of medicine. Results are published in journals that mental health personnel—the people who actually take care of patients with organic psychosis—seldom read, such as journals of neurology, geriatrics, or internal medicine. Relevant research is being done with hyperbaric oxygen, for instance, and with neurosurgical shunting or bypass procedures, in lipid metabolism, and in virology, all at a time when many psychotherapists are breaking away from medicine.

As a result, patients with potentially treatable disorders that sometimes masquerade as organic brain syndrome may easily be misdiagnosed by mental health personnel. For example, patients with myxedema, vitamin deficiencies, abscess, subdural hematoma, aneurysms, tumors, or other conditions that could be successfully treated with chemicals or neurosurgery may be deprived of such treatment and exposed to permanent brain damage, or death. In addition, a small number of persons with a recently described disorder called "normal pressure hydrocephalus," a form of presenile dementia that can be treated by relatively simple surgery, remain generally undiagnosed and untreated.

The whole area of organic psychosis has been grossly neglected in the 30 years since it was discovered that treating syphilis with penicillin could prevent general paresis. Yet research in this area could provide extremely useful information on the development of various kinds of psychopathology. Several clues lead researchers to believe that some forms of dementia are of viral origin. Research on organic brain syndrome will produce better treatment for the millions of people who suffer from some form of this widespread psychosis.

RECOMMENDATIONS FOR RESEARCH ON ORGANIC PSYCHOSIS

1. A thorough reassessment of entire field of the organic psychosis is recommended. As stated above, there is such a paucity of research in this area that work on all aspects is needed.

2. Development of better differential diagnostic techniques would not only advance the whole range of research efforts, but more precise differentiation of organic and psychological disorders would lead, for example, to immediate advances in treatment of affective disorders in the aged.

3. Research on new somatic treatments of organic psychosis should be encouraged.

4. Also significant for this area of research is the fact that recent years have seen a burgeoning of research and findings on the biological processes involved in the so-called "functional psychoses," such as schizophrenia and the depressive disorders. The relevance of these findings to organic psychosis should be examined; similarly research on the organic psychosis might yield new insights about the functional psychoses.

PSYCHONEUROSES

In the present climate of concern with the major psychoses and drug-induced conditions, researchers have tended to pay little attention to the psychoneuroses, probably the most prevalent of all mental disorders. However, certain psychosocial research is closely related to the study of mechanisms underlying the psychoneuroses. For example, basic research supported by NIMH on the effects of anxiety and hostility on behavior has contributed to an understanding of their psychodynamics. Furthermore, the large body of research that the Institute supports on the treatment of mental disorders provides another indirect route to the understanding of the psychoneuroses. This research is described in the chapter on psychological processes and the chapter on treatment.

There are two general categories of neurosis: (1) specific types of disorders, such as hypochrondria, obsessive-compulsive neurosis, and hysteria, all with a relatively low incidence; and (2) repetitious maladaptive behavior in interpersonal contexts, with conflict and pain. Diagnostically, the latter would often fall in the APA category (see table 1) of "Personality Disorders" and show a higher incidence. Together these conditions cause much personal distress and are responsible for, or implicated in, disruption of families, reduced productivity, general disgruntlement and dissatisfaction with the quality of life, criminality, social tensions, and related problems. Their behavior patterns comprise a large public health and social problem.

Sound figures for the incidence of neurosis are nearly impossible to obtain since the definition and classification of these disorders vary from one investigational framework to the next, and the crucial terms are usually not defined at all. Much human behavior is repetitious, for example, and behavior that may be maladaptive for one person would not be so for another.

There are many subforms of neurosis, with names so familiar that they have become common parlance: phobia, obsession, compulsion, depression, etc. A given individual may have a history of many neurotic complaints. In such cases, the investigator chooses for this diagnosis the subform that he finds most salient, but his diagnosis obviously does not encompass the full range of the individual's symptoms.

A distinction between neurosis and psychosis is not always apparent. Some people assume that the neuroses are milder forms of mental illness; twin studies have shown that some neuroses occur in the families of schizophrenics more frequently than one would expect by chance. Others feel that neurosis and psychosis do not belong in the same qualitative category. There is much disagreement, therefore, as to where to draw a boundary line defining the neuroses.

Epidemiological studies of neurosis at present frequently end up with statistics that reflect the investigator's concept of neurosis rather than objective facts. Comparison studies by different investigators in different cultures often lead to additional confusion.

Major questions involve the extent to which psychoneurosis results in extreme subjective distress, interferes with people's ability to contribute to society, and reduces their productivity. Most neurotics who seek treatment apply to psychiatrists and other therapists in private practice, counseling centers, or outpatient clinics.

Research on neurosis has been fragmentary. Much of the existing knowledge has come from psychoanalysis, clinical observation, and basic studies in normal and abnormal psychology. NIMH support for studies on the diagnosis and the etiology of the neuroses has been low.

Many theories coexist with respect to the genesis of neurosis. A large number of them trace their origins to Freud, Adler, or Jung. Others are based on social learning principles. These can be interpreted narrowly, reflecting classical conditioning or Hullian or Skinnerian learning patterns, or much more broadly, involving the quality of the patient's home, intrafamilial relationships, social class, and so on.

In recent years, several new conceptualizations of the neuroses have emerged, such as the hypotheses of "demoralization," and "learned helplessness." Such concepts open up new approaches to research. Other systematic research should address such questions as why some neuroses are chronic while the majority remit spontaneously; what the genetic contribution to neuroses consists of; and how certain neuroses differ at different stages of life.

First, however, researchers must develop clearer definitions and classifications of the neurotic disorders, and work toward their standardization, with help from such coordinating groups as the World Health Organization and NIMH.

RECOMMENDATIONS FOR RESEARCH ON PSYCHONEUROSES

The level of current research activities in this area is much less than its public health and social consequences call for. Research on psychoneurosis should, accordingly, be actively stimulated and encouraged. This research can be productive only if adequate emphasis is placed initially on coping with the basic methodological difficulties, including those of diagnosis and sampling.

PSYCHOSOMATIC RESEARCH

Psychosomatic medicine and research began a period of active growth in this country about the time of World War II. The initial burst of enthusiasm manifested during the early years has since subsided, and so has NIMH research in this area. In the past, NIMH supported a large share of the clinical and preclinical psychosomatic research carried out in this country, which has been generally of high quality. The absolute amounts of resources devoted to this area accelerated in earlier years, plateaued in the mid-1960's, and have declined recently. Proportionately, however, the fraction of total NIMH research devoted to psychosomatic research has declined progressively, as demonstrated by the data on grant support in table 2.

Table 2
Total NIMH Psychosomatic Research

Year	Number of Grants	Amount (In thousands)	% Total Grant Expenditures
1948	4	$ 34	9.6
1951	5	46	3.7
1956	9	150	3.9
1961	27	551	1.8
1966	31	1139	1.9
1971	15	947	1.3

Though the concept, "psychosomatic medicine," has gained widespread usage and general acceptance during this period, the term itself does not appear in any table of organization down to section level of any of the Institutes of Health nor in the titles of any of their public advisory groups.

The research supported has demonstrated conclusively that psychological events can result in reliably measurable changes in hundreds of physically or chemically discernible variables. Many of the changes so demonstrated are similar to changes believed to be causally significant in many somatic illnesses. To date, however, psychosomatic research has provided few, if any, insights that have resulted in major advances in the treatment and prevention of serious somatic illness. Specific accomplishments of this research are characterized by some as primarily extensions, amplifications, and quantifications of a generalization as old as human thought: perturbations of the mind often cause perturbations of the body.

Early psychosomatic research had a substantial psychoanalytic component, and tended to be heavily concentrated in the following illnesses: heart disease, hypertension, Reynaud's disease, dermatitis, hives, pruritis, allergy, peptic ulcer, cardiospasm, asthma, rhinitis, headache, backache, diabetes, hypoglycemia, hypothyroidism, and colitis.

Major trends in research on psychosomatic illness have included:

1. The specificity hypothesis: Do people with a particular somatic illness tend to have distinctive antecedent psychological traits?

2. Predictive studies, which on the basis of psychological evaluation successfully predicted peptic ulcer, hypertension, and coronary heart disease.

3. Psychosocial manipulation of animals and animal disease studies.

4. Advances in instrumental conditioning of visceral and other physiological functions, e.g., heart rate, leading to "voluntary" control of these functions, and the application of this research through "biofeedback" processes to the treatment of a wide range of psychosomatic and medical conditions, e.g., headaches, sleep problems.

Additionally, certain individual study programs have stood out, including those on:

1. The relationship of object loss and depression to susceptibility to illness.

2. Large-scale studies relating illness to simple and objective life-change ratings.

3. A considerable body of psychophysiological research.

The present pattern of research supported by NIMH is quite limited. However, this is a research area in which other Institutes of Health are active.

RECOMMENDATIONS FOR PSYCHOSOMATIC RESEARCH

1. In view of the magnitude of this problem, the present level of support for research in this area is inadequate; active steps should be taken administratively and in terms of resource allocation to infuse greater interest and energy into this area.

2. Sustained collaborative psychosomatic research programs should be fostered in settings which have strong ongoing clinical research programs in many different somatic illnesses and which are not hostile to psychosomatic viewpoints, i.e., a few of the top medical schools and the NIH Clinical Center.

3. Correlations between psychological factors and somatic illness have probably been sufficiently studied from the retrospective viewpoint. High priority should go to prospective longitudinal correlational studies of manifest somatic illness designed to demonstrate mechanisms of onset.

4. Another area of high priority should be prospective studies of high risk populations. NIMH should attempt to involve other institutes and to include psychosocial assessment of subject/ patient participants in a wide variety of prospective studies.

5. Experimental clinical studies of somatic effects of psychosocial manipulations are likely to demonstrate the existence of causal psychosomatic relationships and should be supported.

6. Animal studies relevant to psychosomatic problems should be strongly supported. These should include investigations of long-term somatic results of early experiences, and of the effects of time-remote and

time-proximate environmental manipulations on susceptibility to experimental disease, immune mechanisms, and autonomic and endocrine systems. Further basic research on the nature of visceral conditioning in animals and humans should be supported.

7. Treatment research recommendations:

a. High priority should be given to exploring the potential of operant-conditioning techniques in treating diverse somatic illnesses.

b. Research pertaining to the role of psychotropic drugs in management of somatic illness needs further examination and, probably, more emphasis.

c. Research on psychotherapy in the family setting as it pertains to the management of chronic, relapsing diseases in children should be encouraged.

d. A general and long-term perspective shows a need for research that will define optimal ways to provide all sick people with psychological support, understanding, and treatment as might be indicated.

8. An entity within NIH-NIMH should be given the sole mission of fostering psychosomatic research. The unit should be designed to achieve close working relationships between NIMH and all other categorical institutes.

RECOMMENDATIONS FOR ADMINISTRATIVE AND ORGANIZATIONAL CHANGE

The history of science can teach us several important lessons. First, it is quite clear that the theoretical models with which we operate define the limits of our horizons and predetermine the results. Many important—even epochal—advances have resulted from the development, and application of, radically new models. Second, many important discoveries have been made serendipitously, so their occurrence could not have been predicted. Third, oversimplification of complex issues can lead to a stereotypy of thought and approach, which can, in turn, result in premature closure and loss of innovation. A wide variety of research approaches must be supported in order to avoid stereotyping and too narrowly defining what constitutes good research.

The first four recommendations that follow are viewed as especially useful in implementing this philosophy:

1. The Institute should develop administrative mechanisms to systematically and periodically review programs and overall program balance rather than individual research projects. Such review should weigh the totality of current and projected research resources against questions of the likely yield, and also the relevance to public and scientific need, of different research approaches such as biological versus psychosocial studies. Vigorous disagreement exists between biological and psychosocial investigators as to what constitutes optimal present and future distribution of resources between these two approaches to the study of mental illness.

The Biological Subcommittee of the Mental Illness Study Group reported:

... the compelling evidence that the schizophrenias and the affective disorders are due . . . in part, to a genetically transmitted biochemical defect . . . has not received sufficient attention and . . . the current allocation of research resources does not reflect the increasing evidence of the major role of biological factors in serious mental illness.

Accordingly, that Subcommittee recommended the following:

It is felt by the subcommittee that although the value of basic scientists to clinical research is accepted by most serious professionals in this field, there is a lack of understanding of the critical scientific discipline that is involved in translating selected relevant basic research through clinical research experiments into practical therapeutic and diagnostic procedures. This field involves the development of critical hypotheses and the systematic testing of these theories in human patients. It is our feeling that this discipline is equal in importance to that of basic science and deserves substantial support.

The Psychosocial Subcommittee concluded that:

When one reviews the entire program of Institute extramural financial support for research on the mental disorders, applied and basic, for fiscal 1972, the support appears to be balanced between that apportioned for the biological sciences on the one hand, and that for the psychological and sociocultural sciences, on the other . . . .

(1) [NIMH] supports more basic research in the psychological and sociocultural sciences than it does in the biological sphere, presumably related to the fact that the Mental Health Institute is more heavily reliant on those fields, of all the Institutes of Health, and is probably the major source of support for them.

(2) [NIMH] supports more biological than psychological research which is directly applicable to understanding etiology or to treating the major mental disorders.

The subcommittee believes there has been a recent major shift in apportionment of available research funds for biological research, and a corresponding decline in support for psychological and sociocultural areas in the applied field of clinical research. It believes that the recent notable decline in overall effort in psychological research, relevant to mental illness, is a passing "reexamination" phase which is likely to be followed by a resurgence of research, on a sounder and more innovative base. The subcommittee's recommendation is:

On the one hand, the field with great momentum (biology) should be facilitated, for it requires immediate expansion; and on the other, the new beginnings (psychosocial) require rapid developmental exploitation.

Attention is called to the detailed, eloquent, and extended description of these issues presented by the reports of both subcommittees mentioned above; these are contained in the final report of the Study Group on Mental Illness and the Behavior Disorders.

2. The large bulk of extramural research support should continue to be allocated via the investigator-initiated research grant mechanism based on peer review. This mechanism continues to represent, in most instances, the optimal funding mechanism for basic research. However, special research grant and contract mechanisms do offer greater possibilities of rapid response to applied, clinical, and policy research issues. Therefore, it is further recommended that program managers have more flexibility in allocating resources among these several support mechanisms. Simultaneously, however, it is necessary that administrative and scientific review of research contract proposals be strengthened so as to achieve a degree of credibility and effectiveness equal to that now demonstrated by the grant review process.

3. The Institute should continue a broad-based basic and clinical intramural laboratory of the highest quality as a first-line attack on the problem of mental disorders, as a model for other laboratories in the country, and as a valuable national training resource. This model is an especially important one for maintaining heterogeneity in the field.

4. A new model laboratory for applied research and training in psychopathology should be established. This laboratory, which would provide the resources for the conduct of nationally coordinated, multidisciplinary, collaborative research on critical public health issues and problems, would serve as a central planning base and provide staff and facilities for collaborative national and international programs to evaluate new psychological and biological methods, to develop and test new treatments, to study the bases of mental disorders, and to provide training for young scientists in this field.

The current dichotomy between intramural and extramural programs is basically a sound one, but there should be more communication between scientists in the two realms. The Task Force is reluctant to recommend any specific program of interaction, acknowledging that there are substantial reasons for the maintenance of the current separation.

Other considerations, however, would argue for a new type of organizational unit, one that would bridge the gap between the extra- and intramural programs and conduct the kind of research that currently falls between the functions of both organizations. Such units would have one or more of the following characteristics. They might:

a. Deal directly with critical public health issues, e.g., the simultaneous examination in collaborating laboratories of several biological and psychological indices believed to be causative of major mental disorders, and the evaluation or the development of a new treatment for a major mental disorder.

b. Deal with clinical or social problems that bridge the basic and applied areas, e.g., investigation of a potential biological index of psychosis across several diagnostic classes.

192

c. Facilitate the development and application of new psychological, biological, and social methods.

d. Invite collaborative arrangements and coordination among investigators within and outside the NIMH, e.g., to assemble the sample size required for a given study, or to make maximal use of the limited talent in a specialized field.

The recommended new model laboratory meets these goals.

5. The Institute should construct a physical facility for the integration of the clinical and basic intramural research activities.

In order to convene a "critical mass" of scientists with a common focus of interest in mental health, it is proposed that the work currently underway in four separate geographic locations—Poolesville, St. Elizabeths, Lexington, and Bethesda—be coordinated, and that the latter three be eventually combined into one facility. At the present rate of growth, the 11 wards currently in the intramural research program need to be at least doubled, plus doubled space provided for basic research operations. Research would focus on schizophrenia, affective illness, addiction, childhood psychosis, violence, and neurological problems, with strong representation of all disciplines—biological, behavioral, psychological, and socioenvironmental. Over a period of time such an integrated facility, by eliminating duplication of expensive clinical and support services, would be likely to cost less than the current separate facilities; and, by making possible improved coordination and integration of programs, it would be likely to speed results.

6. The Institute should establish a new genetics program in NIMH composed of a branch in the intramural program and an extramural section within the Division of Extramural Research Programs. Recent findings that genetic factors play a major role in a variety of human psychopathologies, including alcoholism, schizophrenia, and affective illness, and in the determination of a variety of personality characteristics suggest that the area of genetics will continue to have increased scientific and practical payoff for many years to come. It is, therefore, recommended that a new NIMH branch be established to undertake and to stimulate the development of new programs of basic and clinical research in this area.

7. NIMH should establish three new clinical research centers, located in major universities, to test important scientific, primarily biological, theories concerning the etiology and treatment of mental disorders. Since any gains in treatment of patients must eventually come through clinical research, it is suggested that the Division of Extramural Research Programs fund two or three such centers during the next 2 years. The program should have a full-time experienced researcher as its director. It is estimated that the cost of these units would run about $750,000 per year. If three were set up, the total cost per year would be about $2,250,000. A two-phase system for making the grants might ultimately lead to finding the best people and places for these units. Phase 1 would require relatively brief grant applications, which would

be used for initial screening. A number of applicants would then be given 18-month grants for planning the Phase II applications; these would be much more extensive and include commitments from the scientists to work on the project should it be funded. From the Phase II applications, approximately three would be funded. The grants would be for 5 years. If the plan is successful, additional research units can be set up. The units should be designed to provide free research beds, high staff-patient ratios, and facilities to control diet and drugs. Such facilities are expensive, and the basic elements are currently available in only nine or ten university centers in the United States. It is recommended that funding for this program should be additional to rather than in competition with the regular grant program, whose budget is already depleted.

8. The Institute should establish catchment-area-based research centers in which psychological, sociocultural, and biological studies are all carried out in the context of a treatment network. The past decade has seen a major change in locus of the treatment of the mentally ill from the hospital to the community. Such catchment-area research centers might best be located where ongoing patient registers exist and where simultaneous study of a wide range of psychological, sociological, and biological variables could be emphasized. These centers might benefit from being in close relationship with the biologically oriented clinical research centers recommended above. And it is recommended that most new clinical research centers should wherever possible be catchment-area-based. Such an arrangement would make possible the simultaneous study of a wide range of psychological, sociological, and biological variables and, even more importantly, their interactions.

9. The Institute should establish a sabbatical center to provide for the synthesis, analysis, integration, and summarization of existing data, for reflection on this information, and for the generation of crucial new data in the field of mental health. A center devoted to the accomplishment of these tasks could include senior scientists willing to synthesize, integrate, and theorize from existing data; scientists not previously in the field of mental health who wish to offer their specialty to a particular problem area of mental health; and new scientists pursuing a career in mental health research.

This center would cost approximately $300,000 per year for scholars and staff. It would enhance the flow of fruitful ideas and research by inviting outstanding basic scientists and clincial researchers to spend a year or two at NIMH to collaborate in conceptualizing problem areas and designing and conducting mental health research. Other at the center would include scientists with new interests; scientists who require facilities, patient populations, and collaborators; and NIMH scientists who need to spend a limited time in a clinical research laboratory to conduct collaborative research with scientists outside the Government.

In addition, research can be advanced by developing a roster of NIMH consultants who can advise researchers about their areas of expertise, a service to be funded by NIMH.

Table 3
Recent Changes in Extramural Support of Child Mental Health Research [a]

Research Areas	1970			1973			Change		
	No. of Projects	Funds (millions)	%	No. of Projects	Funds (millions)	%	No. of Projects	Funds (millions)	%
Clinical Categories	38	$ 2.7	27	43	$ 2.9	26	+ 5	$+ 0.1	+ 5
Treatment and Services	47	4.0	40	28	2.0	18	−19	− 2.0	− 50
Biological and Physiological Correlates of Behavior	6	0.2	2	14	0.8	7	+ 8	+ 0.6	+ 30
Social and Cultural Correlates of Behavior	35	1.5	15	42	2.1	19	+ 7	+ 0.6	+ 41
Psychological Aspects of Behavior	51	1.7	17	61	2.8	25	+10	+ 1.1	+ 66
Special Categories	1	0.03	1	6	0.5	4	+ 5	+ 0.5	+1400
Total	178	$10.2	100	194	$11.1	100	+16	$+ 0.9	+ 9
Total NIMH Extramural Research Support		$77.8			$43.2			$−34.6	− 44
Primary Child Mental Health Support		$10.2 = 13%			$11.1 = 25%				
Total NIMH Extramural Research Support		$77.8			$43.2				
Secondary Interest in Child Mental Health Support		$ 4.0			$ 5.1				
Primary and Secondary Child Mental Health Support		$14.2 = 18%			$16.2 = 38%				
Total NIMH Extramural Research Support		$77.8			$43.2				

[a] The 1970 figures are from the Ad Hoc Committee on Child Mental Health (1971, p. 26), and the 1973 figures are from an NIMH Division of Extramural Research Program report, dated 9/20/73. Percentages are rounded to 1%. Funds are given in millions of dollars, rounded.
[b] Change of funds % is the funds difference (1973 minus 1970) divided by the 1970 funds.

RESEARCH ON CRITICAL DEVELOPMENTAL PERIODS

NIMH has always devoted special emphasis to research focused on two critical periods in human development—childhood and old age. Reports on the Institute's programs in these areas are given below.

MENTAL AND EMOTIONAL DISORDERS OF CHILDHOOD

Through the years, between one-fourth and one-third of the Institute's research efforts have gone to studies dealing in some way with the mental health of children.

Table 3 shows recent changes in extramural support of research primarily concerned with that subject. In 1970, when child mental health was made the Institute's first priority, research in that area amounted to $10.2 million, or 13 percent of the total extramural research budget (18 percent when projects of secondary relevance to child mental health are included). Three years later it amounted to $11.1 million, or 25 percent of the budget (38 percent, counting secondary projects).

Most of this proportionate gain occurred not because funds for child mental health research were increased—as they were, by $900,000—but because the total extramural budget dropped substantially.

Intramural research on child mental health has also increased in recent years. In 1970 it totaled about $2.3 million or 14.5 percent of the intramural research program's budget. In 1972 it totaled about $2.5 million, or 15.6 percent.

In both extramural and intramural programs, the research deals with a wide range of problems related to child mental health. Basic research relevant to this subject has been reported in the chapters concerned with the processes underlying behavior. These chapters have reported, for example, on the genetic influence in mental illness (a subject also discussed earlier in the present chapter); on the advances in our knowledge of the psychological development of the child; and on some of the social influences on child mental health.

This section is concerned mainly with the areas shown in table 4. The section describes recent research—much of it supported by NIMH—on learning disorders, antisocial behavior, and childhood psychoses and makes recommendations for future work.

Table 4
Extramural Research Support in 3 Areas, 1972

Area	No. of Grants	Amount (In millions)
Learning Problems	42	$2.4
Juvenile Delinquency and Child Behavior Disorders	25	2.1
Child Mental Illness (Chiefly psychoses)	41	2.6
Total	108	$7.1

Learning Disorders

Research has now shown that learning disorders, if they persist into late childhood and adolescence, generally lead to serious emotional and behavioral disturbances. Such disorders represent the major single cause of school dropouts. They also represent one of the major problems observed in children and young people who have been referred to clinics and juvenile courts.

Need for Objective Classification

Research in this area continues to be hampered by the lack of objective means of classifying the numerous types of learning deficiency. There has been a tendency to confuse classification with what is inferred to be cause. But research over the last half dozen years points to many causes, different combinations of them operating in different cases. Included are genetic defects, prenatal and perinatal complications, postnatal brain trauma and infection, inadequate teaching, cultural deprivation, sensory defects, emotional problems, and the complexities of English orthography. Since the classification of a child with a reading disability or other learning handicap may well affect both his treatment and his psychological development, inferential diagnosis is a grave matter.

Desperately needed is an objective classification that focuses on a child's measurable handicap—in reading, arithmetic, perception, or whatever. For example, a learning problem associated with hyperactivity in a child who is not retarded or sensorially impaired should be diagnosed in terms of the type and the extent of the learning disability, and the statement should be made that it is associated with hyperactivity. Nothing more. To infer that the underlying defect is brain damage can only serve to retard scientific knowledge and the child. Wide use of objective classification would facilitate research on the relationships, if any, between specified learning disabilities and such factors as heredity, events at or near birth, developmental milestones, and environmental circumstances.

Studies on Early Detection

The research on early detection has contained serious methodological deficiencies. For example, most studies have been based on small samples and have included both girls and boys, although learning disorders have been shown to be sex-linked, occurring significantly more often among boys. In a notable exception, an investigator supported by NIMH is trying to identify the precursors of reading disability several years before the disorder is apparent. His subjects are 500 boys. Preliminary results show that the battery of tests administered at the beginning of kindergarten had picked out 100 percent of these children who at the end of first grade were found to be severely handicapped in reading and 95 percent of those found to be superior. Validation of these findings would offer parents and educators strong reason for working to help young children acquire those developmental skills shown by the tests to be essential if serious reading problems are to be avoided.

Substantial contributions have been made by two other recent longitudinal projects. In one, every child born within a 7-day period in England, Scotland, and Wales was reexamined at the age of 7. The results confirmed earlier findings that socioeconomic deprivation and birth complications have debilitating effects on early school achievement. They also showed that the rate of prematurity among those children who were failing in reading, writing, and spelling at the age of 7 had been disproportionately high.

The second study accurately predicted developmental-psychological competence at age 7 from prenatal, perinatal, and postnatal data derived from the collaborative child development study at Charity Hospital, New Orleans. All the children were black and most of them disadvantaged. The prenatal and perinatal measures proved to be the most important. The implication: neurological status before or during the first year may be used to forecast normality and abnormality in developmental competence 7 years later.

Another study has implicated a very low birth weight—less than 3 pounds—in the production of a high incidence of developmental handicaps: subaverage intelligence, 90 percent; slower than siblings, 73 percent; behavior problems, 78 percent. Behavior and personality disorders also appear to be common among such premature children. The circumstances of nursery care for some time after birth and of home care thereafter conspire against the development of a normal mother-child relationship, and the situation may be aggravated by the oversolicitude that may persist as a parental attitude long after the premature infant has caught up with his peers.

Effects of Early Intervention

When children with reading handicaps were diagnosed during the first two grades of school, one study found, more than 80 percent could be brought up to normal classroom levels. The proportion dropped to less than 50 percent when the diagnosis was made during the third grade and to only 10 to 15 percent during grades five to seven. Unfortunately, there is a dearth of findings to substantiate this report. Both animal and human studies indicate, however, that intervention should occur early, when the central nervous system is more plastic and responsive—and also, it should be noted, when the child is more likely to be free of the frustrations and emotional turmoil associated with repeated academic failure. An NIMH scientist has shown that variations in the environment have their greatest effect on a characteristic such as speech during the most rapid period of change (ages 2 to 10 in the case of speech) and the least effect during the slowest period of change (ages 11 to 15). Other NIMH-sponsored research indicates that intervention in the case of deprived children can profitably be started as early as the first and second years.

Two Major Needs for Further Research:

1. Development of an objective classification system, like the one discussed earlier in this section.

2. Longitudinal research to uncover the factors involved in the development of specific handicaps. Such research would not only throw further light on how biological and environmental conditions act together in the development of learning problems but would also in-

crease our ability to detect impending trouble, often in time to offset or minimize it.

Antisocial Behavior Disturbances

Children categorized as antisocial or as exhibiting an antisocial behavior disturbance or disorder may be defined as those who repeatedly show resistance to authority. They fail to attend school or complete assignments; they stay out beyond the time allowed by parents; they address those in authority in ways that appear disrespectful. As they grow older, they may engage not only in acts acceptable for adults but considered inappropriately precocious for children, such as smoking, swearing, drinking, and sexual activity, but also in criminal acts—theft, assault, and rape. They prolong, beyond the ages at which it is sometimes tolerated in small children, behavior such as damaging property and lying.

Antisocial behavior disturbance is a common childhood psychiatric disorder. In fact, a recent epidemiological study by an English investigator found that, of all the childhood psychiatric disorders in the area studied, it was the most common. It accounted for 68 percent of psychiatrically disturbed boys and 32 percent of psychiatrically disturbed girls.

Antisocial children include a large proportion of those given other labels—delinquent or predelinquent, hyperactive or hyperkinetic, and underachiever. (Research on delinquency, touched upon in this section, is reported at greater length in the chapter dealing with social problems.) They also include many children with specific learning disabilities.

Psychological and Biological Bases

To the observer, the behavior of antisocial children seems to show a lack of concern for personal safety and comfort, a desire for excitement, a failure to anticipate the consequences of behavior, and perhaps an ignorance of what is good or bad. The last of these hypotheses has been disproved by a number of studies showing that delinquents given a multiple choice test can choose as well as nondelinquents the ethical answer. But the psychological motivation for antisocial behavior is still not well understood. Among the possible explanations offered: Antisocial children (a) fail to feel the anxiety that inhibits the acting-on-impulse of normal children; (b) are unable to fantasize the future and thus foresee consequences of their behavior; (c) have higher pain thresholds, which reduce their ability to learn from experience; (d) have a deep underlying depression, which makes the future look so bleak that regard for personal safety is irrelevant; and (e) have delusions of invulnerability. These possibilities have not been systematically studied.

An association between antisocial behavior and neurological abnormalities—as indicated, for example, by the electroencephalogram (EEG)—has been found by some investigators but not by others. The contradictory findings are possibly explained by the theory that antisocial children are easily bored. In an experimental situation that appears dull to them, inattention might account for the usual EEG abnormality, slow waves; in other situations, brain wave activity might be normal. Similarly, it is possible that the slightly depressed IQ's recently reported in antisocial children result not from a true decrement in intellectual ability but from lack of motivation to excel on the tests, or poor reading ability, or distractibility during the test period.

Prematurity and complications of pregnancy, which are associated with lack of good prenatal and postnatal care and with poverty, are known to increase the incidence of minimal brain dysfunction. And minimal brain dysfunction appears to be involved in many cases of hyperactivity, learning disorder, and childhood psychosis.

An investigator in the intramural research program has reported a high incidence of minor physical anomalies in some hyperactive children. The observations suggest "chromosomal irregularities or some kind of insult affecting embryological development."

Although antisocial children have no marked intellectual impairment, if indeed any, they do have high rates of reading disability and school failure. Whether these are a cause of behavior disorder or an effect is not clear.

Family Factors

Several investigators have reported evidence of a genetic mechanism at work in some cases of psychopathy. It is clear that antisocial parents are more likely than other parents to produce antisocial children, but this is true of both natural and adoptive parents. Also associated with the development of antisocial behavior in children is erratic discipline or negligent child-rearing practices. Nevertheless, some antisocial children have conforming, nurturant parents.

Almost without exception, research shows broken homes in the background of delinquency. However, it is not the brokenness as such but the various associated factors of tension, neglect, and poverty that predispose to delinquent behavior.

Evidence of the extent to which parent-child interaction influences children's behavior comes from a longitudinal study that has given special attention to the development of behavior disorders. The strongest predictors of such disorders were found to be patterns of behavior that differed from the modal in four characteristics: intensity, adaptability, regularity, and mood. However, not all children with amodal patterns developed behavioral disorders, nor did all children with such disorders have amodal patterns. Parental reaction to the child apparently could influence the pattern's effect. The few markedly amodal children whose parents had a high tolerance of difficult behavior seemed to have less persistent problems. On the other hand, mild and undemanding children with calm and unresponsive parents sometimes developed behavioral disturbances after the parents ignored their mildly expressed legitimate demands. In sum, neither the characteristics of the parents nor the temperament of the child had an independent influence on the child's development: they were interdependent.

Natural History of Antisocial Behavior

Although children exhibiting antisocial behavior usually first come to the attention of therapists between the ages of 10 and 16, research has shown that they typically have histories of problem behavior in school and at home dating back at least to their first school years. Early maturation has been suggested but not confirmed as a contributing cause.

Girls have been much less likely than boys to develop antisocial behavior; they have tended to develop it later, and the family settings of antisocial girls have usually been more disturbed than those of boys. Whether or not the continuing changes in social mores will alter these findings remains to be seen. It is a fact, however, that the developmental rates of girls and boys do differ, and these rates are biologically determined.

Followup studies have found that antisocial behavior in childhood is frequently continued into later life. Among children referred to a child guidance clinic because of such behavior, one-quarter turned out to be sociopaths as adults, one-twelfth were alcoholics or drug addicts, one-ninth were psychotic. Only 16 percent recovered before the age of 18 and had no further psychiatric problems by the age of 40. On the other hand, serious antisocial behavior never began in adulthood among those child guidance clinic patients and controls who had been free of it in childhood. This observation, first made by an NIMH-supported investigator studying white clinic patients and normal white school children from lower-class homes, has recently been confirmed in a study of black schoolboys.

Drug Abusers

Several studies have found that habitual drug users are more likely than other young people to come from unstable families with little cohesiveness and a great amount of stress and conflict. Of the addicts in a study of minority groups, 97 percent had families affected by divorce, desertion, or open hostility among family members.

White young people who were addicted, one investigator found, were considerably more likely than their Puerto Rican and black counterparts to come from intact homes, earn more money, graduate from high school, not have addicted relatives, and not be on welfare. However, they were less likely to have had good relations with their families prior to their addiction.

Prevention and Treatment

Projects aimed at preventing the emergence of antisocial behavior or of more serious antisocial behavior than the child has yet shown have been uniformly disappointing. The traditional social casework tried in most of the studies has failed. So have the efforts by one project that provided work-study programs along with tutoring (failure in this case occurring in part, perhaps, because the boys found selection for treatment a stigmatizing experience).

The children in these programs were chosen on the basis of family patterns, underachievement in the early school years, and teacher selection of potential delinquents and dropouts. A large proportion of the children selected have, indeed, shown serious antisocial behavior in adolescence.

In contrast to preventive programs, treatment regimens aimed at reducing the existing level of behavior problems in children who have already been referred for psychiatric care or been classified delinquent have shown some short-term success, but there have been few adequate long-term evaluations. A notable exception is the work of two investigators who developed a vocationally oriented psychotherapy program for delinquent boys and evaluated its results several times over a 10-year period. They found that the benefits of such treatment for delinquents were maintained at least for a decade.

Among other findings are the following:

- Stimulant drugs given to children labeled hyperactive or hyperkinetic improve behavior at home and in school—by reducing hyperactivity, distractibility, and impulsiveness—on at least a short-term basis, and enhance performance on a number of cognitive-motor tasks. Controlled long-term followups have not been conducted, however, and one investigator reported that drug-treated children, from 4 to 6 years later, included many more cases of school failure and delinquency than found among normal children. Authorities disagree on the advisability of prescribing stimulant drugs for hyperactive children. They disagree, too, on the appropriateness of ascribing hyperactivity to minimal brain dysfunction unless there is hard neurological evidence, such as abnormality in the EEG, and not merely soft, or equivocal, signs, such as behavioral traits like fidgetiness.

- Treatment in conventional child-guidance clinics or in residential educational centers or by conventional psychotherapy has shown little or no advantage over no treatment. Behavior modification techniques appear to be more effective than psychotherapy; they have not been sufficiently tested to know whether or not they will work over the long haul.

- Some forms of treatment appear to be worse than no treatment at all. Children who have committed offenses that could require appearance in juvenile court seem less likely to be recidivists if they somehow avoid contact with the courts, and particularly if they avoid being sent to a reformatory. However, carefully controlled studies of the effect of diversion of delinquents from the juvenile courts system have not been done.

Among the Needs for Further Research:

1. Studies to test genetic theories. Twin studies of antisocial behavior such as those that have been made of identical twins discordant for schizophrenia would be a start.

2. Followup studies to learn if school failure can precipitate antisocial behavior.

3. Evaluation of current educational efforts with disadvantaged children in order to determine their effect on social behavior and not merely on IQ and school achievement.

4. Exploration of the effects of lack of discipline on child behavior.

5. Systematic study of antisocial children to learn more about their

depression level and their ability to feel anxiety, to tolerate pain, and to fantasize.

6. Scientific, long-term evaluation of treatment techniques, including those that have been shown to be effective on a short-term basis—behavior modification and stimulant drug.

Childhood Psychoses

In the psychoses of childhood, perhaps even more so than in those of adult life, accurate diagnosis and meaningful classification constitute a major research problem. One commonly used plan divides the psychoses into three main groups: (1) infantile autism; (2) the rarer psychoses, sometimes called either "disintegrative" or "regressive," occurring between the ages of 3 and 5 years following a period of normal development; and (3) schizophrenia beginning later in childhood. Though it is a useful division, a substantial minority of psychotic children do not fit easily into any of these categories. This minority includes: a few cases of disorders that look like autism but begin after the usually accepted age limit for onset of infantile autism, which is about 30 months; disorders that begin at the age of 3 or 4 years but do not show the profound regression characteristic of the disintegrative psychoses of this age period; and a larger number of nonspecific disorders of psychotic intensity having some but not all of the essential features of autism.

Very little systematic research has been conducted into the similarities among the main varieties of child psychosis.

Infantile Autism

As a recognized syndrome, infantile autism is a little older than the Institute. The first systematic account of it appeared in 1943 and was confirmed by a host of observations over the next decade. For years, however, little progress was made on important research questions—the limits of the syndrome, its relationship to other conditions, its etiology—partly because many authorities regarded it as either impossible or inappropriate to study psychotic children with standard physiological and psychological measures, and partly because diagnostic confusion made many research projects of little value.

The first controlled study in which the symptoms of autistic children were compared with those of children of the same age, sex, and intelligence was published in 1966. It suggested that the three cardinal features of autism were a particular type of failure to develop normal social relationships, a special variety of language retardation, and ritualistic or compulsive phenomena.

Research on Causes of Autism

Most of the many studies on specific factors that might cause autism have neglected sound scientific strategy. This would include specification of the autistic behaviors to be explained and a hypothesis about the disordered functions that might underlie such behaviors. Studies would have to be made to determine both (a) whether these functions are actually disordered in all autistic children and (b) whether disorder of these functions always leads to autism—and, if not, what additional factors are required for autism to develop. After that, it becomes reasonable to ask what kinds of biologocial or psychological damage might have caused disorder of these functions in the first place. No cause of autism has yet been established because no research program has yet gone through all these stages.

Nevertheless, a mass of evidence has now accumulated to suggest that the symptoms of infantile autism are probably caused in large part by a cognitive, perceptual, or language deficit. The precise boundaries of this deficit have not been found, and the cause of it is not clear.

Overt neurological disorders appear only infrequently in autism. However, several investigators have independently found that a least a sizable minority—possibly a majority—of autistic children do have indications of some kind of organic brain dysfunction. Whether there is anything specific about the type of dysfunction found in autism is unknown. It is possible that these findings apply only or mainly to autistic children with low IQ's.

Genetic studies of infantile autism have been quite inconclusive.

Research on perinatal complications suggests that autistic children may have been slightly more at risk to them than other children. But the difference, not yet confirmed, is not great enough for such complications to be regarded as a common cause of autism.

A number of attempts to discover neurochemical and metabolic defects in autistic children have proved negative. Biochemical research on autism definitely should continue but probably should not have a very high priority until there is a better indication of what sort of abnormality might be present.

Family Factors

Very little, if any, scientific evidence has been found to support the hypothesis that pathological behavior on the part of the parents can lead to autism in a child. However, it has not been possible to determine satisfactorily just how parents did behave during their children's early infancy, before the onset of autistic symptoms.

One observation made years ago appears to be still valid: that the parents of an autistic child tend to be of higher intelligence and higher socioeconomic level than either the general population or the parents of children with other psychiatric disorders. With only one important exception, numerous studies have attested to the difference, though suggesting that it is not quite so great as first appeared. The reason for the one exception is not clear.

Intelligence Level

Clinicians for many years tended to regard all autistic children as having normal intelligence. Research has now shown, however, that autistic children tend to have a characteristic pattern of abilities, with low scores on any tests involving language or sequencing and higher scores on tests involving visio-spatial skills or short-term memory. The overall level of intelligence is normal in about a quarter of autistic children; the others are mentally retarded to a greater or lesser degree. These findings have methodological implications. First, since many autistic children are also retarded, mental age must be taken into account in making any kind of comparisons with other groups.

Failure to do so—as is the case in a distressingly high proportion of studies—means that the differences may be a function of low mental age rather than of autism. Second, it may be that low IQ and normal IQ autistic children have rather different conditions. One investigator recently found not only that the prognosis was very much worse for low IQ children but also that the indications of organic brain damage were very much more frequent. Epileptic seizures developed in adolescence among a high proportion of severely retarded children but in only a small minority of those of normal intelligence.

Research on Treatment of Autism

Research by NIMH-supported and other investigators has demonstrated that behavior modification techniques can be very useful as means both of treating childhood autism and of investigating its nature. As a result, the work on these techniques with autistic children has moved from the laboratory into the home, and parents are being used increasingly as therapists. (Behavior modification is discussed in the chapter on psychological processes and in the chapter on treatment.)

In the past there has tended to be a gulf between behavioral and psychodynamic approaches to treatment, but several groups of investigators and clinicians have now shown that much may be gained in some cases by combining the two. One authority claims that the outcome of psychotherapy with children at his residential center has been good or fair in four cases out of five. Like many others, this report cannot be evaluated in the absence of adequate criteria and controls.

Several studies have shown the value of special schooling, and progress has been made in defining the type of education needed.

Promising Areas for Further Research on Autism

1. Particularly rewarding should be research seeking to delineate the boundaries of the cognitive, perceptual, or language deficit that now seems to be a principal factor in autism. In such research it will be essential to control for mental age and desirable to choose as pure a group of autistic children as possible. The question should not be, "What cognitive deficits are associated with autism?" but "What cognitive deficits have to be present for autism to develop?" Autistic children of normal nonverbal intelligence, even though they are a minority of autistic children, provide the best opportunity to delineate the cognitive deficits specific to autism. The next step is to learn if these deficits are found also in multiply handicapped autistic children.

    For controls, retarded children, children with developmental language and perceptual disorders, and children with organic brain disorders should be considered. Research has shown that autistic children have much in common with such children (though not with normal children, who have often been used as controls). But they differ in the behavioral features specific to autism, so a comparison with these groups may help determine if the specific behavioral differences are associated with specific cognitive differences.

Other questions that such research should seek to answer include: In addition to the cognitive deficits, what environmental or personality variables, if any, are required for autism to develop? How may cognitive deficits lead to social and behavioral problems? To what extent are these problems inevitable and to what extent preventable?

2. Full use should be made of advances in fields of research apart from autism. For example, during recent years there have been important advances in psycholinguistics that have not only furthered our understanding of language development but also provided tools for investigation. Since the language deficit in autism probably concerns semantics and concepts more than syntax, work on these aspects of language also is important. Leads and methods relevant to the study of autistic children are to be found also in the fields of perception, memory, and cognition generally and in speech and language pathology.

3. A detailed study of individual behaviors, with a functional analysis of which factors induce them and which reduce them, may be just as informative as studies of the syndrome as a whole. An Institute-supported study of social behavior with respect to cognitive success and failure offers a model of how this may be done. Particularly requiring study in this way is the failure of social development in autism. Self-injury, repetitive movements, and attachment to objects are other symptoms warranting analysis.

4. In the area of treatment, research should pay more attention to the handicaps of the children studied, in order to provide better measures of treatment outcome. The studies should also focus on those children—of preschool age—in whom secondary handicaps have not yet become established.

The process of treatment, including parent-child interaction when parents are used as therapists, and teacher-child interaction in the case of special schooling, also needs to be studied. What little work has been done to determine those specifics of education that bring particular benefits to particular groups of children suggests that further research here would be definitely worthwhile. Another important question: to what extent can the techniques used to increase the efficacy of teaching with other groups of handicapped children be extended to the teaching of autistic children?

Childhood Schizophrenia

Much of the research supposedly on schizophrenia beginning in childhood cannot be assessed because the children studied were not clearly

206

described. Many reports appear to refer to groups largely comprised of autistic children. Since this condition has been subjected to very little systematic study of any kind, a wide range of investigations is needed. Among those that should be included and are likely to prove rewarding are studies of precipitating factors, of developmental factors before the advent of psychosis, of family influences on the course of the disorder, and of genetic factors.

Disintegrative or Regressive Psychoses

This group of childhood psychoses has been studied least, probably because cases are rare. Practically nothing is known about them. Post-mortem studies have usually, but not always, shown cortical degeneration. However, these investigations need to be repeated with modern methods of histopathological examination.

Dead Ends in Research on Child Psychoses

Most of the dead ends stem from methodological deficiencies, such as failure to put forward a testable hypothesis, to use adequate controls, and to recognize the influence of developmental changes.

However, some research topics themselves have not led anywhere and probably should not be pursued further at this time. These include the view that infantile autism is primarily a psychogenic disorder and that family factors contribute to its cause. (However, the influence of the family and of other environmental factors on the course of the disorder probably does warrant further study.)

Metabolic studies into all types of psychoses have so far proved to be a dead end. Probably they should not have a high priority until there is more promise from research of this kind.

Psychotherapy with autistic children of the kind designed to provide insight has not proved effective and in the light of our knowledge about autism is unlikely to do so.

SUMMING UP: MAJOR REQUIREMENTS FOR RESEARCH ON MENTAL AND EMOTIONAL DISORDERS OF CHILDREN

1. Two needs are of paramount importance. The first is the proper identification of problems in child mental health. Improper labeling of children, among other results, denies children access to the services they need, as documented by the DHEW Classification and Labelling of Exceptional Children Project. Worse, the consequences of classification—particularly the institutionalization of children labeled retarded or delinquent—may exacerbate the original condition. Examples of overlapping diagnostic categories are frequently found in antisocial behavior disorders, hyperactivity—often termed minimal brain dysfunction—and learning disorders. Diagnostic overlap is also found among infantile autism, childhood schizophrenia, mental retardation, and brain damage. The Institute should do everything within its power to advance the formulation and use of clearer standards of classification.

2. Of equal importance and of help in meeting the need for better classification standards is the need for additional longitudinal studies (a) to determine more precisely the factors involved in the behavioral disorders of childhood and in child mental illness and health, (b) to identify potential problems early, (c) to test preventive and remedial measures over long periods as well as short, (d) to ascertain the natural history of learning disabilities, antisocial behavior disturbances, and the psychoses of childhood.

    The dangers inherent in retrospective studies have been demonstrated by investigators who explored the backgrounds of normal, well-functioning adults. The investigators reported that if many of these individuals had complained of gross inhibitions, incapacities, phobias, or psychosomatic illness, there would have been background factors to account for them. The factors included shyness, nervousness, irritability, tantrums, insomnia, fears, speech defects, hypersensitiveness, and tics—all of them unrelated to psychiatric outcome. Moreover, several cross-sectional studies have shown that a large proportion of supposedly normal children exhibit symptoms or behavior that in a clinic setting would be judged pathological. There is an implication that many disturbances of behavior are no more than temporary exaggerations of widely distributed patterns of reaction to developmental stresses.

3. In the case of research on treatment, long-term followup studies are needed to compare the various treatment approaches—drug, nondrug, and combined—for the different disorders. Particularly important are high-quality longitudinal studies of the natural history of minimal brain dysfunction, with and without pharmacological intervention. As an NIMH authority puts it: "Admittedly, these studies require great dedication and involve serious ethical issues, but these studies must be done lest we find that community and political pressures preclude the use of an effective treatment modality."

    Since the impact of parent on child and child on parent is critically important, research is needed also to develop treatment services to help parents of disturbed children and of children at risk to mental and emotional disorders.

4. Much research on childhood mental and behavioral disorders has been of little or no value because of methodological deficiencies. NIMH should take a much more active role in promoting methodological rigor through one or more ways such as the following: (a) technical assistance to grant applicants in setting up methodological procedures; (b) a publication on methodological concerns, for interested applicants; (c) encouragement of studies aimed at verifying important but unreplicated earlier findings.

RECOMMENDATIONS FOR ORGANIZATION AND MANAGEMENT OF RESEARCH ON MENTAL AND EMOTIONAL DISORDERS OF CHILDREN

1. The Institute should classify child mental health research into three areas:

a. Research of paramount importance to the Institute's mission, such as research on childhood psychoses, hyperactive behavior, and methodology. For this category, NIMH should be the primary funding source.

b. Research of major interest to both NIMH and other organizations, governmental and private. Examples include research on the causes of child abuse and on the effects upon the family of chronic illness or mental retardation in a child. Research in this category should be planned and funded jointly by NIMH and the other interested organizations.

c. Research that is of some interest to NIMH but falls into neither of the preceding categories. Here the Institute would simply be available for technical assistance or information.

The preliminary categorization should be made by NIMH scientists and senior research administrators and by consultants.

2. To ensure a reasonable division of funds between basic research, which is essential to progress, and applied research, for which public pressure has mounted, NIMH should constitute a child mental health research committee to allocate funds to the various research areas. The allocation would be done in consultation with the National Advisory Mental Health Council. In making its decisions the committee would consider the research efforts of other governmental agencies and of private organizations.

3. The Institute should establish a child mental health coordinating center within the Office of the Director (a) to assist the Director in implementing those recommendations pertaining to child mental health research that are acceptable to him; (b) to keep an up-to-date record of child mental health activities within the Institute and outside of it; and (c) to improve coordination not only among NIMH units concerned with child mental health but also among NIMH and other agencies sharing this concern.

STUDIES OF MENTAL HEALTH PROBLEMS IN AGING

Aging is a combination of biological, psychological, and social processes. But the social processes play an unduly heavy role because American culture glorifies youth and considers people old at 65, whatever their capacities. In a society that emphasizes productivity and a hopeful future, the older person faces mostly loss—of occupation and financial status, of esteem, of strength, of friends and social comfort, and inevitably, of life itself. Imposed on these losses and on the organic deterioration of the aging process is the rejection that even the physically healthy aged person may face in our youth-oriented, work-oriented society. American culture, unlike a number of others, has no honored place for elders. It follows that old people, who are subject to the same mental disorders that can strike any age group, also face special mental health problems.

As some indication of the prevalence in this age group of problems labeled mental, people over 65 occupy 29 percent of all public mental hospital beds, or three times their proportionate share. To be sure, a number of them have been hospitalized mainly because their families and communities have seen the mental hospital as the simplest solution to the problem of where old people can live.

There are now more than 20 million people—one-tenth of the total—over 65 in the United States, and the older population is growing more rapidly than the population at large. In another 30 years, almost one-third of Americans will be over 65, and more than 40 percent of these will be over 75. For all its accent on youth, America is becoming a country of elders.

All health problems affect one or another proportion of the population, but the problems associated with old age in our culture affect or will affect almost everyone.

Overview of NIMH Support of Research on Aging

Studies of the mental health aspects of aging have been supported by the Institute since the beginning of its efforts in 1948 (see table 5). During the 7-year period, 1966 through 1972, grants for basic behavioral research on problems related to aging totaled about $1.1 million and those for clinical research, $2.8 million. Grants for applied research, including the demonstration of services for elderly people, came to $9.2 million, or more than twice the other two categories combined.

Table 5
Extramural Studies on Aging

Year	Number of Grants	Approximate Amount
1948	1	$ 6,000
1958	30	868,000
1962	44	1,600,000
1966	32	1,839,000
1970	26	1,807,000
1972	28	1,716,000

Research by the Institute itself, conducted by the Section on Aging established in the intramural program in 1953, constituted the first organized government effort to explore the mental health aspects of the subject.

During the early 1950's, NIMH intensified its efforts to stimulate professional interest outside the Institute. The Center for the Study of Aging and Human Development was established at Duke University and, with NIMH support, a research project initiated on the relationship of physiological, psychological, and social factors to the process of aging. More recently, an investigator at the Center has been attempting to isolate the normal changes of aging from the abnormal or pathological. With Institute help, other research programs in aging were established at the University of Chicago, through its Committee on Human Development, and at the Langley Porter Neuropsychiatric Institute, in San Francisco.

210

In sum, during the 1950's and the early 1960's, NIMH played a strong role in initiating and supporting gerontological research, particularly in cross-disciplinary and longitudinal studies of aging and in the areas of cognitive and learning functions in the aging organism. With the establishment of the National Institute of Child Health and Human Development in 1960, a large proportion of the applications for grants to support research on aging began going there, and the intramural Section on Aging was later closed out.

Since 1966 the Institute's efforts in this field have been centered in the Section on Mental Health of the Aging in the Division of Special Mental Health Programs. This section has two general concerns. First, the section works to have mental health considerations incorporated into programs for the aging where such considerations have been neglected. Second, it encourages and aids the establishment of new service programs—usually either exploratory in nature or intended to serve as models—and of research studies in areas where more information is needed. The section administers no research money of its own; it depends on the Institute's various divisions to fund projects in its field.

Research on the Aging Process

Probably the single most influential research project on aging since the founding of the Institute was the landmark investigation by intramural scientists in which normal healthy aged men were studied over a period of 12 years. As noted earlier, this project countered the common view that significant physical, psychological, and social deterioration is an inevitable accompaniment of the aging process. Small declines can be expected, but severe deterioration apparently is indicative of disease—coupled probably with social isolation—rather than of normal aging. Further baseline studies of this nature are badly needed.

The results of other research on aging are reported in the chapter on psychological processes. Needed is research to explain such findings, to devise means of slowing down or preventing decline in perceptual and cognitive capabilities, and to develop ways of increasing the ability of older persons to acquire new knowledge and skills.

Defining Old Age

The question of when a person becomes old remains unanswered, since one person may be decrepit at 55 while another is creative and active at 90. A number of NIMH and non-Institute studies suggest that a person encounters old age according to the customs and expectations in one's social milieu. One NIMH-supported investigator interviewed 800 people in eastern Kentucky, where he found that old age seems to arrive early. In this rural region people consider the peak years of influence and respect to be 22-45, while in cities the peak years are 45-65. The image of aging has had negative overtones in our culture, but there are societies, such as that of the Hunza, where a ripe old age means 135, and elders are valued.

In one of the few formal studies of centenarians and people over 100, an investigator with NIMH support collected information from more than 750 men and women who had reached or passed the century mark. In general, the investigator found, these very old people were to a remarkable degree physically active and mentally alert.

Psychiatric Disorders of Older People

Elderly people are particularly susceptible to organic psychosis, also known as organic brain syndrome or disease, and to depression. As discussed earlier in this chapter, researchers have grossly neglected the senile dementias and other forms of organic psychosis. However, a great deal of new information about the affective, or depressive, disorders has been acquired in recent years, much of it through Institute-sponsored research. Great advances in treatment have also been made. In fact, existing treatments—including antidepressant drugs, electric shock, and lithium carbonate—have been found effective in approximately 80 percent of patients suffering from depressive psychosis.

The high incidence of suicide among older people, however, is one indication that what we know about treating depression is not being optimally applied; another indication is the frequency of behavior that may be summed up as "withdrawal from life" and is characterized by failure to make use of life-sustaining activities, such as maintaining good nutrition and taking required medication.

Diagnostic Difficulties

The problem of properly diagnosing psychiatric illness in older persons is illustrated by a study of differences in diagnostic processes in the United States and the United Kingdom. This Institute-sponsored study finds that in the United States nearly 80 percent of the people 65 years and over who are admitted to a mental hospital for the first time are diagnosed as having an organic brain disorder; the rest are diagnosed as suffering from depression. In the United Kingdom, on the other hand, the diagnosis of organic brain disorder accounts for only 47 percent of the first admissions in this age group. Clearly, means for more careful diagnosis are badly needed.

Mental Health Services for the Elderly

NIMH-supported projects have shown how to reduce substantially the number of elderly persons entering mental hospitals, and how to improve the care in such facilities so that many elderly persons can return to the community. Other projects are tackling the problems of community care. Examples are given in the following sections.

Reducing the Need for Hospitalization

The aged constitute a disproportionately large number of those admitted to State mental hospitals, as pointed out previously. Evidence that this number can be substantially reduced through the provision of comprehensive community services comes from an Institute-supported project in Houston. With the cooperation of the judge responsible for geriatric commitments to State mental hospitals, the project developed an intervention program that used existing community resources and the services of a geriatric team for treatment and rehabilitation. All persons referred to the program received extensive medical and psychiatric examinations. Where indicated, patients were sent on to the State hospitals. Others received medical or psychiatric treatment, or both, in the community; assistance in finding housing, where needed; and through a variety of community agencies, help of other kinds. Of 100 patients who participated in the program, 41 were hospitalized; in a comparison group the corresponding number was 72.

Improving Institutional Care

The efforts to prevent and cure mental impairment in the elderly and to sustain the aged in the community can and should be greatly increased, but even under the best of circumstances a large number of aged persons will need institutional care. Projects supported by the Institute have demonstrated that this care can be improved. Since its inception in 1963, the Hospital Improvement Program (HIP) has provided an effective means for improving the quality of care provided by State mental hospitals and for demonstrating improved approaches to dealing with geriatric patients. HIP projects have demonstrated over and over that when elderly patients are subjected to modern treatment programs, a significant proportion of them can be rehabilitated and leave the institution.

At one State hospital, for example, HIP funds were used to establish a Geriatric Treatment Center to provide intensive care for all patients with a potential for independent living. During a 2-year period, more than half of the newly admitted patients were accepted for treatment in the project. And of this group of 200, almost 90 percent could be discharged to alternative care facilities within 90 days after admission to the center.

Even when old people must remain institutionalized, much can be done to increase their well-being. At one home for the elderly, for instance, it was found that even severely impaired persons could participate in and benefit from a program in which they worked for wages on tasks done under subcontract with various industries. In a research project at another home, elderly people with chronic brain disease were treated for their "excess disabilities"—those greater than warranted by the degree of impairment. The work demonstrated the value of active treatment even with patients suffering from disorientation and loss of memory. Similar results have been reached in a number of other NIMH-supported studies.

Improving Community Care

Many older persons discharged from State hospitals end up in poorly kept facilities, including welfare hotels, apartment houses, and boarding houses. For the most part, these people comprise an impaired and socioeconomically deprived group living a marginal existence. In large cities, in particular, a serious problem has arisen because of large numbers of older persons living in rundown hotels. One NIMH-supported study is addressing itself to this problem in New York City. It is determining the effect of a comprehensive onsite treatment program on the social, psychological, and physical health of aged tenants of a welfare hotel. Social, psychological, and medical services are provided through a private general hospital.

Research on the Housing Problem

NIMH has pioneered in stimulating and supporting studies of the role that housing plays in the lives of older persons. One group of projects, for example, has delineated the wide range of housing facilities in which older persons live and has evaluated the role that housing plays in adjustment to old age. These studies indicate that the most important factor from the older person's standpoint is self-selection: The older person likes to feel that the decision to live in a particular kind of housing was made by him, not forced on him. Other projects have studied the effects of providing (a) information and referral services in public housing for the aged, (b) medical and social services in such housing, and (c) apartments as an alternative for older persons who have applied for entrance to a home for the aging.

More evidence of the value of self-selection comes from a study of elderly people in a nursing home. Those who elect to live in such a home and see it as one of several options, the results indicate, live longer than those who are sent to such a home without options. Self-selection—that independence so deeply ingrained in the young—is often removed after 65. For many old people, even the right to die where they please is denied; a vast number, often connected to machines, die in an impersonal hospital situation rather than with family and friends.

One outstanding study of death and dying found that in many cases people went through definable stages of anger, depression, and acceptance of death and that most of these people needed help in ventilating stored frustrations and negative feelings. Too often, the psychiatric and spiritual needs of the elderly and dying are neglected.

Retirement

For many older people, forced retirement brings a crisis that seriously interferes with their adjustment to later life. With NIMH assistance, the Senior Citizen Center in Nashville, Tennessee, has shown one way of helping the retired person meet this crisis and find a rewarding role. The center added to its recreation and rehabilitation program a training course to prepare elderly persons for community service activities—in particular, work with disabled or disturbed children. The graduates were in such demand that some were paid for their services. Some graduates went on to become auxiliary therapists and several established other senior citizen centers. The idea led to the development of the highly successful Foster Grandparent Program of the Office of Economic Opportunity. Other research led to a report dealing with patterns of successful retirement.

Experiment to Help Meet the Manpower Problems

The shortage of trained mental health personnel is felt particularly in activities concerned with care of the elderly. In one of a number of Institute programs to provide suitable education and experience in working with older persons, inner city residents are being trained in both classroom and field for a paraprofessional role in helping old people maintain themselves outside of institutions. Seven agencies signed agreements to employ the graduates if they met agency standards and if funds were available. Both these requisites were met. Of the 23 students enrolled in the first 10-month training cycle, 19 graduated and got jobs.

RECOMMENDATIONS FOR RESEARCH ON AGING

1. NIMH should join with other Institutes of Health to vigorously stimulate research on organic psychosis. NIMH should also collect and disseminate the results of recent work in this area.

2. Workers in other areas of medicine are doing research on organic psychosis, while mental health personnel are taking care of the patients afflicted by this group of disorders. NIMH should discuss this situation with the National Institute of Neurological Diseases and Stroke, the Institute of Child Health and Human Development, and the Heart and Lung Institute. The American Board of Neurology and Psychiatry should participate in the discussion because it can request a change in programs of education if that is desired.

3. Good research on the relationship between aging and depression should be encouraged. Among the questions to be answered: What factors work to prevent, and what factors contribute to, depression among older people?

4. Studies are urgently needed on the environmental stresses that speed up deteriorative processes and the environmental supports that contribute to the mental health of older persons.

5. Emphasis needs to be placed also on (a) critical changes in learning processes—such as information storage and the acquisition of new knowledge and skills—in normal aging and (b) biological-psychological-social interrelationships in the process of aging. (Descriptive work on reaction time, memory loss, and personality traits should be deemphasized; so should gross comparisons of "young" vs. "old" on psychological measures.)

6. It is essential to continue to study, test, and evaluate new methods of delivering mental health services to the elderly.

7. The ramifications of demographic change now taking place cannot be considered in mental health terms without taking into account existing Federal policies underlying the support of the nonworking population. At present most older people rely upon some kind of retirement pay: pensions, Social Security, or, for the poorest, public assistance. Retirement programs and their financing should be evaluated in terms of their mental health implications.

8. Progress on research programs to prevent or ameliorate mental health problems of elderly people depends heavily on progress in related problems of Federal concern, such as poverty, nutrition, housing, education, medical care, and retirement financing. NIMH should work for greater coordination between its own and these other programs. It is futile to emphasize the treatment of symptoms of elderly people while overlooking their conditions of life.

References

Bellak, L., and Loeb, L. The Schizophrenic Syndrome. New York: Grune and Stratton, 1969.

Bunney, W.E., Jr., Goodwin, F.K., Murphy, D.L., House, K.M., and Gordon, E.K. The switch process in manic-depressive illness. Archives of General Psychiatry, 27:295-317, 1972.

Cancro, R. (ed). Annual Review of the Schizophrenic Syndrome, Vol. 3. New York: Brunner/Mazel, 1974.

Friedman, R.J., and Katz, M.M. (eds). The Psychology of Depression: Contemporary Theory and Research. New York: Wiley, 1974.

Garmezy, N. Process and reactive schizophrenia: Some conceptions and issues. In: Katz, M.M., Cole, J.O., and Barton, W.E. (eds). The Role and Methodology of Classification in Psychiatry and Psychopathology. Washington, D.C.: U.S. Govt. Print. Off. DHEW (HSM) 72-9015,1968.

Hingtgen, J.N., and Bryson, C.Q. Recent developments in the study of early childhood psychoses: Infantile autism, childhood schizophrenia, and related disorders. Schizophrenia Bulletin, No. 5:8-54, 1972.

The International Pilot Study of Schizophrenia, Vol. 1. Geneva, Switzerland: World Health Organization, 1973.

Katz, M.M., Cole, J.O., and Barton, W.E. (eds). The Role and Methodology of Classification in Psychiatry and Psychopathology. Washington, D.C.: U.S. Govt. Print. Off. DHEW No. (HSM) 72-9015, 1968.

Kety, S.S. Biochemical theories of schizophrenia. Science, 129:1528-1532 and 1590-1596, 1959.

Kohn, M.L. Social class and schizophrenia: A critical review and a reformulation. Schizophrenia Bulletin, No. 7:60-79, 1973.

Marks, I.M. Research in neurosis: A selective review-1. Causes and courses. Psychological Medicine, 3:436-454, 1973.

Mosher, L.R., Gunderson, J.G., and Buchsbaum, S. Special report: Schizophrenia, 1972. Schizophrenia Bulletin, No. 7:12-52, 1973.

Psychopathological Disorders in Childhood: Theoretical Considerations and a Proposed Classification, Vol. 6. New York: Group for the Advancement of Psychiatry, 1966.

Quay, H.C., and Werry, J.S. (eds). Psychopathological Disorders of Childhood. New York: Wiley, 1972.

Rechtschaffen, A. Perspectives on Research on the Biology of Sleep, 1972. Report prepared for NIMH (unpublished).

Reiser, M.F. Changing theoretical concepts in psychosomatic medicine. In: American Handbook of Psychiatry, Vol. 4. New York: Basic Books, 1974.

Rosenthal, D., and Kety, S.S. The Transmission of Schizophrenia. Oxford and New York: Pergamon Press, 1968.

Sachar, E.J. Some current issues in psychosomatic research. Psychiatric Annals, 2:22-34, 1972.

Schildkraut, J.J. The catecholamine hypothesis of affective disorders: A review of supporting evidence. American Journal of Psychiatry, 122:509-522, 1965.

Secunda, S.K., Katz, M.M., Friedman, R.J., and Schuyler, D. The Depressive Disorders, Special Report: 1973. Washington, D.C.: U.S. Govt. Print. Off. DHEW No. (HSM) 73-9157, 1973.

Slaby, A.E., and Wyatt, R.J. Dementia in the Presenium. Springfield, Ill.: Charles C Thomas, 1974.

Slater, E., and Cowie, V.A. The Genetics of Mental Disorders. New York: Oxford University Press, 1971.

Wender, P.H. Minimal Brain Dysfunction in Children. New York: Wiley, 1971.

Williams, T.A., Katz, M.M., and Shield, J.A., Jr. (eds). Recent Advances in the Psychobiology of the Depressive Illnesses. Washington, D.C.: U.S. Govt. Print. Off. DHEW No. (HSM) 70-9053, 1972.

Winokur, G., Clayton, P.J., and Reich, T. Manic Depressive Illness. St. Louis, Mo.: Mosby, 1969.

Wyatt, R.J., Termini, B.A., and Davis, J. Biochemical and sleep studies of schizophrenia: A review of the literature—1960-1970. Schizophrenia Bulletin, No. 4:10-66, 1971.

CHAPTER 9

Research on Alcohol Abuse and Alcoholism

INTRODUCTION

This chapter reports on the alcoholism research programs of the National Institute of Mental Health from 1967 through the first year's operation, beginning in 1972, of its successor in this area, the National Institute on Alcohol Abuse and Alcoholism (NIAAA). The chapter describes and evaluates the current status of research on the social, behavioral, and biological aspects of alcohol abuse; the determinants and medical consequences of the disease of alcoholism; and the patterns of alcohol use and abuse in the Nation.

A BRIEF HISTORY OF NIMH-NIAAA RESEARCH IN ALCOHOLISM

Prior to 1966, relatively little research on alcoholism was sponsored by NIMH, and there was no concerted, coordinated Federal program in this area. In October 1966, in recognition of the magnitude and social impact of the problem, NIMH established the National Center for Prevention and Control of Alcoholism (NCPCA). As the focal point of Federal programs in alcoholism, the center was responsible for stimulating research on the control and prevention of alcohol-related disorders and for accelerating communication and application of research findings to service activities in alcoholism. Under the new thrust, funds allocated for alcoholism research increased from $2.8 million in 1967 (the first full year of NCPCA operation) to $5 million at the time of the program's first reorganization 3 years later.

In 1970, the NCPCA was redesignated as the NIMH Division on Alcohol Abuse and Alcoholism (DAAA), a move calculated to provide the program increased visibility and autonomy within the Institute. Although some funds were appropriated for DAAA service activities, the bulk of the new division's funds went for research. Research funds in 1971 for DAAA totaled $5.8 million.

Formation of a National Institute on Alcohol Abuse and Alcoholism in May 1971 represented the third bureaucratic upgrading of the Federal alcohol program. The NIAAA succeeded the division within NIMH through congressional enactment of Public Law 91-616, the Comprehensive Alcohol Abuse and Alcoholism Prevention, Treatment, and Rehabilitation Act of 1970. The act expanded the mission of the Federal alcoholism program and, for the first time, funds were directly allocated for the delivery of health care services through formula grants to the States and through a community assistance program. Funds for research during the first full year of NIAAA amounted to $10.2 million. This sum included $7.5 million from the Institute's research budget plus $2.7 million specially designated by the Administration for stimulating innovative research into the treatment and care of alcoholic persons.

OVERVIEW OF NIMH-NIAAA ALCOHOLISM RESEARCH: 1967-1972

The research program can be subdivided into two major areas of emphasis:

a. Biological studies have focused on physiological and biochemical aspects of alcohol abuse and alcoholism; the effects of alcohol on metabolic processes, central nervous system function, the liver, and other organs and systems; genetic influences on alcoholism; the nature of the addictive process in alcoholism; animal analogs of human alcoholism; the alcohol withdrawal syndrome; and the biomedical treatment of acute and chronic effects of alcohol abuse.

b. Psychosocial research has focused on patterns of drinking; etiology of problem drinking; the identification of alcoholic and potential alcoholic persons; the effects of alcohol on behavior, memory, sleep, affect, perception, motor function, and cognition; factors in treatment, rehabilitation, and prevention.

Over the 6-year period (1967-1972) under consideration, less than $34 million was invested by NIMH-NIAAA in alcoholism research. These funds were divided about equally between the two major areas. About a third of the total went to university-based centers, which conducted multidisciplinary programs of basic research.

The design and funding of multidisciplinary research centers had been an early priority of the NCPCA. Prior to 1967, research on alcohol-related problems was not viewed as highly prestigious, and comparatively few scientists devoted their skills and energies to such studies. To recruit qualified scientists into alcoholism research, grants were awarded for the establishment of research centers that would focus on diverse aspects of alcoholism and alcohol abuse. Seven such centers were funded, and by 1969, 47 percent of the NCPCA research budget was allocated to them. As the need to recruit scientists into the field became less urgent, funds for the support of research centers were redirected to project grants for individual scientists. In 1972, the three centers then in existence received approximately 9 percent of the NIAAA research budget.

MAGNITUDE OF THE PROBLEM

Alcoholism has long been recognized as the Nation's major drug abuse problem. In an effort to determine more precisely the prevalence of problem drinking and the patterns of drinking practices, a number of studies were sponsored by NIMH-NIAAA between 1967 and 1972.

The NIAAA's First Special Report to the U.S. Congress on Alcohol and Health, presented in 1971, estimated that nine million persons—including nearly 10 percent of the Nation's workforce—were alcoholics or abusers of alcohol. The report stated that at least half of the more than 50,000 annual highway fatalities in the country are alcohol related. Cirrhosis of the liver, stemming in most cases from alcohol abuse, was designated as the fourth leading cause of death among young and middle-aged urban males. The economic cost of alcohol abuse in the United States has been estimated at $15 billion per year; social costs and disruptions of alcoholism include the breakup of marriage and family, and loss of job.

It is generally acknowledged that alcoholism is a complex behavioral disorder, and that many interrelated psychological, biological, sociological, and economic variables affect drinking patterns and the development of alcohol abuse. While the concept of alcoholism as a disease is often criticized, it has served to stimulate research and to redirect the attention of physicians to the medical aspects of this disorder.

BIOLOGICAL STUDIES OF ALCOHOLISM

Approximately a third of the alcoholism research funds have been allocated for studies of the biological aspects of alcohol abuse and alcoholism. There has been a relatively consistent balance between the proportion of money devoted to studies of the central nervous system function (24 percent), alcohol metabolism (18 percent), liver function (18 percent), and the effects of alcohol abuse on other physiological systems (23 percent). Relatively little research has been funded on pharmacological and other biological forms of treatment (2 percent) or on the development of animal models that could facilitate the development of such pharmacological or related treatments (11 percent).

Effects of Alcohol on Central Nervous System Function

Alcohol appears to affect the central nervous system (CNS) more than any other part of the body. This conclusion is based on several facts: (a) The most obvious effect of alcohol and the primary reason for its use are the marked psychological effect it produces; (b) the development of tolerance to alcohol is characterized by a progressive diminution of response to it following chronic exposure to alcohol; and (c) physical dependence on alcohol, expressed as the alcohol withdrawal syndrome, is characterized by psychomotor and autonomic hyperactivity associated with heightened CNS activity.

The role of biogenic amines in alcohol addiction has been the focus of several NIMH-NIAAA research grants. Three projects investigated the neurochemical effects of alcohol on these amines, which are thought to be neurotransmitters, and four sought to identify and assign a role to products of biogenic amines that are aberrant as a consequence of chronic alcoholism and barbiturate abuse. The latter studies, still active, are testing the hypothesis that morphine-like alkaloids may play a role in such addictions. Although it seems doubtful that alcohol and barbiturate addiction have a common biochemical basis, the studies are contributing to the development of analytical tools for measuring alkaloid derivatives; the analysis of their effects on neurochemical systems will contribute to the understanding of brain chemistry.

Limited effort has been directed toward the study of other possible neurotransmitters. Relevant projects supported by NIMH-NIAAA include studies of the role of acetylcholine in mediating the effects of alcohol on the CNS; the effects of alcohol on the endogenous levels and turnover of a number of "excitatory" and "inhibitory" amino acids in the brain; and the effects of alcohol on the rate of formation and turnover of melatonin, a substance found in the pineal gland. Findings from these studies clearly suggest a need for much more emphasis on the interaction between alcohol and putative neurotransmitters in the brain.

Little is currently known of the status of the endocrine system in alcoholic persons; only three grants have been awarded for research in this area. These studies point up the possible role played by the endocrines in alcohol-related behavior. It is not yet known whether constitutional-genetic factors in the endocrine system may render a person more vulnerable to alcohol's effects or whether alcohol and/or nutritional factors alter endocrine functions, thus contributing to alcohol's pathological effects. Answers to such questions may be valuable in treating patients in the various phases of alcoholism.

Research on the effects of alcohol-induced changes in the brain's electrical patterns also has received support. Projects have studied the effects of alcohol on electrical activity and evoked responses in (a) neural systems involved in emotional behavior and vision, and (b) the neural mechanism involved in regulating autonomic nervous system function. Results of eight projects have shown that alcohol profoundly affects neurophysiological events in the brain. For instance, one study demonstrated large differences in the alcohol-sensitivity of neurons in the hypothalamus; some neurons show markedly decreased firing rates, while others seem relatively unaffected.

These advances notwithstanding, the scope of research on alcohol and the brain has been limited. Little attention has been paid to important biochemical processes, such as carbohydrate, lipid, and protein metabolism. Our understanding of alcohol's action on the brain will advance only when information has been acquired on how alcohol affects the overall chemistry of the central nervous system.

Effects of Alcohol on Metabolic Processes

Alcohol is a substance that is chemically degraded in the body and utilized through normal metabolic pathways. But alcohol and its intermediary metabolites have the capacity to disrupt the normal balance of metabolic activities in tissues that have the enzymatic machinery to utilize them. Consequently, a sound theoretical basis supports the belief that abnormal consequences of alcohol use are somehow related to the metabolism of alcohol in the tissues, or to the effects of alcohol or its products on normally existing metabolic processes, or to both.

Research on metabolism supported by NIMH-NIAAA has varied widely. Precise analyses have been made of the kinetic properties and mechanisms of action of specific enzymes in the pathway of alcohol metabolism. At the other end of the spectrum have been gross examinations of such physiological-chemical phenomena as intestinal absorption, overall fat metabolism, and electrolyte transport. In general, the research has been of good quality but too often narrowly focused. The most clearly defined and promising basic studies were confined to research on enzymes of alcohol metabolism. These studies may provide important fundamental knowledge from which scientists may derive suitable testable hypotheses about the malfunctions in alcoholic states. However, in the future, metabolic studies should be broadened to include other important biochemical processes such as carbohydrate, lipid, and protein metabolism in the brain, as well as exploration of additional metabolic systems.

Effects of Alcohol on Other Bodily Systems

Liver Function

One of the earliest and most profound consequences of excessive alcohol use is liver damage. Relevant questions that have been studied with NIMH-NIAAA grants include the role of diet in the development of liver disease; the effects of alcohol on lipid metabolism in liver and intestine; the contribution of genetic factors to alcoholic liver disease; hepatic function and metabolic tolerance for alcohol; and the effects of alcohol on the metabolism of other drugs.

Some studies already have yielded significant answers. For instance, liver disease of the alcoholic person was originally attributed exclusively to malnutrition. This led a number of physicians to believe that, given a nutritionally adequate diet, continuous alcohol abuse would not injure the liver. However, NIMH-supported studies have shown that, even in patients whose diets are enriched in protein, minerals, and vitamins, alcohol produces striking changes in the liver, including ultrastructural changes in the mitochondria. Significant changes in the liver could be demonstrated after only a few days of heavy drinking. Other studies of liver function are helping to explain why persons develop a transient metabolic tolerance to alcohol and a cross-tolerance, when sober, to the effects of a variety of other drugs.

The pathogenesis of cirrhosis is still obscure, but further development of experimental animal models should facilitate progress in this area. One particularly promising achievement is an alcohol-induced liver lesion in the baboon that resembles lesions in man more closely than do lesions in the rat, both in terms of the magnitude of fat accumulation and the nature of ultrastructural changes. This new experimental model can now serve for the study of long-term effects of alcohol on liver function.

Cardiac Function

Studies of cardiac function in chronic alcoholic persons have shown cardiomyopathies with resultant left-ventricular failure. Whether these are caused directly by the administration of alcohol or are due to dietary deficiencies or to toxic effects of congeners, remains open to question.

Research funded by NIMH-NIAAA has sought to elucidate the mechanisms whereby alcohol affects cardiovascular hemodynamics; to date, these studies have not yielded sufficient findings to shed light on alcohol-related cardiomyopathy. In addition to experimental studies in this area, epidemiological studies are needed to determine the incidence and prevalence of alcoholic cardiomyopathy.

Hematology and Circulation

Alcohol has been shown to cause sludging and aggregation of formed elements of blood in man's circulation. Furthermore, alcohol seems to decrease the lifetime of platelets and other formed elements of the blood. This may be related to a deficiency of folic acid and vitamin B12 produced by chronic alcohol ingestion. Alcohol also induces alterations of red blood cell lipids, leading to a loss in the integrity of the red blood cell and rendering the chronic alcoholic person prone to hemolytic anemia.

Although hemolytic anemia, sludging, and thrombocytopenia are not considered the principal toxic manifestations of alcohol consumption, one group of investigators seems to have identified biochemical mechanisms that account for the effect of alcohol on platelets and platelet metabolism. In retrospect, NIMH-NIAAA research may have paid too much attention to the formed elements and too little to the serum proteins of blood as they are affected by alcohol ingestion. The latter are crucial because they relate to the transport and activity of most hormones present in blood and bound to the proteins. These hormones affect every organ system known to exist in man.

Gastrointestinal Function and Nutrition

The first attempts to understand the mechanisms of nutritional deficiencies in alcoholic persons are found in research sponsored by NIMH-NIAAA on the relationship of gastrointestinal function to ethanol administration. These studies suggest that alcohol acts to decrease absorption of vitamins and other essential nutrients. Research in this area is clinically important, for new findings will help us understand the nutritional imbalance found in alcoholic persons.

Genetic Aspects of Alcoholism

Research has suggested frequently that alcoholism "runs in families." For example, about 30 to 35 percent of alcoholic persons' brothers and fathers are themselves alcoholic. Moreover, 20 to 30 percent of the children of alcoholic persons develop alcoholism as adults. Since most persons are reared by their biological parents, it is difficult to separate the contributions of hereditary factors from those of environmental factors in the development of drinking patterns. An Institute-supported study in Denmark may point to the answer. In that country, which has good adoption records and a relatively stable population, more than 5,000 persons who were adopted by nonrelatives have been studied. Data already tabulated suggest that children of alcoholic persons are more likely to have drinking problems than children of nonalcoholic persons even though the children were separated from their parents early in life.

The results of animal research by a number of investigators suggest that in mice and rats a preference for alcohol, rather than other liquids, may be genetically determined. The Institute has awarded grants to study the relationship between alcohol preference and biological kinship in rats and to analyze the biochemical and metabolic differences between strains of mice that have markedly different alcohol preference patterns.

At present, the evidence for a genetic basis for alcoholism cannot be considered conclusive, and one cannot assume that research results are generalizable to large, broader populations. In view of the importance of determining the role of heredity in human alcoholism, research in this area should be continued and encouraged. Research using genetically inbred animals should focus on cellular and subcellular levels in the brain to determine what differentiates strain-sensitivity to alcohol. Such projects are well suited to investigate other little understood aspects of the psychopharmacology of alcohol. Innovative research designs for further investigation of alcoholism in human family groups also should be encouraged both to corroborate previous findings and to establish new hypotheses for testing.

Animal Analogs of Human Alcoholism

Precise biological research on alcoholism—in particular, studies of the addictive process at biochemical and neurophysiological as well as behavioral levels—frequently needs an animal model of addiction. A model also would facilitate the development and testing of pharmacotherapeutic agents for the ultimate purpose of treating alcoholic persons.

Research issues pertaining to animal models investigated in NIMH-NIAAA projects have included: attempts to influence alcohol preference by operant conditioning; the influence of stress or conflict on alcohol preference; the effects of stimulating various brain sites on alcohol self-selection; and attempts to modify alcohol preference with neurobiological and pharmacological interventions.

However, alcohol addiction is difficult to produce in animals, and so far, self-selection of alcohol by animals to the point of dependence has not been achieved. The taste of alcohol seems to be aversive to most animals, and such factors as stress and conflict have not proved effective for inducing addictive drinking.

Some success has been achieved in using forced alcohol administration procedures through intragastric and intravenous routes to produce physiological dependence on alcohol in animals. Once "addicted" through these procedures, several kinds of animals have displayed a typical alcohol withdrawal syndrome when alcohol has been withheld. Though the rapid induction of physical dependence through forced alcohol administration is useful for research, it is still necessary to work toward an analog of the behavioral aspects of human alcoholism. Such research should involve self-administration, should produce intoxication and physical dependence, and should indicate that the drug is a positive reinforcer.

Pharmacotherapy

The low success rate of currently available treatment approaches underscores the need for an effective pharmacotherapy for alcoholism. Drug treatment would permit other types of therapeutic intervention—psychological and social—to occur under conditions where the confounding effects of continued drinking were significantly reduced.

Current research on drugs that might block the intoxicating effects of alcohol has not yielded definitive results, and it is premature to evaluate this approach to treatment. Progress in this line of research, however, may have profound effects on the entire field of alcohol abuse and alcoholism.

PSYCHOSOCIAL STUDIES OF ALCOHOLISM

From 1967 through 1972, less than a third of the funds for research was allocated for studies of psychological and sociological aspects of alcohol abuse and alcoholism. Detailed examination of support patterns reveals a steady dwindling of funds for research in these areas. In 1966 approximately 74 percent of the research budget went into psychological and sociological studies, while in 1971 the proportion was at a low of 18 percent. An increase to 38 percent in 1972 included funds designated for the President's Health Initiative Program. One consequence of this erratic support pattern is that more than half the funded psychosocial research is still in progress or has been completed only recently, with results not fully reported.

Projects related to the psychosocial aspects of alcohol use and alcoholism have been highly diverse in terms of academic fields of investigators, methods utilized, problems studied, and cost and quality of investigations. Research questions addressed in these projects may be categorized as follows: distribution, etiology, diagnosis, natural history, consequence, treatment and rehabilitation, and prevention.

Distribution of Alcoholism

A fundamental step in understanding a given disease or disorder is to determine its incidence and prevalence in a particular society by age, sex, ethnicity, religion, social class, and other demographic factors. Approximately half of the NIMH-NIAAA funds in this category was awarded for survey studies at the national and local level; two monographs issuing from the studies are now considered to be standard works on American drinking practices and problem drinking. Other studies have focused on drinking among specific population subgroups such as teenagers, women, and American Indians, including Eskimos and Aleuts.

NIMH-NIAAA research has enhanced our understanding of the epidemiology of alcohol use and abuse in the broad context of American society. Future endeavors should focus on populations at high risk for developing alcoholism and on groups that have not been well studied (e.g., women). In addition, the relationship of alcohol use to social change could be studied through long-term epidemiological studies that point up changing patterns of alcohol use in specified populations.

Etiology of Alcoholism

Why people develop drinking problems is ultimately the most fundamental question in studies of alcoholism. Six Institute research projects have addressed it from the psychosocial perspective. One currently active, major project is a longitudinal/cross-sectional study of teenagers. It focuses on the development of delinquency, aggression, and the use of drugs and alcohol as they relate to socialization processes, personality factors, and social relationships. This study is valuable both for the substantive data produced and for the theoretical model used, which should facilitate more sophisticated and rigorous research on deviant behavior.

Other etiological studies have compared alcoholic patients in the United States and France, sought to determine the effects of frustration on drinking, and assessed social-personality factors leading adolescents into careers of problem or heavy drinking.

There is a paucity of reliable information and research efforts on the etiology of alcoholism; the fact that only 1 percent of the NIMH-NIAAA psychosocial research expenditures was awarded for etiological studies is discouraging.

Diagnosis of Alcoholism

A major goal of research in diagnostic techniques is to develop means for an early screening and identification of the alcoholic or potentially alcoholic person. But the problem of diagnosis involves a broader question: What is an alcoholic person? The field's existing terminology reflects the uncertainty that has hampered research; alcoholic, problem drinker, heavy drinker, alcohol addict—all terms are frequently used interchangeably. NIMH-NIAAA has awarded only three grants for research pertaining to diagnosis. One project sought to develop a drinking scale based on consumption; another attempted to develop an inexpensive drinkometer; and the third study, using factor analytic methods, aimed toward developing an alcoholism scale based on observations of hospitalized alcoholic patients.

One diagnostic formulation is commonly agreed upon: The "true" alcoholic person is defined by the observation that the use of alcohol interferes with "normal" functioning on the job, as a parent, and as a responsible member of society. This formulation undoubtedly has evolved from our understanding of the alcoholic individuals in treatment, on Skid Rows, or in drunktanks. This highly biased sample is the source of much of what is known about the process of alcoholism. Yet, there apparently is another type of alcoholic individual: namely, the enormously heavy drinkers whose drinking permits them to remain responsible members of society. People whose lives are filled with stress and anxiety may find excessive use of alcohol the necessary crutch to maintain social functioning and prevent social-psychological breakdown. Possibly there are persons who drink heavily but who titrate the alcohol, or spread its intake, leading to a consistent, moderately high blood-alcohol level with which they have learned to function quite adequately. Their alcohol use still would result in physiological symptoms and minor social problems occasionally, but possibly not to the point that their lives and careers are totally disrupted. In view of the high regard accorded to the "man who can hold his liquor" in large segments of our society, and considering that some jobs virtually require heavy drinking, it is likely that there are large numbers of heavy drinkers who never come to the attention of investigators in alcohol research.

Thus, the accepted diagnostic criterion—that the alcoholic person is one whose drinking interferes with his functioning—may be a tautology which has limited our ability to understand the relationship of alcohol consumption to the development of social and behavioral symptoms. This is not to say that such a formulation is not useful to the extent that early casefinding techniques are needed to identify incipient or hidden drinkers. Considering the theoretical problems involving the relation of intake to functioning, as well as the more immediate problem of early casefinding and screening, there is no doubt that more sophisticated research is needed.

Natural History of Alcoholism

What is known about the natural history of the development of alcoholism tends to be derived from retrospective accounts of identified alcoholic individuals, usually those in treatment; the utility of the data, therefore, is limited. Longitudinal investigations of cohorts studied early in their lives and followed for considerable periods of time would yield invaluable information on numerous aspects of alcoholism. Yet there are enormous difficulties in conducting such studies on populations of sufficient size to provide data. NIAAA now has research projects underway that will trace the development of drinking behavior in adolescents. Previously mentioned studies of native Americans and a cross-cultural comparison of French and American drinkers have focused on symptom development and subsequent changes in social role as important factors in the development of alcoholism.

Consequences of Alcoholism

The consequences of alcohol abuse can be conceptualized in terms of physiology, psychology, personality, social relations, and the like. Three projects, conducted in the laboratory, dealt with cognitive and physiological responses to alcohol use in a driving simulation task. Other studies investigated the effects of parental alcoholism on the children; they dealt with such questions as how an adolescent copes with a parent's alcoholism and what influence the parent's alcoholism has on the adolescent's personality, behavior, and achievement motivation.

The consequences of alcohol consumption and alcohol abuse represent central issues of continuing concern to workers in the field. Generally, the better designed studies tend to cluster around minor problems, while the studies of more significant problems evince some confused conceptualization and methodology.

Treatment and Rehabilitation

This area comprises research in behavior modification, treatment, referral, patient motivation, treatment outcome, the family, and minority group factors. Twenty-one projects on treatment and rehabilitation were funded over the period under consideration.

Behavior modification enjoyed the largest investment of resources, with nine of the twenty-one studies in this area. At present it is premature to propose conclusions as to the efficacy of behavior modification treatments for alcoholism (at least half a dozen NIMH-NIAAA sponsored studies are presently in progress). Such factors as small sample sizes, symptom relief criteria, control problems, and the generalizability of laboratory findings suggest limited utility in this research approach.

Research on the referral process has emphasized that early contact with and engagement of problem drinkers have encouraged them to seek treatment and have promoted their commitment to treatment for longer periods. Effective motivation for treatment continues to be a particular

226

problem for the delivery of services to alcoholic persons, with research providing few insights into factors that influence motivational processes among problem drinkers.

Treatment outcome studies continue to demonstrate that recovery from alcoholism is the result of a series of treatment experiences over an extended period of time. There is slowly evolving a body of research that attempts to evaluate the relative influence of social pressures from family members and employers in identifying, referring, and sustaining the alcoholic person in long-term outpatient treatment programs.

Certain populations are consistently at high risk for alcoholism—the American Indians, for example. Yet the peculiar social/cultural influences that contribute to the development of alcoholism, or to its successful treatment, in those populations are so little understood that it is difficult to establish priorities for service or research efforts that might ameliorate the problem.

Since the causes of alcoholism are commonly viewed as psychological and learned (as distinguished from physiological and inherited), the fact that so few grants were awarded in the psychological treatment areas is a basis for concern. Specific gaps exist in our understanding of treatment-related issues such as individual and social facilitators of treatment motivation, developmental factors that promote and sustain early problem drinking, and community and society restraints and supports for accelerating and relieving problem drinking and alcoholism. In addition, the areas previously noted—behavior modification, treatment referral, and treatment outcome—still require more definitive study. In view of the existence of these important research needs, psychological treatment research remains underdeveloped.

Prevention of Alcoholism

Research on the identification and manipulation of factors that reinforce the development of alcoholism-prone behavior is virtually nil. Only two studies were funded over the 6-year period. One was for the purpose of developing health education approaches on alcoholism to be used with school children. The other was a preventive intervention program concentrating on young persons arrested for criminal offenses associated with alcohol use. This study found that, at the adolescent ages studied, preventive intervention was difficult to achieve and that such programs must be started at an earlier age.

Prevention of alcoholism holds such priority that the NIAAA has established a Division of Prevention to initiate, stimulate, and coordinate efforts in this area.

INTRAMURAL RESEARCH ON ALCOHOLISM

In addition to the research support provided by NIMH-NIAAA to scientists outside of Government, research also is conducted in the NIAAA's Laboratory of Alcohol Research. The intramural research program has focused on the basic biological and behavioral correlates of alcoholism in man and on the experimental development of alcohol addiction in animals. The program is currently organized into three components: behavioral, biochemical, and clinical research.

A historical account of the program's activities shows that the research effort has concentrated on a wide range of topics, including psychoendocrine factors in intoxication and withdrawal, aggression, alcoholic cirrhosis, the withdrawal syndrome, and a variety of behavioral effects of alcohol on alcohol addicts.

A descriptive summary of the major findings from the intramural program follows.

Psychoendocrine Factors in Intoxication and Withdrawal

Contrary to common belief, prolonged intoxication in alcohol addicts is usually associated with marked and progressive increase in anxiety and depression. During the course of experimental chronic intoxication, rising blood alcohol levels were accompanied by sustained elevations of serum cortisol levels, which increased further during withdrawal. Excretion of urinary catecholamines and metabolites increased dramatically during intoxication and remained elevated during withdrawal. Comparable adrenomedullary and adrenergic activation is seen in natural and experimentally induced stress situations. These observations have several practical implications. For example, there is no reason to give adrenal steroids during alcohol withdrawal.

Alcohol Effects on Serum Testosterone and Aggression

Serum testosterone was examined in alcohol addicts during sobriety, chronic alcohol ingestion, and alcohol withdrawal. During chronic alcohol ingestion, testosterone levels consistently fell to far below the normal levels, but no simple relation was apparent between changes in testosterone levels and changes in mood or aggressiveness. When the subjects were abstinent, aggressive behavior was observed in approximately half the sample; testosterone levels of these subjects were outside (above or below) the normal range. Analysis of alcoholics during sobriety showed no relationship between testosterone levels and a history of aggressive behavior.

Alcohol Withdrawal Syndrome

The physiological basis of withdrawal signs and symptoms is not understood. Intramural studies have focused on three factors that may be involved in the increased neuromuscular excitability associated with alcohol withdrawal: changes in magnesium metabolism, respiratory alkalosis, and ethanol-induced accumulation of methanol.

The studies found that decreased serum magnesium levels are not always associated with alcohol withdrawal, or with significant changes in total body magnesium. A rapid change in acid-base balance during withdrawal appears to be the major determinant of serum magnesium level change.

During withdrawal, a respiratory alkalosis develops and is correlated with susceptibility to stroboscopically induced seizures and with the onset of delirium tremens, the most severe form of alcohol withdrawal syndromes. Attempts at treatment with CO_2 inhalation have yielded promising results.

Using the sensitive techniques of gas chromatography investigators learned that methanol, an alcohol derivative with poisonous metabolites, accumulated in blood and urine during 10 to 15 days of heavy drinking. Methanol levels increased as a function of time but not of alcohol dose, requiring about 2 days to disappear when drinking was stopped. A possible relation between methanol accumulation and withdrawal symptoms has not been determined.

Water and Electrolyte Balance and Mineralocorticoids

Intramural scientists have found that during chronic drinking diuresis is transient, and there may be an increase in total body water rather than dehydration; that serum osmolarity (mainly due to sodium increase) is increased; and that aldosterone secretion and renin (the kidney protein) concentration are increased. Aldosterone secretion increases initially but falls to baseline levels while renin rises or remains elevated, suggesting a direct suppression of aldosterone secretion by alcohol.

Behavioral Effects of Alcohol on Alcohol Addicts

Direct observation of intoxicated alcoholic persons does not support the usual view obtained from retrospective self-reports that drinking dissolves the alcoholic's anxieties and produces a diffuse sense of omnipotence. On the contrary, alcohol addicts become progressively more dysphoric, anxious, agitated, and depressed during chronic drinking episodes, but usually do not recall this when sober. Consequently, these adverse experiences cannot modify future behavior.

In experimental settings, alcoholic subjects prefer to alternate between periods of drinking and working for tokens exchangeable for alcohol. Furthermore, partial withdrawal symptoms do not necessarily result in increased consumption. This observed cyclicity of drinking and the finding that no subject drinks all the alcohol available are inconsistent with the notion of alcohol craving. These data are more compatible with the commonsense view that physical dependence on alcohol can be only one of the reasons that addicts drink excessively.

No significant impairment of short-term memory was found in alcoholic subjects with a "blackout" history or in control subjects, even at very high blood-alcohol levels. A comparable study using rhesus monkeys had similar results. Therefore, it is unlikely that "blackouts" can be accounted for by an alcohol-specific disruption of short-term memory.

CONTRACTED RESEARCH ON ALCOHOLISM

In high priority research areas, NIAAA has used the contract support mechanism to direct scientific attention and efforts toward the solution of specific problems pertaining to services for alcoholic persons. Used for basic and applied research, contracts complement the long-term support mechanisms of the extramural grant program by providing relatively prompt answers to specific problems. The relevance and quality of contract research are ensured through staff review, participation of outside consultants, and competitive bidding.

Allocating about $2.5 million to contract research over the past 2 years (1972—$741,390; 1973—$1,760,285), the NIAAA has enlisted the talents and interests of highly qualified investigators. At the time of this report, it is too early to evaluate their progress.

The following research contracts have been awarded:

Contracts related to biological research
    Relationship between alcohol and cancer
    Alcoholic beverages in the etiology of cancer
    Alcohol consumption and heart disease
    Study of the effects of ethanol absorption on the gastrointestinal tract
    Report on chemical agents to induce rapid alcohol detoxification
Contracts assessing relationships between race and alcohol
    Study of cirrhosis of the liver in nonwhite males
    A study of the distinctive problems of alcohol abuse among black
    Americans in selected communities
Contracts pertaining to psychosocial areas of research
    Study of the relationship between alcohol and personality
    Basic needs of alcoholic persons
    Study of the relationship between alcohol and violent crime
    Old age and alcohol effects
    Survey of adolescent drinking
    Social contexts of alcohol use
Contracts related to legislation effects and economic costs
    Impact of Uniform Alcoholism and Intoxication Treatment Act
    Study of the impact of alcoholic beverage control laws
    Economic costs of alcohol abuse and alcoholism
Contracts related to prevention
    Model learning system in alcoholism prevention

RECOMMENDATIONS FOR RESEARCH ON ALCOHOL ABUSE AND ALCOHOLISM

Analysis of the NIMH-NIAAA research support programs has led to the following set of recommendations regarding future research directions and strategies for their implementation, including manpower development and administrative organization.

Research Emphases

It is impossible to assign any research priority on the basis of the estimated potential contribution of any single discipline to our understanding of alcoholism. Therefore it is recommended that a balanced support program between the basic biological and psychosocial areas be maintained. Research efforts must explore all aspects of the problem, for significant progress in any discipline affects research in other disciplines.

In the following sections, specific recommendations within the two general areas of biological and psychosocial research will be made.

Basic Biological Research

Neurotransmitters and Neuropharmacology

Little is known about the interaction between alcohol and the numerous possible neurotransmitters in the brain, e.g., norepinephrine, dopamine, serotonin, gamma-aminobutyric acid (GABA), acetylcholine, and other excitatory and inhibitory amino acids. Since neuronal transmission of nervous impulses in the brain is exclusively chemically mediated, studies of the effects of alcohol on these substances can help explicate the overall effects of alcohol on brain function.

Other Neurochemical Systems

Neurochemical systems other than neurotransmitters have been virtually ignored. Research is needed on pathways of carbohydrate, amino acid, and lipid metabolism, and on energy-linked systems and the electron transport chain.

Electrophysiology

A potentially useful means of examining alcohol's effect on the brain is to determine the influence of the drug on recorded electrical activity of the brain. Therefore, research in this area should be encouraged.

Cell Physiology

Little is known about the effects of alcohol on neurons, and studies on the mechanism of action of alcohol and its metabolites on nerve membranes are of primary importance in understanding the effects of alcohol on the CNS. Biophysical and biochemical studies of nerve function should be given high priority for research support.

Neuroendocrinology

It is not yet clear whether constitutional genetic factors in the endocrine system may render a subject more vulnerable to the effects of alcohol, or whether alcohol and/or nutritional factors may alter endocrine function, thus contributing to alcohol's pathological effects. The advent of sophisticated research techniques in endocrinology, resulting in a vast amount of well-established knowledge in the field, suggests that the time is ripe for vigorous investigation of the relationship between alcohol and hormones. Beyond the development of basic knowledge, findings from such studies might be clinically applicable to the treatment of alcoholic persons suffering from both acute and chronic effects of alcoholism.

Effects of Alcohol on Other Systems

Among the most profound biomedical complications of alcohol abuse is its deleterious effects on the body's physiology and function. Alcohol is implicated in many potentially lethal medical problems, which include: cirrhosis of the liver, cardiac myopathy, gastrointestinal dysfunction, and peripheral neuropathy. These are secondary complications of alcoholism, which have no direct role in initiating or maintaining the condition of alcohol addiction. However, because these medical complications create untold human suffering, high mortality, and enormous medical cost to society, research needs in this area are critical. The prevention or effective treatment of these pathological states would constitute a major contribution to the health of the Nation.

Liver Function

Alcoholic persons are commonly affected with liver disease, including fatty liver, hepatitis, or cirrhosis. The pathogenesis of cirrhosis is not yet understood, but preliminary findings are encouraging. Research objectives achieved to date are significant; goals currently pursued fully justify sustained, amplified support of research dealing with a major, common, and potentially lethal complication of alcoholism.

Circulation

Further clinical and experimental studies of alcoholism-associated heart disease should be encouraged, and epidemiological studies should be initiated to determine the incidence and social cost of this problem. Blood disorders that have been observed in alcoholic patients should be studied further with the best current techniques, including electron-microscopy and enzyme assay. Studies of the formed elements of the blood should be supplemented by research on the effects of alcohol on the binding proteins of blood.

Gastrointestinal Functions

The development of irritation in the stomach (gastritis) from alcohol and the increased incidence of ulcers in patients consuming large quantities of alcohol are common findings. Chronic alcoholic persons also exhibit an increased incidence of malnutrition, which may be related to abnormal absorption of vitamins and nutrients. Research on these topics is of immediate clinical interest.

Metabolism

The NIMH-NIAAA research focus on metabolism has not been sufficiently broad to lead to major advances in understanding the problem of alcoholism. Alcohol clearly changes the functions of the central nervous system, and therefore must change the functional capacity of nerve cells. But until the nature of these changes is understood, it will be difficult to design pharmacological interventions effective in modifying the intoxicating effects of alcohol. The study of metabolism warrants continued and expanded support.

Genetic Aspects of Alcoholism

Questions on alcoholism as an inherited trait are important and pressing. At this time the evidence is equivocal. High priority should be given to imaginative and innovative approaches to this problem, including familial studies of alcoholism as well as research on inbred strains of animals.

232

Animal Models of Alcohol Addiction

Successful development of alcohol dependency in an animal would permit study of the addictive process at the behavioral, biochemical, and neurophysiological levels. A more rapid induction of alcohol dependence in experimental animals could clarify the neural, endocrine, and metabolic changes that may be critical for the expression of physical dependence upon alcohol. Moreover, testing the adequacy of pharmacotherapeutic agents on alcohol-dependent animals has obvious advantages over premature clinical trials in man.

Although it is possible to demonstrate physical dependence upon alcohol using several techniques in several species, a number of important questions remain unanswered. These include: time-dose relationships necessary to establish alcohol dependence via intravenous, intragastric, and oral administration routes; neurophysiological, metabolic, endocrine, or behavioral correlates of the developing addictive process; pharmacological interventions able to block the acute effects of intoxication; and prevention of the addictive process.

Basic Psychosocial Research

The general thrust of the following recommendations is that psychosocial research should concentrate less on individual psychopathology, and should seek, instead, to identify and weigh the pervasive influences—in society generally and in subcultures, ethnic groups, social classes, and families—that affect the occurrence of alcohol abuse and alcoholism.

Distribution

Future research should focus on theoretically oriented approaches designed to test hypotheses on interactions among individual attributes and broader social forces. Examples include: How do social contexts within which drinking occurs shape drinking behavior? To what extent are pressures to drink excessively coupled with such activities as conduct of business, sociability, or recreation? To what extent are varied drinking patterns among ethnic groups reflections of Old World cultures and values, and to what extent are they shaped by interaction with the prevailing American culture? Do differences in beverage control laws affect prevalence of alcohol abuse and alcoholism? Studies are also needed to describe accurately the extent of alcohol use and abuse among American Indians, blacks, and women.

Etiology

Research should be formulated in a broad conceptual framework in an effort to clarify the interplay of factors that traditionally have been the subjects of several social science disciplines. Increased emphasis should be directed to a concern with adults whose alcohol use becomes a problem as a function of changes in life situations.

Diagnosis

Research on diagnosis should consider not only the problem of screening and early identification as a necessary prelude to treatment but also the broader question of what is an alcoholic person and what distinguishes the alcohol user from the abuser.

Appropriate questions for study include: What are the routes by which people become labeled "alcoholic" and get involved in treatment alliances? What is the process that leads to the self-labeling of problem drinking and what are the stages in its development? What are the processes that lead to imposed labeling, e.g., marital problems, financial, school, job, or legal problems? What enables some heavy drinkers to remain responsible members of society? What are the cultural beliefs and value systems that engender help-seeking activities with respect to self and others?

Natural History

Longitudinal studies of cohorts studied early in their lives and followed for considerable periods of time would yield invaluable information on numerous aspects of alcoholism.

Consequences

More studies of the social consequences of alcohol abuse should be undertaken to supplement the studies of alcohol's effects on physiological, cognitive, and psychomotor functioning of the individual. In particular, well-conceived, well-designed studies of the effects of alcohol abuse on institutional efficiency, family relationships, children, and suicide are recommended.

Rehabilitation and Treatment

The causes of alcoholism are so many, and appear in such differing constellations from person to person, that one cannot consider treating alcoholism as if it were a single illness with an identifiable and specific etiology, a known course, and a proven response to a particular treatment. Since a variety of treatment techniques are available, further research should seek to determine which approach works best with what types of people. Treatment evaluation studies should incorporate, insofar as possible, sound underlying theory and those features of rigorous research design that are practical and feasible.

Interdisciplinary Collaboration

The desirability of collaboration across disciplines has been articulated repeatedly in virtually all disciplines concerned with research on health and social problems. But the noticeable lack of such collaboration reflects the real difficulties inherent in cross-disciplinary research. Investigators from different disciplines speak different languages, and use different concepts, procedures, and methods. Collaborators must make a large investment in order to learn enough of another discipline's concepts and techniques to make such collaboration worthwhile. For this reason, a blanket recommendation for interdisciplinary collaboration is unrealistic. Selected areas of a problem, however, may profit from such collaboration, and in the field of alcoholism two research areas fall into this category: epidemiological studies and investigations into treatment and rehabilitation of the alcoholic person. Alcohol problems represent a mosaic of etiological factors, natural history factors, and treatment factors, and the dynamic collaboration of biological scientists and social scientists appears to have the greatest potential for theory development and practical utility in epidemiology and treatment.

Mechanisms of Research Implementation

Contract Mechanisms

This mechanism is a useful device for stimulating research in high-priority areas. To ensure that quality research will be supported, it is recommended that a research contracts review board be established to encourage and initiate research contracts, to oversee the issuance of requests for proposals (RFP's), and to provide advice on solicited and unsolicited contract proposals. In addition, RFP's should be widely advertised in scientific as well as commercial publications.

Peer Evaluation System

The existing peer evaluation system should be continued and strengthened; it should be the principal basis for awarding all funds in extramural research activities.

Selection of Review Committee Members

The review group itself should formally recommend a number of qualified individuals to succeed any departing member of the committee.

Multidisciplinary Research Centers

The "center" concept remains a viable one. But projects contained within a request for "centers" grant support should be evaluated separately, and approval should be recommended only for quality projects. This would permit more efficient use of funds and resources, the training of young investigators, and the stimulation of interdisciplinary collaboration.

Research Manpower Development

In addition to encouraging and supporting high-quality research, the NIAAA should initiate such research and should attract new researchers into the field. If natural scientific selection processes do not lead to the development of research and manpower, the NIAAA should take the lead and make a concerted effort to stimulate training and research at all levels.

Senior Research Scientist Awards

In order to attract well-established research scientists of the highest caliber into alcoholism research, a Senior Scientist Award should be established and awarded on stringent criteria of academic excellence to persons in the biological and psychosocial areas.

Research Fellowship Awards

Principal investigators working on alcohol-related problems should be encouraged to apply for funds to support predoctoral and beginning postdoctoral fellows. Such fellowships would provide training in the context of ongoing research programs related to alcoholism. Selection of individuals qualified to request such fellowships would be based on teaching experience and academic excellence.

Center for Advanced Studies of Alcoholism

The establishment of this center is recommended in order to provide advanced study for well-established senior investigators in the area of alcoholism. The center would also facilitate both communication among scientists in different disciplines and the preparation of major scholarly works in the area of alcoholism.

Scientific Achievement Awards

In order to encourage higher quality research, annual awards, prizes, and recognition should be given for the best published studies in a number of areas relating to alcoholism.

Intramural Research Programs

It is recommended that the intramural efforts of the NIAAA be continued and strengthened, and that the intramural research program be subject to periodic, rigorous scrutiny, comparable to that given to extramural grant applications by the initial review group. In order to develop a critical mass that would allow more interaction and collaboration among more investigators and that would minimize duplication of bureaucracy, staff, and equipment, it is recommended that the NIAAA Laboratory of Alcohol Research be transferred administratively to the NIMH.

Finally, it is recommended that the intramural research functions of the NIMH be returned to the administration of the National Institutes of Health and be renamed the National Institute of Mental Health Research.

Annual Evaluation and Communication of Research Activities

a. It is recommended that NIAAA prepare an annual report that would describe all research expenditures, subdivided in terms of research grants, research contracts, and intramural research. The report should further describe support provided in accordance with the topical categories used in this report. The report should be made available to the public.

b. An annual review of alcoholism research should be written and disseminated to all interested scientists.

c. The National Clearinghouse for Alcohol Information should publish a quarterly compendium of outstanding research papers, drawn from high-quality journals, on all aspects of alcohol research. Review articles providing a meaningful integration of data in a particularly high-priority area of alcohol research should be published periodically.

References

Alcohol and Alcoholism. Washington, D.C.: U.S. Govt. Print. Off., PHS No. 1640, 1967.
Alcohol and Health. First Special Report to Congress. Washington, D.C.: U.S. Govt. Print. Off., DHEW No. 73-9031, 1971.

Alcohol and Health. Second Special Report to Congress. Washington, D.C.: U.S. Govt. Print. Off., No. 74-124, 1974.

Bourne, P.G., and Fox, R. (eds). Alcoholism: Progress in Research and Treatment. New York: Academic Press, 1973.

Chafetz, M.E., Blane, H.T., and Hill, M.J. (eds). Frontiers of Alcoholism. New York: Science House, 1970.

Jellinek, E.M. The Disease Concept of Alcoholism. New Haven: Hillhouse Press, 1960.

Kissin, B., and Begleiter, H. (eds). The Biology of Alcoholism Volume 1: Biochemistry. New York: Plenum Press, 1971.

Kissin, B., and Begleiter, H. (eds). The Biology of Alcoholism Volume 2: Physiology and Behavior. New York: Plenum Press, 1972.

Kissin, B., Platz, A., and Su, W.H. Selective factors in treatment choice and outcome in alcoholics. In: Mello, N.K. and Mendelson, J.H. (eds). Recent Advances in Studies of Alcoholism. Washington, D.C.: U.S. Govt. Print. Off., No. (HSM) 71-9045, 1971.

Perrine, M.W. (ed). Alcohol, Drugs, and Driving. Washington, D.C.: U.S. Department of Transportation, 1973.

Plaut, T.F.A. (ed). Alcohol Problems: A Report to the National Cooperative Commission on the Study of Alcoholism. New York: Oxford University Press, 1967.

Proceedings of the First Annual Alcoholism Conference of the National Institute on Alcohol Abuse and Alcoholism. Washington, D.C.: U.S. Govt. Print. Off., DHEW No. (NIH) 74-675, 1973.

Proceedings of the Second Annual Alcoholism Conference of the National Institute on Alcohol Abuse and Alcoholism. Washington, D.C.: U.S. Govt. Print. Off., DHEW No. (NIH) 74-676, 1973.

Proceedings of the Third Annual Alcoholism Conference of the National Institute on Alcohol Abuse and Alcoholism. Washington, D.C.: U.S. Govt. Print. Off., DHEW No. (NIH) 74-677, 1974.

Roach, M.K., McIsaac, W.M., and Creaven, P.J. (eds). Biological Aspects of Alcohol. Austin: University of Texas Press, 1971.

Roebuck, J.B., and Kessler, R.G. The Etiology of Alcoholism: Constitutional, Psychological and Sociological Approaches. Springfield, Ill.: Charles C Thomas, 1972.

Wallgren, H., and Barry, H. Actions of Alcohol. Vol. 1. Biochemical, Physiological and Psychological Aspects. Vol. 2. Chronic and Clinical Aspects. Amsterdam: Elsevier, 1970.

CHAPTER 10

Research on Drug Abuse

INTRODUCTION

This chapter reports the progress of research on drug abuse and addiction. It deals mainly with the following drugs or classes of drugs: opiates (particularly heroin), marihuana, hallucinogens (particularly LSD), stimulants (amphetamines and cocaine), and sedatives (barbiturates and minor tranquilizers). The most commonly abused drug, alcohol, is discussed separately in the preceding chapter. However, the drugs discussed here and the abuses to which they give rise have much in common with alcohol and its abuse; there are also some important differences. Where it is necessary for proper perspective, therefore, alcohol is compared and contrasted with the other drugs of abuse. Recommendations at the conclusion of the chapter also take this commonality into account; those pertaining to the drugs of primary interest in this chapter are followed by recommendations that apply to research in both drug and alcohol abuse.

Definitions and Commonalities

Four terms, not mutually exclusive, will be used frequently in this chapter and are defined as follows:

1. Drug Use: Self-administration of a psychoactive drug for its desired effects on feeling state or state of consciousness.

2. Drug Abuse: Drug use that results in harm to self or to others or that conflicts with the law.

3. Drug Dependence: Compulsive drug use that may or may not be associated with addiction.

4. Addiction: A condition that may result from repeated drug use, in which abrupt withdrawal of the drug causes physical signs and symptoms (abstinence syndrome), and in which there usually is also relative tolerance to the drug so that greater amounts of it must be taken to experience the desired effects.

Cause and Cure

The necessary precondition for all drug abuse or addiction is the voluntary self-administration of one or more drugs. The natural origin or synthetic production of these drugs, their chemical structure, and the ways they reach the user are all well known. Viewed superficially, therefore, drug abuse problems seem less mysterious than many other human health problems: There is an obvious "cause" (a drug), and an obvious "cure" (abstinence). But such a view does not confront the persistent reality of drug abuse—the user knowingly seeks the cause and avoids the cure. One must eventually account for a kind of conscious, goal-directed behavior which, despite foreknowledge that it may be harmful or self-destructive, is reinforced psychologically, socially, and sometimes also organically.

Problems of Identification

In terms of drug use, the extremes—abstainers and addicts—can be unequivocally identified and described; however, many ambiguities of identification and description comprise a long continuum between them. The criteria for defining "normal" drug use or drug abuse are elusive. They vary across time, culture, and setting.

Differential Effects of Drugs on Different People

Drugs differ greatly in their addiction potential. Further, the addictiveness of drugs varies among individuals. Some persons have a greater need than others for the reinforcing properties of various addicting drugs. Why this is so is not understood completely; however, some data suggest that it may be related to the individual's personality, his responsivity to stress, and his previous drug-using history.

Underemphasis on Research and Treatment

Until recently, the attention given by the public and the biomedical profession to drug abuse problems was clearly not consonant with the seriousness of the problem. Historically, attempts have been made to manage drug abuse problems by legal efforts; these efforts, although helpful, have not been adequate. Further, physicians have not been successful in treating problems of drug abuse, in large part because relatively few addicts seek therapy. Society's need to solve this problem and the relative ineffectiveness of current intervention efforts underscore the need for additional research into the understanding and treatment of drug addiction.

The Medical Model

Certain consequences of drug abuse traditionally have been treated in medical settings. Through their contact with drug abusers, medical personnel increasingly have accepted responsibility for treating the abuse or addiction problem itself. This trend has served to channel money into basic and clinical research and into treatment services. It has also created a legitimate field of inquiry both for multidisciplinary research and for health education efforts within the public schools. However, few would take the extreme view that all drug use and abuse are manifestations of medical illness.

Societal Needs

Because of the harm to others and to oneself that may result from a drug user's lifestyle or impaired judgment and performance, society has a stake in preventing and in treating drug abuse. Prime evidence of this is seen in disruptions of family life, abuse of children, crimes against persons and property, and accidental injuries or deaths—all of which may be associated with drug abuse and addiction. Thus, society's requirements may override the wishes of the user and legitimately support regulatory and protective laws related to dangers of drug use.

Psychosocial Influence

A variety of social and psychological factors influence a person's decision to use a drug, his choice of drugs, and his pattern of drug use. Research has linked to some extent specific patterns of drug use to specific cultural groups, to characteristics of families, or to individual characteristics. Nevertheless, there is no precise definition of the nature or extent of influence that the individual's psychological makeup or his cultural milieu has on drug use.

Central Nervous System Effects

The drugs that are of concern in the area of drug abuse are all "psychoactive drugs." They all pass the blood-brain barrier and enter the brain. They are all taken because of their effects on the brain, manifested by altered feeling states or states of consciousness.

Treatment

To date, there are insufficient adequately controlled treatment and followup studies to determine what combination of treatment modalities is optimal for what type of patient in which overall life situation. Significant immediate effects have been demonstrated for a variety of treatment modalities, both to facilitate detoxification and to bring about short-range changes in addiction and behavior. Nonetheless, we do not know, on the basis of empirical data derived from life history followup studies, what the long-range or permanent effect of various treatment regimens may be.

Drug-Specific Features

In spite of the common features that mark them, drug abuse problems have a number of aspects that depend greatly on the particular drug or class of drugs. These include:

Prevalence of Use and Abuse

Imprecise as estimates of prevalence and definitions of abuse may be, there is little doubt that alcohol is by far the most used and abused. Of the drugs discussed in this chapter, marihuana probably ranks first in prevalence of use, and heroin first in prevalence of abuse identified by harmful effects. Therefore, alcohol probably causes the greatest drain on society's resources, while heroin exacts the next highest toll.

Legality of Use

Alcohol is available legally to a unique extent; amphetamines and sedatives much less so; heroin, marihuana, and hallucinogens essentially not at all. These differences complicate both the issue of criminality with regard to use/abuse, and issues of confidentiality in identifying and treating drug users.

Addicting Potential

The opiates, particularly heroin, carry the highest probability that use will lead to addiction. In contrast, the danger that abrupt withdrawal may be lethal (delirium tremens, convulsions) is greatest for alcohol and the other sedative drugs.

Potency

While effective doses of most drugs are measured in thousandths or millionths of grams, effective doses of alcohol are measured in ounces and grams. Alcohol, in other words, is the least potent of all the drugs of abuse. One practical consequence is that covert distribution and use of the other drugs are much easier than in the case of alcohol. On the other hand, the risk of lethal overdose is considerably greater for alcohol than for some of the more potent drugs.

Routes of Self-Administration

Of three main methods of self-administration—injection, ingestion, and inhalation—injection (usually used for opiates and occasionally for amphetamines, cocaine, sedatives, and hallucinogens) is the most dangerous. This is true because of drug potencies as well as the risk of infections.

Historical Notes

The story of the beginnings of drug abuse research by the U. S. Public Health Service is in large part the story of the beginnings of NIMH. Two central figures were PHS psychiatrists, Walter Treadway and Lawrence Kolb, Sr., who had entered the Service at about the time of the First World War and the enactment of the Harrison Narcotics Act. Federal prisons soon were filled with opiate and cocaine abusers convicted under the new Act. The overcrowding was remedied partially through PHS use of an "Annex" at Fort Leavenworth, Kans., acquired when the Army disciplinary barracks became surplus at the end of the war. Medical care for all Federal prisoners at that time was rudimentary; the PHS was not then responsible for prisoner care.

Treadway and Kolb saw that this situation could be used as "an opening wedge" (Treadway's words) that could lead to a greatly expanded Federal role in mental health research and treatment. Kolb began to conduct research on opiate and cocaine abuse in the early 1920's. Within a few years he had published epidemiological, clinical psychiatric, and preclinical pharmacological studies. He showed that over the preceding decades there had been marked changes in the prevalence and patterns of opiate use and abuse, resulting largely from enforcement of the Harrison Act. He contradicted the misconception that opiate use led to criminal behavior other than stealing to support a habit, and he identified several types of individuals who became addicted to opiates. He showed that monkeys given frequent and increasing doses of morphine and heroin always became addicted.

Meanwhile Treadway seized other opportunities. With James Bennett of the Justice Department and Congressman Stephen Porter he drafted legislation which provided the basis for a 1929 act that established two U.S. Narcotics Farms and a 1930 act that made the PHS responsible for all medical care in Federal prisons. Treadway was a member of the Committee on Drug Addiction established in 1929 by the Division of Medical Sciences, of the National Research Council. Its objective was to find a nonaddicting pain-relieving substitute for morphine. The committee established two new laboratories at universites for the purposes of synthesizing and testing new agents. The PHS took responsibility for a third phase—clinical evaluation of any agents that passed the preclinical screens.

The PHS now had access to an appropriate clinical facility, the Leavenworth Annex, but no one in or out of the Service had devised methods to evaluate the abuse potential of narcotic-analgesics in man. C.K. Himmelsbach, who entered the Service in 1931, was chosen for the job; he studied pharmacology for 2 years before going to Leavenworth. There he devised the substitution method of assessing addicting properties of drugs and a method of quantifying the abstinence syndrome. The first drugs evaluated and found to have addicting properties were codeine and Dilaudid (trademark for dihydromorphinone).

By the time the Lexington Hospital opened in 1935, Kolb was well prepared to be the first Medical Officer in Charge, and Himmelsbach already had organized a research department. It was predictable that the first director of the National Institute of Mental Health would be an alumnus of that seminal facility in Kentucky, and indeed Robert Felix was. Treadway's wedge had been well driven.

NIMH RESEARCH ON DRUG ABUSE

Until recently, most NIMH drug abuse research was done in facilities at Lexington, Ky. A new building for the research department, with 40 hospital beds, opened in about 1940. In 1948 the research department was renamed the Addiction Research Center (ARC). Funding of the ARC has increased steadily and exponentially since then, at an average rate very close to 16 percent per year, from $51,000 in 1948 to $1.77 million in 1972.

Extensive research has been done at the ARC, and a condensed listing of major accomplishments fills several pages. The main approach has been medical-pharmacological, but significant research has been done by all relevant disciplines. The work has led to better understanding of all of the classes of drugs discussed in this chapter.

In the early and mid-1950's, workers in the Institute's intramural laboratories in the Washington area did numerous studies of several of the abused drugs, although no part of that program focused on drug abuse. It was hoped that the hallucinogens were the key to a biochemical etiology of schizophrenia, and they received attention from several disciplines. The actions and metabolism of opiates, stimulants, and sedatives were also studied in that period. Recently research related to drug abuse has increased again, taking advantage of the advances in methods of studying drug effects on brain function and of the availability in pure form of marihuana's main psychoactive substance. Clinical studies of dependence and addiction are being started.

In comparison to ARC and other intramural research, extramural support of research related to drug abuse was modest during the Institute's first decade and a half—$35,000 in 1951, $75,000 in 1961. Since then, grant funding has increased exponentially at an average annual rate of about 60 percent (quadrupling every 3 years) to nearly $21 million in 1973. This constitutes one-sixth of all Institute grants and one-quarter of the grant dollars spent.

Epidemiology

Throughout its relatively brief history the NIMH Center for Studies of Narcotic and Drug Abuse (CSNDA) has emphasized the development of better assessment methods for the problem of drug abuse. When the center was established in 1966 there were few hard data on the extent of the drug problem. What little information existed on the use of marihuana and other hallucinogens was either speculative or based on limited surveys of atypical heavy user populations. The information typically available went little beyond inquiring whether individuals had used various drugs, and there was little study of psychosocial correlates or impact on lifestyle.

Responding to public concern, NIMH focused its first surveys on drug use by students. At present CSNDA supports ongoing national surveys of high school and college populations as well as longitudinal and cross-sectional studies to determine the relationship of drug use, lifestyle, values, satisfactions, and academic and professional achievement. Epidemiological investigations also have extended to elementary school students and to school dropouts.

The relationship of childhood experiences to later drug use—with special emphasis on high risk populations—is under study. Investigations have focused on drug use among Job Corps trainers and trainees, hippie populations, specific cultural groups, and industrial workers. Investigators are seeking a comprehensive picture that emphasizes the relationships of drug use to other aspects of life history.

Studies of drug use may be a better starting point for epidemiological research than attempts to describe exactly what constitutes drug abuse. Such studies avoid, for example, the conceptual difficulties involved in the use of the terms "addiction," "habituation," "dependence," and "nonmedical use of drugs." These terms are sometimes used interchangeably, sometimes differently. Few of them, with the possible exception of "addiction," are clearly linked to observable events.

Data needed to clarify the extent and patterns of drug use include:

1. Use of drugs (prescription and nonprescription) by age, sex, education, IQ, family size, socialization, socioeconomic class, occupation, residential area, and type of drug.

2. Rate of drug use, specific to the above variables, focusing on the type of drugs used, as well as methods of use.

3. Trends in the type of drugs used by particular groups.

4. Special characteristics of drug users, including such items as age of and nature of initiation to drug use, persistence and frequency of use, differential characteristics of users of different types of drugs, progression of drug use, sources from which drugs are obtained, sources of drug information, and motivations for drug use.

Definitive epidemiological studies as described above are just getting underway. The extended controversy and the lack of conceptual clarity in regard to drug-related terminology (e.g., addiction, habituation, dependence, abuse), coupled with the fact that many of the drugs in question are illegal, have made research difficult. In addition, there has been resistance to specific differentiation schemes which would allow the depiction of hierarchies of danger (physical and psychological, both to the society and to the individual) in the use/abuse of certain types of drugs. Finally, well-trained practitioners in drug use epidemiology are rare, in part because of the required combination of medical and psychosocial skills, and in part because of the concern for confidentiality of the data collected. A remedy for this situation, as well as new insights, might be found in releasing original data for secondary analysis by social science students interested in epidemiology. Also, greater protection for researchers and subjects is needed. At present, DHEW has not established administrative regulations to implement the protection promised to researchers under PL 91-513.

Until the Government solves some of these problems and develops some objective measure of the nature and extent of drug dependence and other types of drug use, it cannot reliably assess the need for different types of prevention and treatment programs, nor can it appropriately allocate resources to meet these needs.

Opiates

Research on addiction to opiates and other narcotic analgesics is the oldest and largest single component of the Institute's drug abuse research program. The research has encompassed such diverse topics as the mechanisms of action of the opiates, characterization of the nature and course of physical dependence and withdrawal, assessment of the dependence-producing potential of analgesics, detection of opiates in body fluids, psychological studies of addicts, development of animal models of addiction, evaluation of treatment methods, epidemiology of addiction, and the development of narcotic antagonists.

Nature of the Drug

Opiate abuse in this country means, for most practical purposes, heroin abuse. Heroin is diacetylmorphine, a semisynthetic compound made from, but not naturally present in, raw opium. Heroin has no therapeutic advantage over the natural opium alkaloid morphine, and its production is prohibited by law. Usually it is self-administered intravenously. It is roughly two to three times as potent as morphine, probably because it penetrates the blood-brain barrier more readily. In the body, it is rapidly converted to morphine. Research findings on morphine's pharmacology generally are valid for heroin and are presented below without further distinction.

Nature of the Problem

Estimates of the total number of opiate users and addicts in the United States approximate one-half million people. Despite this number, the pattern of opiate abuse is clear. Today, the largest proportion of abusers are low-income young men of minority status living in urban areas. With such pronounced concentration, the effects on the communities most involved are profound.

Opiate abuse also imposes a heavy burden on society generally. This social cost includes a high proportion of reported property crimes and crimes against persons, costs of law enforcement and private protection, costs of prevention and treatment efforts, and welfare payments to addicts and their families. While the accuracy of the estimates of these costs is dubious, the total probably exceeds $2 billion annually.

The greatest economic cost to society resulting from heroin addiction is often obscured by the criminal aspects of the problem. One must consider the loss of an addict's potential contribution if he were legitimately employed, and the potentially productive years which are lost by premature death. (It is estimated that a young heroin addict's life expectancy is one-half that of the average person.) Such costs have been estimated at $4 billion annually. Added to the figures previously given, this brings the total cost of heroin abuse to well over $6 billion each year.

Addiction

Heroin has a high addicting potential. Tolerance and physical dependence can be quickly produced in animals and under some circumstances occur rapidly in man. The majority of heroin users do not use it frequently enough to become addicted. Nonetheless, the rate of addiction among heroin users is probably higher than it is among users of any other abused drug, with the possible exception of amphetamines administered intravenously.

Although much remains to be learned about addiction to the narcotic-analgesic drugs, more has been learned about it than about addiction to other drugs for the following reasons: (1) Because of morphine's great medical value, a concerted multinational effort over several decades has sought to discover nonaddicting drugs with comparable narcotic analgesic action. (2) The NIMH Addiction Research Center has studied the problem productively for 40 years. (3) The nature of these drugs facilitates precise, informative pharmacological study—they exhibit highly structure-dependent effects, users show a lack of cross-tolerance/ dependence to other types of drugs, and there exist structurally related specific antagonists for the drugs. (4) Hundreds of incarcerated addicts at the NIMH Lexington facility have participated voluntarily in essential research.

Research at the NIMH Addiction Research Center (ARC) demonstrated that the abstinence syndrome associated with opiates is a manifestation of physical rather than psychological dependence. But, as is generally the case, tolerance to the opiates cannot be attributed to the development of an increased rate of systemic metabolic inactivation. Adaptive changes in the central nervous system must be presumed responsible for tolerance.

The signs and symptoms that follow withdrawal and that constitute evidence for physical dependence can be extremely distressing but are rarely life-threatening to otherwise healthy individuals. Gross signs and symptoms are relatively short lived, but NIMH research has shown that subtler evidence of tolerance and the abstinence syndrome persists for weeks or months.

Experiments at the ARC with both animals and humans have demonstrated that the abstinence syndrome can be conditioned. Further studies have suggested that both conditioning and protracted abstinence may play a role in subsequent behavior. Laboratory observations of these conditioned responses are consistent with the observed behavior of addicts who, after remaining drug free with relative ease in the hospital setting, may experience abstinence phenomena upon their return to the environment where their prior addiction was initiated and sustained.

Researchers have hypothesized that prolonged abstinence-induced hyperresponsivity to stressful stimuli is an important factor in relapse; indeed, this represents a partial "pharmacological genesis" of the psychopathy so often observable in addicts.

Abstinence signs and symptoms are abolished by doses of heroin that, because of tolerance, are insufficient to have euphoriant-narcotic effects. This fact, coupled with the expensiveness of heroin, explains why addicts' resources are used mainly to get sufficient amounts of the drug to counter early abstinence phenomena. The prevailing mood of the "strung out" addict is dysphoric, self-deprecatory, and hypochondriacal. Relief of abstinence phenomena by each dose of drug is said by some addicts to confer some positive pleasure, analogous to the pleasure of satisfying one's appetite by eating; however, the usual experience is merely a temporary lessening of persistent and pervasive dysphoria.

The timing of the onset of withdrawal symptoms during abstinence and the severity of those symptoms are closely related to the rate of metabolic inactivation of the opiate. Heroin is rapidly metabolized to morphine and has a duration of action comparable to that of morphine (3 to 6 hours). The synthetic opiate methadone is much more slowly inactivated and converted to active metabolites; it was this observation that led ARC scientists in the 1940's to suggest methadone might be useful for treating opiate addiction.

Experimental addiction can be prevented by pretreatment with certain pharmacological agents, notably opiate antagonists and, in animals, inhibitors of protein synthesis. Conversely, antagonists (see following section) used as treatment modalities precipitate withdrawal symptoms in addicted humans and animals.

Central Nervous System

Much of the NIMH research has been concerned with the study of the mechanisms of action of opiates, including the development of tolerance and physical dependence.

Their stereospecificity, highly structure-dependent effects, and the phenomena of specific antagonism are all compatible with some action of opiates at discrete receptor sites of nerve cells, but the normal function of such receptors is not known. Narcotic-analgesic-euphoriant effects, addicting effects, and respiration-depressant effects are dissociable by variation of drug structure, indicating some specificity of the receptors involved in these effects.

Many opiates have both "agonist" and "antagonist" effects. "Agonist" effects are the direct effects on nerve activity resulting from the drug-receptor interaction when only one drug is present. "Antagonist" effects are revealed when the drug prevents or terminates the agonist effects of another opiate. A "pure" antagonist has high affinity for receptor sites and thus blocks or displaces other opiates, but its own occupation of receptor sites does not detectably alter neural function.

There is much evidence that opiates alter both brain concentrations and turnover rates of neurotransmitters; whether this is achieved by direct or indirect action is still unclear. There is some evidence that stimulation of noradrenergic or dopaminergic systems is involved in the primary euphoric effects and that tolerance and dependence may involve a serotonergic system.

The depressant effect of opiates on the brain's respiratory center—their most physically dangerous property—probably accounts for the majority of the several thousand heroin-related deaths that occur each year. Respiratory deaths are mainly an unfortunate result of heroin's exclusively illegal manufacture. While the user of a drug diverted from legal sources knows his dosage, the user of heroin is often uncertain just how much of the drug he is about to give himself.

Systemic Effects

In general the opiates themselves do not have serious harmful effects other than those on the central nervous system. The many detrimental physical complications of opiate abuse are largely the result of inadvertent intravenous injection of bacteria, viruses, and nonliving contaminants.

Neonatal Addiction

Although neonatal addiction as a consequence of being born from an addicted mother is not uncommon, research on the problem has been limited, and little is known about the biological and behavioral implications of such addiction. Recently, there are indications that offspring of women who are on methadone maintenance may have more difficulties in detoxification than addicted babies born to women who are taking other drugs. An important current emphasis of the Institute's drug abuse research program is the systematic investigation of the effects of maternal addiction on the newborn as well as the implications for later childhood development. Both human and animal research is being encouraged in this area.

Drug Detection

An important area of biomedical research on the opiates entails drug detection in body fluids. No present methods reach the ideal of being rapid, sensitive, relatively simple, specific, inexpensive, quantitative, and accurate. Since improved detection methods are important both to the clinical management of patients and to research, considerable effort has been expended to quantify and to improve present methods and to develop new approaches to the problem. Work thus far supported is resulting in improved reliability of urinalysis techniques and in specification of the parameters of detection for various drugs of abuse. In addition, such techniques as radioimmunoassay are proving to be highly sensitive means of detection that are especially suited to research applications.

Assessing Abuse Potential

An important aspect of NIMH research has been that of assessing the abuse potential of analgesics. Carried out at the Addiction Research Center, this effort has probably been one of the most successful of all endeavors in limiting drug abuse through principles of preventive medicine. Since the initiation of this program just after World War II, no narcotic analgesic that has had any substantial abuse potential has come into uncontrolled use.

Psychosocial Factors in Addiction

Psychosocial aspects of opiate abuse have been investigated for some time. Dr. Lawrence Kolb, Sr., the first Medical Officer in Charge of the Lexington Hospital, early emphasized the importance of psychological factors both in becoming addicted and in relapse following treatment. He developed a typology of addiction that included two kinds of psychopathic personality orientations—a psychoneurotic classification and a classification of addiction accompanied by psychoses.

Numerous typologies have been devised since then. While concepts such as psychopathic or sociopathic personality have been useful in describing addicts, antisocial aggression has been the most agreed upon characteristic of addicts who have been studied. Researchers have sometimes distinguished between deviant behavior that is accompanied by guilt ("neurotic psychopathy") and that which is not accompanied by guilt ("primary psychopathy").

The development of personality tests led to extensive testing of many types of addicts. On the Minnesota Multiphasic Personality Inventory (MMPI), addicts were found to score highest on the Pd (psychopathic deviancy) scale. While some addict groups, a neurotic type for example, show elevations on the neurotic triad (Hs, D, and Hy scales), the typical addict has low scores on the other clinical scales of the MMPI.

In developing its own Addiction Research Center Inventory, the ARC attempted to include questions that tapped psychopathology, personality characteristics, and subjective reactions to drugs. Using this inventory it has been possible to distinguish a variety of responses that are more or less specific to a given drug or state (e.g., morphine, pentobarbital, chlorpromazine, LSD, amphetamine, alcohol, chronic opiate use and opiate withdrawal, etc.).

It has been found that during chronic opiate use there is less motivation than normal for physical, mental, social, and sexual activities. During withdrawal there is a greater degree of hypochondriasis and other indicators of neuroticism, along with a range of physical symptoms and general irritability.

Attempts have been made to distinguish the measured psychological characteristics of addicts who remain in treatment from those who do not. While some average differences have been found, they generally are not useful for individual prediction.

The Hospital in Lexington was the locus for a large number of studies aimed at better defining the nature of addiction and its etiology within a sociocultural framework. This research has been responsible for significant contributions to the social science literature concerned with the methodological problems of studying addiction. Research has included the problem of followup studies, the reliability and validity of social science techniques used with addicts, and other methodological issues. A range of demographic characteristics of various addict populations has been examined, and attempts have been made to define subgroups of special interest.

Over the past 6 years, extramural social science research on opiate addiction has attempted to better understand the addiction careers and life history of addicts, to more sharply define the nature and extent of the problem, and to study the ways in which heroin use spreads and is maintained by social forces in addict groups. One of the more promising of these studies originally focused on "copping areas" (geographical areas in which addicts congregate to obtain drugs). This study of patterns in various ethnically distinct parts of Chicago has led most recently to an attempt to determine whether or not epidemics of heroin use can be aborted by early intervention, aggressive casefinding techniques, and strong encouragement to seek treatment.

Despite extensive research, the nature of the psychosocial factors that contribute to opiate addiction still is not well understood. While heroin addiction is considerably more common among economically deprived minority groups, most members of such high risk groups do not become addicted. Recently, NIMH-DNADA has been successful in encouraging several projects designed to examine more carefully the specific and differentiated origins of addiction in a variety of ethnic and racial groups.

Multiple Drug Use

A factor complicating the picture of the opiate addict is the increasing frequency of multiple drug use in which heroin is only one of several drugs used. Some of these drugs, for example, alcohol and methadone, may be obtained legally. As patterns of drug use change, some characteristics originally found in earlier addict populations may also change; therefore, there is a need to study new and evolving patterns of drug abuse and their origins.

Prevention

It may be that there are significant biological as well as psychosocial factors that determine the likelihood of becoming seriously involved with narcotics. There has been little study of the possibility that genetic factors play a role in disposing an individual toward addiction; the Institute recently has funded a study of twins that bears on this question. Continued research may prove useful in the early identification of those who are at high risk of becoming addicted.

Eventual forms of prevention efforts may entail biological as well as socially oriented approaches. Narcotic antagonists, for example, hold some promise for prevention as well as for treatment. Also, preliminary work is underway that may eventually make it possible literally to immunize potential users from the effects of opiates. At present, this remains only a distant possibility.

Marihuana

Nature of the Drug

Marihuana is the general name used for several preparations of dried, chopped parts of hemp plants; in the United States the preparations generally are rolled into cigarettes and smoked. Hemp contains several "cannabinoids," including delta-9-tetrahydrocannabinol (delta-9-THC), which is believed responsible for most of marihuana's psychological effects.

Marihuana has been used as a psychoactive agent for centuries in some parts of the world. But, primarily because it has had no accepted use in modern medicine, marihuana's chemical nature and pharmacology have only recently come under study.

Largely owing to NIMH efforts, marihuana research has progressed more in the past 6 years than in all the time preceding. As late as the mid-1960's, when marihuana use was already widespread, systematic scientific study of the drug was extremely difficult. The marihuana available was of unknown origin and widely varying potency, and bureaucratic barriers to research were formidable at all levels. Accordingly, an early goal of the NIMH marihuana research program, administered through the Center for Studies of Narcotic Addiction and Drug Abuse, was to develop research supplies of adequately specified natural materials for the scientific community. The synthesis of delta-9-THC added another source. At the same time the natural and synthetic materials were supplied in various dosage forms—radioactively labeled and unlabeled. While these supplies were being developed, the mechanisms for gaining more rapid research approval and drug distribution were established through cooperative work of NIMH and the Food and Drug Administration. This drug supply program, which now includes hallucinogens and heroin, supplies commercially unavailable drugs at no cost to the scientific community. By spring 1973, drugs had been supplied for more than 750 research projects.

Nature of the Problem

The National Commission on Marihuana and Drug Abuse in 1972 estimated that nearly 25 million Americans had used marihuana at some time; of this group the commission estimates that more than 8 million are current users. Attempting to combine data from a number of epidemiological studies, one investigator estimated that among all those who have ever used marihuana, 3 percent use it daily, ll percent use it 3 to 6 times per week, 40 percent use it l to 8 times per month, and 46 percent stopped using it or used it less than 10 times altogether.

All polls have shown that users are most heavily concentrated in the young adult age group, and studies of students have predominated. Such studies on individual college campuses show a great variety in use rates, from a low of 23 percent to a high of 78 percent.

250

Only recently have nationwide studies been conducted that give some information on the nature and extent of marihuana use throughout the United States. A 1970-71 survey of persons in the 18-29 age group revealed that about 37 percent of respondents from the Western section of the country had used marihuana—about three times as high as the proportion of respondents in the Northeast, North Central, and Southern regions. Sixteen percent of Western respondents reported that they had used marihuana more than 50 times, while less than 4 percent of the respondents reported that level of use in the Northeast, North Central, and Southern regions.

A second nationwide interview survey of a younger adolescent group, age 12-17, showed that the proportion of that group which had ever used marihuana was as high or higher than that of the 18-29-year-old group. The use rate among 12-17-year-olds rose rapidly with age, and introduction to the use of the drug often began at the junior high school level. In the Nation as a whole, 15 percent of the youngsters had tried what they identified as marihuana, and 3 percent reported having used it 60 or more times.

Use of marihuana by persons in different occupational groups, on and off the job, is of interest and concern. Data from New York State indicate that occupational groups show some variation, from a high of 9 percent for regular users among salesworkers to a low of 0 percent among farmers.

Marihuana use is related statistically to the use of most other drugs, including alcohol and tobacco; frequency of the use of marihuana is related even more closely to the use of other drugs than is mere incidence of use. Heavy marihuana use apparently tends to involve the user in a drug-oriented group or subculture that may increase the opportunity to try other drugs.

Comparing teenage youth who have used only marihuana with those who have used marihuana and other drugs, investigators have found much more deviant and illegal activity among the latter. There is little evidence that marihuana use in itself causes criminal behavior.

Effects on Users

It is well recognized that marihuana use, like most other illegal drug use, occurs first in a social group, is supported by group norms, and functions as a shared social symbol. In the case of marihuana, some of the drug effects themselves appear to occur only when learned in the presence of others.

That a strong placebo effect may occur in habitual users of marihuana was adduced by an NIMH-supported investigator, who used smoked cigarettes or placebos. As might be expected, such effects are more likely to occur when subjects have strong feelings about the drug or when they are exposed to threshold doses. Expectation, set, and setting affect response to almost every psychoactive drug to varying degrees.

The clinical syndromes resulting from a variety of doses of marihuana have been fully described. The usual pattern is a biphasic sequence of stimulation and euphoria followed by a later period of sedation and tranquility, and, with higher doses, sleep. Some of the effects of usual "street" doses of marihuana are similar to the subjective effects of small doses of hallucinogens, but "bad trips" and florid psychoses are infrequent. Delta-9-THC in large experimental doses is definitely a hallucinogen, but there is no cross-tolerance to the other hallucinogens, and there are some differences in physiological effects. For these reasons marihuana is usually classified separately from the hallucinogens.

While a "reverse tolerance," or sensitization phenomenon, for marihuana has been suggested and widely publicized, no evidence for such a mechanism has been adduced. Some tolerance to the effects of marihuana may occur after prolonged use of the drug, but this is not well established. Addiction, i.e., a clear abstinence syndrome, does not occur.

Studies of marihuana effects on driving and cognitive function indicate varying patterns of impairment, depending on dosage. Tests involving immediate memory functions seem to be most sensitive to impairment, and motor tests seem to be most sensitive to deterioration under influence of the drug. The most consistently demonstrated perceptual alteration is a distortion in time sense, a hallmark of drugs with hallucinogen-like activity.

Pharmacology

The contract program of CSNDA, in addition to supplying materials for studies involving actual use of marihuana, has also made possible much of the systematic basic pharmacological investigation of cannabis and related materials.

Evidence to date suggests that delta-9-THC is the most important component of marihuana. More precise information is needed about the activity of other marihuana constituents and their metabolites. Such studies will be of value in determining further structure-activity relationships among THC-like compounds and can settle the question of whether THC has intrinsic activity or is the precursor to an active metabolite.

Metabolism and Systemic Effects

Delta-9-THC is readily absorbed from the gastrointestinal tract and from the lungs. The temporal sequence of subjective effects correlates well with the time course of blood concentrations of delta-9-THC.

The metabolism of the cannabinoids is complex, and some effects may be caused by metabolites, particularly 11-hydroxy-THC. Delta-9-THC is detectable in the blood for many days after a single dose, probably because it is taken up avidly by body fat, which then acts as a slow-release depot. The rate of metabolism is moderately increased in frequent users.

Acute systemic effects include reddening of the eyes, rapid heart action, some impairment of postural circulatory adjustments, and moderate increase in sympathetic nerve and adrenal medullary activity.

Long-Term Use

No harmful long-term effects have been documented. It must be emphasized that the same was said a generation ago about tobacco cigarettes, which have in common with marihuana the method of use and stimulation of the sympathetic nervous system.

Preliminary studies by a number of NIMH-supported groups indicate that modest doses of marihuana used for relatively brief periods of time do not induce much tolerance or decrement in function, but the critical question of consequences of long-term social use is virtually impossible to answer in the laboratory. Two major retrospective studies of chronic cannabis use have been conducted under NIMH aegis. The first, in Jamaica, indicated few significant differences between carefully matched samples of users and nonusers on a wide range of biomedical and psychological measures. Preliminary findings on the second study, in Greece, also suggest few significant differences. Similar studies are being mounted in other locations, and it is hoped that future studies will involve the study of significantly larger samples of users, in which less common adverse effects related to cannabis use might be detected.

CNS Effects

Current studies in animals have shown that delta-9-THC is localized in brain synaptosomes (nerve endings) and that it alters in vivo the rates of uptake and efflux of amine neurotransmitters.

Drug Combinations

Because the combined use of social drugs is a frequent phenomenon, it may be of some importance to study interactions with other drugs. These might include concurrent use of alcohol as well as stimulants, hallucinogens, sedatives, or opiates.

Treatment and Rehabilitation

Except when marihuana initiates a pattern of social drug use that spreads to other agents, or when it causes a rare toxic psychosis, no clear agreement exists concerning what the indications for treatment or rehabilitation should be.

Hallucinogens

The term "hallucinogen" includes several natural and synthetic drugs that have similar effects but differ greatly in potency. Most are either indolealkylamines (LSD, psilocybin, substituted tryptamines) or phenylethylamines (mescaline, substituted amphetamines). Quite aside from immediate problems of abuse, since the early 1950's these drugs have generated a great deal of research because of their distinctive "psychotomimetic" effects and their chemical similarity to the important neurotransmitters, serotonin and norepinephrine.

LSD (lysergic acid diethylamide) is the best known and most used of the hallucinogens. Like heroin, it is a semisynthetic compound that is readily made illicitly from diverted supplies of medically useful drugs—in this case the derivatives of ergot.

Research on the hallucinogens was "rescued" by NIMH in 1967 when the commercial manufacturer of LSD stopped providing supplies directly because of the negative publicity LSD was receiving. The entire supply was given to NIMH. The Institute made arrangements to supply materials for suitable research projects and through the years has remained the sole source of research supplies of LSD and some of its congeners, psilocybin, and other similar drugs. As the distributor of the material, NIMH has been in a position to identify and track all of the research being conducted in this country.

Areas that have been significantly advanced with NIMH support include structure-activity relationships, neurochemical transmission, cytogenetic studies, psychopharmacology, therapeutic potential, abuse potential, and epidemiology.

Patterns of Hallucinogen Use

The use of LSD and/or other related hallucinogens has been most heavily concentrated among middle- and upper-class youth in the United States rather than in lower-class groups. Among the general population, the most recent (1972) national surveys have found that less than 5 percent of those between the ages of 12 and 17, as well as those over 18, have ever used hallucinogens. Among college and senior high school students less than one in seven has ever tried these drugs and, typically, has used them only once. National figures have not been available long enough to establish clear trends, although many observers and some local surveys suggest that use has plateaued and among younger groups may well have diminished.

Addiction

So far as is known, addiction to the hallucinogens does not occur. Marked tolerance to the psychological effects occurs very rapidly and also disappears in a few days, but there is no clear-cut abstinence syndrome. This unusual dissociation of tolerance from dependence, along with the intensity of the experience—satiation—may account largely for the fact that hallucinogens are rarely used more than twice a week.

Biological Research

The main emphasis of early research was on LSD-induced "model psychoses" as the key to the biochemistry of schizophrenia. NIMH intramural research covered CNS effects, metabolism, and structure-activity studies of the lysergic acid, indolealkylamine and phenylethylamine types of hallucinogens. Although much useful information resulted, the hope for a unifying hypothesis of schizophrenia was not realized.

Work at the Addiction Research Center demonstrated that the hallucinogenic actions of LSD differed in some respects from those of delta-9-THC. This work has served as a model for identifying hallucinogens of the LSD type. Further, it first demonstrated that delta-9-THC is hallucinogenic in large doses.

At the Addiction Research Center, interest focused on the psychotomimetic actions, the phenomena of tolerance and cross-tolerance, and the subjective and physiological effects of other hallucinogens and LSD congeners. These included the nonpsychoactive brom-LSD; dimethyltryptamine, psilocin and psilocybin, mescaline, scopolamine and the scopolamine-like hallucinogen N-ethyl-3-piperidylbenzylate.

254

An offshoot of these studies has led to discoveries about the role of tryptamine in the central nervous system. Findings from a series of investigations indicate that tryptamine may be a naturally occurring neurohumor or neurohormone and that LSD-like hallucinogens may act as agonists at tryptamine receptors. In man, tryptamine has been shown to share many of the actions of LSD, elevating blood pressure, facilitating the patellar reflex, and dilating pupils, as well as producing certain LSD-like subjective changes. More recently, enzymes N-methylated by tryptamine have been found in brain and lung; this has raised the possibility of endogenous production of potent hallucinogens. Indeed, several investigators have reported urinary excretion of N-methylated tryptamines by schizophrenic patients. Thus the "model psychosis" rationale of early LSD research now has been resurrected in a new form.

CNS Effects

It has been found in animal experiments that injected LSD is concentrated in a few parts of the central nervous system. Its major effect seems to be to suppress the activity of serotonergic systems, evidenced by reduced firing rates of serotonergic nerves and decreased rate of turnover of serotonin. These observations fit well with LSD's serotonin-related structure.

General Effects

Apart from adverse psychological effects, there is no good evidence that the hallucinogens themselves are dangerous. Death from overdose does not occur. Pure LSD, in doses comparable to those taken by humans, does not cause chromosomal breakage or spontaneous abortions. Nevertheless, "street" LSD users have more structural chromosomal changes than controls and probably more spontaneous abortions; possible reasons for this include inadvertent contaminating ergot derivatives, other drugs deliberately used, and the generally unhealthful lifestyle of the drug subculture.

Psychological and Social Research

Virtually every psychological test has been used to study persons under the influence of LSD or other such hallucinogens, but the research has contributed little to our understanding of the bizarre and potent effects of this drug.

Recent investigations have been concerned with the characteristics of those who use the drug repetitively in a social pattern. These individuals cannot be characterized by any specific psychiatric label, but they usually are more fascinated by the occult (mysticism, magic, astrology, clairvoyance, extrasensory perception, etc.) than are most people.

During the past several years, relatively little human research has been done with LSD, with most effort going into recording the consequences, both immediate and delayed, of its social use. Attempts to use the drug over the years, either as an adjunct to traditional psychotherapy or as a special type of psychotherapeutic intervention, have not clearly defined a therapeutic use.

Long-Term Psychological Effects

The panic states and psychoses that may occur during LSD trips are not always self-limited. When such adverse reactions continue or recur, it is not known whether the psychopathology would have occurred eventually without the drug. Similarly, it is not known whether prolonged frequent use of LSD can permanently impair brain function. The alleged memory deficits, diminished affect, and passive behavior noted in some "acid heads" suggest that it can.

Treatment and Rehabilitation of Users

The adverse mental consequences of using hallucinogenic drugs are generally managed by usual psychiatric treatments, including the use of sedative, antidepressant, or antipsychotic drugs when these are indicated.

Stimulants

Nature of the Drugs

The stimulant drugs mainly abused at present are amphetamines and cocaine. Amphetamines are synthetic drugs, originally developed and manufactured solely for legitimate medical uses. They are members of the large family of "sympathomimetic" phenylethylamine congeners, which includes the natural amines epinephrine, norepinephrine, and dopamine. However, their peripheral sympathomimetic effects are less than their CNS-stimulant effects.

Cocaine is a structurally dissimilar natural compound, long used by Andean Indians for its stimulant effects, but introduced into European medical practice as the original local anesthetic, and now largely supplanted in that legitimate role by synthetic drugs.

Nature of the Problem

There are at least two major types of chronic amphetamine abuse—oral and intravenous. In oral use, the individual often takes a moderate dose of the drug for several weeks. He increases the dose, and, as tolerance develops, he gradually increases his use of amphetamines. He commonly begins to experience insomnia and irritability at night; he sometimes uses sedatives or alcohol regularly to induce sleep. Specific types of people have been identified who commonly fit this category of abuse: housewives for whom amphetamines initially were prescribed for weight reduction; businessmen and professionals using them for antifatigue or weight reduction effects; students, often high achievers, who use the drugs to cram for exams and extend study periods; truck drivers who use drugs to sustain alertness over 24- to 48-hour periods in long distance hauling; and individuals who take the drugs orally, often with alcohol, for the "high."

The other major pattern of use is one in which the individual injects massive intravenous doses of amphetamine at short intervals over a period of 4 to 6 days, during which he does not sleep.

Amphetamine abuse over the past 25 years has had a tendency to appear suddenly in epidemic proportions in a given locale, and to diminish just as rapidly to its original level. Epidemics appeared in Japan between 1950 and 1956, in Scandinavia (primarily Sweden) between 1964 and 1968, and in the United States between 1965 and 1969.

There are no adequate prevalence studies for either the epidemic or the endemic abuse of amphetamines. Most data have been gathered from biased samples or are based on estimates or on information about legal supplies.

Cocaine use has had a resurgence in the past few years. A nationwide household survey in 1971 reported that 5 percent of the teenage respondents aged 12 to 17 years had used cocaine at least once; only I percent of older respondents had done so. Its use seems now to be especially popular among narcotic addicts in methadone maintenance programs.

Although the last few years have seen a dramatic decrease in the number of amphetamine prescriptions written, in 1967 at the height of the U.S. amphetamine abuse epidemic there were 3I million prescriptions for anorexic stimulant drugs, 14 million of which were new prescriptions. At this rate, 6 to 8 percent of all persons over 18 could have used amphetamines by prescription, and perhaps another 2 percent received them from informal but not necessarily illegal channels (for example, obtaining pills from a friend). A New York State survey confirmed that a considerable proportion—12 percent—of the population had used diet pills, and this figure did not include individuals obtaining amphetamines from an illegal market.

FDA sources estimate that in the past 90 percent or more of the amphetamines produced went into illegal markets, and the actual amounts of amphetamines manufactured by legal pharmaceutical companies attested to an oversupply of the drugs in this country. Beginning in 1972, the Federal Government took action to curb the legal manufacture of the drugs. The resulting great decrease undoubtedly will change the nature of amphetamine abuse patterns.

It is probable that fewer sole users of stimulants exist than is the case for other types of abused drugs. Polydrug use, with heroin, hallucinogens, marihuana, and sedatives among the drugs taken appears most often to be the pattern with those who use stimulants.

Amphetamine Effects

In general, the reasons for use of stimulants fall under five categories: to enhance motor performance, to enhance attention and vigilance, to depress appetite, to enhance mood, and to produce euphoria.

The oral, subcutaneous, and intramuscular use of amphetamine produces a sustained sense of euphoria associated with an energizing effect. The intravenous use of amphetamine is alleged to produce an immediate ecstatic, exalting, orgiastic experience; the (much rarer) intravenous use of cocaine produces a similar effect, but it has a shorter duration. Tolerance develops to the positive effects of amphetamine.

Experimental studies with human subjects typically have used low dosage ranges and oral administration of amphetamine, but the most serious street use pattern is one of intravenous administration of very large doses.

As early as 1944, workers at the Addiction Research Center carried out what was probably the first experimental study of chronic amphetamine intoxication in man and the first demonstration of amphetamine psychosis. Because it is a frequent concomitant of amphetamine intoxication that is easily reproduced experimentally, amphetamine psychosis holds research interest as a possible model for paranoid schizophrenia.

Violence related to amphetamine abuse has not been studied decisively, but reports from law enforcers, psychiatrists, and drug abusers themselves have indicated that amphetamines and cocaine may be related to aggressive behavior more specifically than any other group of drugs.

Abuse Potential

The substantial abuse potential of amphetamines and other psychomotor stimulants has been documented by clinical case reports and by clinical and animal laboratory studies.

The primary reinforcing properties of amphetamine-like drugs can be assessed in man through the use of subjective effect questionnaires. In many case reports the time from the first amphetamine experience to dependence is short, often 2 to 6 months. As mentioned earlier, excessive use can lead to amphetamine psychosis, and psychiatric admissions for this syndrome are not unusual.

Laboratory evidence of addiction potential comes primarily from self-administration studies in which animals perform a lever-press response to obtain intravenous injections of amphetamines. These studies have demonstrated such rapid habituation and tolerance that amphetamine abuse potential can be said to compare with that of narcotics. In fact, many animals when left in a free choice situation will continue to inject until they soon die. In monkeys the response patterns, pharmacological response, and toxicity of amphetamines are similar to those seen in humans.

Withdrawal

The amphetamine withdrawal syndrome is characterized by hypersomnolence, followed by depression. It is said that such physical dependence differs from that associated with opiates, alcohol, and depressants in that it does not indefinitely reinforce the use of the drug. This statement is not supported by experimental evidence, however, and the entire question needs further investigation.

Biological Research

Much of what is known of the mechanism of action and biotransformation of amphetamines has resulted from work done at the NIMH Laboratory of Clinical Science. The routes of metabolic alteration and physiological disposition of amphetamines and related drugs were elucidated by several NIMH investigators. The action of these drugs on central neurotransmitters, especially norepinephrine and dopamine, has been extensively studied, especially in relation to the behavioral effects these drugs produce. Some of the few studies of cocaine have been done by the NIMH intramural programs, including a current clinical trial of this drug in the treatment

258

of depressed patients. Cocaine resembles the amphetamines in many respects, including its blocking of the reuptake of norepinephrine by sympathetic nerves.

CNS Effects

The question of how amphetamines exert their stimulant effect is complex. Amphetamines release monamines from nerves, inhibit their reuptake into nerves, inhibit monomine oxidase, and act directly on aminergic receptors. The clinical effects may arise from the interplay of several direct and remote actions on various systems. Inhibition of uptake appears to be the mechanism responsible for cocaine's similar clinical effects, but evidence for the possibility that this is the major contributor to the clinical effects of amphetamines is equivocal.

General Effects

Stimulants are self-administered intravenously in doses much larger than are compatible with safe clinical investigations. Estimates of the peak acute effects of such doses on human circulation therefore are conjectural, but are certainly frightening. Perhaps the paucity of documented amphetamine-related deaths can be explained by the fact that most intravenous users are young and their circulatory systems are therefore able to tolerate the stresses imposed.

The effects of long-term use of these stimulants on general health again are not clear. Data revealing increased cardiovascular morbidity among those whose stimulant use is confined to caffeine or nicotine could perhaps be pertinent. The prevalent practice among abusers of chemically inducing repeated episodes of sleeplessness for several days may well be deleterious to general health in the long run. More informed assessment of this commonsense view will depend on better understanding of the role of sleep in the body's general economy.

Psychosocial Research

These drugs produce some subjective effects quite similar to those produced by narcotic analgesics. Further, there is increasing evidence that many amphetamine abusers show an elevation on the Psychopathic Deviate Scale of the MMPI. Thus it is possible that amphetamines, like the narcotic analgesics, have an especially high positive valence to psychopathic individuals.

There is some evidence that amphetamines taken orally are used excessively by "high achievers" who value their increased productivity more than any risk associated with the drug. Another postulated cause for dependence is that amphetamine users are essentially depressed individuals who are treating their own depression. Neither of these uses for amphetamine accounts for the new pattern of large doses taken intravenously.

Prevention of Abuse

To date most prevention strategies have involved regulatory methods. A number of the amphetamine drugs have been moved to Schedule 2 of the

Controlled Substances Act, and pressure has been applied to physicians to curtail their prescription of stimulants. Over the past 3 years the rate of prescriptions for stimulants has decreased by two-thirds, but a comparable decrease in nonmedical use of the drugs probably has not occurred.

Treatment and Rehabilitation

Since these drugs are often administered intravenously, treatment for the familiar medical complications arising from this method of use is a common need. Similarly, the treatment of the undernutrition which accompanies stimulant use is easily accomplished. Drug-induced psychoses or depressions typically are self-limiting diseases. The use of pharmacological antagonists to the euphoriant effects of stimulants is still experimental.

Depressants

The contributions of NIMH, particularly the intramural research programs, have helped to explicate the actions and effects of barbiturates. Extramural support for studies of these drugs has increased only since their abuse has increased substantially.

Nature of the Drugs

Barbiturates are a large class of drugs comprised of synthetic compounds developed for legitimate medical use. They have much in common with alcohol in that they have widespread lawful use and they produce sedative-hypnotic effects; the major difference is that depressant drugs are much more potent than alcohol. They are mostly prescribed and used to promote sleep, for daytime sedation, and, much less frequently, as anticonvulsants and (in hospitals) as anesthetics.

Their large number is the result of efforts to achieve a wide range of durations of action suited to their various uses, and to separate desired effects from lethality and abuse potential. The former goal has been well achieved, the latter only partially.

The short-acting barbiturates and a few nonbarbiturate depressants are the drugs usually sought and diverted into illicit channels for nonmedical use.

Nature of the Problem

Depressants are the most prescribed class of drugs in this country. In a survey in one large eastern State it was estimated that roughly 1 in 12 adults use them regularly (at least 6 doses per month). It is hard to estimate what fraction of this medically sanctioned use actually constitutes abuse, but NIMH studies of patterns of prescription and use suggest that the fraction is quite small and that prescription by physicians and consumption by their patients are not excessive by present standards. Nonetheless, to some it is a matter of concern that such a large proportion of adults are judged by physicians, whether rightly or wrongly, to require chemical sedation. In addition, prescribed depressants are the chosen means of at least 2,000 suicides each year—a figure comparable to that of opiate-related deaths.

CNS and General Effects

The sought-after sedation effects of these drugs probably result mainly from depressant action on the midbrain reticular activating system. Overdose deaths result from depression of the respiratory center and of cough and swallowing reflexes. Overdose is not usually inadvert because, in contrast to heroin, abused sedatives are diverted from legitimate channels, and the user can be sure how much he is taking. Inadvertent deaths do occur when sedatives are taken with opiates or alcohol. A prevalent but little-publicized hazard of the alcohol-sedative combination is fire from neglected cigarettes.

Probably enough people have used large amounts of sedatives long enough to justify the general conclusion that, except for occasional allergic reactions, harmful effects are limited to the effects on CNS.

Biological Research

Research done at the Addiction Research Center since the early 1950's elucidated many of the phenomena of dependence on sedative drugs. A dependence model in dogs demonstrated that the brain substrate for barbiturate abstinence syndrome is subcortical; it also showed that there is a great similarity between physical dependence on alcohol and physical dependence on barbiturates.

Because of the similarity between some barbiturates and alcohol in their withdrawal reactions, pentobarbital sodium was proposed as a treatment for alcohol withdrawal states and has long remained the model for pharmacological treatment of this disorder.

Clinical studies demonstrated conclusively in man that the chronic administration of either barbiturates or alcohol induces tolerance and physical dependence; when these drugs are withdrawn, two major signs of abstinence emerge—grand mal convulsions (rum fits) and delirium tremens. Both clinical observations and laboratory findings demonstrated that these phenomena were indeed signs of abstinence, negating the widely held hypothesis that they might be signs of alcohol and barbiturate intoxication or of vitamin deficiencies. Other pertinent results of these studies were a method for diagnosing barbiturate dependence and a method for treating both barbiturate and alcohol dependence. Electroencephalographic investigations were proven useful in the diagnosis of barbiturate dependence and its withdrawal syndrome.

Psychological Research

As judged by the Addiction Research Center Inventory, barbiturates produce some subjective effects that are similar to those produced by alcohol and chlorpromazine. Further ARC research showed that tolerance developed in whole or in part to various impairments produced by chronic administration of barbiturates, but at varying times and to varying degrees. This concept of differential degrees and timing of tolerance subsequently has been extended to most drugs.

It has been postulated that sedatives are used excessively by persons especially prone to becoming anxious, but the psychopathology of barbiturate addicts has not been investigated or described.

261

Prevention

There has been no operating system for studying the abuse potential of sedative-hypnotic drugs and having them scheduled appropriately prior to general use. Methaqualone, which probably has many barbiturate-like effects, has not yet been scheduled in the United States although experience with the drug in other countries suggested that it had a high potential for abuse, even before abuse became common in this country.

Treatment

The principles of treating withdrawal reactions to sedative-hypnotic drugs are clear: substitute a more manageable drug and gradually withdraw it. No such clear principles guide the treatment of those who use sedatives in a spree fashion, or who do not reach the stage of physical dependence. Quite possibly, treatment might be best modeled after programs used for helping alcoholics, but the abuse of sedatives often is complicated by the use of several kinds of drugs.

Drug Abuse Prevention Research

The past few years have seen enormous investments of material resources and human effort in drug abuse prevention campaigns; such preventive approaches largely have taken the form of education-information programs. There has been an apparent high priority on "doing something" in the name of drug abuse prevention, but little priority has been assigned to research on the effectiveness of preventive measures. Little or no effort has been made to assess the impact of the vast majority of prevention programs; certainly there is no well-established body of data on the effectiveness of drug education programs. Some prevention efforts employing mass media techniques for educational efforts have even been accused of contributing to the spread of drug abuse.

A fundamental problem in the assessment of prevention programs is the establishment of realistic goals for the prevention efforts, and thus the kind of criteria that can be considered as indicators of program effectiveness. Many information/education programs have stated their objectives in global terms such as "curbing drug abuse" or "making the public aware of the problem"—objectives that do not lend themselves to precise assessment. Optimally, one would like to know the impact of a particular program on an individual's long-term drug-using behavior. Practically, this is extremely difficult to assess, not only because of the period of time involved, but also because of the many other influences that may play a role in encouraging or discouraging drug use. If prevention programs are to be evaluated, therefore, they must be aimed toward goals that can be defined and measured with some degree of precision. And, until we learn more about how to design and conduct constructive information/education efforts, such factors as drug availability and law enforcement policy may have far greater influence on behavior, especially in the short run, than even the most thoughtfully conceived prevention program.

Criteria that have been used as measures of the effectiveness of drug abuse prevention include changes in knowledge about drugs, changes in reported drug use, and records of drug-related arrests or treatment. But none of these criteria represents a direct measure of optimal outcome for a prevention program.

To the extent possible, evaluations of prevention programs should be based on principles of sound research design and analysis. Program designers and program evaluators should work together throughout the entire course of a prevention program—from its conception through its conclusion and followup. Such cooperative effort is essential to specifying realistic goals of prevention, to designing programs focused on those goals, and to devising measures of progress toward the goals. Without careful research evaluation of the wide spectrum of printed materials, films, and multimedia prevention programs, it is hard to continue to justify present expenditures. With such evaluation it should be possible to develop better focused attempts at prevention that have at least some significant constructive impact.

·In the 1960's, speculation that LSD use might be linked to chromosomal fragmentation apparently led some individuals to reassess the positive aspects versus the potential risks of the drug, thus leading to a decline in its use. Also, firsthand observation of chronic drug users by their peers may have had a negative influence on the popularity of some drugs.

A potentially fruitful line of research that has been relatively neglected entails studies of the relationship of child development, family attitudes and behavior, peer relationships, and other social experiences to later drug involvement. Such studies may provide useful clues to what it is that protects some from serious drug involvement even when they are part of a larger group at high risk. Training research scientists with racial and ethnic backgrounds like those of the high risk groups should facilitate this type of research.

At the same time that prevention programs and their accompanying evaluation strategies are carried out through studies of education, communications, and human development, the prospects of drug abuse prevention also must be explored biologically. Epidemiological studies involving medical/biological measures combined with social/behavioral measures may eventually uncover biological differences between those who are prone to excessive drug use and those who are not. If such differences were to be identified, it might be possible to devise selective preventive strategies acceptable to all concerned.

Treatment Research

Research on the efficacy of treatment and the development of more effective treatment approaches to drug abusers remains a priority need. Answers to the complex question, "What works best, with whom, under what circumstances?" are elusive.

A number of factors impede definitive research on treatment: It is expensive; therapists often resist evaluation research efforts; subjective reports provided by patients are often of questionable reliability; the treatment process is defined in different ways by different people; there is little agreement on valid criteria of improvement that can be reliably assessed; and long-term followups are difficult.

Despite the formidable problems of doing adequate research on treatment, such research has been of concern to the NIMH and its antecedent components from their inception. When regulations were developed for carrying out the Narcotic Addict Rehabilitation Act of 1966, a basic requirement of the so-called Title IV programs was that evaluation be a part of the rehabilitative effort. The Narcotic Addict Rehabilitation Branch of the Division of Narcotic Addiction and Drug Abuse has continued to place heavy emphasis on treatment evaluation, and the Center for Studies of Narcotic and Drug Abuse has actively encouraged treatment research.

Early research at the U.S. Public Health Service hospitals showed that the success rate in terms of patients treated there who remained drug-free subsequent to release was quite low. One explanation frequently offered for the high rate of drug abuse recidivism was the fact that treatment took place at locations (Lexington and Fort Worth) which were typically remote from the areas in which most addicts lived. When patients returned to their usual environments, the original conditions conducive to drug use were once again present, and there was no provision for continued followup services that might assist them in their posthospital functioning.

In 1957, the NIMH established the New York Demonstration Center in the belief that increased use of community resources would be of significant value in helping to rehabilitate addicts discharged from the Lexington treatment facility. The center was intended to determine the needs of returning patients, to prepare them for referral to community agencies, and to serve as an information and consultative resource to the local agencies.

During its 5-year existence, the New York Demonstration Center had significant success in improving availability of services to addict patients and in encouraging agencies to modify their traditional approaches to meet the addict's specific needs. Greater success was achieved when the agency had some degree of control over the patient because he was on probation or for other reasons required to remain in treatment.

In addition to funding treatment services, NIMH has attempted to establish treatment data systems with uniform reporting practices so that characteristics of addicts and the relative success of specific treatment techniques can be studied across large samples. An initial system collected uniform data from a representative sample of 45 NIMH-supported treatment programs. The Institute now operates a much larger system, the Client-Oriented Data Acquisition Process (CODAP), which collects uniform admission and progress information. Neither system, however, is designed to follow patients after they complete treatment or patients who drop out. The Narcotic Addict Rehabilitation Branch is developing contracts and grant applications for support of work emphasizing longer term followup and more rigorous research methods.

It should be emphasized that the relative paucity of research designed to explore the efficacy of the various treatment programs does not represent any lack of NIMH commitment to research in this area. The extremely rapid expansion of programs to meet an unprecedented need, the lack of well-qualified researchers in this area, and the many difficulties inherent in the conduct of treatment evaluation have all been serious impediments to high quality work.

It is generally agreed that valid research on treatment outcomes should include longitudinal studies that follow specific cohorts of patients during their participation in a treatment program, as well as after termination. But the most strategic sampling parameters to be employed and the specific indicators of treatment outcomes to be used are still matters of considerable debate. In addition, the validity of self-report data from addicts in treatment programs is questionable.

As data accumulate from patient reporting systems it will be possible to select some of the most salient variables to be considered in sampling for outcome studies.

Chemotherapeutic Research

Research on drug abuse chemotherapy is hardly a decade old. Although there were attempts to treat narcotic addiction in the United States by regularly administering morphine-like drugs in narcotic clinics from 1919 to 1923, the effects were not systematically evaluated.

NIMH has pioneered in the development of narcotic antagonists for the treatment of narcotic addiction. The concept that these agents might be useful in the treatment of narcotic addiction by extinction of conditioned abstinence and drug-seeking behavior originated at the Addiction Research Center. The ARC has been responsible for identifying the salient pharmacological characteristics of cyclazocine, naloxone, and naltrexone in man that gave the drugs a special role in therapy. Further, the evaluation of depot forms of antagonists has been going on at the ARC for the last 3 years.

Methadone

In the late 1940's ARC scientists reported on the addiction liability of methadone and subsequently proposed its use as an agent for detoxifying morphine- and heroin-dependent patients. It was not until 1965, however, that the first report was published of success in using methadone as a maintenance drug for 22 addicts in New York City.

Since that modest but bold beginning, methadone maintenance programs have expanded to the point that an estimated 50,000 persons were maintained on methadone in 1972. But even though there has been a great deal of research on methadone maintenance, questions on long-range effects on a variety of aspects of biomedical, psychological, and social functioning remain unanswered or inadequately answered. NIMH grantees are currently studying various biological and psychological aspects of methadone maintenance, including the problem of neonatal addiction.

The introduction of LAAM (l-alphaacetylmethadol), a longer-acting opiate chemically related to methadone, has provided a possible alternative maintenance drug, and several current studies are evaluating its clinical usefulness.

Use of addicting drugs in treatment continues to be questioned on ethical grounds, and it has not been possible to prevent completely the diversion of methadone into illicit channels.

Antagonists

Antagonists can be used in three distinct ways to combat opiate abuse problems: (I) Their use in treating overdose by reversing respiratory depression is well-established. (2) Given to abstinent addicts, they discourage repeated self-administration by blocking the primary euphoriant actions of the opiates. (3) The more sophisticated concept developed at the ARC entails supervised, repeated self-injection of heroin under antagonist blockade, with the aim of achieving "active extinction" of conditioned abstinence.

Research to date confirms the initial impression that cyclazocine, despite some drawbacks, can be a useful tool in treating the addict. Most recently naltrexone, one of the newer antagonists with few agonist effects and long duration of action, has shown indications that it may prove to be significantly more effective than either of the older antagonists (naloxone and cyclazocine).

Although work to date has concentrated most heavily on the development of antagonists that are specifically useful in treating opiate addiction, activity is also being encouraged to develop possible antagonists to other drugs of abuse such as the amphetamines. In addition, the possible development of means for providing extended duration of action over many weeks or months may provide a treatment regimen far less dependent on the day-to-day continued high motivation of the patient than those that are currently in use. Recent findings in animals indicate the feasibility of a biodegradable depot preparation that releases naltrexone in effective levels for about a month.

It should be emphasized that much remains to be learned about antagonists. Their efficacy, as compared to other treatments, has not been sufficiently evaluated, nor has the possibility been ruled out that the antagonists may be subtly harmful in the long run. Even if antagonists prove to be extremely effective in a strictly pharmacological sense, it is crucially important in rehabilitating the drug abuser to provide a full range of ancillary services (counseling, employment assistance, etc.). These nonmedical aspects of treatment also require systematic evaluation for full understanding of what constitutes optimally effective rehabilitative strategies.

Targeted Research for Developing Antagonists

The NIMH contract program for accelerating the development and testing of antagonists has provided for obtaining materials, preclinically screening them, and further clinically evaluating compounds that appear most promising. Clinical contracts have been let to evaluate the clinical pharmacology of new narcotic antagonists, to test them for clinical efficacy, and, in one contract, to study the effects of antagonists on drug-seeking behavior under controlled conditions.

Future Treatment Techniques

The possibility of developing active immunization in order to treat and conceivably even prevent various types of drug abuse is being investigated, although it is now a theoretical rather than a practical possibility. Several Institute-supported scientists are exploring ways in which

266

specific antibodies could be developed which might prove useful in this way. Even if it were to prove possible to counter the usual effects of self-administered drugs by some such method, the possibility of serious and even fatal allergic reactions would require intensive exploration. If this were solved, there would remain an ethical dilemma. Would it be proper to deliberately make anyone immune to the pain-relieving benefits of the opiates?

The possibility of inactivating or blocking receptor sites for drugs of abuse, which would not depend on continuously circulating molecules of an antagonist, also exists. The use of affinity labeling, now supported by several grants, is a first step in the possible development of irreversible inhibitors that will work in this manner. Again, this is still only a theoretical possibility and poses another ethical question.

Behavioral Approaches to Treatment

Animal laboratories have had a long history of systematically exploring the reinforcement conditions that maintain a wide range of behaviors, including the self-administration of drugs. While a number of studies have shed light on possible behavioral contingencies that operate in human drug abuse behavior, comparatively few attempts have been made to explore the usefulness of behavior modification techniques in human drug treatment situations.

The Institute is now actively encouraging and supporting extramural research exploring behavior modification approaches to treatment. The program has two aspects: (1) the detailed analysis of the reinforcing contingencies that play a role in initiating and maintaining drug use in natural and experimental situations, and (2) the application of such techniques as aversive conditioning, token economies, contingency contracting, and biofeedback techniques in modifying drug-related behavior. It is hoped that the current research will evolve into a larger scale effort to explore more systematically the application of learning principles to treatment in the various subgroups of drug users.

Most treatment research to date has been focused on the use of opiates. Little research has been conducted on treatment for abuse of other drugs. With the proliferation of various kinds of drug abuse has come a similar expansion in the number and variety of activities designed to assist the drug abusers. These have included free clinics, "hot lines," religious education, folk healing, transcendental meditation, self-help groups of all types, residential treatment facilities, and more traditional psychiatric facilities. Few of these methods have been systematically evaluated, and fewer still have been compared with alternatives, but all apparently are sometimes effective. As some of the techniques and facilities become more stabilized, research on their effectiveness as compared to others is essential if we are to have a rational basis for treatment choice.

RECOMMENDATIONS

Three sets of recommendations follow. The first applies generally to the drugs of abuse considered in this chapter. The second applies to specific drugs, or to specific classes of drugs, taking into account the unique characteristics that create unique research questions within each category.

The third, and longest, set of recommendations applies to the entire field of abuse and addiction research—including alcohol. NIMH has administered its drug abuse and its alcohol programs as separate entities, and the Research Task Force studied and evaluated them separately. Nevertheless, the similarity of continuing problems in the two areas is reflected in the two study groups' common recommendations, which constitute the third set of recommendations included here.

Recommendations Pertaining to All Drugs of Abuse Except Alcohol

Research Emphases

1. Immunological approaches to the detection and possible treatment of drug abusers should receive continued support.

    Immunoassay techniques for the detection of various drugs of abuse, including the opiates, have considerable promise as highly sensitive indicators of drug use. A second aspect of this research is aimed at the possibility that specific circulating or mobilizable antibodies can be produced in the body which can bind injected drugs in the plasma, thus preventing the drugs from reaching the receptor site and having their characteristic effect. Although it poses many difficulties, possible use of this technique should be pursued because of its obvious potential for both the treatment and prevention of drug abuse.

2. The development and testing of treatment models based on the application of behavior modification approaches should be actively encouraged.

    The behavior modification approach, based on systematic application of learning principles, has not been extensively tested in the treatment of drug abuse. The application of these approaches to human problems of addiction and drug abuse holds considerable promise for more effective therapy. Moreover, applied behavior analysis may enhance our understanding of the reward conditions associated with drug use and may be used to improve existing therapeutic modalities.

3. Cross-cultural, anthropological research designed to determine social and cultural factors which control drug use and prevent serious abuse should be undertaken.

    One of the more noteworthy aspects of drug use and abuse on a worldwide basis is that the degree to which such use poses a problem is not simply a matter of availability and/or legal sanctions against use. Indeed, there are societies in which various psychoactive drugs are widely available with minimal restriction and yet abuse of these drugs is minimal. By studying possible factors which serve to guard against abuse or tend to regulate moderate use, we may well discover societal and institutional deterrents to drug abuse that are more effective than those functioning in the United States.

4. Epidemiological research should be encouraged, with particular emphasis on studying the extent, patterns, and trends of drug abuse among ethnic and racial minority populations, in industrial settings, and among children and youth.

An improved understanding of the nature and extent of drug abuse is essential, but equally important is concentrated study of the majority of these populations who do not become drug abusers. Followup studies of addicts should be encouraged. Consideration should be given to the establishment of a nationwide elementary and high school drug abuse monitoring system. Research in industry should include studies of drug types favored by blue-collar versus white-collar workers, methods of measuring impairment, and ways of dealing with the problem in the work setting. All epidemiological research should meet rigorous standards with regard to confidentiality of data collected for research purposes, and each research design should include adequate safeguards for investigators and respondents.

Implementation of Research Programs

5. Attempts should be made to develop a manpower inventory of researchers presently available in the field of drug abuse epidemiology, and specific plans to increase this pool should be developed.

Describing the nature and extent of an illegal activity obviously involves complex ethical and legal questions. There are few qualified researchers who have been able to design studies so well that they obtain reliable data and at the same time build adequate safeguards for responding subjects and for research personnel. Further professional training in epidemiological approaches to drug abuse is a prerequisite to building a substantial body of knowledge about the patterns of drug use and abuse.

6. NIMH should establish an intramural treatment research facility in the field of drug abuse and addiction.

With the closing of the Clinical Research Center at Lexington it is important that NIMH have a clinical research facility where well-controlled treatment studies of drug abusers can be conducted. The presently used contractual arrangements for narcotic antagonist treatment programs have serious deficiencies for carrying out efficient and well-defined targeted treatment research.

7. Additional manpower to monitor extramural grants and contracts should be hired.

An adequate number of qualified personnel for monitoring research projects is essential to the maintenance of high scientific standards and the assurance of adequate reporting in the extramural program.

8. There should be a director of research programs in the area of drug abuse, and that person should be a scientist.

9. An intramural social science branch should be created and should be of sufficient size to carry out an effective program.

From the standpoint of total funds available, the treatment, education, and training divisions or branches currently dwarf research endeavors, both intramural and extramural. In the judgment of the Research Task Force, the development of strong intramural and extramural research programs would benefit treatment, education, and training through the application of sound scientific methodology in assessing their endeavors. Thus intramural and extramural research programs should have substantive input into the conduct of the activities of the entire drug program if the most beneficial potential of these interactions is to be realized.

10. FDA regulations regarding clinical research with marihuana on female volunteers should be reexamined and eased.

   This change, if feasible, would facilitate more definitive research on marihuana.

11. All research training programs should involve research scientists in their direction and administration.

Recommendations Pertaining to Specific Drugs

Opiates

1. The efficacy of narcotic antagonists in programs of extended treatment should continue to be examined.

   Such studies should include: the types of addicts with whom this form of therapy is successful; the possible importance of duration of action in antagonist efficacy; possible mode of action of antagonists in relation to protracted abstinence and conditioning paradigms; and the role of other treatment program aspects in outcomes.

2. The possible role of narcotic antagonists in the prevention of addiction in high risk populations should be explored.

   One major potential role for antagonists is that of discouraging opiate use by blocking the action of these drugs. Thus, voluntary treatment of high risk individuals who may be experimenting with opiates may serve to prevent more serious involvement.

3. More detailed research examination of the effects and implications of methadone maintenance should be carried out.

   Although methadone maintenance has been employed for some years, a variety of questions remain unanswered or only partially answered. These questions pertain to the effects of prolonged use of methadone on physical functioning and intellectual or physical performance, adverse effects of the drug, interaction of methadone with other commonly used drugs, termination of methadone maintenance, effects of protracted abstinence after methadone maintenance, methadone's effects on offspring of women taking the drug during pregnancy, and the effectiveness of methadone programs compared with other treatment modalities.

Marihuana

1. Studies of long-term users both here and abroad should be continued and expanded.

   Research should include studies that focus on the sociocultural aspects of use and the methods of social control involved. In studies that involve eventual physiological, psychiatric, and psychological testing, efforts should be made to enlarge the sample size in order to detect possible effects that may have been missed in smaller samples. Long-term studies of American users should be undertaken as soon as is feasible. Research on the mutagenic effect of marihuana should be encouraged, and special attention should be paid to the effects of marihuana use on female users.

2. Possible carcinogenicity of marihuana should be investigated.

   Because the mode of typical use is smoking by deep inhalation, it may have serious public health implications.

3. The metabolism routes and products of marihuana should be further investigated.

   The metabolic fate of the drug in the body is likely to be enormously complex; it appears that eventually the metabolic products may be measured in the hundreds. Their identification, their persistence in the body, and their pharmacological or toxicological actions should be ascertained, as any subtle toxicity of the drug may be dependent upon these products.

4. The actions of various marihuana constituents, homologs, and metabolities should be ascertained.

   Where possible, such studies should describe mechanisms of action in man, although more detailed investigations will be based on experiments with animals.

5. Therapeutic uses of the drug should be further explored.

   Studies should include controlled comparisons with established agents when these are indicated. These uses may be especially relevant to synthetic homologs made in an attempt to isolate or emphasize certain desirable pharmacological actions.

6. Methodology for the quantification of marihuana and its components in body tissue and fluid should continue to be developed.

   There is an obvious need to develop relatively simple tests that can be used to determine the amount of marihuana that becomes physiologically active. Wide availability of such tests would not only insure comparability of research, but also would be helpful in assessing the role of marihuana in impairing driver performance and other everyday functioning.

7. Systematic studies of the role of social pressures in altering attitudes toward marihuana should be encouraged.

   Such studies would be part of a fabric of studies pertaining to attitudes toward the use of all kinds of mind-altering drugs, either positively in starting fashions of use, or negatively in terminating them.

8. The behavioral effects of marihuana at the usual range of single doses have been adequately investigated, and the findings have largely confirmed previous reports. However, further studies are needed of the mechanism underlying these behavioral changes.

9. Specific actions of the drug that may be important clinically should be studied, such as the mechanism of the lowering of intraocular pressure, the possible aggravation of diabetes by impairment of glucose tolerance, and the effects on pulmonary and caridovascular function.

10. Development and testing of psychological tests to be used in countries where cannabis use is common, other than major Western industrial nations, should be encouraged for the purpose of assessing the effects of long-term marihuana use on brain function. This would also involve encouraging psychologists who are knowledgeable in cross-cultural testing to enter this field, as well as cultural anthropologists.

Depressants

1. Coordinated research on alcohol and depressants should be encouraged.

   Because of the close relationships between depressants and alcohol on a pharmacological, epidemiological, clinical, and therapeutic level, it is likely that major findings involving one would also pertain to the other. NIMH should stress coordinated research efforts and shared findings in these important areas of drug abuse.

2. Improved tests for screening sedative-hypnotic drugs for abuse potential should be encouraged.

   The obvious economic potential in the development of less abusable sedatives is likely to be exploited by private industry. The single NIMH role in the effort should be to ascertain that abuse potential of new products can be accurately and reliably assessed.

Stimulants

1. Studies of amphetamine psychoses should be continued.

   These studies are particularly important with regard to understanding the underlying CNS mechanisms in the development of the psychoses.

2. The pharmacology of cocaine should be investigated.

   There has been practically no recent pharmacological research with cocaine despite the fact that it is becoming a more widely abused drug. Pharmacological investigations of the drug, both in single and repeated doses by sniffing and intravenous administration, especially as compared with the amphetamines, should be undertaken using modern pharmacological approaches. Such support should include clinical pharmacological study of the drug.

Hallucinogens

1. Basic research on the pharmacology of hallucinogens and on their actions in the brain should be encouraged.

   The hallucinogens, as a class of drugs causing unique effects, hold great potential as a tool for enhancing our knowledge of brain functions. Of particular importance are studies on hallucinogen-receptor interaction, structure-functional relationships of the hallucinogenic series, molecular chemistry of the hallucinogens, and the significance and mechanism of brain changes in turnover of brain amines after administration of many hallucinogens.

2. Continued support for the development of sensitive immunoassay techniques should be given.

Sensitive indicators of drug ingestion are important both from a scientific point of view and in connection with treatment. Methods that can detect very small quantities of drugs are particularly applicable to study of the hallucinogens, an outstandingly potent class of drugs.

3. A study of former heavy LSD users should be encouraged.

A followup study of former heavy LSD users to determine whether there is evidence of persistent brain dysfunction would be desirable. Although many users have been multiple drug users, it should be possible to develop a sample in which the primary difference between the experimental and the control group is persistent LSD use.

4. Scientific study of hallucinogen-derived "mystical" experiences should be encouraged.

There has been little study by scientists of these experiences, even though they are described as powerful and sometimes transforming. Such study may be of use in exploring means of inducing similar states of consciousness without drugs. It might also enhance understanding of brain mechanisms involved in such experiences, and it may improve our understanding of motivation, beliefs, and value systems as related to development of drug cults.

5. Prospective studies on brain function and possible chromosomal damage of patients who have received LSD therapeutically should be encouraged.

This is an important followup among subjects whose drug intake levels and frequencies of use are known.

Volatile Solvents

1. The pharmacology of volatile solvents should be clarified by supporting animal experiments using high concentration, intermittent exposure to these agents with and without hypoxia.

Much of what is known about the pharmacology of these agents is based on low concentration, continuous exposure experiments designed to assess possible dangers of industrial exposure to these materials. Studies of the type recommended would more closely approximate patterns of abuse.

General Recommendations for All Research on All Drug Abuse and Addictions

This set of recommendations applies to research on drug abuse in general, including alcohol.

Research Emphases

Within Biological Areas:

1. Basic research, with emphasis on the study of the effects of drugs on the central nervous system, is of utmost importance. It has potential for contributions not only to treatment and prevention of drug abuse and alcoholism but to the general understanding of brain function as well.

   Clarification of the basic mechanisms of the addictive process in the brain is essential to the development of effective therapies and highly pertinent to the development of preventive strategies. Better use of existing technologies and the concomitant development of new technologies are essential to productive work on the central nervous system, and promising methodological advances must be encouraged.

2. Studies should be encouraged which investigate the interactive effects of drugs that are commonly taken together.

   Since there are innumerable compounds and dosage interactions that potentially could be studied, research should be restricted to those drugs and dosage levels that are most likely to be used. In addition to the drugs considered in this chapter, such research should include tobacco as well as widely used over-the-counter and prescribed drugs.

3. High priority should be given to imaginative approaches to human or animal studies of the genetic aspects of addiction.

   The question of whether or not humans may inherit a predisposition to addiction is an important one and should be answered. Evidence to date suggests a genetic basis for some cases of human alcoholism, but the hereditary factors and environmental factors that influence any form of drug abuse have not been defined, and their relative contributions to the addictive process have not been quantified or explained.

   Within Psychosocial Areas:

4. Psychosocial research should concentrate less on individual psychopathology and should seek to identify and explain the forces in societal groups that influence the development of drug abuse and addiction.

   The Institute should encourage comprehensive studies of addict, nonaddicted user, and nonuser populations, especially in high risk groups. Intense study should be directed to adolescence, since that is the development period in which many people make choices that may lead to the establishment of drug use habits; also there is particular need for definitive epidemiological studies of drug abuse among minority groups and among women. Investigations should search for aspects of lifestyle, family constellations, institutional characteristics, childrearing practices, peer associations, etc., that may influence the development and maintenance of drug use and that may be instrumental in creating effective prevention programs. Such studies also should attempt to identify psychosocial, personality, and psychopathological factors that predispose to addiction.

   Longitudinal studies of cohorts studied early in their lives and followed for considerable periods of time would yield invaluable information on drug abuse as it occurs in relation to processes of normal development and change. It would be of interest to know how and when an individual is "labeled"—by himself or by others—as a drug abuser and how he gets channeled into avenues of help and treatment services. Studies of psychosocial phenomena and influences on drug abuse should be based on a broad conceptual framework that can clarify the interplay of factors traditionally the subjects of several social and behavioral science disciplines.

Concerning Treatment of the Drugs of Abuse and Addiction:

5. Intensive research programs should be aimed toward the goals of developing effective pharmacotherapeutic agents and developing new experimental paridigms for the early identification of promising compounds.

Development of effective pharmacotherapies is inextricably bound to and dependent upon the success of basic biological research, particularly the study of drug effects on the central nervous system. Pharmacotherapeutic approaches may enable addicts to use effectively the various psychosocial resources that contribute to complete rehabilitation.

6. All treatment research should seek to determine which treatments and which approaches work best with what types of drug abusers.

The causes of drug abuse are so many and so varied that one cannot consider that optimal treatment would be invariable across large numbers of people. The success of treatment, like the development of dependence, appears to depend on a complex interaction of multiple factors. Characteristics of the user himself, his environment, the drug he has used, and the treatment technique—all influence the process and outcome of treatment as well as the chance for rehabilitation or for relapse. Treatment research that sheds light on any of these factors can contribute to the development of more precise theory and research on psychosocial aspects of drug abuse and addiction. Since a variety of treatment techniques are available, treatment evaluation studies hold high priority, but at present adequate assessment of the efficacy of treatment is more often the exception rather than the rule. Methodological advances in theory, instrumentation, experimental design, or other techniques should be sought for the sake of better treatment evaluation. Where therapies have been proven effective, the emphasis should be directed toward increasing their utilization; preliminary psychological and sociological studies may be useful in defining strategies and institutional structures needed to provide such treatment.

Concerning Prevention:

7. To the extent possible, prevention programs should incorporate principles of research design and should be evaluated to determine what kinds of prevention programs are most effective with what kinds of groups.

Prevention programs should take into account the characteristics of target groups, their receptivity and perceptions of the need for drug education as a function of their use of drugs, their social norms, and the extent to which they perceive drug abuse as an important issue. In addition, systematic studies of the constructive personal strategies of those who use drugs with no apparent harm would have important implications for education and prevention programs.

Concerning Interdisciplinary Collaboration:

8. Interdisciplinary collaborative studies are most important in the areas of epidemiology and treatment of drug abuse problems.

Collaboration between biological and social scientists could be useful in determining what distinguishes the drug abuser or addict from the "normal" drug user in epidemiological studies and could enhance the potential for successful application and evaluation of combined medical and psychosocial treatment techniques. Drug abuse problems represent a mosaic in terms of etiological factors, natural history factors, and treatment factors, and there is general agreement that no single factor accounts for all or even most cases of abuse or addiction. Competent collaborative research should facilitate progress toward solving the problem.

Implementation of Research Programs

Concerning Contract Research:

9. The contract mechanism, as a useful means of stimulating research, should be used for its most valuable function—to provide data on specific, restricted questions in priority areas.

10. Research contracts should be undertaken in such a way as to assure that the highest scientific merit is represented in requests for proposals (RFPs), potential contractors, review of proposals, and continued staff monitoring of the contractor's work.

11. Requests for contract proposals should be published in the scientific press.

12. Issuance of RFPs, review of proposals, and negotiation of contracts should take place throughout the year instead of being concentrated at the end of each fiscal year.

13. The peer evaluation system should be strengthened and extended to apply to all extramural research activities, i.e., to contracts as well as grants.

While the grant differs from the contract mechanism in its mode of initiation and in the set of demands and regulations that apply to the recipient of an award and to the Government, the necessity for scientific rigor applies equally to all research projects. Over the years certain procedures have been built into the research grant mechanism that offer more assurance of scientific merit than the procedures that operate in the contract mechanism. It is felt that the implementation of recommendations 9 through 13 would constitute a step toward assuring that all contract research meets stringent criteria of design and execution.

Concerning Research Manpower:

14. NIMH should establish a system of awards for training and for recognition of outstanding research achievements in order to attract qualified researchers into studies relevant to the addictions and drug abuse.

Consideration should be given to Government-sponsored periodic awards, prizes, and professional recognition of scientific achievement in drug abuse research. Research awards to outstanding experienced investigators and to pre- and post-doctoral trainees should be encouraged.

Concerning Evaluation of Research:

15. NIMH should undertake systematic, periodic evaluative review of all its research on the addictions and drug abuse.

The results of such an evaluation should be made available to the scientific community and to the public through publication in professional journals or through Federal publication and distribution mechanisms. Results of the study should be used to strengthen, modify, or redirect existing research programs.

Concerning Administration:

16. Better coordination of drug abuse research activities of the Institute should be encouraged by the creation of formal mechanisms of coordination.

17. The administration of the alcohol and the drug abuse programs should remain separate in the immediate future; however, NIMH should consider a merger of the two programs in the context of long-range planning.

References

Blum, R.H., and Associates. Society and Drugs. San Francisco: Jossey-Bass, 1969.

Braude, M.C., Harris, L.S., May, E.L., Smith, J.P., and Villarreal, J.E. Narcotic Antagonists. Advances in Biochemical Psychopharmacology. New York: Raven Press, 1973.

Chein, I., Gerald, D.L., Lee, R.S., and Rosenfeld, E. The Road to H: Narcotics, Delinquency and Social Policy. New York: Basic Books, 1964.

Clouet, D.H. (ed). Narcotic Drugs; Biochemical Pharmacology. New York: Plenum Press, 1971.

Cohen, S. The volatile solvents. Public Health Review, 2:185-214, 1973.

Commission (Canadian) of Inquiry into the Non-Medical Use of Drugs, Final Report. Ottawa: Information Canada, 1973.

Connell, P.H. Amphetamine Psychosis. Maudsley Monograph No. 5. Institute of Psychiatry. London: Oxford University Press, 1958.

Costa, E., and Garattini, S. (eds). Amphetamines and Related Compounds: Proceedings. New York: Raven Press, 1970.

Glasscote, R.M., Sussex, J.N., Jaffe, J.H., Ball, J., and Brill, L. The Treatment of Drug Abuse—Programs, Problems, Prospects. Washington, D.C.: Joint Information Service, American Psychiatric Association, 1972.

Goldberg, L., and Hoffmeister, F. (eds). Psychic Dependence. Bayer Symposium IV. Berlin—Heidelberg—New York: Springer-Verlag, 1973.

Isbell, H., and Fraser, H.F. Addiction to analgesics and barbiturates. The Journal of Pharmacology and Experimental Therapeutics Part 2, 99:355-397, 1950.

Josephson, E., and Carroll, E. Drug Use: Epidemiological and Sociological Approaches. Washington, D.C.: Winston-Wiley, 1974. In press.

Martin, W.R. Opioid antagonists. Pharmacological Review, 19:463-521, 1967.

Martin, W.R., and Jasinski, D.R. Physiological parameters of morphine dependence in man—tolerance, early abstinence, protracted abstinence. Journal of Psychiatric Research, 7:9-17, 1969.

Martin, W.R., Jasinski, D.R., Haertzen, C.A., Kay, D.C., Jones, B.E., Mansky, P.A., and Carpenter, R.W. Methadone—a reevaluation. Archives of General Psychiatry, 28:286-295, 1973.

Martin, W.R., Jasinski, D.R., and Mansky, P.A. Naltrexone, an antagonist for the treatment of heroin dependence. Archives of General Psychiatry, 28:784-791, 1973.

McGlothlin, W.H. Drug use and abuse. Annual Review of Psychology, 1975. In press.

National Commission on Marihuana and Drug Abuse. Marihuana: A Signal of Misunderstanding. Washington, D.C.: U.S. Govt. Print. Off., 1972.

National Commission on Marihuana and Drug Abuse. Drug Use in America: Problem in Perspective. Washington, D.C.: U.S. Govt. Print. Off., 1973.

O'Donnell, J.A. Narcotic Addicts in Kentucky. Washington, D.C.: U.S. Govt. Print. Off. PHS No. 1881, 1969.

Rubin, V., and Comitas, L. Ganja in Jamaica: A Medical Anthropological Study of Chronic Marihuana Users. The Hague (Netherlands): Mouton, 1974. In press.

Wikler, A. (ed). The Addictive States. Research Publication, Association for Research in Nervous and Mental Disease, Vol 46. Baltimore: Williams and Wilkins, 1968.

Wikler, A. Dynamics of drug dependence; implications of a conditioning theory for research and treatment. Archives of General Psychiatry, 28:611-626, 1973.

Zarafonetis, C.J. (ed). Drug Abuse: Proceedings of the International Conference. Philadelphia: Lea & Febiger, 1972.

CHAPTER 11

Research on Social Problems

AN OVERVIEW OF SOCIAL PROBLEMS RESEARCH

Breadth of Perspective

The field of social problems research is in a state of productive ferment. In the not very distant past, the field was marked by a distressing parochialism of perspective: Research was focused on descriptions of the biological or, more often, psychological functioning of individuals within some narrowly defined segment of the population (prisoners, treated addicts, mental patients, or "bigoted" whites) and generalized uncritically to a much more heterogeneous population (criminals, drug users, the mentally ill, or all prejudiced persons). Moreover, even when the focus of the research went beyond description of the narrow and often atypical population segment subjected to study, the research went little beyond inquiry into the socialization process—induction into juvenile gangs, for example, paths to the mental hospital, or the processes by which little girls are socialized into adult female sex roles.

There has been a dramatic change in the past few years, not in all research, but certainly in the leading research in social problems. The best recent research shows a much greater breadth of perspective and deals with the complex interrelationship of individual, situational field, and institutional and social-structural loci. This shift can be illustrated in virtually all fields of social problems research; a few important examples are offered here.

Sex-Role Differentiation

In research on sex roles, despite a few notable early studies of cultural variations in sex-role differentiation, the modal work was clearly focused on describing psychological differences in American men and women, as evidenced in tests and in experimental situations, the subjects almost always being white and middle class, the research usually making little effort to delineate subcultural differences even within white, middle-class America. Insofar as these studies went beyond description of performance on tests or in experimental situations, the focus was almost invariably on behavior within only one institution, the family. And insofar as research interest went beyond description, it focused on socialization processes, the question being how girls (sometimes boys) learn their appropriate adult sex roles.

Description of existing differences in sex roles in middle-class America has turned into comparative study, across cultures, social structures, and historical epochs, of the many possible arrangements known to human society, some emphasizing sex differences, some minimizing sex differences, and together illustrating that a very large array of human potentialities can be seized upon by one or another society as sexually differentiating behavioral characteristics. The institutional focus of sex-role research has gone far beyond the family, to sex-role differentiation in other spheres of life, notably occupational, educational, political, and recreational. In what may be the most profound shift of all, the focus is now in process of changing from describing sex-role differentiation to analyzing its historical and its social structural bases. The question becomes why some societies make more of sexual differentiation than others do, and why they focus on some of the many potential differences rather than others. The field has moved from a narrow interest in describing sex-role differences in the American middle class to a broader interest in understanding the social, structural, economic, and historical determinants of why we have the particular pattern of sex-role differentiation that we do.

Race Relations

In research on race relations, the broadening of perspective has also been impressive. A quarter of a century ago, it was still widely believed that discriminatory behavior simply reflected prejudiced attitudes; the sole research emphasis was the psychodynamics of prejudice. But then it was learned that most discrimination results not from blatant bigotry but from the ordinary behavior of people who, at worst, are "the gentle people of prejudice," people who simply follow standard institutional practices, be they discriminatory or nondiscriminatory. The questions have more and more become: Why are institutional practices as they are? What forces make for continuity and for change in patterns of race relations?

With this broadening of research perspective has come a number of concomitant shifts in the nature of the research. From being almost entirely concerned with measuring prejudice and its place in personality dynamics, the research has shifted more and more to studying institutional practices and the complex interaction of individual personality, situational context, and larger institutional organization. From being preoccupied with assessments of personality, particularly with devising adequate tests of prejudice, the research has shifted more and more to studying behavior in its natural contexts, particularly the comparative study of how the same individuals behave in a variety of discriminatory and nondiscriminatory situational and institutional contexts. From being preoccupied with the individual, the research emphasis has shifted more and more to studying larger social and economic structures, including political-economic systems as a whole. And in what may be the most important shift of all, research that was once almost entirely preoccupied with static arrangements has come more and more to realize the strategic research value of studying the processes of social and individual change.

Poverty

In research on poverty, too, there has been a significant broadening of perspective. In the recent past, the focus was on the psychology of the poor, an underlying and often explicit assumption being that a "culture of poverty," transmitted from generation to generation, kept the poor from rising in the stratification system. Out of a raging controversy over the validity of such an attribution of cause has come a recognition that the values and attitudes of the poor represent adaptation to a set of social and economic conditions. These values and attitudes are readily modified by changing conditions. Moreover, recent evidence on intergenerational mobility clearly demonstrates that the culture of poverty has little to do with determining who in any generation falls to the bottom of the social scale. The underlying factors are to be found more in the educational and occupational systems, in racial discrimination, in the treatment of the aged, and in our system of financing medical catastrophies.

The focus in poverty research has thus been enlarged from a preoccupation with the values and psychological functioning of the poor to a broader concern with understanding the overall relationship between the system of social stratification and psychological functioning, as discussed in the chapter on sociocultural processes. Along with this has come a renewed emphasis on studying the multiple reasons for poverty—those general reasons built into the social and economic system, and the particular reasons why various types of people, defined, for example, by race, or age, or state of health, as well as by limits of aspirations or ability, are peculiarly likely to become impoverished.

Some of this research raises questions about long-held asumptions—that, for example, the main function of education for occupational attainment is the transmission of substantive knowledge; recent studies indicate that education may be more important for giving credentials, for instilling occupationally appropriate values, and for engendering a degree of intellectual flexibility. Other research has called into question the assumption that intelligence (as measured by IQ tests) is an important determinant of occupational attainment. In these and many other areas, the field of poverty research has raised fundamental doubts as to whether the causes of poverty lie in the values, the aspirations, or even the abilities of the poor. It should be noted that in all these respects the perspective of the research field has moved far ahead of that embodied in governmental policy, which still seems to be based largely on a deficiency theory of poverty.

Crime and Delinquency

Research in crime and delinquency provides still another example of a broadened perspective in social problems research. At one time, research in this field was predicated on the assumption that one could neatly dichotomize the adult population into criminals and noncriminals, the juvenile population into delinquents and nondelinquents. The object of research was to characterize the personalities, life histories, or genetic endowments of the criminals or delinquents; the natural subjects of such research were those convicted of and incarcerated for criminal acts. The assumption that it makes sense to thus dichotomize the population has proved to be false; there are very few members of the population who have not committed some violation of law at some time in their lives. The genesis of criminality, though still not precisely known, is at least known to lie in the interaction of biological potential, life experience, personality, situational exigency, and social structural locus. And incarcerated criminals and delinquents have long since been shown to provide a very biased sample from which to generalize.

Along with this widening of research perspective has come a renewed interest in defining, indexing, and interpreting the social and legal processes that result in the official labeling of the "criminal" act. What at one time seemed simple and even obvious is now known to be the resultant of a delicate and often happenstantial interplay of complex situational determinants. And since the official labeling of a person as criminal or delinquent can have profound consequences for his entire future career, the labeling process has been given considerable research attention.

Finally, research in crime and delinquency has come to question and to evaluate the entire system of criminal justice, incarceration, and imprisonment much more rigorously than ever before. The system itself, both its rationale and its operation, has become the focus of systematic inquiry.

Similar illustrations of an expanded perspective could be elaborated in every other field of social problems research: from an exclusive focus on the biological and psychological functioning of the incarcerated heroin addict, for example, to a broader concern with the social epidemiology of addiction in the urban community; or from an exclusive focus on the psychodynamics (or physiology or some other aspect of the individual functioning) of the hospitalized mental patient to the interaction of genetics, family relationships, and social class position in the genesis of schizophrenia. The movement is from description to analysis, from the study of individuals already "having" the problem to the study of conditions important in the genesis of the problem, and from an exclusive concern with the individual to a broader concern with the interaction between the individual and the larger social structure.

Conceptual Commonalities

Along with a growing breadth of perspective within each of the major fields of social problems research, and of even greater potential importance for the field, has been an increasing recognition of the apparent interconnection of social problems in their consequences and possibly in their underlying conditions. Each field of social problems research has tended to be an island unto itself, with the people in one field often not even reading the research literature in other fields. Most research attention has been focused on the specifics of some given social problem—juvenile delinquency, discrimination, mental disorder, or whatever—with relatively little attention addressed to the search for commonalities in the conditions underlying a variety of social problems. Not surprisingly, the greatest achievements of this era of research have been descriptive: For many social problems, we have come to know the phenomenon and in particular to understand its manifestations. The corresponding weaknesses of such work have been largely analytic; each problem has been seen as if it were unique, with too little attention paid to its underlying conditions or to its interrelationships with other social problems. Even when investigators in several areas of social problems research found the same variables to be involved, they often failed to notice the commonalities. To cite just one striking example: it was the students of social stratification, not the students of mental disorder or drugs or criminality, who noticed the ubiquitous importance of social class for these and other social problems.

A fundamental change in the field of social problems research has been the growing recognition that in determining the focus of research efforts, one of the most serious errors to be avoided is to confuse labels with conceptual relevance. The fact that a study is being done on alcoholics, schizophrenics, or criminals, it is now recognized, does not necessarily make it relevant to our understanding of social problems; its relevance or lack of relevance depends upon the adequacy of conceptualization of the research. Conversely, the fact that a study does not focus on any of these problem populations does not necessarily indicate that it is irrelevant to social problems research. The study may indeed be irrelevant, but it may also be broadly relevant for a range of social problems. The field of social problems research has come more and more to emphasize research that has conceptual relevance for understanding factors basic to the prevention or amelioration of social problems, rather than just studies of people already designated as having (or causing) some particular social problem.

Methodological Rigor

A review of social problems research must also note that, at least until recently, the field has been characterized by a serious lack of methodological sophistication. Some of this lack stemmed directly from the conceptual limitations noted above: an individualistic bias tended to produce studies that failed to take into account or even to control for situational and social structural factors; a parochial view of "causality" led to an overemphasis on static, descriptive studies, with insufficient comparative research, little cross-national research, little longitudinal research, and little study of institutional arrangements or of social change. Too little attention was paid to developing better indices, better instruments, better analyses of the induction and labeling processes. Much of the work on treatment and rehabilitation took for granted the institutional systems that presumably provided the treatment or rehabilitation. Where the systems (or institutions or treatment modalities) were scrutinized, the methods of evaluation tended to be thoroughly inadequate. These issues are so basic to the entire field of social problems research that we shall dwell on them in greater detail in the context of our substantive recommendations. For now, it is enough to say that the standards of the field are still very much in flux, better than they once were but with a long way to go before they catch up with the best work in the behavioral sciences generally. It must also be said, though, that the most exciting recent advances in method—multivariate analysis, estimation of reciprocal effects, methods for longitudinal analysis—are especially appropriate for many of the most important theoretical issues in social problems research. So the field might well leap forward from being the methodological backwater of the behavioral sciences to a position of leadership in methodological innovation. NIMH could help that process.

ROLE OF NIMH IN SOCIAL PROBLEMS RESEARCH

Historical Role of NIMH in Social Problems Research

The Institute's role in supporting social problems research can be traced back to its earliest days. Implicit support appeared in the National Mental Health Act of July 3, 1946 (P.L. 79-487), which provided for the establishment of NIMH as an organizational entity within the Public Health Service. The history of this legislation is significant in that both the original House and Senate bills called for creation of a National Neuropsychiatric Institute that would be concerned with research, training, and service activities related to neuropsychiatric disorders. During the hearings on these bills, Surgeon General Thomas Parran, among others, suggested that the name of the proposed Institute be changed to the National Institute of Mental Health in order to emphasize the primary concern of the Public Health Service with the prevention of mental disease. This suggestion was accepted by the Congress and led to a significant broadening of the legislative mandate.

Explicit congressional interest in social problems first appeared in 1955, in a preface to the Mental Health Study Act of 1955 (P.L. 84-82). In legislation authorizing the expenditure of funds to support a nationwide study of mental health problems by the Joint Commission on Mental Illness and Health, the Congress indicated which mental health areas required greater attention and study. Concern was expressed over the great number of mentally ill and retarded hospital patients in the country, the outmoded reliance on custodial care in mental hospitals as the chief method of dealing with mental illness, the great lag between the discovery of new knowledge in the mental health area and the practical application of such findings, and the extent to which it appeared that many emotionally disturbed children were being placed in mental hospitals without appropriate treatment facilities. At the same time, the Congress also identified a number of social problems as being of special mental health concern: alcoholism, drug addiction, juvenile delinquency, broken homes, school failures, suicide, absenteeism and job maladjustment in industry, and similar problems. The Act was passed as a Joint Resolution of Congress without a dissenting vote.

The next major legislative milestone occurred in 1963 with the Community Mental Health Centers Act (Title II of P.L. 88-164), which emphasized the growing concern of Congress with problems of alcoholism and drug addiction. In budget hearings that year the congressional committee urged that NIMH further "imaginative approaches to such difficult problems as alcoholism, delinquency, and drug addiction." The Institute's program expanded quickly in these problem areas as well as in the areas of school mental health and suicide. At the hearings of the House Appropriations Committee the next year, NIMH Director Robert H. Felix reported that NIMH had made a policy decision to fund selected research grants despite their relatively low scientific review ratings because they dealt with problems that the committee had specifically asked NIMH to address—namely alcoholism, mental retardation, juvenile delinquency, and drug addiction. By 1966, the budget of the branch that funded most social problems studies had reached a total of about $20 million.

In 1966, the Institute organized a symposium to help define its responsibility for the social problems area. A major outcome of this symposium was the recommendation that the National Institute of Mental Health focus its research activities on selected social problems. The list went beyond the congressional specifics. It included not only such explicit congressional concerns as mental retardation and crime and delinquency but also aging, minority problems, metropolitan problems, poverty, disenfranchised groups, homosexuality, marital discord, mass violence, and housing and related issues.

The mechanism recommended for bringing about a focused approach to these problem areas was that of "centers." The "center" concept was explained by NIMH Director Stanley F. Yolles in a draft memorandum for the Surgeon General as follows:

> . . . The current extramural organization of the NIMH, designed primarily on traditional vertical lines of research grants and training grants and reporting to a single Associate Director for Extramural Programs, is no longer responsive to the expanded program needs of the Institute. . . . A principal innovation will be the use within NIMH of "Centers" to insure that basic and applied research, training, demonstrations, technical assistance and consultation, scientific communication, and related activities are devoted to critical program targets in an intensified and coordinated way.

A major reorganization of NIMH then took place. Nine centers were established in 1966, although only five were "total" in that they had their own grant funds and could encompass the variety of extramural mechanisms and the range of services described by Yolles. The others were "coordinating" centers, without grant money but charged with stimulating and coordinating support activities elsewhere in the Institute. Some of the "coordinating" centers later became "total" centers, and some of the total centers later became "divisions" and finally "institutes." These myriad administrative reorganizations need not be detailed here. What is important to note is that the creation of the centers brought into explicit cognizance the Institute's concern with research in a large array of social problems, including not only mental disorders, alcoholism, and drug abuse, but also crime and delinquency, aging, urban problems, and minority mental health.

The mission of these centers includes not only the support of research aimed at increasing understanding of the nature, etiology, processes, and mechanisms of social problems, but also the dissemination, application, and utilization of such knowledge. Information is collated, evaluated, and disseminated to policymakers, agency administrators, community organizations, and the public at large for the purpose of improving social policies and practices relevant to the prevention, treatment, and amelioration of social problems. A further aim is that of enhancing the delivery of adequate services to those who need help.

Present Organization of Social Problems Research

The question is no longer whether or not NIMH has a role to play in social problems research, but how it can best play the role that it already has held for a long time. As various social problems have come into prominence, organizational entities have been created to do research on each of them. Where once a single branch funded all extramural research on social problems, eventually each problem acquired a branch, a committee, a center, or even an institute of its own. Moreover, these various entities have been established within, or assigned to, or reassigned to, a number of larger divisions, so that even before the reorganization of NIMH into ADAMHA, social problems research was being supported in several separate divisions, with no responsible person short of the Institute director himself having overall responsibility for their coordination.

To some significant degree, this "fragmentation" of the overall program of social problems research has been the price paid for coordinating within a single organizational unit all research and nonresearch activities relevant to some particular social problem. To bring all the Institute's activities with respect to crime and delinquency into one center, for example, necessarily means truncating the organizational ties between research on crime and delinquency and research on other social problems. The fragmentation also results, in part, from the deliberate decision to support some social problems research through problem-focused organizational entities (e.g., the centers); some in direct competition with disciplinary-oriented research, through the Division of Extramural Research Programs; and some intramurally. Such organization has its virtues, mainly the gain in quality that comes from a diversity of approaches. It must be recognized, though, that there are also losses entailed in such fragmentation. By treating each social problem in isolation from the others, the Institute is making it difficult for the field to detect commonalities in the antecedent conditions and consequences of the various social problems. Both substantive and administrative recommendations on these issues will be made later in this chapter.

It must also be noted that the Institute's organizational history with respect to social problems research has been marked by an extraordinary amount of flux and change. Organizational entities have sprung up with bewildering frequency. Programs have been reassigned repeatedly. The support of programs has not always been continuous with the enthusiasm attendant upon the initial birth processes. The challenge now is for the Institute to create organizational forms that will provide a continuity of effort regardless of the particular category of problem that is at the forefront of public attention at any particular time, and to do this while recognizing both the important role of science and scientists in conceptualizing social problems research and the essential fact that the ultimate goal is not just the growth of science but also the solution of societal problems.

AN ASSESSMENT OF NIMH'S PAST EFFORTS AND FUTURE POTENTIAL IN SOCIAL PROBLEMS RESEARCH

In the area of social problems, NIMH functions have included the enhancement of service delivery and dissemination of information. These significant efforts are reviewed in the chapters on research on mental health services, and on the dissemination and use of research information. Social problems research in the areas of mental disorders, alcoholism, and drug abuse will not be reviewed here, for these areas are dealt with in the chapters on mental illness and behavior disorders, alcohol abuse, and drug abuse respectively. These omissions from consideration here are not to be construed as evidence of a narrow interpretation of the total NIMH social problems mission or as an implicit statement of values or priorities. This chapter reviews other aspects of the field of social problems research pertinent to NIMH interests and attempts to provide an overview of the field as an entity.

To survey NIMH's role in social problems research, Institute activities must be examined from two distinct perspectives: from the perspective of a project-by-project review of the studies supported by the Institute, regardless of which organizational unit has supported them; and from the perspective of a program-by-program overview of the principal centers of social problems research in the Institute.

A Cross-Sectional Examination

One perspective on the role of NIMH in supporting research on social problems is afforded by a systematic examination of the research projects actually supported in 3 recent fiscal years—1968, 1970, and 1972. Again, since research on mental disorders, alcoholism, and drug abuse is reviewed in detail in other chapters, this analysis is limited to research on or directly pertinent to all other social problems. The analysis is based on initial review group summaries for extramural studies and annual reports for the few pertinent intramural studies. Altogether, 222 research projects were assessed.

A simple statistical analysis of the main objectives of these research projects shows that the principal thrust of NIMH-supported research in these social problems has been on treatment and amelioration, nearly half (46 percent) of all the studies falling into that category. A secondary emphasis has been on descriptive studies of the problems themselves (16 percent of the studies) or of their consequences (23 percent). Only a small proportion of NIMH-supported research has been addressed to studies of causes and underlying conditions (7 percent) or to theoretical or methodological studies (8 percent). The main foci of the NIMH effort in recent years, then, have been on amelioration and on description. This emphasis is, of course, consistent with the needs of the field and prerequisite to rigorous research.

Further analysis of the NIMH-supported research on amelioration shows that much of it has been based, explicitly or implicitly, on the belief that the problems are essentially individual and psychological; the remedy is to be sought in some form of therapy for the affected individuals. There has been little real experimentation, and the evaluations of remedial programs have been relatively rare and, when undertaken, generally have been rather limited in focus and often less than fully objective in method. Moreover, where systematic evaluation has been undertaken, the evaluators have too often been the program initiators themselves, and only infrequently have they included the clients or affected populations.

The descriptive research that NIMH has supported on the phenomenology of the various social problems and on their consequences has been impressive for its richness. But it is also true that this research has been largely focused on the full-blown manifestations of the particular social problems, mainly on their psychological consequences, with little attention paid to the social contexts in which they occur and within which society attempts to deal with them.

Even the research on etiological and underlying conditions has been rather limited in focus—little of it dealing with the interaction of biological, psychological, and social conditions, most of it limited to only one level of analysis, the psychological. The social has been largely ignored. And it is the rare study that is concerned with identifying commonalities in the conditions underlying a range of social problems.

In short, NIMH-supported research in social problems differs from the field generally only insofar as it still retains a bias in favor of studying the individual and emphasizes treatment and amelioration. There is little that marks NIMH-supported research as being substantively distinctive or at the leading edge or in the vanguard of social problems research. The suggestion will later be made that, worthwhile as it may be for the Institute to support the methodologically best of the studies that are submitted to it, there is also a useful role for the Institute to play as a proponent and even initiator of more broadly conceptualized research in this area.

Examples of Core Ongoing Programs

A distinctly different perspective on NIMH's past record and future potential in social problems research is afforded by a close inspection of its core programs. Since the Institute's specialized programs on mental disorder, alcohol, and drugs are discussed in other chapters, our attention is confined here to programs focused on other social problems or pertinent to social problems in general. These programs have been small in scale, undersupported in staff, funds, and in some cases administration, but they have nevertheless had some important accomplishments. Judged against the field of social problems research as a whole, or even against the Institute's own programs in other research areas, these programs have been miniscule. Their importance lies in their demonstration that where the Institute has tried to develop even modest programs of thoughtfully planned research in areas of direct pertinence to social problems, it has succeeded. Moreover, there are several successful "models" of NIMH endeavor in social problems research, each of which could well serve as a basis for future development.

One such model is the problem-oriented center, devoted to a broadly based program of intramural and extramural research and to the application of research results to some particular social problem or cluster of problems. These centers are relatively new, having their origins in the 1966 reorganization of the Institute, and none of them has been fully staffed or adequately funded. None has yet been able to mount its intended program of intramural research. None has as yet been able to devote the staff time necessary to fully formulate its program. Yet they have taken hold, and if one only reads through the summaries of social problems research projects supported by the Institute, one can easily differentiate the areas in which NIMH has active centers from those in which it does not: in the former, the projects have enough in common that one can discern organized, coherent programs; in the latter, though the individual projects are often impressive, their sum total is more scattershot.

Among the best organized of the centers are those concerned with crime and delinquency, urban problems, and minorities. Since the Center for Studies of Crime and Delinquency is furthest advanced in formulating and instituting its program, it can serve as a prototype.

Center for Studies of Crime and Delinquency

This center's program is marked by comprehensiveness, in two senses. It is comprehensive in its explicit recognition that a sensible program of research in this area has to be concerned not only with basic research on the biology, psychology, and sociology of aggression, but also with methodological research on indices of crime and criminal behavior, with research on the social structural conditions conducive to criminality, on the interrelationship of biological, psychological, and social conditions in the genesis of various types of criminal behavior, on the functioning of the criminal justice system, and on the effectiveness of prisons and of treatment and rehabilitation systems. It is also comprehensive in its explicit recognition that research and research utilization must be coordinated, and that part of the responsibility for this coordination rests with those who do research and those who support it. Although still lacking an intramural program, the center provides a model of the usefulness of the Institute's taking the initiative in formulating and sponsoring a coherent program of research and research-related activities with respect to an important social problem.

Illustrations of research into biological, social, and psychological factors associated with crime and delinquency are briefly summarized:

- Individuals who suffer from postencephalitic disorders or tumors located in the limbic system sometimes manifest increased sexual, aggressive, or psychopathic types of behavior. However, the incidence of specific brain disorders among individuals apprehended for crimes associated with sexual, aggressive, or psychopathic behaviors is quite small.

- Abnormal electroencephalographic (EEG) findings continue to be reported among high proportions of violent criminals, especially those showing patterns of recurrent violence in addition to mental illness. Deviant EEG patterns appear to correlate with erratic or poorly controlled behaviors in general rather than with criminal behaviors in particular.

- Genetic contributions to psychopathic and "psychopathic spectrum" disorders have been inferred from the study of children of psychopathic parents (twins and adoptees) raised apart from their biological parents.

- While early reports of a strong association between the presence of an XYY chromosome in males (instead of the normal XY) and aggressive or violent behavior have been somewhat modified by subsequent research, studies continue to report that the incidence of XYY individuals within mentally disordered offender populations is 20 times greater than would be expected by chance. The prevalence of this chromosome anomaly is, however, quite low.

- Gang delinquency appears to be associated with the opportunity for such acts, and the existence of mores that encourage delinquent acts as a means of maintaining status within the group.

- In urban slums, where the proportion of delinquent youth is several times the national average, research found that the parents and even the delinquents frequently had had an initially strong desire to abide by middle-class family and moral values but became "demoralized" after repeated frustration by their environmental circumstances.

- Delinquency is related to both poor socialization and poor social adaptation independent of social class. Patterns of impaired social functions are clearly evident as early as the age of 8. This suggests that early intervention with such high risk groups may be appropriate.

- Delinquent and criminal acts far exceed those that actually come to the attention of the authorities. Almost 90 percent of the young people interviewed in a self-report study of delinquent behavior confided that they had committed an act for which they could have been brought before a juvenile court. However, fewer than 3 percent of the acts reported were detected by the police and fewer than 1 percent of these offenses were recorded as juvenile delinquency.

- A study based on a cohort of 10,000 boys found that 46 percent of the youngsters committing their first offense had no further involvement with the law, while an additional 35 percent of these subjects appeared to stop engaging in law-violating behavior following their second offense. Six percent of the sample had five or more police contacts. This group also accounted for a disproportionate amount of serious crime. Thus, while delinquent acts are committed, at one time or another, by many youths, repeated and serious delinquent acts are traceable to but a small group.

- Aggressive delinquent acts appear to be attributable to modeling of such behaviors by salient individuals and exposure to poor child-training and socialization practices.

- Similar emphasis on maintaining appearances was found in families at both ends of the socioeconomic scale. Upper, middle-class, and lower socioeconomic class parents of sociopathic children often were unaware of their children's activities and behavior. When they became informed, they evidenced more concern with appearances than with ethical or social values.

- An important element of deviance appears to be found not in the "psychopathology" of the individual but rather in his accepting an antisocial role and transforming his social identity in accordance with this social role.

Research on the treatment of delinquents is exemplified by the following studies:

- In terms of both parole success rates and before-and-after results on psychological tests, community treatment not only was more effective than traditional institutional programs for youths who would otherwise have been committed to correctional facilities, but it also provided a considerable savings for the State in construction and maintenance costs of institutional facilities for juvenile offenders. Of special importance to the community was the finding that parole agents, through intensive contact and surveillance, could assure citizen protection.

- Achievement Place, a home for delinquent and predelinquent boys that utilizes principles of behavior modification, has demonstrated that such treatment is a viable alternative to usual institutionalization. Based on the success of Achievement Place, 45 homes modeled after it were scheduled to begin operating throughout the country in 1974, supported largely by State and local funds.

Mental Health Study Center

A second model of NIMH-supported research into social problems is provided by the Mental Health Study Center. Many lessons can be learned from the long history of this center, not the least of which is that it is wasteful to move a research group from division to division and to change its assigned mission repeatedly over the years. Yet, despite the organizational buffeting that this center has endured, it has proved the usefulness of having a multiproblem research center located in the field, away from the main geographic locus of the Institute, and responsive to the needs of the local community in which it is housed and with whose problems it is concerned.

The Mental Health Study Center has been characterized by its receptivity to community needs and concerns and by the realism of its problem-definition. One illustrative series of studies focused on achievement values:

- A study of the lifestyles of lower-class black men found that much of their behavior reflects a defensive compensation for the repeated failures and rejections they have experienced in their attempts to achieve the goals and values of the larger society.

- Dropping out of school was found to be only the end point of a long-developing process extending for many dropouts back to their first school experiences. Factors of school performance and school experiences distinguish dropouts from graduates more than social background. As a consequence of such studies, three out of four high school dropouts may be identified as early as the third grade.

- A study of the social and personal characteristics associated with running away indicated that only a portion of the runaways—all adolescents—reflected psychopathology, delinquency, or family instability. Runaway behavior appeared to be an effort to cope with adolescent stresses.

- Peer group standards and pressures, other research found, strongly determine the social behavior of lower-class black adolescents. Such groups exert influence by setting standards for membership and conditions for achieving status within the group. These socializing experiences affect subsequent patterns of adaptation and the development of adult roles.

- The treatment of adolescent delinquent boys by a program that included job placement, remedial education, and psychotherapy achieved success even with boys labeled "unreachable." A 10-year followup study showed that the treated group maintained their social adjustment to a far higher degree than the untreated control group.

These and other studies illustrate the utility of a research model that is not restricted to a single social problem or to one discipline but rather emphasizes a multidimensional concern with social problems as they emerge, as they are experienced, and as they are dealt with by some local community. The work of the Mental Health Study Center is further described in the chapter on services research.

Laboratory of Socio-environmental Studies

A third model for useful NIMH support of social problems research is exemplified by the Laboratory of Socio-environmental Studies, in the Intramural Research Program. Although relatively little research on social problems is done in this program, this little is enough to demonstrate that the working conditions for science so well-established in the program are as conducive to good research on social problems as they are to good research on, say, biochemistry.

The laboratory for more than 20 years has done fundamental research on the processes by which social structure and culture affect personality development and behavior. Only incidentally has this research been directed to social problems, per se, but even so, much of the laboratory's work has been pertinent. Members of the laboratory have done a substantial amount of research on mental disorder, a few studies of other social problems, and some intensive explorations of issues fundamental to the study of social problems.

Mental Disorder

Particularly in the 1950's and early 1960's, studies of mental disorder constituted a major focus of the laboratory's activities. Some of the most important studies have been:

- A pioneer study of the processes by which mental illness is recognized and dealt with by the family of a schizophrenic and by outside agencies, and the processes by which the family copes with mental illness in one of its members. The study is notable for its description of the "normalization" process by which family members and public officials regard even bizarre psychotic symptoms as somehow situationally explainable and thereby normal.

- An investigation of social factors in the development of schizophrenia, which showed that social isolation is only a concomitant, not a causal factor, in schizophrenia, and which also showed that the family relationships of schizophrenics are different from those of normal middle-class families but similar to those of normal working class families.

- Three major studies of the organization and functioning of the mental hospital, all based on research at St. Elizabeths Hospital:

  A participant-observation study of the hospital, notable for its portrayal of the mental hospital as a "total institution," similar to many other types of institutions that manage people's lives on a 24-hour-a-day basis.

  A survey of nursing personnel, which isolated social structural factors crucial to nurses' orientation to and treatment of patients.

  A systematic examination of patient case records from before and after the advent of drug therapy, which showed that in the early days of drug therapy, before its widespread use, patients who did not get drugs benefited as much as those who did—the major effect of the drugs being to change the social atmosphere of the hospital.

- A continuing series of experimental studies of the social behavior of chronic schizophrenic patients, documenting that schizophrenic patients are singularly fearful of interpersonal relationships, and that many physiological and psychological findings about schizophrenia can be traced to this aversion to interpersonal processes, including those interpersonal processes inherent in the interview situation.

Other Social Problems

There have been only a few studies of social problems other than mental disorder, the major ones being:

- A study of the effects of maternal employment, which showed no difference in quality of child care between working and nonworking mothers—but a distinct deficit in quality of maternal care by nonworking mothers who would rather hold a job outside the home.

- A cross-disciplinary study of the aging process in normal men, conducted by investigators in several intramural laboratories, including an analysis of social psychological processes.

- Experimental studies of cheating and conscience development and of how parental pressures for achievement contribute to children's cheating.

- A field-experimental study of the effects of racial integration on stereotyping and interpersonal process.

These studies each have considerable substantive interest and clearly are pertinent to one or another concrete social problem. It could hardly be claimed, though, that they add up to a coherent program of research on social problems.

Fundamental Issues Underlying the Study of Social Problems

Many, perhaps most, of the laboratory's studies have long-term theoretical relevance for understanding social problems, even those studies that were not explicitly designed for this purpose. Research on social determinants of children's conceptions of self, for example, is broadly relevant to any formulation of deviant behavior; research on the inculcation of prosocial behavior in young children is basic to designing desirable alternatives to social processes that ordinarily have antisocial outcomes. Similarly, most of the laboratory's other research on personality development has long-term applicability to the prevention or amelioration of social problems.

One series of studies that is particularly pertinent to social problems, because it focuses directly on the psychological impact of larger social structure, is the research on the psychological effects of social class position. Begun over 20 years ago in research designed to untangle the inter-relationships among social class, family process, and schizophrenia, these studies have gone on to a systematic exploration of the reasons why social class affects not only the incidence and prevalence of schizophrenia but also psychological functioning in general. The research has been noteworthy for its efforts to go beyond establishing correlations between class and psychological functioning, to examine the systematic differences in life conditions that account for these correlations. In particular, the research—more fully described in the chapter on the sociocultural processes underlying behavior—has delineated class differences in occupational conditions that play an important part in molding class differences in conceptions of reality—in self conception, social orientation, and even in intellectual functioning.

These studies illustrate a type of research, fundamental to the study of social problems, that the Intramural Research Program is admirably equipped to undertake. They also illustrate how a concern with one social problem, in this case schizophrenia, can lead to research of basic interest to a much larger range of social problems. If the record to date is a valid indicator of future potential, the Intramural Research Program is particularly well-suited to fundamental research on processes relevant to social problems in general, most particularly to research requiring a long time-span of concentrated activity. The forte of IRP research on social problems would seem to be conceptually relevant basic research.

OVERVIEW OF NIMH PROGRAMS

Except in the fields of mental disorder, alcoholism, and drug abuse, NIMH has not been a dominant or even a major force in social problems research. In other social problems areas, NIMH has from time to time supported significant work, but it has not maintained sizable programs over long enough periods of time to have been of major importance in shaping the fields. The Institute has done enough, though, to demonstrate its capacity to support and conduct fundamental work in such diverse fields as crime and delinquency, urban problems, discrimination, and poverty. And it has supported a few major studies of considerable conceptual relevance for the field of social problems research as a whole.

For NIMH to play a constructive role in its future support of social problems research, it cannot simply rely on choosing the best applications submitted to it but must help improve the level and scope of conceptualization of research in this field.

RECOMMENDATIONS FOR RESEARCH IN SOCIAL PROBLEMS

In keeping with the perspective of this chapter, no attempt has been made to provide a set of specific research priorities either among or within traditionally defined social problem areas. Instead, the chapter will outline some basic strategies that should be taken into account in planning any research in the field. These recommendations are based on the following premises:

- That there are several serious deficits in most current research on social problems: an underemphasis on underlying and predisposing conditions, particularly social conditions; a lack of attention to the probability of social structural commonalities in the causes and consequences of social problems; an underemphasis on the interplay of social-structural, psychological, and biological factors; an underemphasis on processes of change; and a more than occasional lack of objectivity and rigor in the evaluation of the effectiveness of ameliorative programs.

- That social problems are not merely the expression of individual psychopathology. The definition of what constitutes a social problem is fundamentally social. The problem behavior stems from the interplay of social, psychological, and biological conditions.

- That many social problems are interrelated and that what we learn about one problem may have important implications for others.

- That both research on the underlying causes of social problems and research on amelioration of the consequences of such problems are necessary. It is imperative, however, that any project of either type be clear in its intent and rigorous in its methods.

- That NIMH, in its role as a specialized research institution, is better equipped to sponsor and conduct some types of research than others. NIMH has no expertise, for example, in the economics of poverty; but the Institute is well-equipped to undertake research whose goal, either proximately or as a longer term objective, is to understand the impact of poverty as it affects psychological functioning. The Institute also should coordinate this work with that of other agencies that do focus on the economics of poverty.

An Appropriate Present Role for NIMH in Social Problems Research

Given the assumption of interrelatedness of social problems in both their causes and their consequences, it would be foolhardy to draw up a list of problems that fall within the Institute's proper purview and another list of social problems that fall outside the Institute's appropriate area of concern. But it is nevertheless possible to delineate the focus of the Institute's proper efforts. Two criteria seem pertinent.

First, the Institute's focus, in line with its legislative history and its very name, should be on problems that have major psychic or behavioral implications. Thus, bad housing per se would not be a proper focus of Institute interest, though bad housing could certainly be assessed as a possible factor associated with the production of juvenile delinquency or race riots or psychological impairment. It must be emphasized that we are defining the Institute's focus in social problems research in terms of the dependent variable's being psychic or behavioral. This says nothing about the independent variables, which may be biological, psychological, social, or any combination thereof.

Second, the Institute should build on its strengths and not try to be expert in everything. NIMH has the capacity at present—and even more in potential—for supporting and conducting a broad spectrum of research in the biological, psychological, and some of the social sciences, notably sociology and social psychology. But broad though that spectrum may be, it does not include numerous other fields better represented in other agencies of Government—architecture, economics, law, and industrial medicine, to name just a few. We do not argue that these fields are irrelevant to social problems research; quite the contrary. But we do argue that, as of late 1973, it would be better for the Institute to focus its social problems research on the problems and approaches where NIMH is best equipped to make a distinctive contribution.

It is pertinent to add that since social problems are so interrelated, the Institute's mandate for research on social problems should be significantly broader than its mandate for operating programs. As a consequence, the NIMH research could advance understanding of social problems and thereby contribute to fields in which other governmental agencies appear to have primary operating responsibilities.

Substantive Recommendations

These considerations lead to the recommendation that NIMH should emphasize the following eight approaches in its support of social problems research. Each represents a distinct way of approaching some major aspect of the study of social problems, rather than a specific project or even program of studies.

Develop Better Measures of Social Problems

This first recommendation is elementary but nonetheless needs reiteration. Fairly complete, up-to-date, reliable, and accurate data are essential if we are to have even a reasonably precise accounting of the nature and extent of the problems to be addressed and their dimensions. The need is particularly acute for studies of change, because inadequate baseline data preclude (or at least make very difficult) the proper testing of policy and program effectiveness and the weighing of policy alternatives.

For example, given the present state of our crime statistics, we are usually uncertain as to whether changes in crime rates represent changes in people's behavior, changes in the definition of crime, changes in the extent to which criminal behavior is being reported, changes in the apprehension of criminals, or changes in official recording practices of law enforcement and related agencies. Examples could as well be given in virtually every other field of social problems research: There is a great need for accurate epidemiological information with respect to mental disorder, alcoholism, and drug abuse; our information on the extent of racial discrimination, and on changes in patterns of discrimination and nondiscrimination is far from adequate; the list could be extended indefinitely.

Research is also needed to devise better measures of, and to improve the collection of data on, indicators of social strain; and studies are needed to devise new and more refined measures to identify and locate forces that interfere with the optimal functioning of our social systems. Moreover, while many statistical studies dealing with social problems are available, the data need to be so compiled and analyzed as to facilitate the assessment of the scale, the costs, and perhaps even of some of the determining factors of societal dysfunctioning.

Basic to all the above recommendations is the overriding need for methodological research. The inadequacies in existing data on social problems result not from any reluctance of the appropriate governmental agencies to collect such data, but from very substantial difficulties in developing reliable and valid indices. Such methodological research deserves far greater support than it has heretofore been given.

Analyze the Assumptions Underlying Proposals for Dealing With Social Problems

Proposals for the prevention or the amelioration of social problems necessarily make assumptions about the likely outcomes of the proposed remedies or preventive measures. For example, proposals for welfare reform, income maintenance, and negative income taxes necessarily make assumptions about the motivations of the target populations and how these motivations might be affected by the proposed plans. Most of these proposals are based on untested assumptions; only recently have rigorously designed experiments been conducted to determine what their consequences actually are. Other proposals extrapolate from research conducted on one segment of the population to other, often dissimilar, segments of the population to whom the original research might or might not apply. For example, Moynihan's famous report on the black family assumes that findings of the psychological consequences of father-absence in middle-class white families are equally applicable to lower-class black families.

One of the most important and useful aspects of research on social problems is to make explicit the assumptions underlying current and proposed social policies and to test these assumptions empirically. In the case of Moynihan's recommendations, for example, the pertinent research would be comparative studies of how the patterns of family relationship found in underprivileged segments of the society actually affect the psychological development of children in these segments of the society. It would also be useful to study systematically how family patterns are themselves affected by other social institutions. Moynihan himself discussed the ways that the occupational structure affects family patterns, an obviously important but little explored area of social problems research.

On the most fundamental level, definitions of what constitutes a "social problem" are themselves based on largely untested assumptions. A restricted definition of the nature and source of the problem may lead to self-defeating definitions of what can be done to prevent or ameliorate that problem. It is important, therefore, to conduct historical research on the "natural history of social problems," in order to determine how social phenomena come to be defined as social problems and how such definitions affect society's efforts to deal with these phenomena.

Study the Processes by Which Social Structural Variables Have Their Psychological Impact

Studies of the conditions underlying some particular social problem, whether it be schizophrenia, crime, or alcoholism, ordinarily focus on variables believed to play some critical role in the production of that problem. Such research tends to emphasize what is unique to that problem and to obscure that which may be common to a range of problems. This approach results in constricted conceptualizations of the problems and may overlook potent opportunities for social intervention. It may even focus attention on marginally differentiating variables rather than on those that have widespread effects.

The variables that are broadly conducive to a number of social problems are likely to be those embedded in the structure of the society as a whole—variables such as social class, race, gender, ethnic background, religion, and urbanicity. For example, many of the social problems of greatest concern to the Institute occur disproportionately among lower-class segments of the society; this is true, in particular, of schizophrenia, heroin addiction, and many types of criminal behavior. This finding strongly suggests the need for research designed to trace and to understand the social psychological concomitants of social class position. But although studies have documented the relationship between social class and many aspects of human behavior in this and other urban, industrial societies, relatively few have gone beyond the correlational level to investigate why social class has widespread psychological and behavioral ramifications. And there has been little research addressed to deciphering the psychological concomitants of other major facets of social structure, such as those named.

It is recommended that greater emphasis be given to research on the psychological and behavioral concomitants of social structure. It is particularly recommended that greater emphasis be given to research addressed to unraveling the processes by which social position has its psychological effects. This approach focuses attention on variables whose importance for understanding a spectrum of social problems may be much greater than appears in investigations concerned with only one such problem. It also gives some basis for considering possible alternative outcomes of varying constellations of factors, e.g., that similar social conditions may lead to differing behavioral outcomes in varying situational contexts or in different subcultures. It provides a rational basis for assessing the social costs and benefits of proposals for prevention and amelioration of social problems. That is, it enables one to determine what price must be paid for reducing some social problems and what gains and losses are potentially available if existing social arrangements are changed. Finally, the study of social structural variables offers possibilities for purposive social change on a larger and potentially more efficient scale than does the study of variables rooted in individual functioning.

298

Analyze the Processes of Social and Individual Change

Along with, and complementary to, the study of social structure there should be greater emphasis on processes of change, both social change and individual life-cycle change. The two types of change should be distinguished, for although both are important, they imply substantially different types of research:

1. Studies of social and cultural change. Social change refers to changes in the organization of society or its component institutions that affect the life conditions of large groups of people, for example, the impact of racial desegregation, natural disasters, adoption of new personnel policies, or modification of major social values. Social change implies that major transitions are taking place, not simply in the life cycles of individuals, but in existing social arrangements. To conduct research on social change requires the repeated—or preferably, continuing—observation of some institution, locale, or situation during periods of major transition.

    Studies of social and cultural change may provide a useful corrective to any assumption that the structural arrangements of the moment are immutable. (Prejudice and discrimination, for example, are much more volatile phenomena than one would think from studying stable situations.) The study of social change also brings research to bear on the natural history of social problems. Moreover, studying social change offers unique opportunities to learn of possibilities for social intervention. Finally, studying social change may also offer greater opportunity for gaining insight into the processes by which social structure affects psychological functioning than does cross-sectional research. As structure changes, one can see consequent, not simply correlative, changes in people's values and behavior.

    It would also be of great value to focus more research attention on the factors that facilitate and inhibit social change. Particularly in programs designed to remedy social problems, often what is most lacking is not knowledge of what is needed but knowledge about institutional, bureaucratic, and sociopolitical aims and structure that may obstruct the implementation of what is needed. Such obstacles have often stood in the way of change despite the availability of considerable information clearly pointing to the need for institutional changes. For example, despite our longstanding knowledge about the deleterious effects of long-term institutionalization of infants and small children we continue to send many children to these public facilities.

2. Studies of change in the life circumstances of individuals. By this is meant "longitudinal research," that is, repeated study of the same individuals over time, but with this difference in emphasis: the intent is not so much to study the natural development of individuals as to assess the psychological consequences of the normal progression of changing circumstances that occur in people's lives—for example, changes in occupational conditions that occur in the course of people's careers. Such research need not be restricted to any particular phase of the life cycle. Instead, the strategy of such research would be to choose times of strategic importance for the changes being studied.

In the example of occupational conditions, one would want repeated measurements of job conditions and of psychological functioning at different stages of people's careers.

There are two primary reasons for doing such longitudinal research. First, the direction of causality in the relationships between social conditions and individual functioning cannot be definitively determined without such repeated measurements. Moreover, and more importantly, repeated measurements provide an essential basis for studying the processes by which social conditions affect psychological functioning.

Emphasize Studies of the Interaction of Social, Psychological, and Biological Conditions

Most research on the causes of one or another social problem conceptualizes the interpretive task from the perspective of one academic discipline—for example, studies of the genetics of schizophrenia, the sociology of juvenile delinquency, or the psychology of prejudice. Such research overlooks the possibility that there may be important interconnections among variables ordinarily thought to be the province of different academic disciplines. Research into stress is a good example, for it spans an array of disciplines. Sociologists may focus on the conflicts and frustrations resulting from the demands of social roles; clinical psychologists on how individuals defend themselves against potentially stressful experiences; psychiatrists on the relationship between these experiences and the presence of physical ailments for which no organic basis is evident; physiologists on the alteration of cells; chemists and endocrinologists on changes in the production of steroids. Disciplinary boundaries have tended to isolate different aspects of stress and have obscured their dynamic interconnectedness in the total functioning of people in society.

Some argue that the findings of the pertinent disciplines can be pieced together after the fact; this assumes that the effects of social, psychological, and biological variables are additive. However, it is likely that many social problems arise out of the joint occurrence, the interaction, of social, psychological, and biological conditions. Some or all of these conditions might not be important except in the presence of the others. By ignoring these interactions, one may fail to discover important causal conditions that come into play only when certain other conditions are jointly present. Moreover, in ignoring these interactions, the power of many research studies is needlessly limited, because investigators fail to see that varying combinations of the same basic conditions may give rise to a variety of outcomes, some of them clearly social problems and some, perhaps, socially valuable.

By way of illustration, present research evidence suggests that both genetics and social class are involved in schizophrenia, and that neither genetics alone nor the experiences attendant on social class position are able to provide a sufficient explanation of this disorder. Some interaction of genetics, class, and undoubtedly other variables appear to be involved in the etiology of schizophrenia. One will not learn if there are particular constellations of variables that produce schizophrenia by studying any of

300

the variables in isolation from the others. Nor will one learn if different constellations of these and other variables produce different behavioral outcomes. In the absence of a genetic predisposition for schizophrenia, would the pertinent social conditions lead instead to heroin addiction, criminality, suicide, or compensatory efforts at achievement or creativity?

What is needed is an approach that emphasizes the interaction of social, psychological, and biological variables, together with the examination of alternative possible behavioral outcomes of differing constellations of these variables.

Encourage Cross-National Research

Whatever research we do within the United States—whether it be on the conditions underlying social problems, on amelioration, on change, or on social experimentation—conclusions are necessarily limited to the social and cultural conditions applicable in the United States. For many purposes, this limitation is not serious. But for many of the central issues of social problems research the limitation may be crucial: The very definition of what constitutes a social problem is often greatly affected by social and cultural conditions; the conditions underlying a given social problem may have different consequences in different social and cultural contexts; and the possibilities for prevention and amelioration may be different in different cultures and different social and economic systems. For all these reasons, well-designed cross-national comparative studies can be invaluable in social problems research.

Insofar as possible, cross-national studies should be truly comparative, with parallel methodology for studies conducted in the United States and in one or more other countries. Obviously, this cannot always be done: some phenomena that shed much light on social problems can only be studied here, and some only elsewhere. Sometimes one wants to study a problem in another country precisely because that country's social conditions or culture are in pivotal respects dissimilar to our own. But for most problems, the maximum research value comes from carefully selecting another country or countries that are similar to ours in some important respects and different in other important respects, and using methods of research that are as parallel as possible. For example, in interpreting U.S. studies of the effects of social stratification on psychological functioning, it is impossible to determine which effects are the generic results of social stratification and which are the particular results of how the stratification system functions in the particular economic circumstances, historical traditions, and culture of the United States. For properly ascribing the effects, it is necessary to study the relationships between social stratification and psychological functioning in one or more societies with similar stratification systems but different cultural, economic, and/or historical circumstances. Even one such study, properly executed in a well-chosen society, can be immensely informative.

Study Institutional Constraints on the Utilization of Research

Much of the research that has been done on the amelioration of social problems has neglected to develop an understanding of the ways in which current organizations and institutions fail to remedy problems or neglect the study of the commonalities in their failures. Institutional constraints on the utilization of research knowledge in service programs are clearly in need of investigation, as are strategies for institutional changes that are carried out—not so much from the perspective of the managers as from the perspective of such relatively powerless participants in the system as patients and prisoners.

It is important to determine what common issues emerge in different institutions as they attempt to develop effective mixes of treatments, treaters, and treatees in designing programs; to explore the areas of overlap between different systems, such as criminal justice and welfare; and to determine their implications for clients as well as for administrators. Research is particularly needed on models to describe the operation of social systems; on the identification of critical decisionmaking points in different service systems, and the contingencies of effective-ineffective action at those points; on the selection of intervention points; on models of effective planning and evaluation; on the issues involved in using internal or external structures for system monitoring; on conflicts in the perspectives of different interest groups; and on the organization and use of power and authority in treatment institutions.

Build Experimentation Into Operating Programs

The definitive way to test assumptions about the nature and alleviation of social problems is to put them to experimental test. NIMH's potential role in this type of research may be more limited than in those already discussed, for many operating programs fall outside the Institute's province. Nevertheless, there is much the Institute can do in service of its own programs and those of other operating agencies. The basic considerations in designing and supporting experimental research on prevention and amelioration of social problems include the following:

1. There should be rigorous evaluation of programs. In particular, differential evaluations should be made to determine which procedures work well and which less well, in whose hands, and for which segments of the population. This is in contrast to global evaluations of whether or not some complex program is generally successful or unsuccessful.

2. Social experimentation should be an integral part of the design of new programs. For example, it was unfortunate that the comprehensive community mental health centers program was not designed as an experiment, systematically trying out a variety of staff arrangements and programs, for varying segments of the population.

3. Efforts should be made to look for commonalities in the operation of diverse social programs, so that what is learned about the reasons for success or failure in programs dealing with one social problem may be carried over to programs dealing with other social problems. Institutions have much in common, and the comparative study of their operations has much to teach us.

4. Efforts should be made to determine how programs in one sector of the society affect problems in other sectors—for example, how programs for dealing with truancy (the educational system) ultimately affect the juvenile and criminal justice system.

5. Greater attention should be given to the development of ameliorative techniques aimed at larger social units, e.g., community organizations and institutions. There should be corresponding efforts to develop techniques for evaluating the impact of such interventions.

RECOMMENDATIONS FOR ORGANIZING SOCIAL PROBLEMS RESEARCH

To implement the substantive priorities recommended above, the following organizational recommendations are proposed:

Adapt Organizational Devices for Broadening Representation of Sectors of Society that Contribute to Formulating the Institute's Research Programs on Social Problems.

The definition of what constitutes a social problem is an essential part of social problems research and is influenced by people's values, social position, power, and interests. Therefore:

1. Ad hoc consultants and conferees should be recruited to broaden the base of those who define and give urgency to social problems research and have program responsibility. These consultants should include people from groups directly and indirectly affected by social problems, as well as from the academic and political sectors of society.

2. Review committees that consider the funding of social problems research should include representatives of the population groups that are the subject of, or are affected by, such research. Theoretical and methodological issues should still be reviewed primarily by the representatives of the research community, while representatives of the affected population groups should focus their attention on the meaning of the research for, and impact upon, the population under investigation.

3. To make the most effective use of social problems research, it is necessary to strengthen ties with policymaking sectors of Government. The Institute should be responsive to the research needs of those who must make policy decisions.

Support Coordinated Research Efforts Across Existing Social Problems Research Organizations

Several organizational units within NIMH are now concerned with research on discrete areas of social problems. Such organizations include the National Institute on Alcohol Abuse and Alcoholism, the National Institute on Drug Abuse, virtually all parts of the Division of Special Mental Health Programs, and segments of the Division of Mental Health Services and the Division of Extramural Research Programs. The social problems research of the Intramural Research Program has ranged over target populations and social processes. These geographically and administratively separate units appear to function largely in isolation from one another, rarely coordinating their research activities. There should be explicit recognition of the need for a unified program of support for social problems research. While the advantages of current focused indepth research on specific social problems is recognized, attention is now called to the potential usefulness of coordinating research efforts across currently existing organizational boundaries. Not only would this provide the opportunity for collating and integrating research information that would be useful both in specific research areas and in collaborative efforts, but, of perhaps greater importance, research coordinated across organizations would provide an opportunity to test the hypothesis that a variety of social problems have common antecedents and common consequences. As suggested earlier, the present approach to social problems research may obscure the identification of commonalities which could be important for social action and policymaking related to prevention and treatment. To this end, it is proposed that:

1. Insofar as possible, the hierarchical structure of the Institute be arranged so that all chiefs and directors of organizational entities dealing with social problems research report to the same higher official(s). This official should have the duty to see that these programs are mutually reinforcing.

2. Each organizational unit responsible for research on any social problem be "taxed" a proportion of its resources, say 10 percent of its personnel budget. This tithe would be used to support intra- and extramural research on the interrelationships among social problems and on the common conditions underlying social problems. Such research could utilize personnel from any intra- or extramural program of the Institute, and a large proportion of this research should be interdisciplinary.

3. The Institute create seminar programs and information exchanges to ensure that all organizational entities dealing with social problems research are kept aware of the others' programs and findings.

4. An ad hoc group be created to review the form in which research information is currently stored in the Institute's computer system. This group, which should represent research workers, program planners, and administrators, as well as computer experts, should have the responsibility for devising a system that facilitates information retrieval in a form that will reveal the commonalities of research into various social problems.

Increase Utilization of Intramural Research Capabilities

The Institute has underutilized the possibilities for intramural research in the field of social problems. Whatever the reasons, the Institute's failure to develop a substantial program of intramural research in the field of social problems is a great loss, for much needed research can be done effectively through intramural programs, and some of it (e.g., longitudinal research) probably can be done more effectively through an intramural investigation than through any other mechanism of research support.

In principle, there are three ways of organizing intramural research in the Institute: all intramural research can be placed in a single administrative entity that has no responsibilities other than the conduct of such research; each operating division can have its own intramural component, with the Institute having no organizationally separate division or divisions of intramural research; or there can be a mixed mode, with a relatively large, organizationally separate intramural research program and smaller intramural programs in whichever other divisions need them. At present, the Institute comes closest to the first model of a single, organizationally separate intramural research program, although there is a small amount of intramural research done elsewhere. To facilitate intramural research in the field of social problems, it would be desirable to move closer to the third model. Specifically, it is recommended that:

1. The present Mental Health Intramural Research Program be maintained, rather than broken up and dispersed to operating divisions. There are important organizational advantages to separating intramural and extramural functions. Experience has shown that when the conduct of intramural research and the administration of extramural research are carried out by the same organizational units, administrative duties leave little time for research. Furthermore, most scientists are not equally qualified for or interested in both types of activity. A third advantage—perhaps the most important—to keeping intramural and extramural functions separate is that the administrative requirements and program leadership for the two types of research activities are so different that it is administratively wise to handle them separately.

2. Smaller intramural research components be established (or where already established, continued and supported) in other divisions of the Institute as well. These units can take advantage of opportunities not readily available in the centralized Intramural Research Program, such as the opportunity to conduct community-based research, as now exemplified by the Mental Health Study Center. These research units can also serve as a mechanism for problem-oriented centers and other parts of the Institute to conduct research focused on their special interests.

   But if intramural research is to prosper outside of the Intramural Research Program, its practitioners must be partially insulated from the administrative pressures of their divisions, perhaps by organizing intramural research activities as separate organizational components of the appropriate centers or divisions.

   The existence of a strong Intramural Research Program offers a safeguard to research workers in other parts of the Institute, for it establishes standards and conditions of work appropriate to the conduct of research. These should apply to all intramural research.

3. Efforts be made to "bridge the gap" between the Intramural Research Program and other parts of the Institute.

   The major disadvantage of a separately organized Intramural Research Program is that intramural and extramural scientists who share similar research interests are kept organizationally separate. This is disadvantageous to the scientists, for intellectual gains are more likely to come from individuals who share substantive interests than from people working in distant research areas. It is also disadvantageous to the overall research program, for it means that the intramural and extramural scientists are not as mutually informed as they might be, and are not as able to utilize each other's talents and resources. To overcome these problems without sacrificing the advantages of a separately organized Intramural Research Program, it is recommended that:

a. There be flexible arrangements for intramural scientists to work for individually negotiated, specified periods of time in extramural programs and for extramural scientists to conduct research in the intramural programs of the Institute.

b. There be greater flexibility in the utilization of intramural facilities for conducting research of high priority to other parts of the Institute, and greater flexibility for the funding of intramural investigations by other parts of the Institute.

c. Intramural scientists be appointed as liaison members to initial review groups appropriate to their research interests, in order to maximize communication between the intramural and extramural programs.

Increase Utilization of Research Results

While recognizing that valuable research does not necessarily produce knowledge whose usefulness is immediate or direct, the Institute should increase its efforts to maximize the use of its research findings. It is recommended that:

1. The effectiveness of present communications and public information efforts be reevaluated, and there be created better liaison between those who conduct research and those who communicate research results.

2. The functions of existing review groups and committees be expanded to include the review of possible uses of the research supported by the Institute.

3. Since facilitation of the actual utilization of research results is a major goal of the NIMH research programs, a portion of Institute funds be explicitly allocated to support more active efforts to address this need.

RECOMMENDATIONS FOR SUPPORT OF SOCIAL PROBLEMS RESEARCH

The final set of recommendations deals with implementing the foregoing substantive priorities and organizational recommendations for research on social problems.

Funding

The primary reason why there has not been a greater emphasis on social problems research is that the Institute and the Government have not given it a sufficiently high priority. This reflects in part the scarcity of positions and funding available to the Institute for all purposes; but it also reflects a conscious or unconscious set of priorities. It is recommended that the Institute make every effort to secure greater resources for research on social problems. This effort should be made on behalf of intramural research as well as on research to be conducted outside the Institute.

It is also recommended that the allocation of research resources be made in accordance with program objectives and priorities rather than organizational units. There should then be a deliberate and flexible choice of modes and combinations of modes of research activity to pursue these objectives. Thus, a given allocation of personnel and budget would be made to social problems research, with portions of these resources allocated to the Intramural Research Program, to the Division of Extramural Research Programs, to appropriate centers, and to any other organizational units appropriate for the conduct of social problems research.

It should also be recognized that in pursuing single-mindedly the research problems that seem most exciting and potentially fruitful at the moment, we may fail to build the scientific base for the exciting possibilities of the future. It is recommended that a portion of the Institute's resources for research on social problems be concentrated on studies believed to be directly pertinent and important (e.g., those discussed in the foregoing substantive recommendations), but also that a significant portion of available resources be allocated to research that seems only tangentially relevant, to the development of methodology, and to nontargeted research whose objective is the theoretical development of the sciences from which more focused inquiries draw their inspiration and concepts.

Increase Flexibility in the Use of Research Support Mechanisms

Judged from the perspective of the substantive recommendations made above, all the mechanisms of research support now employed—intramural research, contracts, regular grants, special or collaborative grants, small grants, and conference grants—have proved to be useful and necessary. The major problem in their utilization has not been any inherent limitation in these mechanisms of research support, but administrative and organizational arrangements that sometimes interfere with the rational choice among these mechanisms by program officials. It is recommended that there be:

1. More flexible use of both regular and special grant mechanisms in the achievement of Institute priorities. Both regular and special grant mechanisms should be readily available for stimulating and carrying out fundamental research of special pertinence to social problems. Often the Institute's specification of areas of special interest will be enough to elicit first-rate research proposals; sometimes it will be desirable or even necessary to work collaboratively with outside investigators.

2. More effective use of the contract mechanism. The use of the contract mechanism is a valuable resource in those situations where flexibility of operations or timing is important or when the Institute is in need of specific information. But the rigid separation of grant and contract funds makes it difficult to use grant funds for purposes best accomplished by contracts and contract funds for purposes best served by

grants. There are also difficulties that result from centralized control of contract funds, which makes them available to program managers on the basis of individual request rather than on the basis of program allocation. It should also be emphasized that the most effective use of the contract mechanism requires rigorous evaluation by ad hoc peer review, rigorous monitoring by program staff, and adequate staff time for timely and effective monitoring.

3. Combined use of existing mechanisms. Under present organizational arrangements, intramural research, contracts, and grants are often treated as if they were completely separate ways of conducting research, rather than as administrative tools that can often be effectively combined to maximize the values of each. For example, difficulty is encountered when attempting to combine the use of intramural research and contracts for conducting longitudinal research. The intramural mechanism maximizes the likelihood of continuity in the conduct of such research, but the periodic fieldwork required in longitudinal research requires occasional contracts with nongovernmental organizations that have the requisite trained manpower. Since the funding for intramural research is relatively stable from year to year, a major financial crisis occurs each time a new field operation is begun. A more flexible arrangement that makes use of the continuity of personnel in intramural research, together with the flexibility of adequately funded contract mechanisms for supporting the periodic and expensive data-collection operations, is needed.

4. Support of multidisciplinary research. Since social problems involve multiple causes and multiple consequences that cannot be encompassed by a single academic discipline, the Institute should encourage studies employing levels of analysis that cut across different academic disciplines. This may require special or modified initial review groups for adequate review.

5. Organizational supports for cross-national research. To facilitate a renewed emphasis on cross-national research, it is recommended that:

a. The funds available for comparative cross-national research should be markedly increased. These monies should be available to foreign nationals as well as to Americans, including Institute scientists, for research abroad.

b. The panels that review proposals for cross-national research should be composed of individuals, U.S. citizens or foreign nationals, who have firsthand knowledge of the societies to be studied.

c. The Institute should participate in facilitating communication among scientists from different countries who have similar interests in social problems research.

6. Flexible support mechanisms for studies of social change. Research on social change requires even more flexibility than other social problems research. One requirement of such research is the commitment of financial support over several years. Another requirement is a set of flexible procedures for the approval of general plans that can be modified and implemented quickly for the study of rapid changes, emerging crises, and the like.

CHAPTER 12

Research on Treatment of Mental Disorders

AIMS AND SCOPE OF TREATMENT RESEARCH

Treatment research is designed to increase the effectiveness and availability of therapy by developing new techniques, improving existing methods, and increasing the precision with which patients with particular problems can be offered the most appropriate treatment. The body of research encompasses studies of psychosocial and physical interventions, explorations of their mechanism of action, and assessments of their effects under specified conditions.

Techniques for treating mental disorders have multiplied rapidly during the past quarter century. At the time when the National Mental Health Act was signed in 1946, Freudian psychoanalysis was the most highly developed form of psychosocial treatment, and behavior modification had not yet emerged from the laboratory. The major somatic treatments included electroconvulsive therapy, insulin "shock," and prefrontal lobotomy. Treatments for central nervous system syphilis and psychosis associated with pellagra were also available. Few psychoactive drugs were known and these were typically used to manage rather than to treat mental patients.

Today the scene has vastly changed. Psychotropic drugs appear to have revolutionized the treatment of schizophrenia. In the past, a schizophrenic patient was likely to spend years in a mental hospital; nowadays many are treated in general hospitals or as outpatients. Patients are discharged into the community to their families, halfway houses, or foster families. Drugs also have enhanced the efficacy of the treatment of affective disorders. The full range of emotional disorders is treated—in individual and in group settings—by a panoply of techniques ranging from chemotherapy and classical and modified psychotherapy to behavior therapy and physical manipulation.

Commensurate with the expanding universe of techniques is an increase in the range of human problems that are directed to the mental health practitioner. These now include not only "serious disorders"—the psychoses and neuroses—but also diverse "problems in living" and concerns about failure to "self-realize."

Overall, there has been a shifting of emphasis among practitioners and policymakers from psychological illness to psychological health. In part this reflects an optimistic attitude toward the possibility of enhancing functioning rather than merely ameliorating distress, and in part a fear of possibly stigmatizing the client by labels of illness. The borders between normal and abnormal functioning—which were never crisply drawn—have become increasingly fuzzy. The normal-abnormal distinction, it is argued by some, no longer serves a useful purpose and may indeed be mischievous. The very concept of mental illness has been challenged as not only pejorative but as actively limiting the potential benefits that may accrue to the patient from his treatment. However, there is no substantiation or validation for the currently popular and engaging belief that mental illness is a "myth." Mental disorders have not obligingly disappeared in response to their redefinition.

In selecting treatment, a therapist must have some conception of what produces, interacts with, aggravates, or sustains the problem to be treated. Does he view the manifest symptomatology a product of disordered brain function, intrapsychic or interpersonal conflicts, learning deficits, environmental factors, or intricate interaction among all or some of these factors? What weight does he assign to each factor in the treatment of a given individual? The therapist must also decide where to intervene. Some therapists view illness as residing within the individual, while others consider it to be in the family, community, social institutions or society. The therapist's view of the nature and locus of the illness determines which treatment techniques he will consider most appropriate.

For the purposes of this report, three major treatment approaches have been covered: psychosocial, somatic, and behavioral. While behavior therapy is a psychosocial approach, it will be discussed separately to emphasize its distinctive characteristics, principles, and goals. Somatic therapy—based on the recognition that behavior, thought, and feelings are linked to biochemical and neural mechanisms—now includes the extensive and successful use of drugs for the major mental illnesses.

PSYCHOSOCIAL THERAPY

Introduction

The psychotherapies focus on treating the "whole person" through verbal and symbolic techniques in a professional relationship between a socially approved healer and a suffering person. There are many varieties of individual and group therapy, with groups as small as the family or as large as a hospital ward. The agent of change may be a professional mental health worker—psychiatrist, psychologist, social worker, nurse—or simply a compassionate person who has had some training in mental health principles.

By some standards, psychotherapy seems vital and flourishing; by some standards, it is decadent and moribund. The number of therapies and the variety of techniques grow steadily; the ranks of therapists—both authorized and self-appointed—swell; and the number of consumers—both referred and self-diagnosed—grows. The definition of therapy is ambiguous, and professional standards of therapeutic practice have been both broadened and lowered. The initial model of mental illness required the intervention of medically trained or medically supervised professionals; the current model of mental health encourages the services of humanistically oriented, growth-stimulating educators and nonprofessional catalysts.

The nature of a therapist's personality, or perhaps his earlier period of patienthood, frequently is afforded more significance than his professional training. The spectrum of patients ranges from those with psychoses, neuroses, or addictions to those with ennui and alienation. The criterion of successful therapy has been extended from improving to optimizing the patient's well-being and effectiveness.

Psychotherapy has inevitably changed with changes in society, and the modal presenting problem appears to be correlated with prevailing cultural values. Therapists have confronted successive waves of patients, the first of them presenting problems of sexual repression, the second, anxiety, and the third, boredom and meaninglessness. Treatment and underlying theories have been reactive to the changing problems. However, the old therapies have not disappeared as new ones have been added, so that the roster now ranges from psychoanalysis and briefer psychotherapy (individual and group) to behavior therapies (operant and classical) and a new array that includes self-help groups, primal therapy, reevaluative counseling, meditative therapies, encounter groups, sensory awareness, gestalt, transpersonal therapies, and psychosynthesis. Well over 130 "therapies" have been reported in the literature.

Each school reports success in treating a wide range of problems but no school has clearly demonstrated its superior effectiveness, a state of affairs that is complicated by the purported differences in their goals.

Research in psychotherapy today is designed to answer: "What kinds of changes are produced by what kinds of interventions by what kinds of therapists, with what kinds of patients, and under what kinds of conditions?" Despite the improved quality and sophistication of this research, its major impact with but few exceptions has been on other researchers rather than on practitioners. Innovations and modifications of practice are based more on clinical observation than on research findings. But this situation is changing with a growing acceptance of the need to establish firm and scientifically credible bases for psychosocial therapies.

The potential inauguration of national health insurance with mental health coverage makes this research even more urgent. If public funds are to reimburse a wide array of alleged psychotherapeutic services, detailed evidence is needed of their potency and safety. Scientific evidence will be required for the continued public support for such practices as: (1) awarding third-party payments for diagnostic services; (2) licensing through internal professional regulatory process; (3) funding of training, research, and service in the mental health field; and (4) authorizing psychological procedures in human experimentation.

Historical Highlights of Psychotherapeutic Techniques

When NIMH was established, psychoanalytic emphases were beginning to shift from id to ego psychology and to the study of interpersonal relationships. In addition to neoanalytic and Rogerian therapy, a number of new adjuncts were introduced in the 1940's: art therapy, music therapy, dance therapy, play therapy, psychodrama, and bibliotherapy. Group therapy was being explored and the development of behavior modification was beginning. By the mid-fifties, the principles of operant conditioning were

311

being applied to psychotics in mental hospitals, and systematic desensitization was being used to treat fears and phobias.

The 1950's were rich with diverse research studies to analyze the process of psychotherapy—studies of verbal content and of nonverbal content, studies measuring the depth of interpretation or the patient's emotions, and studies on the characteristics of the therapist, the transmission of values during therapy, and the difficulties of the research itself. By the 1950's the field of psychotherapy that previously had been viewed by many as the exclusive province of psychiatry was being entered by clinical psychologists and psychiatric social workers. They brought with them the techniques of "nondirective" therapy and the richness of casework experience. Existentialist philosophy was also gaining recognition.

By the 1960's, techniques of behavior modification were extended from the back wards of mental hospitals, where they had been found useful, to home settings, classrooms, rehabilitation wards, prisons, nursing homes, etc. Simultaneously and independently the "humanist psychology" movement evolved groups designed for psychotherapy and growth: gestalt therapy, encounter groups, marathons, sensitivity training, sensory awareness, transactional analysis, truth labs, etc., and also supported bioenergetics, structural integration, and the incipient transpersonal therapies.

Group Psychotherapy and Group Dynamics

Aside from behavior therapy, the greatest modification of psychotherapy during the past quarter century may have been the shift in emphasis from individual to group psychotherapy. The utility of the group as a mechanism for increasing self-awareness was demonstrated as early as the 1920's and 1930's. During World War II, group therapy was used to distribute the scarce resource of trained therapists among large numbers of patients. With the demonstration of therapeutic efficacy, however, it was adopted by therapists from all schools. As a consequence, the principles of reality testing, corrective emotional experiences, analysis of the transference, desensitization, contingency contracting, token economy, etc., have all been used in group settings, including family units and "networks," and "therapeutic" milieus and communities. At the same time a combination of factors transformed the mental hospitals from their custodial philosophy back to an earlier tradition of "moral treatment."

Considerable research by social scientists on the dynamics of small groups was finally linked to therapy when the apparent effectiveness of T-groups (T for "training") was brought to the attention of the clinician. This may represent one of the rare instances of psychotherapists adopting principles and techniques developed by researchers.

The T-group was originated as a mechanism for studying group processes and training individuals to function more effectively as leaders and members of natural groups. Many of the T-group techniques were utilized in the development of "growth" groups, which came to be identified generically as "encounter groups." In turn, the popularity of encounter groups influenced the practice of group psychotherapy.

All the group treatment approaches represent a change in focus from altering intrapsychic conflict to changing the individuals' interpersonal relationships, modifying the dynamic relationships that exist among interdependent, interrelated people and their social institutions. Recently some therapists have become concerned with large systems—the community, society, and culture—and have come to view the problems of the patient as a consequence of an oppressive society that must be changed.

Evolution of Research Methodology

In the 1940's and 1950's, psychotherapy research largely depended upon retrospective individual case reports and the therapist's judgments of the patient's progress. Although a few investigators designed careful research, devising special instruments and using adequate controls, interest in measuring the outcome of therapy was considerably dampened when it was initially reported that the effectiveness of psychotherapy did not exceed the spontaneous remission rate—a rate that was mistakenly believed to be approximately 72 percent. Investigators turned to research on the process, assuming that such studies were prerequisite to developing more adequate psychotherapeutic interventions.

Recently an NIMH grantee has assembled evidence that spontaneous remission rates vary widely among different types of neuroses, for some neuroses do not change at all, some neuroses get worse, and the median rate of spontaneous remission appears to be closer to 30 percent than to the earlier reported and widely believed 72 percent.

In the 1960's came a research finding of signal significance: psychotherapy may have deleterious effects on about 10 percent of the patients. In contrast, only 5 percent of untreated patients showed deterioration. Thus, some aspects of therapy may be potent for either good or ill, or both. Moreover, when positive and negative effects are lumped together as group means, the true effects in terms of improvement and deterioration are obscured. It is important, therefore, to identify the specific change-inducing or change-inhibiting processes.

Also in the 1960's investigators accelerated research on outcome through the use of sophisticated research tools, including multivariate designs and multiperspective analyses, and through the inclusion of a variety of control groups.

While studies of somatic and behavioral approaches to treatment derived from traditions of experimental research, studies of psychosocial treatments did not. The psychosocial treatment researcher found it necessary to overcome a pervasive belief among psychiatrists and psychoanalytically oriented practitioners that rigorous research would interfere with the very processes and consequences of the treatment to be studied. It was feared that the richness and complexity of the concepts of psychodynamics and psychopathology, and also the humanistic goals of reintegrating inferred stable personality structures, did not lend themselves to translation into operational terms or simple standardized measures.

The clinicians' resistance to the data-gathering techniques of audio and visual recordings has diminished. Still to be overcome, however, is the grave problem of specifying targets of treatment, interventions, relevant therapist and environmental variables, and measures of change and outcome.

NIMH Support of Research on Psychotherapy

The roster of Institute grantees since 1948 indicates that there is hardly a major researcher in the field of psychotherapy who has not received some financial support from NIMH, yet the total amount of monies expended on all forms of psychosocial treatment research (including behavior therapy) over the past 25 years adds up to about $40.3 million. This is 5 percent of the total NIMH research grant expenditures of $796 million in this period.

A closer look reveals the following apportionment of funds (see table 1):

> Individual psychotherapy, 98 studies, $10.2 million
> Behavior therapy, 95 studies, $13.9 million
> Group therapy, 73 studies, $6.1 million
> Specialized therapies (such as art, hypnosis, self-conducted computer), 42 studies, $7.1 million
> Psychoanalysis, 20 studies, $2.9 million

The declining role of individual and group psychotherapy and the increasing significance of behavior therapy during the past 7 years is clearly shown in table 2, which summarizes the amount and percentage of research support awarded annually to categories of psychosocial therapy during the period 1967-1973 (individual psychotherapy, behavior therapy, group therapy, psychoanalysis and specialized therapies). The proportion of the annual psychotherapy support budget for individual and group psychotherapy declined fairly steadily from 1967 to 1973, while the proportion devoted to behavior therapy increased from 31 percent in 1967 to over 50 percent since 1970. Psychoanalysis has remained at about 7 percent.

Highlights of NIMH Contributions

Over the past 25 years, the catalog of NIMH-supported projects is long, through every fashion ranging. Only the salient findings of studies concerned with outcome research and process studies will be cited here as illustration.

Outcome Research

Approximately half of the studies on psychosocial treatment supported by NIMH concern the effects of treatment on patients and the contribution of such independent variables as treatment techniques, patient attributes, therapist qualities, and patient-therapist relationship. Not only is it difficult for the researcher to identify the nature of the problem the psychotherapist has treated and to measure the effects achieved, but also it is difficult to determine whether the therapeutic intervention has even been noted or accepted by the patient. Numerous events in the treatment setting and in the patient's life may inhibit or enhance the effects of treatment. Thus research can rarely demonstrate an unequivocal effect of treatment.

In view of the fact that outcome studies have failed to specify in comparable terms such variables as patient characteristics, nature of the interven-

Table 1
Amount and Percentage of Psychotherapy Research Support (Extramural) by Major Forms of Therapy in Five Year Periods—1947-73

Years	Individual Psychotherapy	%	Behavior Therapy	%	Group Therapy	%	Specialized Therapies	%	Psychoanalysis	%	Totals	%
1947-51	$ 335,225 (n* = 5)	48	$ (n = 0)	0	$ 251,410 (n = 6)	36	$ 106,170 (n = 3)	16	$ (n = 0)	0	$ 692,805 (n = 14)	100
1952-56	$ 737,783 (n = 19)	40	$ 51,296 (n = 1)	3	$ 665,223 (n = 15)	35	$ 221,949 (n = 6)	12	$ 187,308 (n = 3)	10	$ 1,863,559 (n = 45)	100
1957-61	$ 1,466,962 (n = 37)	36	$ 302,188 (n = 5)	8	$1,090,919 (n = 23)	27	$ 717,589 (n = 9)	18	$ 463,815 (n = 7)	11	$ 4,040,656 (n = 81)	100
1962-66	$ 2,881,944 (n = 40)	33	$ 1,998,407 (n = 24)	23	$1,499,919 (n = 23)	17	$1,674,578 (n = 19)	19	$ 744,489 (n = 6)	8	$ 8,799,337 (n = 112)	100
1967-71	$ 3,930,007 (n = 32)	22	$ 7,812,490 (n = 58)	43	$2,119,577 (n = 29)	12	$3,075,312 (n = 17)	17	$1,117,689 (n = 10)	6	$18,055,075 (n = 146)	100
1972-73	$ 868,066 (n = 11)	13	$ 3,756,394 (n = 37)	55	$ 451,992 (n = 6)	7	$1,327,420 (n = 11)	19	$ 450,855 (n = 4)	6	$ 6,854,727 (n = 69)	100
Total	$10,219,987 N** = 98	25	$13,920,775 N = 95	35	$6,078,223 N = 73	15	$7,123,018 N = 42	18	$2,964,156 N = 20	7	$40,306,159 N = 328	100

* n = the number of projects supported within a given time
** N = the total number of discrete projects

Table 2
Amount and Percentage of Annual Psychotherapy Research Support (Extramural) by Major Forms of Therapy—1967-1973

Year	Individual Psychotherapy	%	Behavior Therapy	%	Group Therapy	%	Specialized Therapies	%	Psychoanalysis	%	Totals	%
1967	$ 734,991 (n* = 16)	24	$ 980,681 (n = 22)	31	$ 629,228 (n = 16)	20	$ 548,971 (n = 9)	18	$ 222,330 (n = 4)	7	$ 3,116,201 (n = 67)	100
1968	$ 754,507 (n = 12)	21	$ 1,238,333 (n = 22)	35	$ 669,154 (n = 13)	19	$ 644,628 (n = 10)	18	$ 270,105 (n = 6)	7	$ 3,576,727 (n = 63)	100
1969	$ 853,574 (n = 16)	26	$ 1,500,698 (n = 19)	47	$ 209,931 (n = 6)	7	$ 638,129 (n = 9)	20	$ 19,695 (n = 1)	1	$ 3,222,027 (n = 51)	100
1970	$1,008,242 (n = 16)	22	$ 2,322,920 (n = 26)	50	$ 276,955 (n = 8)	6	$ 662,013 (n = 9)	14	$ 331,144 (n = 4)	8	$ 4,601,274 (n = 63)	100
1971	$ 578,693 (n = 9)	16	$ 1,769,858 (n = 24)	52	$ 334,309 (n = 4)	9	$ 581,571 (n = 8)	16	$ 274,415 (n = 2)	7	$ 3,538,846 (n = 47)	100
1972	$ 448,911 (n = 10)	14	$ 1,961,330 (n = 26)	57	$ 104,443 (n = 3)	3	$ 582,929 (n = 7)	18	$ 229,810 (n = 1)	7	$ 3,327,423 (n = 47)	100
1973	$ 419,155 (n = 6)	12	$ 1,795,064 (n = 27)	51	$ 347,549 (n = 5)	10	$ 744,491 (n = 8)	21	$ 221,045 (n = 3)	6	$ 3,527,304 (n = 49)	100
Total	$4,798,073	19	$11,568,884	46	$2,571,569	10	$4,402,732	18	$1,568,544	7	$24,909,802	100

* n = the number of projects supported in a given year

tion, environmental influences, and indices of change, conclusions about the relative effectiveness of treatment techniques must be made with great caution.

Despite these constraints, the research literature on outcome has, for many years, produced a remarkably consistent finding: 65 percent to 75 percent of nonpsychotic patients treated in outpatient settings benefit from psychotherapy. Controlled studies have repeatedly found that patients afforded psychotherapy showed significantly greater gains than did comparable patients assigned to "no psychotherapy," "wait for psychotherapy," or "minimal" psychotherapy control groups.

A review of 101 studies has recently concluded that about 80 percent of investigations having adequate designs showed positive effects of psychotherapy that were statistically significant and 20 percent showed null or negative results.

People who appear to benefit from psychotherapy tend to be intelligent, highly motivated, experience acute discomfort, anticipate help, show a high degree of personality integration, are reasonably well educated, have had some social success and recognition in the past, are reflective, and can experience and express emotion.

Initially a number of studies indicated that the effectiveness of psychotherapy was directly related to the degree to which therapists exhibited characteristics such as warmth, genuineness, or empathy. However, such findings, or their lack, now appear to be contingent on who assesses the quality of the therapist and on the nature of the patient-change measures used.

The assumption that therapist characteristics will affect the ability to work usefully with patients seems plausible, but therapist behavior is not independent of the patient. The evidence strongly suggests that patient behaviors may seriously influence the therapist's effectiveness. For example, the more responsive the patient, the more "genuine" the therapist's concern. But a patient may also frustrate the therapist's efforts to understand him and to communicate effectively with him.

This problem may contribute to the fact that the middle-class white therapist has often found it difficult to be effective with patients from different cultures, races, or socioeconomic levels. Similarly, male therapists may find themselves less effective with women patients who feel oppressed by culturally imposed roles. Various studies have suggested that actual or assumed similarities in therapist and patient attitudes, interests, and values enhance the therapeutic relationship and the treatment outcome.

A landmark study evaluated three groups of nonpsychotic patients: one receiving individual therapy, one receiving group psychotherapy, and a control group. It found that patients in the control group showed significantly less improvement than those in either treatment form; however, no differences were found between individual and group therapy effectiveness. In followup studies the scientists found that after 5 years patients that had been in the control group had "caught up" to the treated patients. A 10-year followup revealed that the greatest gains had been made within the first 2 years of treatment. Patients who said they had improved tended to credit their improvement to favorable change in their socioeconomic condition or to acceptance of life circumstances, including chronic symptoms.

A recent large-scale study found that the therapist's warmth and congruence differed with different clients, and, regardless of the degree or appropriateness of the therapist's empathy, most clients seemed to improve. Surprisingly, the data suggest a negative relationship exists between level of empathy and patient improvement. Another study indicated that the best predictors of therapeutic success were the patient's psychological health or adequacy of functioning, empathy between patient and therapist, and direction provided by the therapist.

The findings concerning research on outcome of psychotherapy may be summed up as follows:

1. Most forms of psychotherapy are effective with about two-thirds of their nonpsychotic patients.

2. Treated patients show significantly more behavioral and attitude change than untreated patients.

3. Apparent differences in the effectiveness of different forms of psychotherapy gradually disappear with the passage of time; whether or not one form of psychotherapy is superior to another has yet to be convincingly demonstrated.

4. Psychotherapy techniques as generally practiced appear to have some potency for both good and ill. However, work is needed to identify the source of this potency. The so-called "placebo effect" appears to play at least some role in all types of therapy and, therefore, needs further careful study.

Process Studies

Because it is difficult to correlate the patient's ultimate change with specific interventions, many investigators judge process by adopting intermediate goals based on theoretical formulations, i.e., interpretation of transference, depth of interpretation, increasing self-exploration, sensitivity, etc. The ultimate purpose of process studies is to identify what is therapeutic about psychotherapy and what pattern of conditions enhances favorable outcomes for specific patients. During the 1940's and 1950's, such studies were oriented toward psychoanalysis and client-centered therapy, which provide a theoretical stance and some clear notions about mechanisms and techniques of therapy. However, research interest in these forms of therapy has diminished, leaving more recent process studies atheoretical and somewhat haphazard.

Many researchers have developed systems to study the content of therapy interviews or other dyadic interactions, basing their analyses largely on the verbal content of patient's and therapist's speech, but also including linguistic analysis, speech disruptions, and facial and body movements. NIMH-supported researchers have developed scales and systems of analysis that have proven fruitful in providing data about the process of psychotherapy and communication in general.

318

Substantial work by one group of NIMH-supported investigators defines successful therapy as increasingly differentiated awareness of one's inner experiences. Recently, studies using an "experiencing" scale show that: (1) experiencing differentiates gross diagnostic groups, e.g., neurotics experience more deeply than do schizophrenics, and (2) the level of experience is related to the outcome of therapy.

The stability of the patient's verbal behavior has been the subject of considerable study. Analysis of the verbal content of therapy has been advanced by computer methods, and measurement of the linguistic characteristics of speech in psychotherapy has permitted the identification of idiosyncratic communication patterns thought to have diagnostic significance.

The study of speech disturbances, undertaken initially to provide an index of moment-to-moment changes in the anxiety level of patients, ultimately identified lawful relationships that characterized speech disturbances. This work may be a basic contribution to the understanding of thought and speech processes.

Kinesics is the study of patterns of body motions that may have communication value. While clinicians affirm the importance of body cues, research suggests that, unless specifically trained, they make little use of kinesic information.

There have been a number of attempts to relate physiological change in the patient, such as heart rate or finger temperature, to events in psychotherapy, but the complexities of measurement and the idiosyncrasies of patient response have made these studies difficult to interpret.

Each form of psychotherapy is based on hypotheses regarding conditions that are prerequisite to effecting desired change in a patient. A review of the conditions for change espoused by the various schools of therapy suggests considerable overlap. For example, the experience and expression of intense affect is highly valued by such approaches as primal therapy, reevaluative counseling, "growth" therapies, and "release" therapy. By contrast, rational thought is believed to be therapeutic in rational-emotive therapy, reality therapy, structured learning therapy, and general semantics therapy.

Increased awareness of one's feelings and personal experiences is emphasized by client-centered therapy, experiential therapy, gestalt therapy, and others. The lifting of repression is stressed by various analytic schools and hypnotherapy. Awareness of one's behavior and its impact on others is central to many approaches and is particularly emphasized in video-tape playback procedures. Public confession of sins and restitution is proposed by many self-help, repressive-inspirational groups and also by integrity therapy.

In most forms of therapy, however, it is difficult to demonstrate that the techniques assigned therapeutic qualities are indeed responsible for the effects observed, for intervening events may augment or attenuate the therapist's efforts. In short, the conditions for effecting change in psychotherapy remain ambiguous.

One investigator has proposed that all therapies share the same common elements, among them:

>   An emotionally charged relationship with a helping person
>   An "explanation" of the causes of a patient's distress
>   New information about the nature of the problems
>   Possible alternative ways of dealing with these problems
>   Provision of some experiences of success to heighten the patient's sense of mastery

It has been proposed that these common (nonspecific) elements are effective with seemingly dissimilar patients because all patients may suffer from essentially the same sense of "demoralization."

Conferences and Surveys

To expedite the work of researchers—both extramural and intramural—a number of conferences and surveys were initiated:

Three national conferences on research in psychotherapy were sponsored in 1958, 1961, and 1966 by NIMH and the American Psychological Association to promote the development of better methods of studying psychosocial treatments. The three volumes that resulted are classic references for researchers and trainees.

The Clinical Research Branch Conference on Planning of Research on Effectiveness of Psychotherapy resulted in the publication of an article that has become a manual for the conduct of outcome research.

A conference sponsored by the Clinical Research Branch was designed to encourage independent investigators to define independent variables and to use a core battery of outcome measures. A thorough survey of psychometrically acceptable instruments and recommended measures to be included in a core battery will be published soon by NIMH.

An exhaustive survey of the research literature was commissioned by NIMH to increase coordination and integration of existing research findings.

A survey of psychotherapy researchers found that interest in participating in large-scale cooperative research was lacking.

General Studies of Therapeutic Techniques

Psychoanalysis

From 1947 to 1973 NIMH supported only 20 studies and programs in the area of psychoanalysis. These attempted to combine clinical relevance, theoretical complexity, and a commitment to empiricism and objectivity; however, with few exceptions, it has been difficult for psychoanalysis to combine great rigor of research method with the complexity of its explanatory concepts.

In a major 18-year study, supported in part by NIMH, psychoanalysts made a systematic research effort to test hypotheses regarding the process and outcome of therapy. The study was significant not only for its substantive findings but also for its development of the research instrument known as the Health-Sickness Scale.

Psychoanalytic therapy was found particularly effective with patients classified as showing "high ego strength"; with patients of initial "low ego strength" (borderline) neither psychoanalysis nor supportive therapy was effective. The most useful approach with such patients was found to be a combination of hospital milieu and supportive, interpretive therapy.

That psychoanalysts are willing to cooperate in research efforts is evident in the fact that 800 of them provided information concerning their treatment of patients to the Central Fact Gathering Survey of the American Psychoanalytic Association. Further evidence is found in the psychoanalysts' willingness and ability to pool data in a study conducted at the Columbia Psychoanalytic Clinic.

Contrary to popular belief that psychoanalysis is suitable only for the middle class, a form of psychoanalytic therapy offered without medication to lower-class, black, hospitalized schizophrenics is reported to have produced more improvement in thought disorders than did drug treatment alone or drug treatment in combination with ego analytic therapy.

Family Therapy

Therapy with the nuclear family of the outpatient "neurotic" was introduced by a member of the NIMH staff. It was subsequently extended to the treatment of schizophrenics and their families by a number of investigators in the intramural program. The primary purpose of family research in the intramural setting was the investigation of family process, but the clinical findings have been used by practitioners in family therapy. Primarily concerned with the treatment of families having a schizophrenic member, NIMH intramural scientists have focused on the family unit as a vehicle for studying: (1) disordered communication between parents and children; (2) patterns of thought and communication among family members; (3) personality formation as it is shaped by family interactions; and (4) family relationships as precursors to disturbed behavior.

NIMH intramural research has tended to deal with the family as a system, and treatment is not focused on changing the individual but on changing interactions among family members through identifying the antecedents and consequences of their behavior. Despite the prolonged research effort to identify family factors related to schizophrenia, investigators have been unable to determine whether the nature of interactions among family members are products or causes of the illness.

Milieu and Community Care

A number of scientists have investigated the social structure of treatment settings. The movement away from custodial care was supported by evidence—much of it developed by intramural investigators in studies of the mental hospital as a total institution—that institutionalization itself had iatrogenic effects and often retarded the healing process. The interaction between patients and hospital staff thus became the subject of studies that eventually led to a change in the traditional roles of the caretaker and patient. The concepts of the therapeutic community and ward milieu—which call upon all elements of the institution to work together for the well-being of the patient—were developed and were applied to a variety of settings:

hospitals, sheltered workshops, halfway houses, foster homes, day hospitals, and aftercare programs.

Research has shown that the ability of individuals to maintain themselves in the community or to avoid the debilitating effects of long-term hospitalization depends in large part on the nature of social supports and the quality of available human relationships. Consequently, the social organization of the mental hospital and alternatives to hospitalization have been improved. Graduates of a patient-managed, community-based lodge (halfway house) for formerly hospitalized patients have demonstrated better community adjustment than have regular hospital dischargees, and in some instances the lodge system was more economical. Although the Mental Health Services Development Branch of NIMH has energetically encouraged the adoption of the lodge approach, community interest lags.

Other studies have shown that nonprofessional counselors can help discharged patients maintain social and occupational effectiveness, and continued association between patients and counselor appears to facilitate rehabilitation and to prevent relapse. Even this treatment approach is not uniformly encouraging. After serious efforts to mobilize community resources to maintain patients at home by a combination of psychotropic drugs and community care, two research studies reported favorable early results, but 5-year followups showed that the patients' rate of rehospitalization was no different from that of patients who lacked these community services. It is recognized, nonetheless, that the capacity to function effectively at home and in the community even for a year is not a trivial benefit. Research now underway may disclose how to maintain the benefits of the treatment after discharge.

NIMH has also supported the development of part-time hospitalization—days or nights, or weekends—and favorable results were reported with some psychotics, whose symptoms were brought under control within 7 weeks. Their remissions lasted as long as those of patients receiving full inpatient treatment.

Encounter Groups

The term "encounter groups" encompasses a range of small groups that are characterized by face-to-face interactions, focusing on the here and now; intensive group experience; openness, honest interpersonal confrontation, and self-disclosure; and strong emotional expressions. The groups' aim is to effect behavioral and attitudinal change.

It has been estimated that 5 to 6 million people have participated in groups variously identified as personal growth, human relations, sensory awareness, sensitivity, self-awareness, etc., yet very few investigators have attempted to assess the impact, therapeutic or otherwise, on participants. One notable exception, a study of the effects of 10 different encounter group approaches, indicates that one-third of the participants benefited, approximately one-third remained unchanged, and the remaining third experienced a negative outcome. About 9 percent of the latter group of participants suffered serious damage.

322

It had been anticipated that encounter group techniques which lowered patients' resistances, fostered a sense of group cohesiveness, and stimulated intense affect might be usefully adapted to group therapy practice, but the tentative conclusions of recent research suggest that the more exotic techniques have little enduring therapeutic usefulness. The procedures appeared to be advantageous only to the extent that patients clearly understood the emotional experiences.

Hypnosis

The Institute has invested relatively little in research on the uses of hypnosis for psychotherapy ($755,000). A major series of studies of hypnotically susceptible people and the development of a valid hypnosis susceptibility scale have helped to remove some of the onus from hypnosis and render the technique more respectable for both therapist and researcher. Studies of suggestibility and of the "demand characteristics" of experiments have clarified the role of bias or motivation on the part of experimenter and subject. Perhaps for cultural reasons and Freud's abandonment of hypnosis, it has never become a major tool in psychotherapy, and many clinicians who practice hypnosis still believe that only a fraction of the population is amenable to trance induction.

Computers in Therapy

The Institute has supported few grants for studying the therapeutic uses of computers. One researcher has attempted to develop computer programs that simulate the interchanges between therapists and patients in psychotherapy sessions. Experimental subjects have conversed with the machine by typing messages to the computer. Interaction with the computer has resulted in notable language improvement in nonspeaking disturbed children. Children who previously had refused to speak responded vocally to the machine and then in everyday life. Additional computer research has involved the testing of models of psychopathology, the study of decisionmaking processes, patient associations, and language.

New Treatment Techniques

Characteristically, a practitioner of a psychosocial therapy may "hold out to the public" as efficacious any procedure, technique, and/or philosophy without first testing its consequences. The Institute, while not a regulatory agency, has the responsibility to provide objective, accurate, and reliable information to the public. It has the responsibility but not the authority to obtain information based on sound research, yet research-based information is scarce, if not altogether nonexistent, for some therapies.

Although NIMH has supported some research on innovative treatments, e.g., transcendental meditation and biofeedback, "new methods" such as primal therapy, reevaluative counseling, and transpersonal therapy appear to have been relatively neglected. The gathering of reliable research information on the new forms of psychotherapy is thwarted by the following circumstances:

1. Practitioners of such techniques as primal therapy, reevaluative counseling, gestalt therapy, transactional analysis, structural integration (Rolfing), etc., have not submitted applications for research support.

2. Competent investigators are frequently unable to undertake needed research because practitioners skilled in these techniques do not cooperate.

3. There is no mechanism for persuading the practitioners to cooperate in research, nor is the psychotherapist required to pretest a "new" form of treatment or to treat it as an "experiment."

Primal therapy and reevaluative counseling, for example, are designed to aid the patient to reexperience early psychological and physical hurts—in their original form. In primal therapy the release may be accompanied by violent thrashing, screaming, and convulsive behavior, an emotional release that is believed to be curative. Typically a patient is afforded individual therapy for 3 weeks, in 2- to 3-hour sessions. Then the patient joins a "post-primal" group that meets once or twice a week to help the patients establish contact with dissociated experiences and to continue to express emotion by primal screams. This intensive form of therapy is purported to relieve neurotic symptoms and produce a tension-free person, but no systematic, independent research has assessed the validity of the claims.

Two new approaches that recently have become popular among patients and therapists are the "humanistic potential and growth movement" and "transpersonal psychology." The first approach attempts to aid individuals to fulfill positive human potentials; the transpersonal school attempts to aid individuals to achieve the highest possible reaches of human nature, including spirituality. There have been some attempts to investigate the techniques of the human growth movement (particularly encounter groups as mentioned above), but there has been little systematic research in the area of transpersonal psychology. The transpersonal approach includes such treatment forms as psychosynthesis and Arica.

Psychosynthesis was developed by a Florentine psychiatrist to help people develop all of their psychological functions in harmony, as a path to the higher self, and is practiced as a form of psychotherapy by specially trained therapists in several countries.

The Arica Institute comprises an eclectic system that incorporates Middle Eastern and Oriental teachings including Yoga, Zen, Sufism, Kabbala, and the martial arts. Institutes now established in some major American cities offer special diet, sensory awareness, energy-generating exercises, techniques for analysis of personality, interpersonal and group exercises, and various meditations. In Arica and related schools, a small group of trainees meet regularly as a community to help each other and to develop a "group energy" that is helpful to each in attaining his highest goals of consciousness evolution.

Transcendental meditation, a variant of Raja Yoga, has become popular in the United States and Europe. Transcendental meditation has been tailored to the habits of Westerners and does not require special postures, forced concentration, lengthy or arduous training, or religious belief. Each individual is assigned a specific mantra, a euphonious syllable. Twice a day for approximately 20 minutes the practitioner relaxes and focuses his attention on the mantra. The first study of the psychological and physiological changes that accompany transcendental meditation was performed under an NIMH training grant and suggests that the meditation produces a state of deep relaxation, with physiological and metabolic changes that differ from those during sleep and hypnotic trance. A survey of college students indicated that consistent practice of transcendental meditation was associated with diminished drug use. The technique also is being investigated as a possible treatment for hypertension. The claims of profound relaxation, a feeling of well-being, increased energy, and better general health are worthy of systematic research.

BEHAVIOR THERAPY

The goal of behavior modification is to alter the principal presenting problems rather than to alter personality, character structure, or underlying conflicts. In the view of the behavior therapist, maladaptive responses obey the same laws of learning and conditioning as do "normal" responses and are amenable to change through the application of what is known about learning and behavior modification. Perhaps the most characteristic feature of behavior therapy is its basis in laboratory research, its adherence to the empirical tradition of experimental psychology and to the ideal of establishing a science of behavior change. The principles of classical and operant conditioning have been well-known since the 1920's, but were not applied until the 1950's when behavior therapy was introduced as a decisive break with orthodox psychotherapeutic techniques. It dissociated itself from the medical model and from popular assumptions regarding psychodynamics and psychopathology. A discussion of the research leading to behavior therapy appears in the chapter on the psychological processes underlying behavior.

While generalizations from classical and operant conditioning studies provide the foundation and rationale for behavior therapy, studies of verbal behavior, modeling, cognitive learning, and social learning influence its practice. Successful and speedy treatment of anxiety disorders began to draw attention to a procedure known as systematic desensitization that progressively counteracted, weakened, and extinguished the association between a patient's subjective feelings of anxiety or fear and the situations or thoughts that evoked the emotions.

Behavior therapy has become a popular treatment, particularly for managing institutional populations and children's behavior problems, and is a focus for considerable research. Four new journals on behavior therapy have been initiated since 1963. In a random sample of schools that offer doctoral training in psychology, 84 percent had courses in behavior modification. Similarly, courses are given in medical schools, and II percent of psychiatric residency programs require a behavior therapy practicum.

The American Psychiatric Association's recent Task Force Report on Behavior Therapy in Psychiatry recommended that premedical courses contain a course in psychology with special attention to the experimental analysis of behavior, and that training in behavioral psychiatry be made available to all psychiatric residents.

Clinical Effectiveness of Behavior Therapy

Systematic desensitization appears to produce measurable benefits across a range of distressing problems including anxiety, most phobic reactions, anxiety reactions, enuresis, and stuttering. A number of children's behavior problems appear to be responsive to reinforcement therapy: temper tantrums, head banging, thumbsucking, refusal to eat, and excessive scratching.

Behavior therapy has been used successfully to modify disruptive behavior, failure to study, and low academic achievement. Chronic mental patients have been taught a wide variety of appropriate social behaviors, and the verbal and nonverbal behavior of psychotic adults and schizophrenic children has also been positively influenced. Behavior therapy has had less impact on alcoholism, but new procedures are currently being developed and tested.

Behavior therapists require that a symptom must be specifiable in objective behavioral terms; therefore, they do not usually deal with broad existential crises or philosophical problems unless a potential client also shows some specific behavioral deficit.

Illustrative Treatment Techniques

Preliminary to treatment, a "behavioral analysis" is undertaken to determine the specific contexts and settings of daily life that distress the patient and to ascertain the environmental responses that might maintain the patient's maladaptive behaviors. On the basis of the behavioral assessment, a therapeutic procedure is selected and adapted for that patient.

Of the numerous techniques employed by behavior therapists, only five of the major ones will be mentioned here as illustrative: the token economy, systematic desensitization, aversive therapy and punishment techniques, biofeedback, and modeling.

Token Economies

Earlier operant experimental studies demonstrated that the behavior of psychotics was influenced by the same principles of learning and motivational conditions as the behavior of normals. Two NIMH grantees applied this observation in the area of patient management through a procedure known as the "token economy," providing patients with tokens for performing in ways that the institutional staff (or experimenters) deemed desirable. The tokens were exchangeable for privileges in a work-payment incentive system. Token economies appear to help prevent or overcome the iatrogenic deterioration and social breakdown that usually accompany prolonged institutionalization. The efficacy of this type of program has been demonstrated with institutionalized psychiatric patients, delinquents, and the mentally retarded. In classrooms its application has been shown to decrease disruptive behaviors, increase task attentiveness, and improve grades. However, when the reward system is withdrawn, the "good" behavior decreases in frequency, so current efforts are aimed toward replicating the reinforcing environment in the patient's daily life.

Systematic Desensitization (Reciprocal Inhibition)

This technique involves the graded and progressive imaginary or actual exposure of the patient to a feared situation, on the theory that anxiety responses can be weakened if competing responses—such as relaxation, sexual or assertive responses—are stimulated simultaneously.

First, the patient is taught to relax. Then, the anxiety-producing life situation is identified and the therapist and client construct an "anxiety hierarchy" of scenes that are calculated to produce increasing anxiety in the patient. Finally, the deeply relaxed patient is asked to imagine each scene and to signal if the scene proves disturbing. If so, the patient is told to relax, and the scene is repeated and coupled with relaxation until it evokes no anxiety. At this point, the next scene in the hierarchy is presented.

Although this is an extensively researched procedure, the exact mechanism of effect is still being debated; some researchers postulate "extinction" while others implicate the "therapeutic relationship." According to one review of the experimental literature, neither muscular relaxation nor a progressive hierarchy and imaginal rehearsal are essential to the success of systematic desensitization. While there is little question that the systematic desensitization procedure appears to work, there is considerable question as to whether it works for the reasons postulated by reciprocal inhibition theory.

Aversive Therapy and Punishment Techniques

Research literature suggests that the most effective way of eliminating inappropriate behavior is to punish it while reinforcing the desired behavior. Aversive therapy, therefore, involves the administration of some painful intervention—such as electroshock or emetic drugs—to induce the subject to avoid certain kinds of situations or behaviors. It may be supplemented by punishment—such as the removal of a privilege. These procedures are employed with drug addiction, alcoholism, and situations where the problem behavior is manifestly injurious or self-destructive—for example, head banging or self-mutilation by autistic children.

Punishment techniques frequently do not generalize beyond the specific behavior that is being punished, but when destructive or bizarre behavior is eliminated, the patient may become more available to positive aspects of his environment, gaining reward for more appropriate behaviors.

Biofeedback

Not strictly a behavior therapy, biofeedback is included here because it deals with learning to control bodily functions without assuming a need to understand them. The term "biofeedback" has been applied to techniques by which some people have learned to exercise voluntary control over their internal organs and over brain waves, blood pressure, kidney functions, or other internal processes previously believed to be beyond conscious control. From the vantage point of the practitioner, the demonstration that individuals can learn to control their internal functions would represent a long step toward the possibility of their learning to control autonomic processes to correct psychosomatic dysfunctions.

For individuals to learn to control internal processes, it is necessary to provide some means by which they can become aware of changes in their internal states. This is accomplished by using a monitoring device that transforms the information regarding the internal states into cues that are visual, auditory, tactile, or kinesthetic. Biofeedback has been utilized in a number of NIMH-sponsored studies to intervene in psychosomatic problems such as hypertension, cardiac arrhythmias, migraine, tension headache, asthma, ulcerative colitis, peptic ulcer, spastic sigmoid colon, esophageal motility, and gastric hyperacidity. Although biofeedback has great promise and its claims have been flamboyantly heralded in the popular media, there has been no compelling evidence that the procedures have significant clinical effect on patients with serious physiological malfunction. Careful research is necessary to investigate the nature of biofeedback and its mechanisms of action and to perfect techniques for utilizing its therapeutic potential while minimizing possible side effects.

Modeling

Some research shows that a fundamental way of learning new modes of behavior is through modeling. The observation of the behavior of other persons and its consequences enables individuals to acquire even intricate response patterns. For example, well-controlled experiments have shown that children who are afraid of dogs will lose their fear if they watch a film in which a somewhat fearful child gradually overcomes fear of dogs and finally plays with them. This finding suggests that films of children modeling a variety of desirable behaviors might have a significant impact in therapy if shown on children's television programs. Although this work is unquestionably important, it has not stimulated extensive research, and while clinicians have described the useful effects of "vicarious learning" and "identification" with the therapist, the purposeful use of such modeling has not been widely accepted.

Highlights of NIMH Contributions

NIMH-supported scientists have been preeminent in the behavior therapy field. All leading behavior therapists in the United States have been encouraged and supported by NIMH grants, and the following are a sample of the major contributions from NIMH-supported researchers:

- The demonstration that adult psychotics and autistic children are subject to the same principles of operant conditioning and are responsive to the same motivational conditions as normal people.

- The successful application of learning principles to the systematic desensitization of anxiety and fears.

- The application of operant conditioning principles to institutional and ward management problems of psychotic adults, autistic children, retarded children, delinquents, and alcoholics.

- The application of operant conditioning procedures to a wide range of behavioral problems in the home, halfway houses, courts, and community agencies. The problem behaviors included stuttering, aggression, underassertiveness, depressive reactions, enuresis, phobias, anxieties, obsessive-compulsive behavior, sexual problems, gambling, insomnia, nightmares, temper tantrums, and head banging.

- The development of biofeedback procedures via laboratory studies that demonstrated that animals could learn to control functions of their autonomic nervous system. This procedure was subsequently applied to humans and has important implications for the ultimate clinical treatment and control of psychosomatic disorders.

- The demonstration of the importance of modeling as a mechanism for influencing the behavior of children.

- The development of behavioral engineering procedures enabling patients to wear or use instruments in a natural setting to gain control over specific behavioral problems such as stuttering, smoking, and enuresis.

- The extension of the therapist's role into the naturalistic environment by the training of parents, teachers, peers, and others who are in regular contact with the subject to act as therapist and behavior modifier.

- The development of self-control measures that can be taught to the subject so that he can reinforce his own appropriate behavior when the behavior therapist is no longer available to him.

Four units of NIMH and the National Institute on Alcohol Abuse and Alcoholism have funded research on behavior therapy: the Center for Studies of Crime and Delinquency, Division of Special Mental Health Programs; the Division of Extramural Research Programs; the Center for Studies of Narcotic Addiction and Drug Abuse, Division of Narcotic Addiction and Drug Abuse; and the Mental Health Services Development Branch, Division of Mental Health Service Programs. Except for one project conducted within the intramural program by the Laboratory of Human Behavior at St. Elizabeths Hospital, all of the NIMH-funded behavior therapy research originated in the extramural programs.

Over the past 15 years the NIMH support of behavior therapy projects has increased dramatically. During 1957-1961, a total of about $300,000 or approximately 8 percent of the total NIMH extramural budget for researchers in the psychosocial treatment area was invested in behavior therapy (see table 1). In the period 1962-1966, the proportion rose to 23 percent, and this percentage jumped to 43 percent in the period 1967-1971. In 1972-1973, behavior therapy research represented $3.7 million, or 55 percent of the $6.8 million given to psychosocial treatment research.

Since 1967 the number of behavior therapy projects submitted for review has steadily increased, while the number submitted in the other areas has steadily decreased. Behavior therapy proposals also enjoyed a higher approval rate. For example, between 1970-1973, the initial review groups reviewed 72 behavior therapy projects and approved 49 percent, whereas only 31 percent of the 81 nonbehavior therapy projects reviewed during these 4 years were approved (see table 3). Thus increased representation of behavior therapy research projects supported by NIMH reflects both the judgment of the reviewers and a change in the interest of, or project submission patterns from, researchers.

Table 3

Submission and Approval Rates for Proposals Relating to Psychotherapy and Behavior Therapy (CL-T Projects)—1970-1973

Year	Individual	Behavior	Group-oriented	Psychoanalytic	Special	Totals
			Therapy Types			
1970						
Submissions	5	16	10	1	2	34
Approvals	1	9	2	1	0	13 (38%)
Awards	1	9	2	1	0	13
1971						
Submissions	7	16	8	1	6	38
Approvals	1	7	3	1	1	13 (34%)
Awards	1	7	3	1	1	13
1972						
Submissions	8	16	10	0	6	40
Approvals	1	6	3	0	1	11 (28%)
Awards	1	6	1	0	1	9
1973						
Submissions	3	24	7	2	5	41
Approvals	2	13	3	2	3	23 (56%)
Awards	2	11	3	2	3	21
1970-73						
Submissions	23	72	35	4	19	153
Approvals	5 (22%)	35 (49%)	11 (31%)	4 (100%)	5 (26%)	60 (39%)
Awards	5	33	9	4	5	56

SOMATIC THERAPIES

Introduction

All somatic therapies are rooted in the belief that psychological conditions can be influenced therapeutically by nonpsychological methods. Chemical, hormonal, and physical interventions can affect the brain either directly or indirectly, and thus produce or inhibit behavior and alter mood. A clinician may employ drug therapy or convulsive therapy without assuming that the patient's problems are exclusively or even primarily attributable to some biochemical imbalance.

In 1946 the primary somatic techniques for mental illness were the convulsive therapies, insulin shock and electroshock. They were used mainly in the treatment of schizophrenics. Prefrontal lobotomy was widely practiced, especially on chronic hospitalized patients. Chemotherapy was used primarily for generalized sedation or stimulation. Barbiturates, it is true, were used as narcocathartic and narcosuggestive agents—in order, however, to facilitate psychotherapy. At that time psychotherapeutic treatment, especially psychoanalysis, was felt to be the only effective approach to treatment, and the somatic techniques were held in low esteem, particularly in the United States. The reverse may soon be true.

The initial discoveries and seminal hypotheses in the somatic therapies were based more on clinical observation than on research. This was inevitable since the underlying etiological and pathophysiological factors of mental illness were, and remain, essentially unknown.

While a number of factors have contributed to the sharp decrease in the patient population of State and county mental hospitals, there is little question that the use of antipsychotic drugs has not only shortened the psychotic patient's stay in the hospital, but has allowed treatment and rehabilitation in the community. Acutely ill patients have been treated in the community programs of general hospitals and clinics rather than in the large mental hospitals. Whether this has been accomplished without seriously straining the family and community remains a question to be answered by research.

Drugs do not "cure" psychoses, but they do appear to interrupt the psychotic episode and ameliorate symptoms. They can also prevent or lower the rate of recurrence of symptoms, and thus prevent or lessen the need for rehospitalization.

Highlights of NIMH Contributions

Somatic therapy research has included such areas as basic biological studies, psychopharmacological treatment of major mental illnesses (schizophrenia and depression), convulsive therapy, psychosurgery, megavitamin therapy (also known as orthomolecular treatment), and other physiological interventions such as body manipulation. By all odds, the most important somatic therapy has been pharmacological, and it has received the most sizable investment of NIMH funds.

Between 1968 and 1973, clinical and preclinical research on pharmacological therapy (exclusive of alcoholism, drug abuse, and intramural programs) totaled $59.6 million, another $2.9 million was devoted to two other somatic therapies, convulsive therapy, and orthomolecular treatment. The portion of the psychopharmacology budget dealing solely with therapy totaled some $30.1 million, or about 91 percent of the funding for clinical research on somatic therapies. The relative distribution of funds among psychopharmacology and other somatic therapies has remained stable since 1968 (see table 4).

Table 4
Somatic Therapy Research Grants—1968-1973

Year	Psycho-pharmacological (Clinical)	%	Convulsive Therapy (ECT and Insulin)	%
1968	$ 5,155,649	92	$ 60,135	1
1969	$ 5,384,000	92	0	0
1970	$ 5,043,733	90	$107,097	2
1971	$ 4,588,957	89	$119,138	2
1972	$ 4,648,358	91	$ 5,000	<1
1973	$ 5,290,359	94	0	0
Total	$30,111,056	91	$291,370	1

Year	Orthomolecular	%	Totals	%
1968	$ 384,099	7	$ 5,599,883	100
1969	$ 427,940	8	$ 5,811,940	100
1970	$ 492,751	8	$ 5,643,581	100
1971	$ 450,142	9	$ 5,158,237	100
1972	$ 454,170	>8	$ 5,107,528	100
1973	$ 389,884	6	$ 5,680,243	100
Total	$2,598,986	8	$33,001,412	100

The preclinical work necessary for clinical application of drugs absorbed almost half of the Psychopharmacology Research Branch budget in the period 1968-1973. Much of this work—on medicinal chemistry, mechanisms of drug action, development of new therapeutic compounds, and synthesis of compounds for basic psychopharmacological research—is reviewed in other chapters.

Research on Basic Biological Processes

Support has been given to research assessing the pharmacological properties of new compounds and analyzing the physiological and behavioral effects of drugs on animal and human subjects. Substantial investment also has gone into developing knowledge about the synthesis, storage, release, and metabolism of central nervous system transmitters; the anatomical, physiological, and biochemical basis of various emotions and pathological states; the biology of memory; and the role of the endocrine system in the regulation of homeostasis and adaptive behavior. In another line of research, the molecular bases of the action of psychotropic drugs and the undesirable side effects of some of them gradually are being revealed.

NIMH scientists have demonstrated that every psychoactive agent tested interacts with neurotransmitter mechanisms. The integrity of these transmitter systems appears to be essential for mental health.

NIMH laboratories have also developed methods for the measurement of several neurotransmitter amines, their metabolites, and enzymes involved in their synthesis and metabolism. They have developed sensitive and versatile methods enabling investigators to make enzyme and metabolite studies of blood and cerebrospinal fluid. And these same laboratories have been responsible for developing concepts relating biogenic amines to affective disorders and perhaps to psychotic states. This research is discussed further in the chapter on the biological processes underlying behavior.

Psychopharmacology Research Program of NIMH

Since the introduction of reserpine and chlorpromazine, the first antipsychotic agents, literally thousands of psychotropic drugs have been synthesized to treat the pathology associated with schizophrenia, depression, and manic-depressive disorders. (The work leading to the discovery of chlorpromazine is noted in the chapter on basic research activities.) In addition, "minor tranquilizers" such as meprobamate and chlordiazepoxide, surpassing in efficacy the previously available antianxiety sedatives, have been introduced. These minor tranquilizers are among the most widely prescribed drugs in medicine today.

While NIMH played no significant role in the discovery of these drugs, it has been a major influence—perhaps the major influence—in the early and definitive clinical testing of the efficacy and safety of psychotropic drugs. NIMH has stimulated and collaborated on psychopharmacological research, has collated the findings, and has disseminated them to researchers and practitioners.

In 1956, recognizing the need to assess the effectiveness of psychoactive drugs, the NIMH established the Psychopharmacology Service Center (now the Psychopharmacology Research Branch), giving impetus to the development of the new interdisciplinary field of research known as psychopharmacology. This branch has acted as the principal Federal source of support for research in psychopharmacology. The psychopharmacology branch has developed a model methodology for collecting and evaluating data on the clinical effectiveness of drugs and for dissemination of the findings, a major contribution to medicine. Within 3 years of its inception it launched its first multihospital collaborative treatment study project. The branch developed a common research protocol for use in varied settings, and in 1959 nine hospitals agreed to follow it to make a definitive assessment of several kinds of phenothiazines that were being used in the treatment of schizophrenia.

Since then, this single protocol, multiclinic type of study has been used to evaluate the effectiveness of several other types of drugs: the tricyclic antidepressants, the MAO inhibitors, and a variety of minor tranquilizers prescribed both to hospitalized patients and outpatients. The new technology of quantifiable and replicable clinical evaluations has now reached hundreds of hospitals.

Drug Research Information Network

The psychopharmacology branch also has developed an administrative mechanism to coordinate clinical studies by a number of independent investigators. The mechanism known as the Early Clinical Drug Evaluation Units (ECDEU) Program began in 1960 and was further developed with the introduction in 1967 of the Biometric Laboratory Information Processing System (BLIPS).

Clinical drug studies, which had been conducted in various settings such as State hospitals, university hospitals, and outpatient departments, had used such disparate protocols that it was frequently impossible to compare results from studies employing the same drug in terms of the populations studied, the drug dosages used, or the efficacy and toxicity measures employed. The ECDEU Program, a type of collaborative research, established a nationwide network of research units necessary for clinical testing of psychopharmacological agents. BLIPS is an attempt to document the findings through a common reporting system. It consists of detailed input forms with information about the study protocol, the characteristics of each patient, a record of dosages received by each patient, the side effects, a set of rating scales to describe the symptoms, a set of computer programs that edit the input forms, and a data bank in which all information from studies processed by the system are entered. Data can then be selectively retrieved from this bank for specialized research.

The system provides for the accumulation of comparable data, which in turn facilitates scientific inference. As a consequence, the branch has been able to carry on systematic data collection, analysis, integration, and dissemination so that clinical trial rather than clinical impression is now prerequisite for the wide application of therapeutic drugs. (The psychopharmacology branch system for standardizing and sharing research information might be considered a model for dealing with similar problems that exist in psychotherapy research.)

Psychopharmacological Treatment of Schizophrenia

The Cooperative Studies in Psychiatry Group of the Veterans Administration and the collaborative studies of NIMH have contributed to the proof—and to the methodology for that proof—that the neuroleptic drugs (antipsychotic agents), properly prescribed, are effective in the treatment of schizophrenia.

The discovery of effective drugs for treating the symptoms of schizophrenia ranks as one of the salient advances in the field of modern psychiatry. Before the discovery of drugs such as chlorpromazine and the other phenothiazines, schizophrenics were considered to have a poor prognosis. Today, the drug-treated patient is more accessible to other kinds of treatment and we are witnessing a resurgence of psychosocial treatment for even the most seriously ill patients. It is now rare to find an institution that does not offer schizophrenic patients a combination of drug treatment with individual, group, and milieu therapies.

In order to help a schizophrenic patient, it is necessary to reduce the psychopathology so that the patient may avoid hospitalization, or, if hospitalized, be speedily returned to the community. Then the patient must be helped to maintain his gains and to function effectively in the community, thus avoiding rehospitalization. NIMH-supported studies revealed that psychopathology is reduced by drugs such as the phenothiazines, thioxanthene derivatives, and the butyrophenones. However, the rate of rehospitalization has been unacceptably high. To deal with this serious problem, NIMH shifted the focus of research toward the prophylactic action of drugs among recently discharged or partially remitted patients.

At the same time, NIMH researchers are attempting to increase the effectiveness of current drugs with a wider range of patients, and extensive research is being conducted to identify patient subgroups that are differentially responsive to particular drugs. Recently investigators have become interested in identifying patient subgroups that may be adversely affected by drug administration and in determining if such treatment may interrupt natural restitutive processes.

Several studies suggest that there are certain types of patients for whom the major tranquilizers are efficacious and other types for whom they are not. One investigator found that people with a poor premorbid personality adjustment improved on tranquilizers while those with a good premorbid adjustment did not. The short-term hope is that refinement of drug treatment will continue so that only patients who need drugs will receive them—and will get the drug best suited to them. The long-term hope is for more effective drugs. This requires further research on the nature of schizophrenia, the workings of the human brain, and the mechanisms of drug action.

The two major approaches to maintaining patients in the community have been (I) the development of long-acting drugs, and (2) the investigation of possible synergistic effects of various drugs combined with specific psychotherapeutic interventions. Search for long-acting drugs is partly inspired by the finding that many patients suffer relapse when they fail to take their prescribed drug on a regular basis after leaving the hospital. Studies have shown that the relapse rate for chronic schizophrenic patients over a I-year period ranges from about I0 percent when a long-acting, injectable phenothiazine is used for maintenance, to about 35 percent when an orally administered phenothiazine is used, to about 65 percent when a placebo is used. The interactive effects of drugs have been explored in an attempt to diminish or counter undesirable side effects. An NIMH grantee recently reported that the use of perphenazine and amitriptyline in combination appeared to diminish the side effects associated with each drug given individually.

The NIMH Collaborative Outpatient Study in Schizophrenia found that a combination of chlorpromazine and a sociotherapy consisting of intensive individual social casework and vocational rehabilitation counseling was effective in reducing the relapse rate of patients who had been discharged for 12 months. The prophylactic role of drugs appears to be enhanced by sociotherapy following 6 months of treatment, emphasizing the role of human interaction in preventing morbidity.

Psychopharmacological Treatment of Affective Disorders

Although drugs are widely used in treating depression, there is controversy about when they are useful and which particular drug or combination of drugs is most effective for a specific patient. Various typologies have been offered to identify different types of depression, but none of these diagnostic categories has achieved general acceptance. One approach is to identify patient groups on the basis of their differential responsiveness to drug therapy. Lithium has shown great promise in treating the acute manic phase of manic-depressive psychosis and may be effective in preventing recurrences of manic and perhaps of depressive episodes as well. Recently NIMH joined forces with the Veterans Administration to launch a major multihospital collaborative study of the effectiveness of lithium as a preventive agent. The tricyclic derivatives appear to be particularly indicated for people over 40 and those having symptoms of the retarded, psychotic, or endogenous pattern. The need for careful diagnosis is underlined by the finding that lithium administered to people in schizoaffective or schizophrenic states may intensify rather than relieve symptoms. Many studies of lithium's effects and mechanisms of action are underway. Since lithium seems to affect both the natural course of manic-depressive psychosis and the functioning of the thyroid gland, there is speculation that the thyroid itself may play a role in the physiological malfunctioning associated with this form of depressive illness.

Maintenance doses of amitriptyline have been effective in preventing relapse among outpatients with depressions. Imipramine, the reference standard among antidepressant drugs, generally does not afford relief until 2 or 3 weeks after treatment starts, but with small doses of thyroid hormone it may act faster, according to a preliminary study. If this is confirmed, an important and elusive goal of psychopharmacological research will have been attained: rapid drug treatment against psychotic depressions.

Impressive though the recent advances in the biology of depression have been, it would be a mistake to assume that the cause, cure, and prevention of depression will be found solely through the biological sciences and that psychological and sociocultural factors are no longer important.

Electroconvulsive Therapies

Electroconvulsive therapy (ECT) involves the induction of massive electrical discharge over wide areas of the brain which is attended by activation of the peripheral autonomic nervous system, secretions from many endocrine glands, and (unless there is neuromuscular blockade) convulsive movements.

The induction of seizures was introduced as a treatment in the 1930's by means of hypoglycemic coma and pharmacological agents such as camphor and metrazol. Electrically stimulated convulsions were subsequently found to be easier and safer. Until the drug discoveries of the

1950's, electric shock treatment was widely used for mental illness. Fractures, memory loss, fear of treatment, and postseizure confusion and panic were gradually controlled by the use of muscle relaxants, smaller amounts of electrical current, and stimulation of the nondominant cerebral hemisphere. NIMH-supported research has contributed importantly to improving the safety and effectiveness of this technique. With the introduction of the antipsychotic and antidepressant drugs, the popularity of seizure therapy dropped; however, the technique has regained favor. A new variant being tested, "multiple monitored ECT," is reputedly safe and also clinically effective after as few as two treatment sessions conducted over a 3-day period. Validation of this technique for wider use would represent a significant advance in reducing the duration and cost of hospitalization for treatment of severe depressions.

Currently investigators appear to agree (1) that ECT is the most effective and rapid treatment for relieving the symptoms of involutional melancholia and the depressed stages of manic-depressive psychoses and (2) that its use is questionable for other disorders unless there is severe depression. There is little agreement about whether ECT is useful in the treatment of schizophrenia, or whether it causes permanent brain damage even with proper medical precautions.

While the neurochemical bases for the therapeutic effects have not been established, there appears to be evidence that ECT affects the synthesis of biogenic amines and protein in the brain.

To enhance the effective dissemination and use of findings on ECT, a workshop cosponsored by the Clinical Research Branch, NIMH, and the New York Medical College on the psychobiology of ECT dealt with the clinical, biochemical, neurophysiological, and behavioral aspects of treatment of depression.

Psychosurgery

Psychosurgery, the removal or destruction of brain tissue in the absence of organic pathology, for the purpose of altering thought, mood, and behavior, has been practiced since the mid-thirties. Because of the adverse side effects attendant on brain destruction, psychosurgery has been a subject of great controversy throughout its history.

Between 1936 and 1955, perhaps as many as 50,000 psychosurgical procedures were carried out in the United States. Since psychosurgery is performed largely by private practitioners, it is difficult to obtain reliable figures on the extent of past or current use. It is estimated that approximately 500-600 such operations were performed in 1972.

Lobotomy, one form of psychosurgery, initially became popular for the treatment of schizophrenics and other patients with grossly incapacitating and intractable behavioral problems. During the past 15 years, however, psychosurgeons have recommended the extension of their practice to nonpsychotic patients—notably narcotic addicts, homosexuals, children with severe behavioral problems, and persons given to violently aggressive acts.

A major development in psychosurgery has been the attempt to pinpoint the exact locus in the brain that controls the undesirable behavior and to restrict brain destruction to that specific area. Thus psychosurgery moved from the relatively gross lobotomy, topectomy, and undercutting of subcortical connections, to its present technique of stereotaxic positioning of electrodes in the brain. This technique makes structures deep within the brain more accessible for surgery and permits the destruction of the portions of the limbic system that are believed to be involved in emotional behavior.

NIMH has supported research programs on brain function and behavior but such studies have been limited to research on animal subjects. For the most part knowledge concerning behavioral effects of altered brain function in the human has been derived from studies of traumatic brain injury, disease, or clinically essential brain surgery such as tumor removal.

NIMH has supported more research conferences on psychosurgery than research projects. During 1949-1951 three conferences on psychosurgery research reviewed evidence, and their conclusions did not encourage the support of psychosurgery on humans. The only human study supported by NIMH was a contract for research on the control of rage seizure associated with temporal lobe epilepsy. However, the preliminary findings did not warrant destruction of brain tissue and therefore no psychosurgery was performed.

Perhaps the major benefit from NIMH interest in psychosurgery has been the increased sensitivity of investigators to the many complex and profound ethical issues involved, particularly the question of whether irreversible brain damage is ever warrented for purposes of achieving behavior control.

Psychosurgery can only be evaluated as a treatment if there is a systematic collation of information on the extent of use, types of patients treated, the specific surgery employed, and the specific short- and long-term effects on patient behavior, affect, and cognition.

At this point, the most promising direction of research remains within the area of basic brain-behavior approaches. The potential benefits of psychosurgery must be carefully weighed in each instance against possible risks to the patient.

Megavitamin Therapy ("Orthomolecular Psychiatry")

Proponents of megavitamin therapy have claimed to provide an effective treatment for schizophrenia and other disorders. Megavitamin—or orthomolecular—therapy involves the administration of high doses of vitamins to compensate for a postulated defect, presumably in the transmethylation of norepinephrine. The term originally applied to large doses of nicotinic acid (vitamin B3) but has subsequently been applied to the use of other vitamins such as B6 and B12, and "orthomolecular psychiatry" now supplants the original term. It has been hypothesized that schizophrenia is an incipient form of cerebral pellegra; thus people with this disorder require large quantities of vitamins, presumably because of a block between the substrate vitamin B3 and its synthesis into the coenzyme NAD.

The originally modest claims for this treatment now include reports of successes with hyperactive children, childhood autism, alcoholism, arthritis, hyperlipidemia, geriatric problems, and some neuroses.

NIMH has supported research in this area since 1959 and continues to support five research projects, but NIMH grantees have failed to replicate the effects. In 16 controlled clinical trials by different investigators, none has supported the claimed favorable findings.

A Task Force of the American Psychiatric Association has concluded that the research studies claiming evidence in favor of this form of therapy are inadequate and do not meet minimal scientific standards.

Possible long-range toxicity of the continued administration of nicotinic acid has also been investigated. An NIMH staff member in reviewing reports of such investigations concluded that evidences of toxic reactions in man include duodenal ulcer, abnormal liver function, hyperglycemia, and extraordinary increases of serum uric acid. Reviews of these issues occurred during the NIMH-sponsored workshop on the orthomolecular treatment approach in schizophrenia held in 1973. Despite the failure of research to support the claims of clinicians, a number of them report that they have observed impressive changes in patients after this form of therapy.

Miscellaneous Somatic Therapies

Acupuncture and body therapies are not new. They are mentioned together here because their use is relatively new and limited in the United States and they have not yet been subjected to systematic research.

Acupuncture

Acupuncture involves the insertion of needles into special points of the body to effect beneficial physiological and psychological change. It has been part of Chinese medicine for nearly 5,000 years. While there are no scientifically acceptable research studies explicating acupuncture, there is considerable evidence that it has been employed successfully as a form of anesthesia for surgery. One Russian study reported that acupuncture was found to be useful in the therapy of some psychoses and neuroses; the most favorable results were with manic-depressives. In the People's Republic of China, acupuncture is not mentioned as a significant treatment for emotional disorders, perhaps because the Chinese believe that mental illnesses cannot be a significant problem under their political and economic systems. Nonetheless, the Chinese report the use of acupuncture in conjunction with phenothiazines and "heart-to-heart talks."

One basis for studying acupuncture is the possibility that it may present an alternate approach to hypnosis and trance. It is possible that a psychotherapy patient who is accessible to hypnosis and meditation will also respond well to acupuncture.

The effective mechanisms of acupuncture remain unexplained and therefore invite the interest of the Western investigator. It will be important to understand the manner in which acupuncture takes advantage of anatomically or neurophysiologically determined capacities of the central nervous system. The prescientific explanation in terms of altered "energy flow" and restoration of the balance of "life force" in vital organs is neither congenial nor enlightening to Western scientists. However, some psychiatrists claim to see parallels between this view of life-force energy and psychic energy or orgone-energy concepts.

Although it is premature to use acupuncture in the mental health field, a knowledge of the underlying mechanisms might further the understanding of the pathogenesis of some mental disorders. Careful research is necessary to inform and protect the public.

Body Therapies

Bioenergetics, structural integration, and other such body therapies aim at releasing emotional and body energy and restoring natural postures and movements. When originally introduced, bioenergetics was designed to extend analytic psychotherapy to the study of a patient's posture and movements in relation to his personality and temperament. In its current form, bioenergetic therapy has come to mean the use of exercises, stressful postures, and movements to increase the client's awareness of the level, flow, and blockage of his energy. By modifying body configuration, therapists hope to modify character structure.

Structural integration ("Rolfing") assumes that emotional and psychological events may produce chronic postural imbalance attributable to muscular compensation and changes in supporting connective tissue. Treatment consists of a number of sessions of deep manipulation of the muscles and fascial connections in an attempt to stretch them and make them more elastic. The manipulation is painful and often stimulates the recall of old emotional or physical traumas, but treatment usually does not involve conversation, since the emotional and psychological changes are expected to follow from the body manipulation alone.

The techniques of F. Matthias Alexander and the "system" of Moshe Feldenkrais are also based on the belief that systematic body work—including, for example, manipulation, massage, exercise, postures, movements—is an effective way of changing behavior and experience of the world. Within the past few years numerous popular accounts have spread enthusiastic claims for the means and goals of body work, causing great demand. The need is apparent for NIMH to initiate and support careful research on these somatic techniques and their mechanisms and effects.

EFFECTIVE TREATMENT FOR MINORITY AND LOWER SOCIOECONOMIC CLASS PATIENTS

The difficulties of determining the appropriateness and efficacy of a specific treatment are compounded when patients belong to groups that are culturally discriminated against: women, children, the aged, minority groups, or lower socioeconomic classes. Here there are such influences as prejudice, discrimination, cultural idiosyncrasies, communication deficiencies, and resentment, plus, very often, poverty, malnutrition, and unemployment. The identification of deviant behavior in poor communities is often made first by the police. Many people may encounter the mental health care system in a drug clinic or in clinics staffed by inexperienced therapists with rapid turnover of trainees and therapists. Black psychotherapists are likely to receive referrals of other blacks, hippies, and the poor—a covert categorization that has negative overtones, regardless of the quality of either the treatment or the caseload.

Preconceptions about minorities have consistently interfered with diagnosis. For a long time it was thought that blacks had a lower frequency of depression, and depressed behavior was likely to be diagnosed as schizophrenic. Recently it was found that blacks seem particularly vulnerable to depression. In addition, the symptoms that are called neurotic in whites are sometimes called psychotic or psychopathic in blacks. More diagnoses of severe psychopathology are made among the lower socioeconomic groups. This is interpreted by some investigators as evidence of bias, and by others as evidence that people in lower socioeconomic strata are less able to cope with the stresses to which they are subjected. Diagnosis is obscured by folk beliefs among some ethnic groups such as the Spanish Americans, since outsiders to the culture sometimes mistake the manifestations of these beliefs as psychopathology.

Referral agencies, clinics, hospitals, and consulting therapists tend not to recommend individual psychotherapy for members of minority groups. This practice is frequently justified on the grounds that persons from lower socioeconomic backgrounds tend to reject treatment or to drop out of therapy, which has some basis in fact. However, white patients are accepted into psychotherapy to a significantly greater degree than black and Mexican-American patients of the same social class. Moreover, blacks brought into emergency service were found to readily accept the possibility that their behavior was related to internal states rather than external events. Similarly, a large percentage of lower-class outpatients showed improvements in physical and psychological symptoms and interpersonal relationships as a result of brief psychotherapy.

Although some investigators believe that the problems of blacks are social and not amenable to psychotherapies, others have tried to reorient therapy so that it can be effective for blacks and people of lower socioeconomic status.

There has been some experimentation with paraprofessionals who are recruited from minority groups and who therefore are familiar with the subcultures and are unburdened by professional jargon and biases. Paraprofessionals may have advantages over the professional therapists, who often have difficulty identifying with minorities and who misinterpret behavior that is actually adaptive or overreact to possible social oppression while ignoring disorders in intra- or interpersonal functioning.

While treatment should be available to anyone with an expressed need, regardless of geography, race, or socioeconomic status, it is not clear whether new treatment forms must be devised for social, cultural, and economic minorities or whether existing ones can be adapted appropriately. These basic questions remain unanswered: "What is the best kind of treatment for particular ethnic and socioeconomic groups?" and "What is the best way to persuade these groups to come for treatment and to remain in treatment?" Such questions point to the need for research to improve diagnosis and psychotherapeutic orientation, and to adapt therapy to the general racial or cultural milieu and specific needs of each patient.

RECOMMENDATIONS

Research

Since all treatment research is aimed at increasing knowledge of the processes and effectiveness of therapy, it is not surprising that the Psychosocial, Behavioral, and Somatic Treatment Subcommittees of the Study Group on Treatment Techniques independently proposed a number of overlapping recommendations for achieving these shared ends.

Because of the difficulties of specifying variables and of achieving adequate controls, therapy research—particularly psychosocial and behavioral—rarely approximates the ideal research design. Findings obtained from research conducted by independent investigators are rarely replicable, generalizable, or cumulative, because standardization of description and reporting of variables has never been achieved. These facts have been accepted by some as the basis for urging that further efforts toward achieving scientific rigor in the nonsomatic treatment field be abandoned. This counsel of despair was rejected in favor of supporting research that combines clinical complexity with experimental rigor. Research should attempt to specify the treatment task, the nature of the intervention, the process and action mechanisms of "therapeutic agents," and the nature, degree, economy, and durability of effected change. The relative effectiveness of different forms of therapies for specified patients should be assessed. Accordingly, high priority is given to the development of measures for assessing change in a broad range of human functioning. In categorizing kinds of patients, it is important not only to consider diagnosis and personality differences, but also to consider cultural or class differences that might affect response. The role of suggestion and placebo should be carefully assessed. Research studies should be designed to contribute to answering the complex questions of what kinds of changes are effected by what kinds of interventions with what kinds of patients/clients/problems, offered by what kinds of therapists under what kinds of conditions.

Primary Emphasis on Research Concerning the Treatment and Prevention of Mental Disorders

Many have come to believe that all problems which produce dysphoria, unhappiness, discomfort, and "maladjustive behavior," are mental health problems. Three separate classes of problems have been so classified:

1. Classical mental illness—mental disorder and problems of adjustment as psychiatrically defined.

2. Social problems—problems that appear to be predominantly environ-

mentally induced and maintained, affecting such particularly vulnerable segments of the population as the poor, black, young, and aged.

3. Problems of self-actualization and fuller use of potential, i.e., the achievement of "positive mental health." Since mental health is an ideal rather than a definable state, the extension of this view has already led researchers into the study of such subjects as creativity, leisure activities, humor, entertainment, pleasure, esthetic gratification, and spiritual peace.

While it is a proper function of the Federal Government to be concerned with improving the well-being, quality of life, and happiness of its citizens, the NIMH contribution to this goal must be delimited. All Federal agencies share this general aim, but NIMH's distinctive role is that of the treatment and prevention of serious mental disorders. Many—if not all—Federal agencies are concerned with the amelioration and prevention of one or another social problem and the fuller utilization of capacities. The degree to which emotional disturbances (as distinct from temporary unhappiness and dysfunction) are attributable to social structures and institutions should, of course, be identified by careful research in the area of mental disorders. Further, NIMH should continue to have an important advisory and consultative role with regard to prevention and treatment of social problems and for the enhancement of the functioning of the already effectively functioning individual.

Continued Emphasis on the Development of Valid and Reliable Measures of Specified Criteria of Change and Outcome

Treatment research reports have had only modest impact, in part because neither the criteria nor the measures employed by researchers have achieved wide acceptance or credibility among the practitioners and clinicians who are responsible for patient care. It is necessary to identify criteria from diverse domains relevant to theory and practice and to develop well-standardized measures appropriate for use by each of the relevant reporting sources: patient, therapist, and independent observer (professional and nonprofessional).

The interpretation of such measurement should distinguish between "change" and "outcome"—that is, it is important that the investigator indicate what criteria of change he has used in arriving at a judgment regarding degree of improvement. It should be clearly recognized that external behavior and internal experience as types of change may be far from identical. Improvement should be interpreted in terms of the individual patient. The generalizability of findings should, however, be to classes of patients.

- Increase comparability of data derived from studies conducted by independent investigators by use of standardized instruments, core batteries, and standardized report forms. The utilization of comparable measures of criteria derived from specified domains will permit assessment of relative effectiveness of techniques within and between various treatment forms. The ECDEU Program of the Psychopharmacology Research Branch provides a model of such efforts.

- Determine whether different therapies, interventions, therapist styles, and conditions produce different kinds or amounts of change in comparable patients, or produce the same changes more quickly, or with greater durability, and with fewer noxious effects. Despite numerous claims, there is still no firm evidence that specific forms of psychosocial and behavioral therapies produce different kinds or amounts of change in comparable patients.

- Determine whether specific forms of therapy interventions are uniquely suited for some types of patients rather than others. Patients may select or be assigned treatments in part on the basis of their socioeconomic class membership, availability of treatment, and untested assumptions regarding appropriateness. It is necessary to determine more appropriate bases for effecting the most useful matches of patient and therapy and therapist.

- Increase emphasis on identification of patient groups who are positively or negatively affected by specific treatments. For example, careful diagnosis and followup must be undertaken to identify patients who are "drug resistant," who respond differentially to certain drugs, or who are adversely affected by certain types of drugs. Similar concerns are appropriate with psychosocial and behavioral therapies and with environmental manipulations.

  A popular hypothesis to be tested is the belief that there are some patients for whom the psychotic episode may be an opportunity for more effective personality reorganization. For such patients it is thought that premature or indiscriminate use of drugs may interfere with the opportunity to gain maximum benefit from their psychoses.

- Determine whether there are patient categories and problems that do not now respond appreciably to any known treatment form; if there are such categories, attempt to develop appropriate new techniques and approaches. Null or negative response may be characteristic of specific diagnostic categories, minority groups, and lower socioeconomic class groups.

- Continue development and testing of various therapeutic techniques and interventions to increase effectiveness and decrease harmful side effects. Examples of needed investigations include:

a. Study of various forms of therapist styles and training.

b. Study of new psychotherapy techniques and procedures such as transactional analysis, primal therapy, transpersonal therapies, etc.

c. Development and testing of behavior control instruments for patient use in a natural setting.

d. Extension of the behavior therapist's role into the natural environment by the training of parents, teachers, peers, etc., to continue behavior modification.

e. Self-control measures for reinforcement of appropriate behaviors in the absence of the therapist.

f. Extension of biofeedback applications to clinical problems.

g. Development and testing of new drugs and physical interventions to assess efficacy and safety.

h. Increased emphasis on preventing and reducing the incidence of serious side effects of drugs. The chronic use of drugs as a prophylactic agent against relapse to schizophrenia appears to have its hazards—for example, extrapyramidal reactions and neurological complications such as tardive dyskinesia. Such hazards must be reduced.

• Increased emphasis on long-term followup and rehabilitation; maintenance of change. Many studies on treatment and recovery from mental illness have ended when the patient has been discharged from the hospital or clinic. Further research is urgently needed on the total rehabilitation process as it takes place both inside and outside institutions, as it evolves over time, and as it may be affected by crisis intervention and other short-term interventions.

Operant methods have been effective in altering patient behavior and producing dramatic immediate change, but extensive research is needed on methods of maintaining such improved behaviors beyond the treatment period. Followup studies are essential to test the sustained effects of these treatment procedures.

During the past 15 years schizophrenic patients have been hospitalized for shorter periods than previously, but they have been readmitted more frequently. Moreover, unless adequate followup programs are provided, many patients may be unproductive and unable to sustain themselves adequately in family or community living. Further, the absence of adequate community care programs has encouraged the use of neuroleptic agents for prolonged and indefinite periods without proper supervision, a practice that appears to increase the likelihood of dangerous side effects.

• Increased study of effects of combined pharmacotherapy and psychosocial therapies on specified patient populations. Because the combined use of drugs and psychotherapy is common, it is important to study the enhancing and possibly inhibiting effects of such practices. Careful research on interactions is necessary, giving attention to optimal timing, sequence, and combination of psychological and pharmacological methods of treatment.

• Increased research on the early detection of emotional problems, with special emphasis on children and on testing the efficacy of various modes of intervention. The early identification of individuals manifesting disturbances in mood, thought, and behavior may permit the interruption and reversal of processes that could produce serious problems, some of which might be resistant to change at a later time.

Organizational

A Center for Research on Psychosocial Treatments should be established in order to provide a focal point for the NIMH research activities in the broad field of psychosocial and behavioral treatments applied to the full range of clinical populations. Specifically it should undertake to coordinate, analyze, and evaluate current research supported and conducted by NIMH and to support the development of instruments, measures, and research methodology to facilitate the conduct of research on psychosocial treatments. The center will prepare and disseminate information regarding NIMH research efforts and findings related to the mechanisms, processes, and outcomes of psychosocial treatments of the mental and emotional disorders.

Particular emphasis should be placed on stimulating, supporting, and conducting research on new psychosocial treatment approaches aimed at the psychoneuroses, personality disorders, and certain other nonpsychotic mental disorders. Some of these clinical studies could be collaborative undertakings with the NIMH center staff developing specific protocols and working closely with grantees and other investigators.

Coordination, Analysis, and Evaluation of NIMH-Supported Research

In the course of its growth the NIMH support and conduct of psychosocial treatment research has been scattered among different segments of NIMH, NIAAA, and NIDA. Within NIMH, treatment research is the concern of such units as the Clinical Research Branch, the Psychopharmacology Research Branch, Applied Research Branch, the Center for Studies of Crime and Delinquency, and the Intramural Research Program. The Mental Health Study Center includes among its activities studies of some treatment methods and health education. Several branches within the Division of Mental Health Service Programs also sponsor research on psychosocial treatments. The Mental Health Services Development Branch supports a variety of projects involving rehabilitative counseling, milieu therapy, and behavior modification treatments.

Despite the fact that the support of psychotherapy research appears to be widely dispersed within the NIMH, there was no conviction among the Research Task Force participants that administrative reorganization and centralization of all existing psychotherapy research-support units into a single organization such as the proposed research center would better serve the NIMH mission. The existing organizational units reflect different orientations and functions. Some are organized to study the treatment of specific target problems: schizophrenia, depression, addiction, crime, and delinquency; other units focus on investigating systems of treatment delivery; still other organizations sponsor research on the synergistic effects of combining different forms of psychosocial and biochemical therapies. Consequently, reorganization into a single administrative unit would be difficult. It was urged that each parent organization carefully review its own administrative structure to determine if its psychosocial treatment functions would be better served by some reorganization or reintegration of its components.

While there was reluctance to recommend an administrative coordination function for the center (planning, directing, integrating the total NIMH psychosocial treatment research), there was great agreement regarding the potential utility of the center in providing an information coordination function—a function that is not now filled by any existing NIMH unit. This

346

fact became painfully apparent when attempts were made to identify, review, and assess the psychosocial research supported or conducted by NIMH during the past 25 years.

Based on the development of a clinically meaningful project coding system, the center could collate and integrate records and reports of psychosocial research conducted by the NIMH intramural and extramural research organizations. Facts thus derived on the nature and scope of research could be used to explicate research trends and emphases, information which would be made available to program directors and planners for their guidance.

While systematic evaluations of proposed research are effectively performed by the peer review system, no comparable detailed, rigorous, and scientific assessment is now undertaken of completed research projects. The center would undertake to obtain assessments of research results and the credibility of inferences and generalizations. Such evaluations would be sought from highly qualified independent reviewers and staff who would be asked to assess specified projects and research areas; resulting information would be made available to NIMH scientists and administrators. Such reports should be of particular value to those charged with the responsibility of encouraging practitioners and administrators to implement, adopt, or test treatment innovations based on the NIMH-supported research.

Support for the Development of Instruments, Measures, and Research Methodology

By its own efforts or through suitable mechanisms the center would encourage development of needed instruments, measures, and research methodology. For example, the field still lacks instruments to measure the mental health aspects of change, such as positive integration and increased sense of well-being, which are the goal of many therapies. A consultative function could also be performed for investigators in assisting them to increase their awareness of relevant research.

Dissemination of Information

a. Seminars: The center would sponsor demonstration and research seminars lasting for periods of 2 or 3 months. Outstanding practitioners of various schools, teachers, and researchers would be invited to attend and present recorded or live demonstrations of their treatment techniques. The opportunity for prolonged exposure to and searching discussion of their various ways of working would enable the participants to achieve an exchange of views not possible by more usual media of scientific communication, such as conferences and journals. Seminars should lead to vastly improved understanding of similarities and differences among treatments. Such seminars, providing a relatively neutral setting for cooperation and understanding of shared goals and problems, also should contribute to more effective communication and collaboration between clinicians and researchers.

b. Special Reports: These would be issued periodically in an effort to provide reliable and current information to the researcher, practitioner, administrator, educator, and potential patient. Reports would include what has been learned from research on psychosocial treatments sponsored by NIMH and other research organizations. The material to be prepared and disseminated would include not only summaries based on progress reports or final reports prepared by investigators but also critical assessments of the inferences to be drawn from research in specified areas.

Stimulation and Support of and Collaboration on New Psychosocial Treatment Research Concerning Psychoneuroses, Personality Disorders, and Other Nonpsychotic Mental Disorders and Adjustment Problems

While specific research organizations currently direct their efforts toward such mental disorders as schizophrenia and depression, no comparable emphasis has been placed on the study of treatment of the nonpsychotic patient/client. The center would seek to stimulate, support, and collaborate on some of the research. It would seek to integrate and to conduct systematic studies of the process and outcome of a variety of approaches including particularly the new forms of psychotherapy that are widely practiced but not systematically studied.

The center staff would attempt to develop uniform data collection and evaluation procedures that could be used by collaborating investigators. These procedures would facilitate the pooling of data, the central analysis of data, and the dissemination of definitive reports to the professional and nonprofessional world.

Location of Proposed Center

The Center for Research on Psychosocial Treatments could appropriately be located in the Clinical Research Branch of the Division of Extramural Research Programs, and could incorporate and supersede the present Psychotherapy and Behavioral Intervention Section.

References

Ayllon, T., and Azrin, N.H. The Token Economy: A Motivational System for Therapy and Rehabilitation. New York: Appleton-Century-Crofts, 1968.
Baer, D., Wolf, M.M., and Risley, T. Some current dimensions of applied behavior analysis. Journal of Applied Behavior Analysis, 1:91-97, 1968.
Ban, T. Psychopharmacology. Baltimore: Williams and Wilkins, 1969.
Bandura, A. Principles of Behavior Modification. New York: Holt, Rinehart and Winston, 1969.
Bergin, A.E., and Garfield, S.L. (eds). Handbook of Psychotherapy and Behavior Change: An Empirical Analysis. New York: Wiley, 1971.
Bergin, A.E., and Strupp, H.H. (eds). Changing Frontiers in the Science of Psychotherapy. Chicago: Aldine and Atherton, 1972.
Birk, L., Stolz, S.B., Brady, J.P., Brady, J.V., Lazarus, A.A., Lynch, J.J., Rosenthal, A.J., Skelton, W.D., Stevens, J.B., and Thomas, E.J. Behavior Therapy in Psychiatry. Washington, D.C.: American Psychiatric Association, 1973.
DiMascio, A., and Shader, R.I. (eds). Clinical Handbook of Psychopharmacology. New York: Science House, 1970.
Effron, D.H. (ed). Psychopharmacology—A Review of Progress: 1957-1967. Washington, D.C.: U.S. Govt. Print. Off. PHS No. 1836, 1968.
Eysenck, H.J. (ed). The Effects of Psychotherapy. New York: International Science Press, 1968.
Fink, M., Kety, S., McGaugh, J., and Williams, T.A. (eds). Psychobiology of Convulsive Therapy. New York: Wiley, 1974.

Fiske, D.W., Hunt, H.F., Luborsky, L., Orne, M.T., Parloff, M.B., Reiser, M.F., and Tuma, A.H. Planning of research on effectiveness of psychotherapy. Archives of General Psychiatry, 22:22-32, 1970.

Frank, J.D. Persuasion and Healing: A Comparative Study of Psychotherapy. Baltimore: Johns Hopkins Press, 1973.

Franks, C.M. (ed). Behavior Therapy Appraisal and Status.New York: McGraw-Hill, 1969.

Goldstein, A.P., Heller, K., and Sechrest, L.B. Psychotherapy and the Psychology of Behavior Change. New York: Wiley, 1966.

Greenblatt, D.J., and Shader, R.I. Benzodiazepines in Clinical Practice. New York: Raven Press, 1973.

Hamerlynck, L.A., Handy, L.C., and Mash, E.J. (eds). Behavior Change. Champaign, Ill.: Research Press, 1973.

Hogarty, G.E., and Goldberg, S.C. Drug and sociotherapy in the aftercare of schizophrenic patients. Archives of General Psychiatry, 28:54-64, 1973.

Joyce, C.R. (ed). Psychopharmacology: Dimensions and Perspective. London: Tavistock, 1971.

Kiesler, D.J. The Process of Psychotherapy: A Review of Research. Chicago: Aldine and Atherton, 1973.

Klein, D.F., and Davis, J.M. Diagnosis and Drug Treatment of Psychiatric Disorders. Baltimore: Williams and Wilkins, 1969.

Levine, J., Schiele, B.C., and Bouthilet, L. (eds). Principles and Problems in Establishing the Efficacy of Psychotropic Agents. Washington, D.C.: U.S. Govt. Print. Off. PHS No. 2138, 1971.

London, P. Behavior Control. New York: Harper and Row, 1969.

Luborsky, L., Singer, B., and Luborsky, L. Comparative Studies of Psychotherapies: Is It True That "Everbody Has Won and All Must Have Prizes"? Presidential Address. Society for Psychotherapy Research, 5th Annual Meeting, June 14, 1974, Denver, Colo.

Meltzoff, J., and Kornreich, M. Research in Psychotherapy. New York: Lieber-Atherton, 1970.

Parry, H.J., Balter, M.B., Mellinger, G.D., Cisin, I.H., and Manheimer, D.I. National patterns of psychotherapeutic drug use. Archives of General Psychiatry. 28:769-783, 1973.

Prien, R.F., Caffey, E.M., Jr., and Klett, C.J. Prophylactic efficacy of lithium carbonate in manic-depressive illness. Archives of General Psychiatry. 28:337-344, 1973.

Rogers, C.R. On Becoming A Person. Boston: Houghton-Mifflin, 1961.

Rubenstein, E.A., and Parloff, M.B. (eds). Research in Psychotherapy. Washington, D.C.: American Psychological Association, 1959.

Shlien, J.M. (ed). Research in Psychotherapy. Washington, D.C.: American Psychological Association, 1968.

Strupp, H.H., and Luborsky, L. (eds). Research in Psychotherapy. Washington, D.C.: American Psychological Association, 1962.

Task Force Report: Megavitamin and Orthomolecular Therapy in Psychiatry: Report No. 7. Washington, D.C.: American Psychiatric Association, 1973.

Usdin, E., and Snyder, S. (eds). Frontiers in Catecholamine Research. New York: Pergamon Press, 1974.

Valzelli, L. Psychopharmacology: An Introduction to Clinical and Experimental Principles. Flushing, N.Y.: Spectrum Press, 1973.

Wolpe, J., and Lazarus, A.A. Behavior Therapy Techniques. Oxford: Pergamon Press, 1966.

Yates, A. Behavior Therapy. New York: Wiley, 1970.

CHAPTER 13

Research on Mental Health Services

INTRODUCTION

Improvements in the delivery of services to the mentally ill depend on three types of research, other than research on the nature and causes of mental illness and on methods of treatment. These types are (l) epidemiological and biometric studies to tell us where mental health services are most needed, how many people are suffering what types of illness, and at what cost services can be delivered; (2) studies of what appear to be better ways of delivering the services—through innovations in existing delivery systems or through the development of new systems; and (3) studies of the effectiveness and efficiency of both established and new ways of delivering services or meeting other Institute goals related to service delivery.

These three types of research may be considered as one major area—mental health services research—defined as research to provide knowledge needed for the effective and efficient delivery of mental health services. Such research includes studies and plans pertaining to the people to be served: What these people need, what financial resources are required to meet the needs, and how these resources can be obtained and most efficiently used. Mental health services research also includes studies of the means by which the services are delivered: How clinical treatment and other means of helping people meet and master mental health problems are provided in such facilities as mental health centers, hospitals, and halfway houses, and through such programs as education and consultation, aftercare, crisis intervention, referral, manpower, and transportation.

In considering mental health services research, this chapter addresses in turn each of its three principal, somewhat overlapping, components. The chapter describes the Institute's work in each area, points to important unsolved problems, and makes recommendations for Institute activities toward finding solutions.

NIMH ACTIVITIES IN BIOMETRY AND EPIDEMIOLOGY

National Reporting Program

As of l946, the year of the National Mental Health Act, relatively little research had been undertaken on the epidemiology of mental disorders. A limited number of community studies had been done; scattered studies had used data from individual States; the United States Census had periodically counted patients in mental hospitals; Selective Service had found a surprisingly high rate of rejections for mental disorder among

World War II draftees; and the Army and the Navy had found a surprisingly high rate of psychiatric casualties among men who had been accepted. But the incidence and prevalence of mental disorder for the Nation as a whole were unknown.

The Institute took several steps to improve the situation. One was to stimulate and support research on the epidemiology of mental disorders through its research grant program. Another was to undertake similar studies by investigators on its intramural research staff. A third was to use the annual census of patients in mental institutions—responsibility for which had fallen to NIMH when it was founded—for the systematic development of statistics on one large segment of the mentally ill population, those in hospitals.

In 1951, the Institute took the initiative in establishing a national reporting program to produce reliable and comparable data on first admission rates, resident patient rates, movement of patients through the hospitals, and length of hospital stay by age, sex, and diagnosis. This was done in cooperation with 11 States and the Veterans Administration. A few years later, as more and more outpatient clinics were established with funds granted to the States—under the National Mental Health Act—for the development of community services, NIMH led the way in establishing a program for the collection of data on people receiving psychiatric outpatient services. Still later the Institute set up means for collecting data on the characteristics of people using psychiatric services in general hospitals and, following passage of the Community Mental Health Centers Act in 1963, of those using community mental health centers.

The statistical material collected through this national reporting program is a primary national resource for information relevant to research on the delivery of mental health services. Table I demonstrates one important use—to provide a record of changes that have taken place in the use of psychiatric facilities in the United States since 1946. The changes have been particularly dramatic since 1955, when, after more than 100 years of a continous increase, the State mental hospitals began to see a diminishing patient population. In 1955, these hospitals accounted for about 819,000 patient care epidodes—the number of hospital residents at the beginning of the year plus the number of admissions during the year. The rate was 505 per 100,000 people. At that time the State hospital patient care episodes constituted about one-half of the total for all the psychiatric facilities operating in the United States. By 1971, patient care episodes in the State mental hospitals had fallen to some 745,000, a rate of 363 per 100,000. The total was less than one-fifth of the episodes in all facilities then operating. At that time, 8 years after the passage of the Community Mental Health Centers Act, the operating federally funded centers had a higher number of patient care episodes than the State hospitals.

Research and Development Studies

In addition to collecting and analyzing data on the Nation's psychiatric facilities and their patients, the Institute's Biometry Branch through its own resources and through grants and contracts conducts a variety of what may be called research and development activities. Some illustrations follow:

Table 1

Number of Patient Care Episodes and Rate per 100,000 Population, by Type of Psychiatric Facility: United States, 1946, 1955, 1963, and 1971

Type of Psychiatric Facility	1946 (a)	1955 (b)	1963 (b)	1971
		Number of Patient Care Episodes		
All Facilities	870,560	1,675,352	2,235,940	4,081,796
Mental Hospitals	762,108	1,030,418	1,037,286	1,020,022
State and County	587,568	818,832	799,401	745,259
Veterans	91,655	88,355	109,973	176,800
Private	82,888	123,231	127,912	97,963
Psychiatric Services of General Hospitals	108,452	265,934	349,654	542,642
Outpatient Psychiatric Clinics	N.R.	379,000	849,000	1,693,848
Residential Treatment Centers for Emotionally Disturbed Children	N.R.	N.R.	N.R.	28,637
Community Mental Health Centers	N.A.	N.A.	N.A.	796,647
		Rate per 100,000 Population		
All Facilities	629.1	1,032.2	1,197.8	1,989.1
Mental Hospitals	550.7	634.8	555.7	497.1
State and County	424.6	504.5	428.2	363.2
Veterans	66.2	54.4	58.9	86.2
Private	59.9	75.9	68.5	47.7
Psychiatric Services of General Hospitals	78.4	162.8	187.2	264.4
Outpatient Psychiatric Clinics	N.R.	233.5	454.8	825.4
Residential Treatment Centers for Emotionally Disturbed Children	N.R.	N.R.	N.R.	14.0
Community Mental Health Centers	N.A.	N.A.	N.A.	388.2

N.R.—Not reported.
N.A.—Not applicable (community mental health centers were not in existence in these years).
[a] Total excludes outpatient psychiatric clinics and residential treatment centers.
[b] Total excludes residential treatment centers.

Distribution of Mental Disorders

In the absence of more precise information on the prevalence of mental disorders, the data collected on patterns of use of psychiatric facilities—supplemented by whatever information is available from community studies and other sources of vital, morbidity, and social statistics—are used to develop estimates of the frequency of occurrence of specific mental disorders. For example, the branch has applied to a life table the first admission rates of schizophrenia to psychiatric services, as determined in several community studies and in special studies by the Institute. Based on these studies, the branch estimates that about 4.5 percent of all children born in the United States who reach the age of 15 years will develop schizophrenia during their lifetime. Each year there are about 3.7 million births in the United States; by the branch's estimate, approximately 160,000 cases of schizophrenia will develop among them.

Application of Case Register Technology

The Institute, through the branch, has also been instrumental in developing psychiatric case registers, which make it possible to follow individuals or groups with respect to the kind of psychiatric facilities to which they were first admitted, the length of care received, and the intervals between periods of care. Computer programs have been developed and are being used to obtain estimates of the cost of care for persons who enter the mental health care system through different portals and who use the system for different lengths of time.

Admission Rates to Community Mental Health Centers

Some 70 centers are involved. The analyses relate variations in admission rates to such factors as the location of the center (degree of urbanization), years the center has been in operation, and the type of administrative control—public or private.

Mental Health Demographic Profile System

This is a project to provide States with data from the 1970 census that will help them in planning community mental health center programs. Of particular interest is the identification of areas with high risk populations, meaning areas whose social and economic characteristics have been shown in demographic studies to be associated with high rates of mental illness, or social disorganization, or both.

Development of Automated Clinical Data Systems

The Institute has supported several major efforts to automate clinical data in order to provide more fully and more readily information needed for the treatment of patients, institutional and program research and management, and clinical research. Paramount among the efforts is the Multi-State Information System (MSIS), whose participants are New York, Connecticut, Vermont, Massachusetts, Rhode Island, and two mental health centers in Washington, D.C. One major project is using data given the system by four mental health centers to show the extent to which these centers are accomplishing several objectives, including equity in services delivery, accessibility to services by population subgroups, and continuity of care. Two major problems related to MSIS and similar systems are still to be solved. One is to maximize the uses by management and researchers of the data these systems can generate (MSIS at present is considerably underutilized). The other is to develop and demonstrate the usefulness of these systems for the day-to-day clinical management of patients.

Research to Improve Diagnostic Data

The Institute has stimulated two major international research projects that are directed toward developing instruments and procedures for improving the comparability of diagnostic data on the mental disorders. These projects are the Unted States-United Kingdom Diagnostic Project and the World Health Organization's International Pilot Study of Schizophrenia. Both projects are supported by NIMH research grants.

One result of the U.S.-U.K. study has been to clarify the reason for the striking differences between the two countries in the diagnoses of people admitted to mental hospitals. The clarification was obtained by using the same interviewing procedures and diagnostic criteria to examine patients in both countries. It now appears that the American concept of schizophrenia is far broader than the British, embracing many patients whom British psychiatrists would regard as suffering from mania, depression, neurotic illness, or personality disorder. These differences have serious implications for international communication on such problems as the reporting and interpretation of research findings, clinical practice, and the training of clinicians.

The WHO project has developed procedures for identifying comparable cases of schizophrenia in nine countries—Columbia, Czechoslovakia, Denmark, India, Nigeria, Taiwan, the United Kingdom, the United States and the U.S.S.R.—and for assessing the patients' outcome.

Other Research in Biometry

Among other recently completed or ongoing projects are:

- A study to produce statistics that can serve as a model for community mental health centers in analyzing the use of all psychiatric facilities in their catchment areas.

- Development of techniques to measure continuity of care.

- Development of measures—performance indicators—to show the extent to which the community mental health center program meets its objectives.

- Development of statistical methods such as profile analysis and cluster analysis to deal with certain problems occurring in psychiatric and psychological research and of mathematical models to elucidate certain phenomena in basic and clinical research.

Epidemiology Center

The Center for Epidemiologic Studies was established in 1967 as part of the Division of Field Investigations; in 1968 it was transferred to the Division of Extramural Research Programs. Its program includes contracts for the operation of two small field stations—one in Kansas City, operated by the Kansas City Mental Health Foundation, and one in Washington County (Hagerstown), Md., operated by the Johns Hopkins University. Both stations are studying representative samples of the people in their areas to determine the prevalence and depth of depressed moods, changes in these moods over time, and the possible relationships between the findings and (I) stressful events in the lives of the people being studied and (2) a number of other circumstances, including the weather and the rates of homicide, accidents, illness, unemployment. The investigators use a questionnaire developed by the center after a study of existing instruments that had been applied chiefly to clinical populations. Center researchers hypothesize that depressed moods are a good indicator of the extent of mental illness in general. It is hoped that the questionnaire will prove sufficiently reliable for wide use in epidemiologi al studies, including those that attempt to measure the c impact of community mental health centers.

Originally, the center was to have staffed and managed a number of NIMH field stations across the country. These were intended to provide a flow of information about mental health service operations in selected communities and about characteristics of the populations being served. Funds for the stations have never become available. Neither the grant nor the contract mechanism was adequate for the long-term collaboration required for these stations; also lacking was the commitment of top-level field investigators.

The center currently supports through grants about 45 research projects almost all of which have been proposed by investigators outside the Institute. Several projects are concerned with developing instruments to measure psychological well-being; several others, with uncovering the extent and causes of psychiatric impairment among children. About one-fifth of the studies, inherited from the former Center for Studies of Suicide Prevention, deal with suicide. Other current projects deal with such subjects as the epidemiology of mental retardation; the social breakdown syndrome—a pattern of chronic deterioration that develops in some people with a mental disorder; the relationship between social class and mental illness; the mental health of noninstitutionalized adults; the effects of social change on family health; the quality of life following kidney transplantation; the prevalence of psychiatric distress among university students; cultural differences in the perception of mental illness; social and situational factors among driver fatalities; and mortality associated with mental disorders. In addition to research, the center supports half a dozen training projects.

Status of Statistics on Mental Illness

The Institute's efforts in biometry and epidemiology—only a few of which were reported in the preceding sections—have consideralby increased the Nation's ability to plan and evaluate mental health service programs; the efforts have had an impact not only in this country but also abroad. Nevertheless, much further research in these areas is required.

The surveys of the Biometry Branch provide systematic data—in considerable detail for the country as a whole and in less detail for each of the States—on the universe of psychiatric facilities and their patients; however, similar data on the extent of mental disorders in the general population do not exist. Numerous community surveys have indeed been carried out in various parts of the world to determine the prevalence of mental disorders. But the data do not permit precise comparisons because of differences in the definitions of mental disorder and differences in casefinding techniques, diagnostic categories, and data-analysis methods.

Five surveys—two of them supported by the Institute—in different parts of the United States were done during the past 30 years. Their findings (with date of publication) are summarized below:

a. Of the total population of an urban area, 60 per 1,000 were on the active rolls of mental hospitals and/or other health, welfare, social, educational, and correctional agencies that provided services to persons with mental disorders (1941).

b. At least 70 persons per 1,000 in a rural county would have been referred to a mental health clinic had one existed in that county (1943).

c. At least 100 persons per 1,000 of the noninstitutional population of a major urban area had a serious mental disorder (1957).

d. Of the noninstitutional population of a large metropolitan area, 240 persons per 1,000, aged 20-59 years, were seriously impaired by mental disorder (1962).

e. In another metropolitan area, eight persons per 1,000 were known to be under the care of a private psychiatrist, a psychiatric clinic, or a mental hospital during a 6-month period (1958).

None of these surveys has yielded practical casefinding and diagnostic instruments that are highly sensitive and specific and can be applied with a high degree of reliability to individuals in the population being studied. Reliable statistics of the incidence and prevalence of mental disorders as a group, or of individual disorders within the group, do not exist for the United States or any other country.

Priority Areas for Research in Epidemiology and Biostatistics

The success of much of the research to improve the delivery of mental health services depends largely on the provision of better data about the effectiveness of those services. A major effort to obtain and apply such information is required. The most important areas of unsolved problems are:

Measurements of Prevalence and Incidence of Mental Disorders

Studies of the utilization of psychiatric facilities yield patient data that are biased by (a) the many factors that determine who goes where for specific kinds of service, and (b) the fact that many persons are treated—if they are treated at all—at other than psychiatric facilities. Such data must be supplemented by facts on the frequency of occurrence of mental disorders in the general population. This information is necessary both for gauging the need for psychiatric services and for determining their effectiveness.

Followup Studies of Patients Who Have Received Psychiatric Services

There is relatively little systematic information on the fate of patients who have been released from mental hospitals or have received psychiatric services elsewhere. Data are urgently needed on changes in the patient's clinical state, social and familial adjustment, employment status, etc. High priority should be given also to research on the extent to which community programs increase or decrease the burden of mental illness on the family and the community. Instruments for measuring "burden"—analogous to those developed by British investigators—are needed.

Factors Affecting Patients' Use of Facilities

What are the factors—attitudinal, socioeconomic, other—that facilitate access to mental health services? What are the factors that block, hamper, or prevent individuals from seeking and gaining access to such services?

Better Use of Existing Data

Computerized data systems for psychiatric facilities have made available an unprecedented body of systematic data on the demographic and diagnostic characteristics of psychiatric patients and on the treatments they have received. Now it is important to invest funds and personnel to develop methods of training present and potential users of these systems in the most effective means of using the data for planning, administering, and evaluating programs and for clinical and other types of research.

Data are also needed on:

- The extent to which mental health services are delivered, and the type and effectiveness of these services, by mental health professionals (including psychiatrists, psychologists, psychiatric social workers) in private practice; family physicians and medical specialists; and practitioners using nontraditional systems of therapy.

- The characteristics of the multiproblem family and the relationships among its various problems—medical, psychiatric, and social.

- The patterns of use of mental health and other health services at the local level.

Recommendations for Research in Epidemiology and Biostatistics

1. The Institute should expand its efforts in all the research priority problems that have been listed in this section, and it should take whatever other action may be needed to provide descriptions of the mental health care delivery system and its effect, perhaps at 3-year intervals. The description is needed in order to evaluate the system and its components and to plan services research and other measures necessary for the achievement of goals. The description should include information not only on numbers of patients and kinds of facilities but also on types of patients, disorders, therapists, and treatment and on the costs and results of treatment.

2. The Institute should use every means at its command to develop: (a) standardized casefinding techniques capable of being uniformly ap-

plied from place to place and from time to time for detecting persons in the general population with mental disorders; (b) reliable differential diagnostic techniques for assigning each case to a specific diagnostic category; and (c) methods for determining dates of onset and termination.

3. The Institute should develop study centers or field stations in several catchment areas to determine the extent to which disturbed persons, in need of mental health services, are using the available services and to what extent their use reduces the disability caused by mental disorders. Psychiatric case registers would play an important role in such studies.

4. The Institute should sponsor workshops attended by experts in cost-effectiveness research, biometry, epidemiology, and clinical care in order to (a) develop models for cost-effectiveness studies of the various kinds of mental health services, and (b) determine what new data are needed for the application of these models.

EXTRAMURAL RESEARCH ON MENTAL HEALTH SERVICES

A Short History of the Extramural Program

Since its founding, NIMH has supported the delivery of mental health services, although this support was quite limited until the advent of the community mental health centers program. It was in 1956, with passage of the amendments to the National Mental Health Act, that research on services became a discrete, identifiable program. Title V of that act authorized funds to support project grants, studies, experiments, and demonstrations to improve services to the mentally ill and to promote mental health. In effect, Title V officially recognized that the effective delivery of mental health services is a subject for formal scientific inquiry, development, and evaluation.

The first services grant under the new legislation addressed itself to discovering and testing methods of auditing service operations. Since then major contributions have been made through grants dealing with consultation and education techniques, crisis intervention, intensive treatment, partial hospitalization, community alternatives to isolated hospitalization, third-party payments, systems of organizing community agencies, uses of mental health manpower, specialized services for children and for the chronically ill, and many other subjects.

Several community programs served as prototypes of the elements of community mental health centers and helped determine the course of the legislation and the regulations governing such centers. Most concepts embodied in the CMHC model were developed and tested—some several times—as part of the services research program.

In 1966, as noted in the chapter on the history of the research programs, NIMH was reorganized and the Title V program placed in the newly formed Applied Research Branch in the Division of Extramural Research Programs. This branch focused its attention not on demonstrations but on more tightly controlled research and on the dissemination and use of research results. Projects were funded in such special problem areas as alcoholism, drug abuse, crime and delinquency, child and family mental health, and suicide. About the same time, the Institute also began placing greater emphasis on studies to improve treatment for the seriously and chronically mentally ill.

In the late 1960's and early 1970's, special problem areas received further emphasis through the creation of special centers, to which the applied research projects relating to these areas were transferred. In 1970 the mental health services research component of the Applied Research Branch was merged with the Mental Health Services Development Branch, within the Division of Mental Health Service Programs. This branch remains the focal point for the support of mental health services research.

Evolution of Approaches to Services Research

The mental health projects grants program, which encompassed services research and demonstration projects under Title V, operated for approximately the first 10 years as a traditional grants review and administration program. Investigators were encouraged by NIMH consultants to test innovative forms of care and were assisted if necessary in the preparation of proposals, which then moved through the usual grants mechanism. Under such a program, it is assumed that: (a) once awarded a grant, an investigator will complete the project and disseminate his findings, and (b) once the findings have been disseminated, they will be considered and, if useful, applied by other workers in the field. However, a 1966 evaluation study demonstrated that the assumptions were not valid in the case of services research. That study attempted to review findings of all of the services research projects over the previous 10 years. Even after persistent efforts to evoke reports from investigators, however, results could be obtained for only 40 percent of the completed projects.

Beginning in 1966, therefore, changes were made. Projects were monitored, and liaison was maintained with investigators through letters, phone calls, and consultation visits. To improve review and monitoring skills, the variables making the difference between high-payoff and low-payoff projects were studied. Briefly, it was found that the successful projects had been manned by investigators who were receptive to ideas and had energetically solicited the reactions and contributions of other people—including those who might use the findings—as early as the design-formulation phase. Host agencies had shown their interest and involvement by augmenting NIMH funding. Information about the projects had been disseminated widely, mainly through institutes, workshops, and other means of presentation that encouraged exchange of information and ideas. The same open approach had also contributed to more widespread and effective use of the findings. In all, 15 factors were found to differentiate high-payoff from low-payoff projects. These factors were converted into a checklist which was distributed for use in consultation, proposal writing, and application review.

The first generation of services research efforts, beginning in 1956, could be said to have operated under the "traditional grants review and administration" concept. The concept adopted 10 years later might be described as "monitoring toward successful completion."

359

For the first year after the monitoring plan was started, the Institute still fell woefully short of obtaining evidence of completion from all projects. Even repeated calls to terminated investigators—signaling that future grant decisions might be influenced by failure to report—produced little. In 1967, final reports could be obtained for only 53 percent of the projects within 6 months of termination. The unreported projects represented an investment of $6,166,316. In 1968, however, evidence of completion was obtained for 85 percent of the terminated projects; for 1969 and 1970, 95 percent. Evidently the monitoring concept is valuable when employed from the onset of a project.

The program then added a new goal: dissemination of research information. Program efforts increasingly emphasized the importance of effective dissemination; in some cases technical assistance and supplementary grants were offered. Of those projects for which reports were received in 1967, only 45 percent had produced at least two dissemination products, counting conferences and speeches as well as written material. By 1970, the proportion had risen to 75 percent.

Studies by NIMH, however, demonstrated that, by themselves, written materials have little effect on programs. One study found that innovators got their initial ideas from written material in only 8.5 percent of the instances. Another found that even after project results had been published several times in respected professional journals, barely 5 percent of the mental health workers for whom the information was relevant had even heard of the project. So the services research program added another goal: utilization of research results.

Through contract and in-house research the factors that help determine the utilization of project findings were studied, and the results tested. The following example indicates how utilization can be increased. Two books had been written describing the results of a "lodge" program for groups of chronic patients living and working in the community, yet only one hospital in the Nation had adopted the program—and that had been funded through a Hospital Improvement Project grant. After the employment of special utilization techniques, which included brochures about the findings, letters and visits to potential users, and the offer of a consultant to help in applying the findings, approximately 25 hospitals indicated an intention to adopt the program, and none asked additional funding from NIMH.

Only 19 percent of the investigators in 1967 could report that their results, within 6 months after the termination of the grant, were being used at other sites. However, for 1970 the proportion rose to 50 percent.

In 1971, the services research program decided that wide use of results required yet another step: planning the research from the start to meet some widely felt need. This decision was based on the discovery that research results which had appeared promising to the staff and review committee members were often, in fact, of little or no use except in the particular service system where they had originated. Perhaps they were too expensive, or they addressed problems to which most other systems had found solutions on their own, or successful application depended on an unusual set of conditions.

The new governing concept for the services research program has become "research and development." It implies that: (I) service problems are assessed and existing knowledge searched for possible solutions; (2) research is stimulated where necessary and monitored; and (3) techniques for the dissemination and use of findings are applied.

To facilitate the application of processes included in that concept, the Institute has produced a series of publications under the general title, "Planning for Creative Changes in Mental Health Services." Further, to test the research and development concept itself, the Institute is supporting several new research projects. One, a study on the transfer of knowledge, analyzes the processes that take place as mental health facilities— in this case mental hospitals—attempt to solve their problems. Particular attention is given to the role of research information—how it is sought, communicated, and used. Another project focuses on how community mental health centers identify their problems and on what role research knowledge plays in their solution. Both of these projects are testing new ways of facilitating the use of information by providing technical assistance. A third project is a study of the feasibility of having a State mental health consultant serve much as a broker of research information. This is a collaborative project of the Institute and the Utah Division of Mental Health. Through NIMH and other sources, the consultant will keep abreast of research findings bearing upon Utah's mental health problems, and he will try various means of communicating them.

In one way or another, all these projects are testing the idea of providing mental health "change agents" similar to agricultural extension workers who bring information about developments in agriculture to potential users and help in its application. A desirable next step may be to train a cadre of mental health agents to work similarly to bridge the gap between the production and use of knowledge relevant to mental health.

The Institute has evidence that the research and development concept yields benefits. In addition to continuing efforts to apply it, however, a still broader approach is desirable—one that brings together all the Institute's resources and is concerned with all the stages of research, from planning to utilization and evaluation. Such an approach, which might be called "technologic research and development," is defined as a system to develop, evaluate, and use knowledge for the creation of innovations in services delivery to attain specified goals.

The proposed system has these distinguishing features:

- Research is considered to be the entire process of transferring knowledge—from analysis of need and opportunity to evaluation of impact on policy and practice.

- A systems approach is employed, with planned and coordinated stages (both concurrent and sequential) directed toward a predetermined objective. An Institute-wide coordinating panel for mental health services research is proposed, along with research teams—drawing members from all the appropriate NIMH divisions—that would be responsible for the work in specified areas. The proposed system would accommodate findings from unsolicited research projects.

A major recommendation of this chapter is the adoption on a pilot basis of this broader research and development approach to services research.

Description of Extramural Services Research

This review covers a sample of 5 years since the Institute's beginning—1951, 1956, 1961, 1966, and 1972. During those years 46 percent of the projects coded by NIMH as "mental health services research" turned out to be research to produce new knowledge. Twenty-three percent were demonstrations; 18 percent, service evaluations; and 12 percent, training, usually of paraprofessionals.

Community Treatment and Action Programs

Research here was largely on the organization and administration of community health services and innovations in treatment techniques and in services delivery methods. The great majority of grant applications came unsolicited, with shifts in the topics reflecting changes in the needs or interests of the applicants; rarely was a project stimulated by NIMH. Early projects sought to initiate community mental health services within existing social institutions, to develop new short-term treatment procedures, and to evaluate the capability of local programs to initiate and sustain community mental health services. Later work reflected interest in adapting the principles and practices of community mental health centers for use in public mental hospitals and in adapting services more closely to client needs.

Research recently supported in this area has been about equally divided between projects seeking to improve the delivery of mental health services (these projects included epidemiological studies to determine need) and projects addressed to the development and use of new treatment procedures by community mental health programs. This pattern of support reflects the projected needs for the 1970's and 1980's.

A sample of findings from single studies:

- The availability of community mental health services decreased the occurrence of psychiatric deterioration.

- Occupational therapy services in nursing homes, plus training provided to nursing home operators, helped reduce the number of nursing home patients transferred to State hospitals.

- When patients were discharged from State hospitals, consistent support by volunteers helped them adjust to the community and reduced the projected readmission rate. Strong organizational support was needed to sustain the volunteer effort.

- Immediate treatment at critical stress periods in the lives of elderly persons living in low-cost housing apparently reduced the length of treatment and helped prevent breakdown during subsequent periods of stress.

Selection, Training, and Evaluation of Personnel

The vast majority of grants in this area were for training projects of various types to develop nonprofessional persons for adjunctive service with traditionally trained mental health professionals. In 1951 and 1956 only a very small proportion of services research was concerned with personnel. By 1961 it had risen to almost one-third. It fell to 21 percent in 1966 and to about 10 percent in 1972.

Institutional Management

Most of these studies have been conducted at State mental hospitals. A few have been made at community mental health centers and general hospitals, and recently a grant was awarded to a "people's clinic." Among other accomplishments, the State hospital studies have demonstrated the value of (1) token economy, or operant conditioning, programs; (2) the geographic unit system, in which patients are grouped according to where they live; and (3) the "lodge" system, in which groups of patients live and work together in the community.

Of particular promise in current work is a project for further developing and validating an objective, standardized, yet highly individual program evaluation system based on a technique called Goal Attainment Scaling. This scaling was first used to evaluate the relative effectiveness of four kinds of therapy offered in the adult outpatient unit of a county mental health center. The goals were the treatment goals decided upon at the start by the patient and the therapist. More than 30 settings have adopted the scale for planning treatment and for evaluating kinds of treatment, administrative procedures, and training programs.

Before 1969, less than a tenth of the services research grants supported institutional management studies, but by 1972 the proportion had risen and stood at approximately one-fifth. Because more and more of these studies are placing major emphasis on evaluation, the Institute and other agencies have made awards to the American Psychiatric Association and the American Psychological Association to develop standards for the survey and accreditation of psychiatric facilities. Existing standards, based on those of general hospitals, do not represent the broad variety of agencies now providing treatment for mental disorders.

Other recently funded projects are examining the process of discontinuing a State mental hospital and the impact of the hospital's closing, and the impact of judicial decisions—such as the recent one in Alabama stipulating standards of care to be provided by psychiatric hospitals—on mental health service delivery systems.

School Programs

Research and demonstration projects, given about equal emphasis, have been concerned with these main areas: (1) development of mental health components in school programs for persons who need help because of physical handicaps, mental retardation, cultural deprivation, or emotional disturbance; (2) preschool screening and preventive mental health services in the primary grades; (3) the impact of the school experience on the emotional development of children; (4) understanding the school mental health needs of minority groups; (5) development of means to provide mental health consultation to school staffs.

In the early 1950's, Institute-supported research helped to show how the school experience affected the emotional development of children. Later in the decade other NIMH projects led to mental health service programs to improve the learning and school performance of culturally deprived children from minority groups. Demonstrations of the efficacy of school mental health consultation in the 1960's helped lead to the provision of consultation services by community mental health programs and educational facilities.

Systems Research and Computer Studies

Computer technology has been applied to these major areas: (1) analysis of the results of treatment, where it has been particularly useful in studying the outcome of drug therapy; (2) program planning studies in mental health centers, hospitals, and elsewhere, which have been greatly facilitated by computer storage and retrieval of data on patients and by

computer simulation of various organizational arrangements and various configurations of manpower and funds; (3) studies to improve the methodology of information processing.

As mentioned earlier, a Multi-State Information System has been established which enables hospitals and community mental health facilities in participating States to store and retrieve upon demand information about a patient's medical history, diagnosis, treatment, and movement. The system contains safeguards to protect confidentiality. A drug-monitoring system records every treatment with psychotropic drugs and compiles drug-treatment histories of individual patients.

Two special programs have been established to train mental health personnel in the techniques of systems research.

Rehabilitation

Four phases of programing for rehabilitation can be identified: (1) development of rehabilitation and training programs within State hospitals in order to return patients to the community; (2) early demonstration programs to develop the base for community mental health services; (3) service evaluation projects to adapt and apply research findings to the provision of direct services; and (4) pilot projects in special need areas. The period of the 1950's was concerned primarily with phases 1 and 2. Rehabilitation programs were established within State hospitals, with specialized programs for chronically ill and elderly patients. Community-based programs, such as halfway houses and foster care and homemaker services, were demonstrated and provided the basis for social rehabilitation procedures focused on the needs of special groups, such as alcoholics, adolescents, and drug abusers. Service evaluation projects have been supported since the late 1960's.

Institute-supported projects led to incorporating rehabilitation in the treatment of mentally ill people and to including these people in community-based rehabilitation programs. Evaluation of such programs is now in order.

Financial support for rehabilitation studies has steadily declined. The decline may be related to the demonstrated effectiveness of rehabilitative measures and to the emphasis by NIMH on comprehensive community-based mental health services—which include rehabilitation—rather than on particular rehabilitation programs.

Foster Care and Adoptive Services

These services appear as a separate category in the Institute's records only in the years from 1966 to 1972, when 10 studies were supported. The research included: (a) studies to improve the match between foster home replacements and the needs of the person being placed; (b) a demonstration that foster parents can be educated to adequately care for seriously disturbed children; (c) a study, being conducted in Iran, comparing the development rates of infants reared under traditional orphanage circumstances with rates of infants reared under circumstances that have been enriched in various ways; and (d) a study evaluating foster family care in Gheel, Belgium, where such care for mentally ill and mentally retarded people has been provided for centuries. In 1971, there were 1,500 such people placed among 1,100 families—in a town with only 6,600 families.

Day Care and Home Care

The efficacy of day care for mental patients was thoroughly demonstrated by Institute-supported projects during the late 1950's and early 1960's. Projects supported since then have been directed primarily at the improvement of treatment procedures within community programs. It is now clear that community-based day-care and home-care programs (a) can be operated more economically than inpatient care; (b) have reduced transfers to State hospitals; and (c) can help persons who have been hospitalized make the transition to the community.

Program and Facility Effectiveness

The early demonstrations of what was "good" have been replaced by more sophisticated efforts to determine mental health needs, ascertain prevailing treatment patterns, and evaluate programs. One major project is constructing a predictive model intended for widespread use in the development or improvement of treatment facilities. The model makes use of: (1) a comprehensive rates-under-treatment study, to show who is currently receiving mental health care; (2) a prevalence study, involving a random sample of nonpatients in the community, to indicate the frequency of "social psychiatric impairment"; (3) socioanthropological analysis of the Florida area in which the research is being done. A number of Florida agencies have already utilized the research instruments and techniques stemming from this project and have modified their treatment program as a consequence.

An assessment manual is to provide step-by-step procedures enabling organizations to make their own assessments at the community level.

Another study, almost completed, has compared milieu therapy and social-learning therapy (based upon a token economy) with each other and also with traditional hospital treatment. All included systematic aftercare services. The subjects were chronic schizophrenic patients hospitalized more than 2 years. Of those treated in the experimental programs, 95 percent were successfully placed in their communities, in contrast to 46 percent of the patients receiving traditional hospital treatment. Data from a 2-year followup are being analyzed.

A number of projects are evaluating community mental health centers, focusing on such matters as equity of services, integration with other community agencies, continuity of care, cost-benefit comparisons, and the centers' impact on the use of State hospitals. Rehabilitation treatment programs for chronic schizophrenics, children's mental health services, and behavior modification and other techniques are also being evaluated.

Studies of the effect of architectural design on patient behavior have provided guidelines for maximizing the therapeutic influence of physical environments. The results have stimulated schools of architecture to include the design of mental health facilities in their curricula.

A Major Problem: Financing of Services

Research on mental health service financing has become an increasingly important part of the Institute's services research program. It deserves to be given high priority. Most of the grants for this type of research—totaling less than $I million during the I962-I972 period—have been awarded within the last 5 years. The resulting studies have demonstrated the feasibility of providing mental health coverage in private and public insurance programs. One study, for example, found that when short-term, outpatient psychiatric service was made available to patients in a prepaid medical program, the patients who used this service made markedly less demand upon the program's nonpsychiatric physician services and laboratory and X-ray procedures. Other studies have explored new patterns of service delivery, such as group practice and service within the work setting. Partly because of Institute-financed studies, the insurance coverage of emotional illness has significantly increased, particularly among labor groups and for outpatient care.

A number of important questions are critical to the problem of financing services. For example, to what extent do people use mental health services? How has the level of use been changing? What will or may be the level of use in the near future, given the current trends? The recent American Psychiatric Association study of mental health insurance, which NIMH supported, shows that it is rare for more than 2 percent of the covered population to use the services. Yet epidemiological studies, as reported in the first section of this chapter, have produced much higher estimates of mental health impairment, with one study reporting "serious impairment" among 24 percent of the people it surveyed.

Defintions of "serious impairment" vary, so the difference between the 2 percent who are being treated and the much higher proportions sometimes identified as seriously impaired may or may not indicate a need for more mental health services. That is an important question for study. Another is: How would national health insurance coverage for mental health care affect utilization levels? Such questions highlight the need for more attention to epidemiological research, to studies of how services are to be financed, and to manpower needs.

Evaluation of Extramural Research on Services

To assess the substantive aspects of the program, a number of questions were considered by staff of the Mental Health Services Development Branch. These are noted and answered in the following paragraphs. A subsequent section looks at the program's organizational and management aspects.

- To what extent is unproductive, incompetent, or unpromising work being supported? This question was soundly considered, with non-Federal consultants carrying out blind ratings of final reports, in 1968 only. In recent years there have been too few projects in each research category to allow sound comparisons among categories. It is the impression of staff in the Mental Health Services Development Branch, however, that almost all projects dealing with the general area of program evaluation and knowledge transfer meet high standards. Virtually every such project is dealt with as a collaborative special grant, with intensive staff input.

- How relevant has the work been in relation to the mission of NIMH? Both the demonstrations supported under Title V and the services research program itself have been closely related to the Institute's mission. They have tested and provided models for new and improved forms of mental health services. When the main responsibility for services research was vested in the Division of Mental Health Service Programs in 1970, not a single research project was being funded in the field of children's mental health services, which was soon to become the Institute's top priority; 3 years later, more than 50 percent of the new funds for services research were going into this field. Increasingly, as the division's priorities have been clarified, the services research program has taken the initiative in stimulating new substantive and methodological directions to match Institute needs. Response to the priorities is expressed by investing staff time to stimulate grants and to collaborate with investigators on selected topics, and by setting preferences on lists of projects to be funded.

- Are relevant problem areas being overlooked? The area of prevention is being bypassed. Within church and synagogue young people's groups (involving 40 million people at any one time), the program did support the development and testing of a network of training projects to enable young people to reach out and help troubled peers. Identified troubles were reduced, but prevention of breakdown was never tested.

  Investment has been inadequate, too, in research on community mental health center operations—but not because of neglect. Numerous efforts have been made to solicit research proposals, with the response generally being that centers have found it financially impossible to employ research specialists. Moreover, the centers have been so occupied with establishing and maintaining themselves that research seems to many of them something they can well do without for the time being.

- What are the gaps in knowledge, resources, or methodology? Perhaps the greatest gap is the lack of adequate methodology for field research. The control of extraneous variables is extremely difficult, and obstructing the flow of services in order to gather data causes understandable concern. The Institute's considerable investment in methods of program evaluation, such as individualized goal-attainment measurements, should help close the methodology gap. So should a handbook that is being prepared on evaluation methods in field situations.

The services research program is concerned, too, with the need to amplify the role of new knowledge in influencing decisions on policies and practices. When changes are to be made in the delivery of mental health services, the decisionmakers seldom turn to the research literature for guidance. Experiences, inclinations, seat-of-the-pants hunches, new funding resources, or other sociopolitical pressures more often determine what services are going to be offered and how. The wide use of new research findings to improve services is still a goal, not a reality.

- What significant non-NIMH support is presently available? There is support from a few foundations and a little help from the States. The Social Security Administration and the Office of Child Development, both in DHEW, now support projects relevant to mental health services. The new joint-agency funding program and integrated projects approaches are promising, though both still need some Institute funds. Community mental health centers offer some promise of conducting research without Federal support.

Critique of Organization and Management of Extramural Services Research

Staff of the Mental Health Services Development Branch point to a number of problems that plague mental health services research:

1. It seems fair to say that future needs are rarely anticipated—that NIMH-supported services research follows crises rather than anticipates them. By the time sound research findings are available throughout the field—often a period of 5 years—most potential users will have implemented their ad hoc solutions and will be less than eager to change. The approaches recommended in this chapter are intended, among other objectives, to correct this situation.

2. As judged by gross figures, there has been a significant increase in the utilization rate of project findings, but the rate can be improved. By now, approximately 50 percent of investigators who completed their projects at least 6 months ago can name one or more specific users of the results. The transfer of information from its production to its use is one of the greatest problems the Institute faces.

3. Applications for grants have been generally poor. At one recent review session in the mental health services research program, only l5 percent of the proposals were recommended for approval. Though this reflects some conservativeness on the part of the initial review group, it suggests that many investigators need help in designing their work

and in preparing their applications. For example, the general run of proposals and also of final reports indicates that the investigators do not consider the factors that help determine to what extent, if at all, project findings will be applied. Such weaknesses can be remedied through staff collaboration, but this requires a considerable investment of time even for one project; and requests and proposals have almost tripled in 3 years. Preparation of a guidance manual on designing services research is essential.

4. Review committee members are not uniformly familiar with Institute priorities, newer techniques of program evaluation, and designs fostering utilization.

5. Any project that has to run the traditional grant-review gauntlet has a low probability of being funded. Therefore the investment of staff time in soliciting research directed to critical topics and in planning that research with a collaborating investigator is often not warranted.

6. More effective methods of measuring the impact of services research projects have been needed and are now being developed and applied. The evaluations mentioned in this chapter are based upon investigator reports.

7. Until 1972 the services research program had little contact with the Institute's critically important biometry program. Deeper and more systematic coordination is urgently needed. Much the same can be said about the relation between the services research program and the centers within the Division of Special Mental Health Programs.

INTRAMURAL SERVICES RESEARCH

Description and Evaluation

The Mental Health Study Center is an intramural unit that uses a county in the Washington metropolitan area as its base of operations; it is charged with research and development of community mental health services. Founded in 1948 as the Prince George's County (Md.) Mental Health Clinic, its initial function was to demonstrate the application of public health concepts of treatment, intervention, and prevention to the problems of mental illness in the community, and to assist the county in planning mental health clinics. In 1954, the NIMH unit acquired its present name and general mission.

Between 1960 and 1968, the center moved from the Office of the Director, NIMH, where it had been placed originally, to the intramural research program; from there, to the Division of Field Investigations; and then into the new Division of Mental Health Service Programs, where it now is. Each of the moves reflected changes in the balance among community-oriented clinical, and service-related research at the center. The center had its largest staff in 1967, with 50 full-time and 15 part-time members. At present it has 27 full-time and 12 part-time members. Its budget totals $800,000 of which roughly $700,000 goes for services-related research.

A few examples of the research activity, which is discussed also in the chapter on research on social problems, are given below:

Research on Community Mental Health Center Needs

Community research undertaken by the Study Center was applied to the development and operation of its own community mental health center, a demonstration project that helped to lead to the county's three CMHC's. The research showed that if services were to be widely used: (a) they had to be close to potential consumers or at least to adequate transportation; (b) they had to be offered at hours when the potential consumers could use them; and (c) they had to be advertised in terms that meant something to these consumers. To make access easier, the center adopted a decentralized model for its CMHC; the staff worked out of those agencies the prospective clients were accustomed to visit, including clinics, schools, churches, and recreation centers. In gaining access to hard-to-reach groups, choice of sponsor was found to be a crucial factor.

Other research yielding valuable results included anthropological studies, used to identify key caregivers and to understand local customs relevant to service delivery; studies leading to a system for the identification of leaders in community associations; and studies leading to a demographic profile of a catchment area.

In community mental health centers, such as this demonstration project, the achievement of continuity of care is influenced by the degree to which subagency rivalry and territoriality can be controlled. Organizational mechanisms such as case monitors, unified record systems, clear definition or responsibility, coordinating conferences, overall administrators, and neutral ombudsmen do not in themselves counteract the strength of intergroup dynamic forces. Methods to cope with these process interferences in interagency or interunit collaboration are still in their infancy.

On the basis both of an extensive program of consultation and education and of studies on the technical aspect of consultation, the Mental Health Study Center identified a need for widespread training in consultation, a need that has not yet been addressed by the Institute.

Service-Related Research on Children and Youth

Recently completed research on achievement patterns of elementary school children reveals that the majority of children who will experience academic failure and not complete high school can be detected as early as third grade. These studies, which used information routinely kept by many school systems, provide indices for the early identification of high risk children. Methods used in the research have been adopted by several school systems in other regions; they have proved useful in evaluating efforts to prevent school dropout.

Other important projects concerning children and youth have included:

- A major research effort to understand adolescents and their needs and to develop methods for treating teenagers and their families. The results included a method for diagnosing central problems in families, a short-term method of multiple family group therapy, and a method of training therapists to carry out this treatment.

- An experimental program combining work and therapy, which was a forerunner of the national youth employment efforts.

- A study of runaways, which implicated the family, the school, and the lack of recreational activities. This project led to the study of leisure activities of youth in a poverty area, with neighborhood youth trained to obtain the data; these studies led, in turn, to the development of an effective recreation program.

- Work in progress includes studies of models of citizen-agency collaboration and of child advocacy at neighborhood, county, State, and national levels for the development of services for children.

Dissemination and Use of Findings

A study in 1972 showed that staff members were spending 25 percent of their time disseminating the findings of Mental Health Study Center projects. Until recently, the members directed their efforts almost exclusively to the mental health professional community—in clinical and university settings—and to planners and citizen interest groups. At present the primary targets for dissemination are the Institute and other Federal agencies concerned with mental health.

Two Problems Hindering Intramural Research on Services

1. The changing mandate. In studying community mental health service organization and delivery, and in designing methodology, time is needed—to study the problems, test methods to meet them, train staff, negotiate with other agencies, demonstrate, and evaluate. Changes in direction and the withdrawal of support are wasteful to research efforts.

2. Inadequate communication and collaboration between branches and between divisions. More collaboration is required among process research, applied services research (both intramural and extramural), and service development and training. It is also required between central and regional offices, and between research programs and the Office of Communications.

RECOMMENDATIONS FOR RESEARCH ON SERVICE DELIVERY

Introduction

Evaluation of NIMH-supported mental health services research points to the need for continual improvement in methods and focus on critical problems. This need becomes even more imperative when existing problems of services delivery are considered, along with the impact of major shifts in public policy on services research. More sophisticated methodologies must be developed and applied. Research projects must genuinely focus on research and development and not on the support of services themselves partly camouflaged as research. Most important, the services research program must become increasingly concerned with the identification, analysis, and solution of problems affecting entire systems of services delivery. Among these problems are those related to regionalization of services, revenue sharing, national health insurance, consumerism, and the move for coordinating health, mental health, and human services systems.

Solutions of such problems, it is true, requires action at higher levels than the Institute, but the Institute must be constantly ready to influence that action. It must be prepared to answer, through research whenever feasible, a host of questions affecting policy on services delivery. For example: As chronic patients continue to be released from State hospitals, what additional plans and facilities are needed for their care in the community? How can the financial and manpower resources tied up in the operation of State hospitals be channeled, in part, into the kinds of services people will be demanding under a national health insurance plan that includes mental health? Since a person's health is primarily a function of what happens to him outside the health care system, and since mental health workers understand this much better than most general health workers, how can the former be used most effectively under Federal plans to improve the Nation's health status?

The Institute has a more general need, as well, to be able to describe, much more fully than it now can, the country's present system for delivering mental health services and the system as it should be a decade or two from now. Action, including research on services delivery, can be most effectively taken when the discrepancies between what the country has and what it should have are made clear.

Needed: Better Coordination and a New Research Approach

To meet these needs and challenges requires both a greater coordination of all Institute elements having any concern with services problems and a somewhat different approach to services research from that commonly used by the Institute.

For achieving the necessary coordination, an Institute-wide Coordinating Panel on Mental Health Services Research is proposed. The panel would be accountable to Institute-level authority and would include representatives of biometry, epidemiology, intramural and extramural services research, operational evaluation, training, and other programs relevant to services delivery. The panel's responsibilities would include proposing a priority for technologic (or targeted) research on services for the whole Institute and coordination of the pilot research plan.

The different approach—here called technologic research—is basically the same as any other scientific investigation. It spans the same range: determination of need for new knowledge, review of existing relevant knowledge, scientific production of the needed knowledge, and dissemination of the results. However, it places emphasis not alone on the production of knowledge but also on its transfer. It goes beyond the usual research and development project in services research by making a planned, coordinated effort, drawing on all the Institute's resources, to: predict emerging problems requiring new research findings, identify existing knowledge and research in progress as bases for research to be stimulated, coordinate the convergence of knowledge sources, monitor funded studies to ensure maximum benefits, guide technical assistance efforts toward optimum adoption of research knowledge and services problem-solving, and evaluate the process and outcome of such targeted research endeavors.

This approach would be implemented on a pilot basis, and closely evaluated, over a 3-year period. The major part of the extramural program on mental health services research would continue to follow the usual research and development model, with responsiveness to investigator-initiated proposals for research. But in the pilot program the primary initiative would come from an NIMH planning team and an accompanying review panel. Even in that situation, investigators would be invited to address a specified topic and to use their own creativity to design both the techniques to be employed and the methods to test the results.

The recommendations pertaining to organization can be implemented without additional resources for staff or funding. They are placed first because, calling as they do for new directions in the services research program, they are believed over the long run to be the more important.

The substantive priorities are generally similar to those of the Division of Mental Health Service Programs and are set forth in the knowledge that full implementation would be greatly beyond present resources.

Organizational Recommendations for Services Research

The Institute should:

1. Establish an interdivisional coordinating panel for mental health services technologic research and charge it with developing an annual plan of research priorities and estimated funding levels, to be entered in the Institute's research plan. The panel should be appointed by the Director and administered by a full-time executive secretary.

2. Develop and assess over a 3-year trial period a problem-oriented program of research on mental health services—to end almost exclusive reliance on investigator-initiated, grant-supported research. The proposed program should, to a considerable degree, meet the needs for advances in technologic research in services.

3. For the pilot program, establish interdivisional research teams to develop projects in each priority area. These teams should be under the guidance of the coordinating panel, proposed in the first recommendation, which would provide core members.

4. Set aside a portion of the I-percent evaluation funds—discussed in the final section of this chapter—for assessing and refining the pilot program.

5. To help implement the proposed program, convert $500,000 of unobligated grant funds to contract funds for each of the next 3 years.

6. Stimulate new grant applications in targeted research and development.

7. Institute a trial review procedure aimed at improving the quality and quantity of grant-supported research projects in priority areas. Under this procedure, final action would be deferred on more grant applications facing rejection until the applicants had been offered Institute assistance in improving their research designs and their grant applications.

8. Establish a special initial review group for technologic research to review grant proposals stimulated under the pilot program.

9. Make administrative supplements available to successful projects for timely diffusion of their results.

10. Set the Institute's goal for its overall effort in targeted mental health services research at 20 percent of the total. This goal might be achieved gradually during the 3-year test.

Substantive Recommendations for Research on Services

The Institute should initiate or continue research on the delivery of mental health services in accordance with the order of research priorities given below.

The priorities fall into three groups: (l) research on processes basic to the successful delivery of effective mental health services, with financing set as the first priority, and quality of care the second; (2) research on means of supplying services to those needing them most; and (3) research on technological developments. The groups are of equal priority. In general, within each group, the higher the position of a research subject, the greater its priority.

Note that new priorities will continually evolve out of the recommended process under which an Institute-wide panel assesses the needs for services research at frequent intervals and establishes new guidelines.

Order of Research Priorities

Delivery Processes

1. Studies of means to ensure the adequate financing of mental health service programs. Included are studies to determine: (a) the costs of adequate benefit packages, and (b) the actual or probable effect on mental health service costs of such factors as third-party payments, national health insurance alternatives, revenue sharing, and income maintenance plans. Also included are studies of how present mental health agencies, both public and private, are financed.

2. Studies of means of ensuring high quality care and improved standard-setting procedures. Included is research: (a) to define and measure the quality and outcome of care; (b) to determine the cost-effectiveness of alternative means of delivery services; (c) to determine the relationship between type and quality of care, on the one hand, and the impact on the people being served, on the other. Included also are studies of public and private means to regulate the quality of services through the development of standards and a system of accreditation. Means must be found as well to evaluate and set performance standards for the personnel who deliver mental health services.

3. Studies of means to improve mental health service program planning and evaluation at Federal, State, and local levels. Included is research on: (a) methods for measuring continuity of care, and (b) methods of evaluating services.

4. Research on community service systems to determine:

a. Community alternatives to institutionalization. Among the questions to be answered is how the closing of State mental hospitals affects patients and the community.

b. The desirability of integrating services. For example, what are viable mixes of general health services, mental health and mental retardation services, social and legal services, alcohol and other drug services? What impact does integration of services have on patients? How does integration affect costs and efficiency?

c. The roles of public and private networks of services.

d. The importance and role of comprehensive health planning.

5. Studies of means of ensuring that consumers and other citizens have an informed and effective role in mental health services planning.

Group Need Priorities

1. Studies of means to ensure equity of access to services, and also equity of services, for all those needing them. Priority should go to research on services for groups having both the greatest needs and the greatest potential for benefits. These include children and their families, the seriously mentally ill, the poor, members of minority groups, and people living in areas where mental health services are scarce.

2. Research on cultural, social, and ethnic barriers to access and effective use of available services.

Technical Development Priorities

1. Research to develop techniques and methodologies that will enhance both our understanding of and our ability to influence a variety of factors bearing upon the quality of mental health services. Among the requirements are:

a. Means for developing generalizable knowledge.

b. Faster and surer ways of transferring knowledge from the people who have developed it to the people who can use it.

c. Improved ways of training people who provide technical assistance to those who are planning or operating mental health services.

PROGRAM OF THE EVALUATION BRANCH

Introduction

This section deals mainly with the program administered by the Evaluation Branch of the Institute's Office of Program Planning and Evaluation (OPPE) and financed by the I-percent set-aside funds authorized by the 1969 amendments to the Community Mental Health Centers Act. Under that and more recent legislation, federally financed health programs must be evaluated; up to I percent of the money appropriated for those programs may be set aside for the evaluation studies.

From 1971 through 1973, the Institute awarded evaluation contracts totaling about $2 million a year in 1 percent money, the preponderance of the funds going for studies of services. This program represents only a portion of the Institute's evaluation activities, since all major divisions are responsible for making assessments in their areas.

Characteristics and Growth of Program

The Evaluation Branch's studies differ in two principal ways—in addition to methods of financing—from evaluation research elsewhere in the Institute:

1. They assess total programs, not individual projects.

2. They are all planned in the Institute, under the direction of the Office of the Secretary, DHEW, and supported through the contracting mechanism. Proposals for other evaluation studies are usually submitted by investigators in the field, and, if accepted, are usually supported by grants.

Goals and Guidelines

Policy for the program is determined in part by the Assistant Secretary for Planning and Evaluation, DHEW, whose office sets guidelines and approves the final evaluation plan. This office also sponsors evaluation projects itself—those that cut across departmental programs or are considered to require a level of objectivity deemed more likely to be achieved outside the agency sponsoring the program to be evaluated. Funds for the Department-level program, and until recently for a similar HSMHA-level program, come from the 1-percent set-aside funds of NIMH and other agencies. In the case of NIMH, one-half of these funds have gone to support evaluations at higher levels, including the HEW departmental level.

For several years the major goal of the evaluation program was to find improvements that could be made in existing programs. But in 1972 the Institute and the Department decided on a new objective: to determine the validity of those programs. Recently adopted guidelines for deciding which evaluation projects should be funded under the 1-percent program stipulate that evaluation efforts:

- Must focus on the validity of a program's underlying assumptions.

- Must show how a program is organized to affect identified problems.

- Must be so planned and carried out that the findings can be applied either to the entire program under evaluation or to an identified major part of it, no matter where it functions.

Assessment of a program on the basis of effectiveness, efficiency, and impact is to be made only if those stipulations can be met.

The Institute is now reassessing the past results of evaluation studies and the impact of these studies on program policy and planning. Comprehensive plans relating evaluation studies to major mental health policy issues and management decisions will be developed. The aim is to encourage NIMH managers to consider routinely the results of evaluation when making decisions.

To help ensure that the results of evaluation studies are considered, the Evaluation Branch provides them to every major level in the bureaucratic hierarchy. Final reports go also to the U.S. Department of Commerce Technical Information Center, where they are available to the public.

Studies of Community Mental Health Centers

Of the 73 contracts let during the history of the evaluation set-aside funds, 29 dealt specifically with the community mental health centers program. Seven of these assessed the centers' progress toward short-term goals, such as providing a range of services, providing them equitably to all catchment area residents, providing continuity of care, and providing effective relationships with other caregiving organizations in the community. Seven studies have been methodological—attempts to improve methods for assessing advances toward such longer range goals as the centers' impact on utilization of State mental hospitals and on catchment area population, and on the effects of indirect services (e.g., consultation to schools). Other studies have examined a variety of areas such as services for children, sources of funds, community participation, and the validity of the catchment area concept.

By the end of 1973, 20 substantive evaluation studies of community mental health centers had been completed. Analysis of their findings shows that, among a number of other points:

1. Evidence of what impact centers have had on the use of State mental hospitals is equivocal. Data from the centers themselves indicate that the rate at which people in their catchment areas use State hospitals is lower than for the country as a whole. Further, the longer the center has been in operation, the lower the dependence on State hospitals. However, these comparisons are cross-sectional, not longitudinal: They assume there was no difference in rates, between catchment areas and the country at large, before the start of the CMHC program. The Institute is examining additional State statistics in order to compare areas that have centers with those that do not.

2. Centers typically underserve the elderly because old people tend not to recognize that certain problems may be problems of mental health, are often unable to travel to a convenient service location, and frequently find the cost of services a barrier. (Even under Medicare, deductibles pose a problem for those on fixed retirement incomes.)

3. The catchment area concept is a generally effective mechanism for organizing CMHC services to ensure that each citizen in an area served by a CMHC actually receives service.

Among the many current or planned evaluation activities under the 1-percent program, two seem particularly important: (a) stronger efforts to improve local, State, and regional capabilities to undertake evaluations of programs for which administrators at those levels are responsible, and (b) comparative evaluations of components of total systems of care, such as studies of efficiency of community mental health centers as compared with that of private psychiatric care.

377

Major Difficulties in Evaluating Services Programs

The objectives and goals of mental health service programs are much more difficult to delineate and quantify than most other social action programs. "Good mental health" is hard to define, "cure" nearly impossible.

When evaluations must cover both costs and benefits of a program, the problem becomes even more complicated. Most mental health centers, for example, are funded by a variety of sources and provide not only services to patients but also preventive programs, such as consultation to schools. Determining cost-benefit ratios for individual centers in relationship to people served is consequently a most difficult but not necessarily insurmountable problem.

Second only to the problems of definition, perhaps, are the issues relating to privacy. Because of the stigma still attached to mental illness, many people hesitate to talk about their illness even to friends and counselors, let alone evaluator-interviewers. Moreover, it is necessary to preserve the confidentiality of a patient's treatment program.

Another problem arises because people in charge of service programs are subject to many levels of evaluation and reporting requirements. Often administrators feel that a controlled evaluation requiring substantial input from them will infringe on their ability to provide good service. They also feel that, in the final analysis, decisions are made largely at the local level and that evaluators from Washington probably cannot help them. To a certain extent, they are right.

If Federal evaluation is to be viewed as part of the planning and management systems, then utilization of results must be considered. An evaluation study may recommend alterations in guidelines, or technical assistance, or even, at times, termination. Rarely, however, do these studies actually alter operations at the local level. Lack of impact can be blamed in part on studies whose recommendations are based on unconvincing findings. The predominant difficulty lies in regional and State evaluation systems that are insufficiently staffed or in other ways ill-prepared to provide guidance and technical assistance to centers in need of them. As noted above, efforts are being made to overcome this difficulty.

The major roadblock to fully successful evaluation activities in NIMH is the present exclusive reliance on grant and contract mechanisms for supporting evaluation studies. The contracting process takes up so much time that the results of a contracted study frequently arrive too late to influence decisions. The grant mechanism is even less responsive to the needs for evaluation, for several reasons: The subjects to be studied are usually selected by the grantee; the pace of a grantee's study is often geared to his own interests; a grantee may do his best work near the university with which he is affiliated, not always the best site for conducting studies that are to have general applicability.

Recommendations

1. The evaluative activities of the Biometry Branch, the Mental Health Services Development Branch, and the Evaluation Branch should be more clearly and closely coordinated. Quarterly or semiannual

meetings of senior staff members of these branches should be arranged to coincide with the forward planning and evaluation planning cycles.

2. The Institute should develop an in-house capability to conduct evaluation studies. This requires both the allocation of sufficient well-trained staff and the development of field stations staffed to carry out such studies.

MENTAL HEALTH SERVICES RESEARCH: A RECAPITULATION

The preceding sections of this chapter have been concerned with the services research activities of the Biometry Branch and the Center for Epidemiologic Studies, the Mental Health Services Development Branch, and the Evaluation Branch. Each major section concluded with recommendations particularly appropriate to the unit or units discussed.

This final section provides, first, a brief overview of the findings and, second, a synthesis of the recommendations.

Major Conclusions

1. Like the mental health field itself, services research has made substantial progress in the last quarter centry. From an emphasis on demonstrating new services, it has moved toward evaluating existing services, determining what changes should be made, and testing innovations. There is now a need to increase NIMH concern with the analysis and solution of systemic problems.

2. Reports from investigators in the field indicate that both the dissemination and the use of services research results have considerably improved. However, objective ways to evaluate the impact of evaluation studies need to be developed.

3. The Institute's efforts in biometry and epidemiology continue to provide excellent information about the use of psychiatric facilities. However, reliable statistics on the incidence and prevalence of mental illness in the general population do not exist; without such data it is difficult to plan most wisely for the delivery of mental health services and impossible to measure their impact accurately.

4. Activities in services research suffer from two major organizational problems:

a. The Institute's efforts in research on the delivery of mental health services need to be better coordinated so they can be most effectively planned, carried out, and evaluated. Lacking most notably have been strong bonds among the Biometry Branch, the Center for Epidemiologic Studies, the Mental Health Services Development Branch, the Evaluation Branch, and the centers having services research responsibilities.

b. As traditionally administered, the grant mechanism for the support of services research is not only slow and unwieldy but also largely unresponsive to Institute needs.

For a substantial improvement in the Institute's capability to do services research, correction of those organizational deficiencies is essential. Without such correction, efforts addressed to substantive matters will be at best inefficient and at worst useless. The one most important recommendation, therefore, pertains to organization.

Principal Recommendations

1. The Institute should immediately move to establish and test a program of services research designed to overcome the gaps in knowledge and the deficiencies in coordination, planning, and support mechanisms that hamper the present program. Specifically:

a. The Director, NIMH, should appoint an Institute-wide Coordinating Panel for Mental Health Services Research, with a full-time executive secretary.

b. The proposed coordinating panel should develop a pilot program of target-oriented studies that would comprise, by the end of a 3-year trial period, 20 percent of the Institute's total of mental health services research. To do so, the panel should establish, supervise, and provide core members for interdivisional research teams, charged with developing research studies in each priority area. Each research project should address a particular problem and be so designed that its findings will either advance other research in the area or be directly applicable to service delivery.

c. To help finance the pilot program, the Institute each year should convert $500,000 in unobligated grant funds to contract funds. To assess and make adjustments in the program, the Institute should draw upon the l-percent evaluation funds.

d. To make the research grants program more responsive to NIMH needs in services research, the Institute should: (l) stimulate new grant applications in priority areas; (2) establish a special initial review group to review the new proposals; and (3) in priority areas, offer Institute assistance to improve both research design and grant applications, instead of rejecting out-of-hand those grant proposals of less than average quality.

2. Stronger and more systematic coordination should be established among all NIMH components concerned with services research. These include the Biometry Branch, the Center for Epidemiologic Studies, the Mental Health Services Development Branch, the Evaluation Branch, and the centers within the Division of Special Mental Health Programs. While the organizational changes proposed in the first recommendation, above, should go far toward meeting the need for better coordination, still further action may be necessary. In view of the considerable importance of training—both academic and inservice—in the transfer of research knowledge, the Institute should also work for better coordination between its training activities and its mental health services program.

3. As an overriding priority in substantive matters, the Institute should undertake a major research effort to obtain: (a) reliable data on the

prevalence and incidence of mental disorders among the general public, and (b) more nearly accurate ways of measuring the need for, and the effectiveness of, specific mental health services in a given population. Among the actions required to implement this recommendation, one is particularly important: the establishment of several carefully selected field research units for the pursuit of epidemiological, biometric, and evaluative research.

4. The Institute periodically should provide a description of the national mental health services delivery system in sufficient detail for use in evaluating progress toward goals and in planning services research and other action to achieve goals. The questions addressed should include who is providing service, to whom, under what circumstances, at what cost, and with what result.

5. The Institute should support research in three areas of equal importance:

a. Processes essential to the delivery of services. In this group the first priority should go to research on ways to ensure financing of mental health services; the second, on ways to ensure quality of care; the third, on ways to improve the planning and evaluating of service programs.

b. Means of ensuring equity of access to mental health services and equity of services, with priority going to studies concerned with the groups in greatest need of services.

c. Technological developments, with priority going to methods for transferring research results from the investigator to the potential user.

6. The Institute should increase the support of research to identify, analyze, and solve systemic problems in our mental health delivery systems.

7. The Institute should make every possible effort—including the development of in-house training programs—to increase the number of trained personnel to carry out the recommended research activities.

The following chapter describes Institute policies and efforts to further the dissemination and use of information derived from every type of research, including research on services delivery, and makes recommendations for improvement.

References

Conley, R.W., Conwell, M., and Arrill, M.B. An approach to measuring the cost of mental illness. American Journal of Psychiatry, 124:755-762, 1967.

Conley, R.W., Conwell, M., and Willner, S.G. The Cost of Mental Illness, 1968. Statistical Note No. 30. Washington, D.C.: DHEW, NIMH, Biometry Branch, 1970.

Davis, H.R. Innovation and change. In: Feldman, S. (ed). Mental Health Administration. New York: Charles C Thomas, 1974.

Factors Influencing the Success of Applied Research. Los Angeles, Calif.: Human Interaction Research Institute, 1969.

Fein, R. Economics of Mental Illness. New York: Basic Books, 1958.

Follman, J.F., Jr. Insurance Coverage for Mental Illness. New York: American Management Association, 1970.

Joint Commission on Mental Health of Children. Crisis in Child Mental Health: Challenge for the 1970's. New York: Harper and Row, 1970.

Jones, D.R. Staff and Manhours in Mental Health Facilities in the United States: 1970. Statistical Note No. 51. Washington, D.C.: DHEW, NIMH, Biometry Branch, 1971.

Knee, R.I., and Lamson, W.C. Mental health services. In: Encyclopedia of Social Work. New York: National Association of Social Workers, 1971.

Planning for Creative Change in Mental Health Services. (Five-document series) Washington, D.C.: U.S. Govt. Print. Off. DHEW Nos. (HSM) 73-9145, 9146, 9147, 9148, 9149.

Reed, L.S., Myers, E.S., and Scheidemandel, P.L. Health Insurance and Psychiatric Care: Utilization and Cost. Washington, D.C.: American Psychiatric Association, 1972.

Rice, D. Estimating the Cost of Illness. Health Economic Series, No. 5 Washington, D.C.: DHEW PHS No. 947-6, 1966.

Silber, S.C. (ed). Multiple source funding and management of community mental health facilities. Selected Papers from NIMH Regional Office Funding Conference, 1970-1972. Rockville, Md.: DHEW, NIMH No. (HSM) 73-9055, 1973.

Sobey, F. The Nonprofessional Revolution in Mental Health. New York: Columbia University Press, 1970.

Taube, C.A. Staffing Patterns in Community Mental Health Centers, 1970. Statistical Note No. 37. Washington, D.C.: DHEW, NIMH, Biometry Branch, 1970.

Taube, C.A. Distribution of Psychiatric Beds by Geographic Division, 1970. Statistical Note No. 45. Washington, D.C.: DHEW, NIMH, Biometry Branch, 1971.

Taube, C.A. Caseload of Federally Funded Community Mental Health Centers, 1969. Statistical Note No. 38. Washington, D.C.: DHEW, NIMH, Biometry Branch, 1971.

Taube, C.A. State and County Mental Hospital Services, 1970. Statistical Note No. 25. Washington, D.C.: DHEW, NIMH, Biometry Branch, August, 1970.

CHAPTER 14

The Dissemination and Use of Research Information

Mental health research is not an end in itself. It acquires value only when its findings are used, whether the users are scientists, science administrators, practitioners, social agency managers, or the general public. Integral to the conduct and support of research itself, then, is the support of programs to disseminate and promote the use of knowledge that arises from it.

This chapter describes and evaluates NIMH policies and efforts to promote the dissemination and use of research findings and makes recommendations for strengthening these activities. To designate the complex of activities involved, it uses the acronym RIDU—Research Information Dissemination and Utilization.

RESEARCH INFORMATION POLICY

The Institute does not possess an explicit overall policy on the dissemination and use of research findings. Rather, its policies are found in Federal legislation, rules and practices concerning grants and contracts, DHEW and other governmental regulations and procedures, and in the process itself of stimulating and supporting a wide range of research.

Activities on behalf of the dissemination and use of research findings were authorized in the Public Health Service Act, which specifically authorized the Surgeon General to "collect and make available through publications and other appropriate means, information as to, and the practical application of, such research and other activities," and in the National Mental Health Act which includes among its purposes the coordination of researches and related activities, the useful application of results, and assistance to the States in the use of the most effective methods of prevention, diagnosis, and treatment.

Institute regulations and practices regarding research grants, contracts, and intramural research foster the dissemination of research findings to scientists. Scientists in the intramural program are encouraged to attend scientific meetings and to publish results of their research; reprints of their articles are purchased by the Institute and made widely available. Grantees are specifically informed that they are expected to share the results of their research with the scientific community. Costs of travel to scientific meetings and costs of publication in scientific journals may be met with grant funds. Publication of books, monographs, and pamphlets is also an allowable cost.

Grant regulations require the grantee to inform the Institute of results. Interim progress reports must be submitted with all applications for renewal or continuation of support. A terminal report is required within 120 days after the end of the project. If the research findings in the terminal report have been submitted for publication, the report will not be released for 6 months without the investigator's approval. If there is no indication of publication plans, the report becomes available immediately to anyone requesting it, and the information may be disseminated and used.

The Freedom of Information Act and DHEW regulations require release of certain research grant information. A monthly report listing grants awarded during the preceding month is prepared by the Institute, with the following information available upon request: general description of the project, approved budget, totals for each major cost category, and the terminal progress report.

A major difference between grant and contract policy is that the contractor does not receive final payment until the required report or other product called for in the contract is delivered, and the NIMH project officer may reject the product if it is not satisfactory.

In sum, the philosophy of NIMH toward both research and the dissemination of research findings to scientists is the same as that of the scientific community: maximum freedom for maximum creativity, publication in scientific journals, and peer review of research results.

Dissemination of information to practitioners, research managers, policymakers, and the public has not been guided by a specifically stated policy; both the intramural and extramural programs have maintained a low-key attitude toward such dissemination. Recently, however, the extramural program has taken a more active role in dissemination of research results to the public.

Regarding research utilization, the Institute has had a laissez-faire policy. With some exceptions—primarily in mental health services development and the field of delinquency—efforts to stimulate and to ensure the use of research findings have been minimal. The main reason for this lack of effort is found in the widely held philosophy that the Institute should disseminate information primarily to scientists. Moreover, staff members have been made wary by the problems of how and when to stimulate practitioners to use new research findings; they point out, for example, that research utilization demands a delicate balance between premature, risky application of knowledge and overcautious replication in a search for absolute certainties.

Nevertheless, NIMH and much of the scientific community in general have begun to change their philosophy toward RIDU. Influenced both by the public's disenchantment with science and by reductions in funds, scientists are recognizing that, difficulties in utilization notwithstanding, they are accountable for their research, and must demonstrate its relevance to the accumulation of knowledge and the solution of human problems.

Publication of findings in scientific journals, important though it is, goes only part way. It does not make research information readily and widely available to many potential users, such as agency administrators, policymakers, mental health practitioners, and the general public.

Several Institute research programs, as noted in the following section, do make purposeful use of RIDU measures in an effort to bring new knowledge to persons who can use it. Their procedures should be more generally adopted.

ACTIVITIES IN RIDU

A number of the Institute's components are heavily or solely engaged in promoting the dissemination and use of research findings. Their activities are described below. (These descriptions reflect the organizational structure of NIMH at the time this chapter was written in 1973.) All other NIMH components engage to some extent in RIDU activities, but their staffs generally do not regard this work as a primary concern.

National Clearinghouse for Mental Health Information

Until the early 1960's the Institute acted in accord with NIH policy that the dissemination of research findings was the responsibility of the researcher. Two developments made it apparent that the research scientist could no longer carry the RIDU burden alone. One was the increasing problem of scientific communication, brought on by the great upsurge of scientific and technological advances following World War II and affecting all fields of science and medicine. The other was growing congressional interest in, and questions about, the results of NIMH's rapidly expanding program.

Consequently, and with attention to a Senate committee report favoring the establishment of scientific information centers throughout the Government, the Institute in 1962 established the National Clearinghouse for Mental Health Information. The clearinghouse has built up a strong program for collecting, storing, retrieving, disseminating, and publishing scientific information on all aspects of mental health, gathered from worldwide sources. It annually has added about 35,000 documents (primarily journal articles), in abstract form, to its computer files and has handled about 500 inquiries a month from students and professionals in mental health fields.

National Clearinghouse for Drug Abuse Information

This unit, established in 1970, has operated both as a central source for the collection and dissemination of drug abuse information for all Federal agencies and as a coordinating information agency for groups throughout the country involved in drug abuse programs. It has operated a nationwide network of drug abuse information centers, developed drug abuse resource materials, and responded to inquiries from the general public as well as from special groups such as educators or research scientists. It also has operated information systems covering international drug abuse programs, the world literature on drugs, and Federal grants and contracts concerned with drug abuse.

National Clearinghouse for Alcohol Information

Established in 1972, this clearinghouse differs from the others in being operated, under contract, by a commercial firm. It has been a national focal point for the collection and dissemination of information on alcoholism and alcohol abuse. It has answered inquiries from the general public and the professional community, provided reference services, distributed documents, developed new materials and publications, and compiled directories of alcoholism programs and federally supported activities.

Office of Communications

When the Institute became a bureau in 1967, the responsibility for public information was placed in an Office of Communications. The office has worked with researchers and scientist administrators to translate scientific findings and theories into printed and audiovisual messages for the general public and the professional community. It has been the focal point for the production of magazine articles, newspaper feature stories, radio health features, films, TV features, and informational and educational brochures and leaflets on mental health topics. It also organized news conferences and produces a monthly column of news and articles that is published in a magazine for physicians. For all these activities, NIMH research staff have served as consultants and sources of information.

Since 1969, public information officers have been assigned to the divisions, where they act as intermediaries between scientists and administrators and the press and as production managers for Institute publication of scientific and technical materials. They have initiated a variety of information activities. These include, as a service to States and communities, an exchange of information about mental health educational programs and innovative mental health services. The exchange is effected through a newsletter and other liaison activities with State and voluntary organizations. About 50 percent of news releases produced by the Office of Communications have dealt with research information. Over 7,000 copies of each news release have been mailed to the press, mental health centers, academic institutions, and others.

The office has maintained a library (called the Communication Center) with a stock of some 5,000 books and 500 journals. In its weekly "Current Awareness Service," the center has supplied staff with tables of contents from journals and with listings of NIMH publications, tapes, films, and new books. Bibliographies are compiled on request. The center also has offered services not found in the traditional library: television sets for screening mental health films and for closed-circuit monitoring of such events as meetings of the National Mental Health Advisory Council and addresses by the NIMH Director, audio cassettes from a behavioral sciences tape library, and mental health films. NIMH staff have also obtained searches of several computer-based information systems—National Clearinghouse for Mental Health Information, National Clearinghouse for Drug Abuse Information, National Library of Medicine's Medline, and the Education Resources Information Center. The center has supplemented these searches with manual searches of journals and abstract publications.

Program Information Systems Branch

In the late 1950's, information about research grants and fellowships began to be coded for scientific and administrative purposes, including the dissemination of research findings, and entered into an automated system where it was retrievable upon demand. As the Institute grew and more of its programs became mission-oriented, additional information systems were set up. By 1972, there were five in all, operated out of four divisions. Because of a number of pressures—leveling of financial support, questioning of the social value of mental health research, increased concern with cost-effectiveness studies—NIMH management required a centralized, Institute-wide source of program descriptions. This need could be met neither by any of the existing systems nor by all of them put together, since their outputs were not comparable. In 1973 a new system was instituted.

The new information system has covered all NIMH grants and contracts—past and current—in research, training, and service programs. The system has yielded listings of grants and contracts and indicative abstracts, which provided an array of administrative and substantive information. The abstracts have directed the user to sources of additional information, some of which have been maintained in a backup system. Among the items stored there, in microfiche form, have been the summary sheet of the application for a research grant, progress and terminal reports of results, abstracts of published articles resulting from the project, and magnetic card records of any changes in the substantive findings. The shortcomings of this system are described in the chapter on the administration and organization of NIMH research programs.

Program Analysis and Reports Branch

This branch has used research information to prepare narrative-descriptive materials that meet internal management needs and has provided extensive summaries and reviews of NIMH-supported research to readers outside the Institute. Each year the branch has devoted substantial amounts of time and effort to the preparation of materials for budget justification and congressional testimony. The staff has also responded to numerous requests for research information from other parts of the Executive Branch and the Congress. The branch has been responsible for the "policy implication papers" requested by DHEW; these papers inform other governmental units of the results of NIMH-supported research that may have policy implications for other Federal programs.

Psychopharmacology Research Branch

Since the creation of this branch in 1956 under the name of Psychopharmacology Service Center, its efforts to foster the dissemination and use of research information have been a principal activity. A Scientific Information Unit was part of the branch until transferred to become the nucleus of the National Clearinghouse for Mental Health Information (NCMHI). Since 1959, the branch has published the Psychopharmacology Bulletin, which is distributed to 6,000 researchers throughout the world. Psychopharmacology Abstracts (abstracts of published literature) now produced by the clearinghouse was originated by the branch in the early 1960's.

The branch has made extensive use of computers both in analyzing data from clinical drug trials and for information storage, retrieval, and dissemination purposes. For example, an online real-time system that stores data on the protocols of clinical trials reported to the branch has been developed, and searches have been done to inform investigators of ongoing, planned, and completed clinical trials. Three books have been produced using the WYLBUR Text-Editing System and the Linotron Photocomposer, namely, "Principles and Problems in Establishing the Efficacy of Psychotropic Agents," "Psychotropic Drugs and Related Compounds," and "International Directory of Investigators in Psychopharmacology."

Because of the branch's extensive work in information dissemination, the World Health Organization in 1967 asked NIMH to operate a network of centers for information about psychotropic drugs. Subsequently the International Reference Center for Information on Psychotropic Drugs was created within the Psychopharmacology Research Branch; it coordinates the work of over 20 other centers.

Center for Studies of Schizophrenia

This center began a RIDU program in 1966, the year the center was formed in the Division of Extramural Research Programs. One of its first efforts was a national conference on schizophrenia, in which participants assessed the current status of research findings, determined which were ready for application in the clinical field, reviewed the status of traditional and innovative treatment methods, and considered barriers to the assimilation of new research findings in the treatment of the illness. The "Schizophrenia Bulletin," begun in 1968, has been a major vehicle for dissemination of up-to-date comprehensive information about schizophrenia. It has contained the center's annual report of progress in NIMH-supported research on schizophrenia as well as indepth reviews and syntheses.

The center has also sponsored small workshops and conferences on special subjects pertinent to schizophrenia research, such as childhood autism, high risk groups, treatment strategies, and psychotherapy in schizophrenia.

Center for Studies of Crime and Delinquency

In the interest of getting research findings disseminated and utilized, this center—in the Division of Special Mental Health Programs—has made use of publications, conferences, and direct consultation with regional, State, and local agencies. Research utilization has been one of its explicit goals. To that end, the dissemination of information to researchers and practitioners has been one of its major activities.

The center has provided funds as grant supplements to investigators who have shown the effectiveness of some procedure. The investigator has used these funds to develop a utilization kit—a package of materials including special brochures—for disseminating information regarding the research findings and their use to program administrators. The kits have been geared to the appropriate audience and disseminated by both the grantee and NIMH. In addition, the researcher has been able to use this supplemental support to hold workshops for program administrators and to do followup consultation with any agency considering adopting his research findings as part of its program. Some grantees have held 1-day utilization workshops, to which program administrators and policymakers in relevant programs have been invited.

RIDU activities within the center have also included: a series of monographs that review and evaluate important program areas in order to inform program administrators, policymakers, and other interested persons about research gaps and significant findings that could be used in the development and improvement of services; contracts to researchers to write monographs directed at future needs in the juvenile and criminal justice systems; fliers describing innovative research programs and listing names and addresses of researchers; and staff followup of promising research findings on innovative treatment models, with additional research and training project awards used to provide for further refinement of the models and for dissemination of the methods used in them to other communities and project settings.

Mental Health Services Development Branch

This branch, whose work is described more fully in the chapter on mental health services research, has operated a vigorous and carefully planned RIDU program in the Division of Mental Health Service Programs. Its objective has been a three-phase research and development program. The first phase has determined the need for scientific information about a services delivery problem and has tried to meet the need through existing information resources. When new information is needed, the second phase has stimulated research projects, and monitored them to ensure utilizable results. The third phase has promoted the diffusion and use of resulting knowledge; targets are mental hospitals, community mental health centers, State mental health authorities, regional offices, Veterans Administration hospitals, and agencies and organizations concerned with mental health.

The modes of communication have been primarily consultation, formal presentations at professional meetings, and publications. Research results from demonstration projects have been summarized for each content area. Literature reviews have been prepared on rural mental health, sheltered programs, social problems and community participation, systems research and administration, allied services, children's mental health services, clinical facilities, and program evaluation.

This branch has also studied the process of dissemination and utilization of services research information, and has developed and tested solutions to RIDU problems.

Division of Narcotic and Drug Abuse

This division's program to develop an effective narcotic antagonist has been a research and development effort and, as such, has planned from the beginning for the dissemination and use of its findings. The program has included neurochemical and pharmacological research, preclinical studies, and, if the preclinical results have been promising, clinical trials. As a final step, the drug or drugs that have proved useful will be made available for treatment of narcotic addicts.

Close monitoring of contracts by NIMH staff brings promising compounds or other findings to immediate attention. Provisions for tests of the findings can be written at once into new research contracts, thus eliminating the delays inherent in the traditional processes of publication, replication, and eventual application.

Much of the research generated in the narcotic antagonist program, particularly at the neurochemical and pharmacological level, may provide knowledge relevant to other important mental health problems. For example, information from studies of neural transmission across synapses, necessary for an understanding of how narcotic antagonists work, is also necessary for a better understanding of the biochemical basis of the major mental illnesses.

PUBLICATIONS AND OTHER RIDU PRODUCTS

This section describes briefly, mainly by examples, the kinds of publications and other products prepared by the Institute.

The print medium has been used extensively in dissemination activities. Most of the periodicals have been in special interest areas, such as the "Schizophrenia Bulletin," "Psychopharmacology Bulletin," "Psychopharmacology Abstracts," and "Drug Abuse Current Awareness Service." The "Mental Health Digest" has covered literature from the entire field of mental health, and "Mental Health Program Reports" have aimed to interpret the entire spectrum of NIMH research to interested persons.

Other kinds of publications have been monographs and syntheses of current knowledge such as "Mental Health and Social Change," "Urban Mental Health," "Cognitive and Mental Development in the First Five Years of Life," "Alcohol and Alcoholism," "Special Report on the Depressive Illnesses," and a series of monographs on crime and delinquency.

Numerous bibliographies, some with annotations and abstracts, have been published. Examples are: "Bibliography on Racism," "Alcoholism Treatment and Rehabilitation," "Abstracts of the Psychoanalytic Study of the Child," and "Bibliography of Translations in the Brain Sciences."

Technical manuals have included "Documentation of Clinical Psychotropic Drug Trials," "Planning for Creative Change in Mental Health Services," and "Administrator's Handbook on the Application of Operations Research to the Management of Mental Health Systems."

Video tape, film, and other nonprint media have been produced and are now used increasingly for educational purposes. Examples of mental health educational films are the "Social Seminar," a series of 15 films intended to demonstrate to teachers and community groups the complexity of the drug abuse problem, and "One To Grow On," a teacher-training film and discussion series intended to promote mental health in the classroom. Films have not been used widely for the dissemination of research information per se, although training films and video tapes disseminating new techniques and information are produced by grantees for practitioners, students, and researchers.

Conferences and workshops have been used as prime vehicles for sharing research information. Topics of conferences and workshops during the past few years have included child mental health, alternatives to drug abuse, problems of drug dependence, principles and problems in establishing the efficacy of psychotropic agents, mental health aspects of sickle cell anemia, emotional and physical conditions of working people, current research on amphetamine abuse, psychobiology of electroconvulsive therapy, psychology of depression, and verbal learning.

Conferences frequently lead to publications in the form of proceedings or reports, as, for example, "Recent Advances in the Psychobiology of the Depressive Illnesses" and "Proceedings of the Joint Conference on Alcohol Abuse and Alcoholism."

Activities such as television interviews with scientists and exhibits at professional meetings—plus liaison activities such as lectures by NIMH staff at universities and other institutions—also provide forums for RIDU operations.

COSTS OF THE RIDU EFFORT

Support for activities to advance the dissemination and use of research findings has been in the form of grants, contracts, and direct operations.

Research Grants

During the period 1948-1966, grants were classified as "research information and utilization" if they included one or more of these eight activities: conferences, publications, translations, travel, writing a book, bibliographies, history, and indexing and abstracting. The classifications were not mutually exclusive; a grant could be coded under several topics. Table 1 shows the totals for grants that included a provision for some RIDU activity.

On the basis of the figures on these selected grants, 475 grants totaling $14 million provided for some RIDU activity during the 18-year period. It should be emphasized that an unknown number of grants were coded under more than one classification and the figures represent total costs, of which the RIDU element may have been only a part.

Probably the only firm conclusion to be drawn is that the Institute has supported publications and conferences from almost its beginning. Support of professional travel began in the late 1950's; preparation of bibliographies, historical studies, indexes, and abstracts in the mid-1960's. The number of grants providing for information activities rose during the period, but this rise may merely parallel the growth of the entire grant program.

Table 2 shows RIDU grants in 1966-1972. The data for 1966 in table 1 cover extensions of grants made earlier; table 2 covers new awards. Beginning in 1966, grants were coded according to their primary, secondary, and tertiary purposes, and the eight RIDU topics coded earlier were compressed into three: history, publications, and conferences. Here again the same grant could be coded under several headings. During this period, the number of grants coded as having at least a tertiary interest in RIDU activities totaled 232, with expenditures of $13.6 million. When the two

Table 1

Grants Providing for RIDU Activity, 1948-1966

Classification [a]	All Grants [b]		Selected Grants [b]	
	No.	Amount	No.	Amount
Conference	125	$ 4,344,159	100	$ 3,727,840
Support of Publication	68	2,762,001	67	2,751,411
Translation	22	702,710	22	702,710
Travel	173	6,775,077	109	4,048,024
Writing a Book	145	4,385,300	137	1,235,403
Bibliography	23	787,671	6	73,250
History	28	838,142	22	479,174
Indexing, Abstracting	25	1,443,214	12	999,256
Total	609	$22,038,274	475	$14,017,068

[a] These classifications are not mutually exclusive; i.e., a grant may have been coded under more than one of the classifications (as well as under a content classification).

[b] "All Grants" includes grants that may have been minimally involved in RIDU activities; "Selected Grants" includes grants that, on the basis of the grant title, appear to have been substantially involved in RIDU activities.

392

Table 2
Grants Providing for RIDU Activity, 1966-1972

Classification	Primary [a]		Secondary		Tertiary		All Classes	
	No.	Amount	No.	Amount	No.	Amount	No.	Amount
History	22 [b]	$ 491,861	9	$1,209,029	7	$ 78,240	37	$ 1,879,130
Publications	50	2,784,367	34	3,137,166	27	1,311,124	111	7,232,657
Conferences	34	2,319,391	36	1,842,965	14	357,352	84	4,519,708
Total	106	$5,595,619	79	$6,289,160	48	$1,746,716	232	$13,631,495

[a] See text for explanation of primary, secondary, and tertiary.
[b] 22 grants were officially awarded but one was merely a change of principal investigator's location; thus in actuality 21 separate grants were awarded.

periods—the earlier 18 years and the later 7—are compared, it can be inferred that the support of these activities more than doubled in 1966-1972.

Generally speaking, however, the number of RIDU grants declined with time. Probably the main reason was a change in policy under which more information activities were supported through the contract mechanism.

Contracts

Data for contracts dealing with information projects are more detailed than those for grants and therefore are not comparable. Table 3 shows the total number of contracts, and their cost, in six RIDU categories for the fiscal years 1968-1973.

Direct Operations

Estimates of the cost or level of direct operations were difficult to obtain and must be regarded as very rough and fragmentary.

Printing and reproduction services (including those of the drug education program of the White House Special Action Office for Drug Abuse Prevention) cost slightly over $4 million in 1971 and $5 million in 1972.

In the Office of Program Planning and Evaluation, a major portion of the operation of three branches—National Clearinghouse for Mental Health Information, Program Information Systems Branch, and Program Analysis and Reports Branch—was devoted to RIDU, at an estimated cost of about $1.5 million in 1972.

The Office of Communications' budget has been about $500,000 annually, one-half or more of the budget going for the dissemination of research information.

The National Clearinghouse for Drug Abuse Information reported a 1972 budget of about $6.5 million. The National Clearinghouse for Alcohol Information had a budget of $2 million in 1972.

Costs of other direct operations in RIDU are not possible to calculate—a reflection of the fact that such activities are so embedded in most NIMH programs that they have not been accounted for separately. An estimate is that the total annual cost of direct operations devoted to the dissemination and utilization of research information is greater than $15 million.

Total Estimated Costs for RIDU for Fiscal Year 1972

Considering grants and contracts together, the estimated total extramural effort in RIDU activity amounted to some $4 million in 1972. With an estimated figure of over $15 million for direct operations, the total estimated cost of RIDU activities overall was at least $20 million.

EXAMPLES FROM OTHER AGENCIES

Elsewhere in the Government, agencies with audiences comparable in nature to NIMH's also operate dissemination and utilization programs. The Office of Education, for example, has a change agent located in each regional office, on the model of workers in agricultural field stations. The Law Enforcement Assistance Administration has, within its National In-

Table 3
Contracts Providing for RIDU Activities, 1968-1973

Classification	1968	1969	1970	1971	1972	1973	Total
Conferences, Workshops, Seminars	$ 114,562	$ 163,822	$ 55,724	$ 227,466	$ 825,814	$ 167,948	$ 1,555,336
Information Products (Books and Other Printed Materials)	125,642	206,402	187,878	336,070	690,284	172,284	1,718,560
Audiovisual Products	0	85,807	489,851	140,416	254,094	41,996	1,012,164
Information Processing (Abstracting, Indexing, etc.)	663,879	599,305	659,005	343,163	771,943	55,113	3,092,408
Public Education (Primarily Drug Abuse)	493,500	154,503	7,316	334,725	827,725	60,780	1,888,549
Communication Studies	0	7,490	787,806	716,487	292,712	0	1,804,495
Total	$1,397,583	$1,227,329	$2,187,580	$2,098,327	$3,662,572	$498,121	$11,071,512

stitute of Criminal Justice, an Office of Technology Transfer whose task is the dissemination of research findings developed by the Institute's extramural research program. It also promotes innovative criminal justice practices throughout the country. The office uses a variety of mechanisms to disseminate information. These range from publications to onsite advisers who work with State planning agencies. These persons function both as conduits of information and as change agents. The office has a small special dissemination staff that puts out "dissemination packets," and a research information bulletin; in addition, it holds symposia and workshops to disseminate research findings.

Needed is an NIMH-wide program with the goal of promoting the dissemination and use of research findings in practical settings, perhaps somewhat along the lines of these activities in other agencies.

NIMH INFORMATION ACTIVITIES: AN EVALUATION

The Institute has an imposing array of means for disseminating research findings and an impressive record of production, as gauged by the number and variety of publications (including journal articles, books, and other reports by grantees and intramural scientists), conferences, press releases, and the like. The quality of the output, particularly that written by scientists and addressed to scientists or other professionals, has generally been considered good. And a few Institute programs do foster the utilization of findings.

What is principally lacking is an Institute-wide policy on which to base a purposeful, coordinated, and planned effort to make research findings known and, whenever appropriate, to encourage their use. The lack of a central policy seems to result from two situations: Many Institute scientists and program staff members view RIDU—except for the reporting of findings in scientific journals—as neither an important nor a proper part of their activities, and Institute management until recently has maintained a laissez-faire attitude toward RIDU, particularly its utilization aspect. Accomplishments have generally depended upon individual initiative and perseverance.

A number of shortcomings result from this lack of a stated and implemented policy:

- The Institute's RIDU activities are neither coordinated nor integrated. For lack of linkage, there is a serious and sometimes costly lack of cooperation among Institute programs sharing a common interest in promoting the distribution and use of research information. The Research Task Force became acutely aware of this problem. Lack of a consistent base from which both program managers and the scientific community could obtain information about NIMH research programs has been an obstacle time and again to the Task Force operation. Attempts to develop comparable information from different research units, or from the same unit at different times, have been inefficient, expensive, and frustrating. It has been difficult and often impossible to match any one set of data with another.

396

- The Institute's RIDU activities tend to be responsive, not initiative. They rely too often on such stimulants as budget hearings and congressional mandates.

- The feedback from RIDU activities is exceedingly sparse, preventing evaluation of their effectiveness and discouraging any plans for improvement.

- No specific items for RIDU appear in NIMH operating budgets or in research grant applications, making it virtually impossible to obtain accurate information about costs of these activities.

- Although the regional offices are increasingly important in the operations of the Institute, they are only minimally involved in the dissemination and use of research information. No RIDU role has been defined for them.

- Research project files are inadequately maintained. Final reports and copies of journal articles are often missing. Moreover, whatever information the file contains is generally received from the investigator without subsequent review or evaluation. As a result, attempts to use the files as a RIDU resource are frequently frustrating, and information disseminated by the Institute is sometimes outdated and consequently misleading.

- The processing, clearance, and printing of NIMH publications are hampered by cumbersome procedures and an inordinate amount of red tape.

- NIMH mailing keys or lists are uncoordinated and too often outdated. A lack of attention to such basic matters as the accuracy and coordination of mailing keys is further evidence that the Institute has concentrated on producing research information and gives relatively little attention to an activity of equal importance, its dissemination and use.

RECOMMENDATIONS

Policy and Organization

1. The Director should issue an explicit mandate stating that efforts to disseminate and promote the use of research findings are an integral part of the Institute's research enterprise. In view of the generally laissez-faire, and occasionally even negative, attitude of too many staff members toward RIDU activities, such a mandate is basic to all the other recommendations of this chapter. A directive would help lead to the required interaction between those who conduct research and those who communicate and use research results.

2. The Institute should work as rapidly as possible to develop a coherent system for disseminating and advancing the use of research information. The system should have the capability to, among other functions: monitor and evaluate RIDU activities; anticipate research findings and trends and the impact of predictable advances in mental health research; and design effective RIDU strategies for particular purposes.

3. As the first step toward this recommended system, the Institute should assemble a staff group charged with its development and coordina-

tion. This group should be attached to the Office of the Director, NIMH. The group would serve as an advocate of RIDU and as a catalyst for improving it. Each component of the Institute would continue to be responsible for activities in advancing the dissemination and use of research information; the RIDU group would be responsible for coordinating these activities into an effective system and evaluating the system.

4. The Institute should maintain RIDU activities throughout the entire organization and not bring them together in a single centralized structure. What NIMH needs is an interactive network—not central control—but with central coordination and with central development of general policy.

5. The role and functions of the regional offices with respect to RIDU should be clearly defined and operationally set forth. The priority of RIDU in the regional offices should be elevated and one or more staff positions created to promote the dissemination and application of new findings throughout the region served.

Activities

The Institute should:

6. Increase support of syntheses, state-of-the-art studies, and other efforts to consolidate knowledge. The funding policies of Federal agencies and private organizations encourage a proliferation of research studies and do not encourage integrative and theoretical activities. But, as today's information overload attests, there is as great a need for the synthesis and integration of existing information as there is for the generation of new. Creative ability of a high order is required for true syntheses of knowledge. In most cases the ideal arrangement for developing useful syntheses is for a skilled science writer to work with well-qualified scientists. Support for efforts to consolidate knowledge should be available to both staff and grantees.

7. Set up computer data resources as part of the overall system, using the following guidelines, which are based on a review of the problems that have emerged from past program information storage efforts and on the experience of the Task Force:

a. Scientists and administrators must collaborate in the development of the information base and agree on a common set of terms and definitions. Otherwise, no one set of estimates of the extent of NIMH activities, in any given area, will be possible to obtain.

b. Management commitment to the system must be clear and sustained in order that the required information can be elicited from Institute programs.

c. Management commitment must be backed by resources. Since some kind of quick analysis can always be done to meet a crisis, inadequate resources have been given to developing an information system that would, in the long run, eliminate the need for many crash studies.

398

d. The scope of the system must be realistic. The need is for a system that will meet both administrative requirements—for planning, allocation of resources, management—and the need for research-based information. The answer to the problem of how to meet the different needs of different NIMH components is probably the development of a separate but technically compatible system for each major Institute activity.

8. Increase support of research on the dissemination and utilization process. Such questions as the following should be submitted to careful study: (a) What guidelines or criteria can be developed to assist in the wise and timely use of research findings? (b) What is the most effective way to present research information to a given audience? (c) What are the resistances to putting research findings into practice and how can they be overcome?

9. Increase support of conferences, workshops, seminars, and other meetings, with emphasis on those designed to foster utilization of research information, but decrease support for the publication of conference proceedings. Targeted workshops and seminars have been found to be effective devices for conveying information that results in change; there should be more of them. The level of support for meetings at which scientific papers are presented by and for scientists, however, appears to be sufficient.

10. Make more use of press conferences and seminars for dissemination of research information to the mass media. Meetings at which several scientists present research findings and discuss them with science writers serve not only to clarify and interpret the findings but also to inform media personnel about mental health research in general.

11. Prepare more exhibits based on research information, display them at more conventions and other meetings, and have them manned by professional staff.

12. Increase the use of films, radio, television, tape, and other audiovisual media for disseminating research information. More materials should be prepared for scientists and mental health practitioners as well as for the general public.

Procedures

The Institute should:

13. Establish procedures for the review and maintenance of reports and publications emanating from all NIMH-supported projects. Reports include progress and final reports resulting from grants and contracts, and reports and publications written by intramural research staff. Whenever possible, evaluations should state the actual or potential implications of the findings for further research, treatment, delivery of services, or other applications. They should be distributed through a periodically published research highlights document, and a comprehensive file should be maintained for use by Institute staff.

14. Study its publication procedures, with a view toward simplifying and streamlining them. A simplified set of procedures kept up-to-date through regular monitoring would result in better, more timely, and less expensive publications.

15. Work—preferably in concert with other agencies—to improve clearance and publication procedures, practices, and policies within the Federal Government.

16. Construct and maintain a centralized, computerized, accurate mailing list. The list should be coded to yield, for any mailing, the most appropriate audience without duplication.

Standards and Quality Control

17. NIMH should make every effort to ensure that the information it gathers, disseminates, and uses is accurate, timely and as comprehensive as required.

a. Emphasize quality, not quantity in its research information program. If there must be a choice between fewer publications or other information products of outstanding merit and more materials of less merit, the Institute should take the first alternative. An improved RIDU program means better, not necessarily more.

b. Apply the highest standards of writing and editing and of graphic and artistic design to all research information publications.

c. Provide investigators with funds, where needed, for editorial support. Funds for consultation with authorities in one or another scientific field are often provided to grantees. Support for consultation on, or the actual writing and editing of, grant reports is just as important. Some scientists are skilled writers; many are not. This recommendation is made in the interest both of improving and expediting the reports required by the Institute.

d. Build rigorous quality control procedures into all computerized information systems.

e. Foster the education and training of RIDU specialists in mental health. The dearth of competent manpower in almost all phases of information and utilization activities is a serious handicap. Needed are skilled science writers and mental health journalists, editorial personnel at all levels, audiovisual specialists, computer specialists, systems managers, and utilization specialists and consultants.

Financing

The Institute should:

18. Maintain support for RIDU activities at approximately the current level for the next few years. An improved and expanded RIDU program does not necessarily require more funds, since a more orderly, coherent program can result in the more effective use of available resources.

19. Set up an informative and efficient method of recording and accounting for funds expended on RIDU.

20. For those RIDU activities that can be predicted accurately, provide consistent and regular support. Funds for many RIDU activities have been available on a sporadic basis. This kind of fiscal expediency greatly reduces the quality of the program and increases the costs.

Cooperation

21. The Institute should work closely with other agencies and organizations engaged in disseminating and advancing the use of mental health research information to develop a nationwide network or consortium. The Institute should also expand its activities to foster the development of a worldwide mental health information system.

22. As the Institute's RIDU system is developed, NIMH should look toward a coalition or pooling of resources with other organizations, public and private. Pooling of resources may be difficult to accomplish but may become necessary because of the costs of sophisticated information systems.

References

Benn, G. Technology in Retrospect and Critical Events in Science. Chicago: Illinois Institute of Technology, 1969.

Communication Systems and Resources in the Behavioral Sciences. A Report by the Committee on Information in the Behavioral Sciences, Division of Behavioral Sciences of the National Research Council. Washington, D.C.: National Academy of Sciences, 1967.

Crane, D. Invisible Colleges. Chicago: University of Chicago Press, 1972.

Davis, J.M. The transmission of information in psychiatry. Journal of the American Society of Information Scientists, 33:111-115, 1970.

Freedman, D.X. Can We Put Research to Use? Highlights of the 17th Annual Conference, VA Cooperative Studies in Mental Health and Behavioral Sciences, St. Louis, Missouri, March 13-15, 1972.

Garner, W.R. The acquisition and application of knowledge: A symbiotic relation. American Psychologist, 27:941-946, 1972.

Garvey, W.D., and Griffith, B.C. Scientific communication as a social system. Science, 157:1011-1016, 1967.

Glaser, E.M., and Taylor, S.H. Factors influencing the success of applied research. American Psychologist, 28:140-146, 1973.

Gross, S.B. The psychiatric information network: A challenge to psychiatry. Comprehensive Psychiatry, 11:559-567, 1970.

Havelock, R.G., and Lingwood, D.A. R&D Utilization Strategies and Function: An Analytical Comparison of Four Systems. Final Report to Manpower Administration of the U.S. Dept. of Labor. Ann Arbor: Institute for Social Research, University of Michigan, 1973.

Knowledge Into Action: Improving the Use of the Nation's Social Sciences. Special Commission on the Social Sciences of the National Science Board. Washington, D.C.: National Science Foundation, 1969.

Kochen, M. (ed). The Growth of Knowledge. New York: Wiley, 1967.

Nagi, S.Z., and Corwin, R.G. The Social Contexts of Research. New York: Wiley-Interscience, 1972.

Project on Scientific Information Exchange in Psychology, Vols. 1, 2, 3. Washington, D.C.: American Psychological Association, 1963, 1965, 1969.

Rome, H.P. Prospects for a psi-net: The fourth quantum advance in psychiatry. Comprehensive Psychiatry, 8:450-454, 1967.

Science, Government, and Information: The Responsibilities of the Technical Community and the Government in the Transfer of Information. President's Science Advisory Committee. Washington, D.C.: U.S. Govt. Print. Off., 1962.

Sherwin, C.W., and Isenson, R.S. Project Hindsight: A Defense Department study of the utility of research. Science, 156:1571-1577, 1967.

UNISIST. Synopsis of the Feasibility Study on a World Science Information System. Paris: Unesco, 1971.

Yarrow, M.R. Research on child rearing as a basis for practice. Child Welfare, 52:209-219, 1973.

Yolles, S.F. Government activities in health communications. American Journal of Psychiatry, 126:191-195, 1969.

CHAPTER 15

The Administration and Organization of NIMH Research Programs

INTRODUCTION

The Research Task Force had the responsibility of evaluating and recommending programmatic emphases and of identifying administrative and organizational arrangements through which research programs in mental health can best be realized. This chapter provides an overview of the considerations given by the Research Task Force to administration and organization.

MISSION AND POLICY

Basic to consideration of administration and organization are issues of mission and policy. The mission description of an organization is a functional definition of its primary task, an answer to the question: For what purpose does this organization exist? It follows theoretically, then, that assessments of an organization's performance and progress should use its mission as a yardstick. In the case of the Task Force, this principle was made explicit in the NIMH Director's charge at the opening meeting of the Research Task Force in May 1972: The Task Force was encouraged to work ". . . to ensure that this crucial activity [research] be strengthened and fulfilled in a way that advances equally the cause of science and scientists and the mission of our own Institute."

As the several components of the Task Force settled into their work, this apparently straightforward charge presented unexpected difficulties, the reason for which was not immediately apparent. Only after a series of prolonged and intense debates—in meetings of the Task Force staff, Coordinating Committee, and the Task Force consultants—did it become clear that, where NIMH is concerned, the term "mission" has widely divergent meanings for different people. In any group discussion of what the universe of NIMH research should be, a variety of different yardsticks were being applied.

The reason for the ambiguity appears clear. It lies in the essentially broad and open-ended nature of the official mandates with which the Institute is charged. It lies also in the widely divergent views among researchers regarding a valid definition of "mental health," and regarding meaningful criteria for the term "mental illness."

The National Mental Health Act of 1946, Section 2, stated:

> The purpose of this Act is the improvement of the mental health of the people of the United States through the conducting of

researches, investigations, experiments, and demonstrations relating to the cause, diagnosis, and treatment of psychiatric disorders; assisting and fostering such research activities by public and private agencies, and promoting the coordination of all such researches and activities and 'he useful application of their results; training personnel in matters relating to mental health; and developing, and assisting States in the use of the most effective methods of prevention, diagnosis, and treatment of psychiatric disorders.

This Act and the subsequent elaborations and extensions provided in the Health Amendments Act of 1956 and the Community Mental Health Centers Act of 1963 are generally regarded as defining the NIMH research mission.

The broad mandates set forth in these Acts continue to be considered as valid, portraying, as they do, the broad parameters of mental health concerns. It should be recognized also, however, that these mandates accommodate equally well the various and often conflicting interpretations of the Institute's legitimate goals made by members of the increasingly heterogeneous mental health community. It can be safely concluded that all such interpretations were represented in the spectrum of disciplines and problem orientations represented in the Task Force, and hence the continued difficulty in discussions involving "mission." It became apparent within the Task Force that legislative language—the only formal mission statement extant—could not resolve the hard questions that had been posed concerning research priorities, relevance, balance, and evaluation.

The recognition that the NIMH mission is more an umbrella than a yardstick led to a critical and useful distinction between the terms "mission" and "policy." "Mission" has already been defined as the stated purpose for which an organization exists; the term "policy" may be used to signify the prevalent mission "interpretation" that serves to define the organization's functioning at any given time. The policy, then, is derived from the interpretation of the mission by those responsible for developing programs to implement it. This, in turn, generates and elaborates a system of operating principles, guidelines, definitions, objectives, priorities, and imperatives, according to which the members of the organization carry out their work.

Obviously there is no direct correspondence between a mission and the attendant policy; a broad, general mission mandate can be interpreted and implemented in many different ways, depending on the backgrounds, abilities, personal styles, and biases of the policymakers. Indeed, it can be demonstrated that this has been precisely the case in the history of NIMH.

In the late 1940's and early 1950's, Dr. Robert Felix (the first Director of NIMH) and the newly created National Advisory Mental Health Council made a number of decisions that shaped the operating policy in the new agency. They successfully advocated NIH rather than the Bureau of State Services as the organizational base for NIMH, thus establishing research rather than services as the agency's primary task. The new Institute aligned itself with the existing National Institutes of Health in maximizing the freedom of the investigator in both intramural and extramural research programs, a policy seen as appropriate and necessary in stimulating high-quality work in relatively underdeveloped fields.

404

The research policy shaped through these early decisions was simple and straightforward: find and support the best possible research having demonstrable or plausible relevance to mental health problems.

This policy was undeniably productive. There has been solid scientific progress in many fields. The record also shows a phenomenal proliferation of investigators, disciplines, strategies, and problems addressed.

In the light of the Institute's growth and achievements, it may be asked why NIMH research policy should now require reconsideration. The view advanced here is that the world of mental health research today poses issues of management different from those of the past—and that these issues expose the need for more concretely articulated program planning.

In reviewing the research policies of the Institute, the Task Force reaffirmed that the National Mental Health Act of 1946 and the subsequent extensions provided in the Health Amendments Act of 1956 and the Community Mental Health Centers Act of 1963 define the overall purposes of NIMH and its research mission. Existing legislation, it is agreed, provides the guiding force and philosophy for the Institute's efforts.

As already noted, the tacit policy direction that shaped the NIMH programs in the past was appropriate during the years in which mental health research was beginning its growth and proliferation. Two decades ago there were comparatively few scientists devoting their efforts to mental health research, and the Institute's policy was well understood by the small staff around the NIMH Director; the Institute's research programs advanced in quality and scope without need for a clearly articulated policy.

Over the past 25 years, however, the environment gradually changed. Today, hundreds of scientists in many different disciplines are seeking solutions to the incredibly diverse mental health problems besetting the Nation. Both the knowledge base and the numbers of trained investigators are approaching a critical mass; as the body of this report attests, significant progress has been made, and many scientists feel that we stand at the threshold of even more striking advances.

Despite the record of progress, the American research community is facing difficult issues, including problems related to accountability, its scientific approaches to the solution of practical problems, and disappointment on the part of many people with the gap between the promises and the fruits of science and technology. Moreover, the issues now confronting the scientific community are only part of the changed scene in contemporary society. Depletion of natural resources, the complexity of modern living, massive shifts in ethical and moral values, new lifestyles, the rising consciousness of attitudes and actions affecting minority groups, changes in the speed and modes of communication and transportation—these are only a few of the societal forces impinging on mental health research as well as science in general.

Finally, it must be acknowledged that diminished resources, both absolutely and relatively, impose the requirement for careful review of policy. Not all worthwhile mental health research can be supported now or in the future; difficult choices will be forced, and a clearly voiced policy to guide decisionmaking becomes essential. Equally difficult choices would be confronted as well if NIMH's resources were suddenly to undergo a marked expansion.

All of these developments were taken into account in the Task Force's deliberations on research policy. After many hours of discussion, the Task Force was able to formulate a set of principles that it presents as guidelines for NIMH research policy.

GUIDELINES FOR AN NIMH RESEARCH POLICY

The research policy for NIMH recommended by the Task Force evolves from policies of the past. To some extent it highlights aspects of the policy on which the Institute's productive research activities over the years have been based.

An essential element of the recommended NIMH research policy is explicit acknowledgment that the universe of mental health research must be broad and comprehensive, ranging from studies at the molecular level to analyses of whole societies. It is clear from the knowledge accumulated through mental health research since NIMH was founded that, to understand normal and abnormal behavior, it is imperative that the domain of mental health research be characterized by breadth and diversity. The goal of NIMH to find the cause, effective treatment, and means of prevention of mental disorders requires this kind of a diversified approach.

Related to this requirement is the recognition of the intrinsic interrelatedness of mental health research approaches. Although specific research projects may focus on either biological, psychological, or social processes, the NIMH research policy should make clear that these processes are all interconnected and interactive; the Institute must continue to support all these approaches, for to limit one of them would be to vitiate the others.

Flexibility must be maintained. Rigidly prescribed mechanisms and procedures are anathema to research. Just as the individual scientist must be free to pursue new paths as new knowledge emerges, so NIMH as an organization should be able to effect changes easily in its research support programs and procedures.

A corollary of the maintenance of flexibility is that NIMH arrive at decisions regarding its research programs and projects on an inductive basis. Generalizations to guide the research program are better achieved by moving from the particular to the general than by attempting to apply overall formulas. This approach to research management can be viewed as analogous to case or common law, in contrast to the formally stated principles of Roman law—an approach especially important in the process of setting priorities.

NIMH research management should continously analyze program distribution, and decide on specific priorities appropriate to given circumstances. Similarly, the individual scientists—as always in research—will constantly set the day-to-day priorities for their own research. This emphasis on adaptability and rational selection of choice as circumstances change will provide a research program that is truly accountable to the larger society.

Another important policy issue concerns the role of basic and applied research. Effective intervention in many mental health problems depends on knowledge we do not have as yet, and basic research is likely to be the prime source of such knowledge. Private foundations, business, and the States provide minimal financial support for investigator-initiated basic research in mental health. The domain is largely a Federal responsibility, and within the Federal establishment principally an NIMH responsibility.

It should go without saying that in order to apply existing and new knowledge to the end of developing more effective means of treating and preventing mental disorders, a variety of applied research undertakings are also needed. In fact, since research efforts of an applied nature give rise to questions that require more basic investigations, these two general types of research are to an extent interdependent.

Basic research poses accountability problems for a public agency because of the very nature of science. Needed new knowledge cannot be produced on demand; rather, it characteristically emerges from unsuspected directions and in unplanned ways. Since this is the case, the distribution of basic research funds and projects within the context of a set of socially defined problem areas or research goals is an unrealistic exercise. For these reasons, the Task Force recommends that basic and applied research be treated separately in program planning. As the scientific cornerstone of the entire research enterprise, basic research should be allotted a substantial and stable proportion of the entire research budget; the sole criteria for support should be scientific excellence, timeliness, and potential relevance to mental health as these are interpreted in the peer review system.

Applied research, on the other hand, can be more closely planned, managed, balanced, and evaluated. The objectives and the achievements of applied research are more readily categorizable and thus more amenable to planning. By preserving this distinction between basic and applied research, it should be possible to establish a far greater degree of program planning than now obtains, without jeopardizing the freedom of inquiry that is the lifeblood of basic science.

The Task Force draws particular attention to the criterion believed to be critically essential in the implementation of any research policy—that of scientific excellence. Research that is in any way trivial, faulty, or unproductive cannot be supported, and the NIMH must adhere firmly and unwaveringly to the highest standards of quality where scientific endeavor is concerned.

Still another element of NIMH research policy considered by the Task Force is the role and responsibility of the scientist and the managers of research programs in setting policy and in making decisions about NIMH research. The Task Force concludes that scientists and research managers must take an active part in determining the course of the NIMH research program, and must play a decisive role in program planning and priority setting; it recommends that decisionmaking regarding research programs be widely distributed and shared throughout NIMH, thus continuing a viable process of participatory management.

In summary, the Task Force recommends that NIMH make explicit a research policy that affirms the breadth and diversity of mental health research and the necessity for a balanced approach, calling upon efforts in the biological, psychological, and social sciences; a policy that is flexible and adaptable, with appropriate recognition of the differences in basic and applied research for planning purposes, that cleaves to the highest standards of scientific excellence, and that delegates much of the decision-making power for the research program to the research managers and research scientists.

Finally, of central importance to policy issues is the further recommendation that the Director of NIMH should be more directly involved in the Institute's research programs, both intramural and extramural, and in developing and implementing its policies. As is reflected throughout this report, the Task Force is convinced that the Institute's research activity is the fundamental ingredient of its overall program, and that scientific endeavor across all relevant disciplines is basic to the achievement of the Institute's goals.

The Task Force concludes further that in the environment of competing NIMH programmatic priorities, the research activity of NIMH has received insufficient support and understanding. It is recommended, therefore, that steps be taken to ensure that the role and goals of research be better understood and more strongly advocated by Institute management.

A RESEARCH INFORMATION SYSTEM

We have seen time and again in the course of the Task Force the lack of a consistent data base from which both program managers and the scientific community alike can obtain information about NIMH research programs. As noted in the chapter on the dissemination and use of research information, it has been difficult, expensive, and often impossible to develop comparable information from all the different research organizations within the Institute, or even for the same organization over a period of years. As a result, a quantitative description of our past efforts in various research areas has been elusive. Evaluation efforts have been similarly hampered.

The basic fact that NIMH is a public agency dispensing public funds requires that the distribution of those funds by a variety of both management and substantive categories be available on quick notice. In this connection, the Wooldridge report ("Biomedical Science and Its Administration: A Study of the National Institutes of Health" 1965, U.S. President's NIH Study Committee, Dr. Dean C. Wooldridge, Chairman) stated:

> . . . NIH should be able to answer, quite promptly, almost any question about almost any detail of its extramural program. This ability is not only a vital ingredient in effective supervision, but is also perhaps the most impressive evidence that effective supervision indeed exists.

NIMH should have the same capability. What is needed is a system that will meet administrative requirements for planning, allocation of resources, and management as well as for scientific content. In the past, the Institute's program analysis efforts have been geared primarily toward the latter, i.e., describing the substantive content of the program. Current systems aim at describing the richness and complexities of the research, with insufficient attention to the need to describe the overall program.

The Program Information Systems Branch is a continuation of this trend in that it takes as a primary goal the access to groupings of extramural projects according to almost any conceivable type of content. It was not designed, however, to tell anything about the relative distribution of research resources—for example, those for scizophrenia as against those for social problems. The breadth of the system (it covers research, services, and training) and its emphasis on meeting external requests for information have necessitated limits on the data to be maintained. Financial information and progress reports are excluded from computer storage and retrieval, thus severely limiting the system's use in management and evaluation. Coverage of intramural research efforts is intended, but has taken a low priority in face of the demands to maintain information on the many extramural programs presently included.

In addition to concentration on the breadth of research content, a more subtle problem has been the minimal involvement of professional research staff. All managers know their programs and projects, and feel that any attempt to classify or categorize them will do violence to the true nature of the research. This has resulted in situations in which program analysis staffs have developed information apart from the research managers, only to have its validity, and consequently its interpretation and use, challenged by staff who "know" their own programs. Because no common set of definitions, terms, or categories has been agreed upon by the administrative and research staffs, virtually any piece of information can be questioned as being irrelevant.

As suggested in the chapter on dissemination and use of mental health information, a general strategy for approaching this problem would be to establish a central system with compatible subsystems for the various program areas of the Institute. A common set of descriptors and categories, uniformly applicable across all programs, could be elaborated by individual units as needed. This would permit flexibility, and at the same time allow the individual program descriptors to relate back to the common framework. It is essential that manageable information on the outcomes of research be included. This would make possible a wide range of evaluations at the Institute, program, and scientific field levels.

The design and maintenance of such a system would be undeniably expensive. The appropriate cost comparison, however, is not with zero expenditure, but with the cost of all present efforts, plus the total annual expense of the one-shot crash analyses that are so frequently required.

To sum up: The internal research information network in NIMH is not adequate to provide the information needed to institute and maintain overall research coordination, or to answer the wide variety of evaluative and descriptive questions that are posed by scientists, administrators, Congress, and the general public. To be truly responsive to inquiries and to provide research managers with information necessary for program decisions of a scientific, administrative, or policy nature, a concerted, Institute-wide effort to develop a research information retrieval system encompassing grants, contracts, and intramural activities is required. Discussions aimed at coordinating the research effort require that the participants proceed from a common information base about the program. Unless the internal information problems of the Institute are corrected, they will continue to impede, and perhaps even preclude, meaningful coordination, discussions, and decisions by the research managers and the Institute director.

PROGRAM BALANCE AND PRIORITIES

The concepts of program balance and priorities refer here to the processes by which resources are differentially allocated among research programs and objectives. In the course of their work, the Task Force study groups identified a number of issues of balance relevant to their separate areas of concern. These are summarized here. However, it should be stressed that these issues, although important in themselves, do not involve a concern with the problem of overall program balance. This requirement can most wisely be met by continuous and conscious attention to priorities and to their implementation. The recommendations are intended, therefore, as a vehicle for conveying a sense of the broad range and diversity of issues that must be considered in dealing with overall program priorities.

Biological and Physiological Processes

The Biological and Physiological Processes Study Group analyzed the pattern of research support in the biological sciences. In 1972, they found, 61 percent of all basic biological research expenditures were in the related fields of pharmacology, biochemistry, and chemistry, leaving only 39 percent to be distributed over all the other areas of neurobiology combined. To remedy this imbalance, the study group recommends that NIMH support a broader range of biological investigations.

They point out that treatment and prevention of mental illness must be based on knowledge of how the normal brain functions and how abnormalities in fundamental processes become manifest as disease processes. A knowledge of physiology and chemistry of the component parts of the nervous system that give rise to a given set of symptoms and signs must be sought as a basis of rational therapy and the prevention of disease just as it is the basis for preventing and treating diseases of other organs.

Increased effort in several areas is highly recommended. One is the field of genetics at both behavioral and biochemical levels. A full understanding of human behavior and mental disorder requires an appreciation of the phylogenetic origin of the species and the mechanisms of genetic transmission. Another important area for expanded research is studies on how the brain develops; huge gaps remain in our understanding of developmental processes and the factors that can lead to abnormal brain development.

The Institute supports little basic research in this area. It is also essential to support work on how cell membranes function, on trophic factors in neural transmission, and on the physiology and chemistry of the brain as related to learning, memory, perception, sleep, consciousness, i.e., to normal and abnormal behavior in general. In the area of neurochemistry, it is

410

of fundamental importance to understand more about the neurotransmitters, receptors, enzymes, and hormones involved in the metabolism of drugs and other chemical substances. Other specific areas requiring further study include rigorous analyses of neuronal events underlying complex sensory and motor sequences, and attention to neuronal systems other than the classical motor and sensory apparatus. To aid in accomplishing these myriad research efforts, the development of new methodologies and techniques is also needed.

Psychological Processes

The Brain and Behavior Subcommittee of the Psychological Processes Study Group calls attention to the steady decrement in extramural research support for projects evaluated by the Neuropsychology Initial Review Group, to the point where few new approved applications are now being funded. Unless this trend is reversed, they submit, many potentially significant advances in understanding the biological bases for mental illnesses will have been aborted. The Brain and Behavior Subcommittee recommends that emphasis be placed on integrative research based upon the combined application of techniques of anatomy, physiology, biochemistry, endocrinology, and pharmacology to problems of brain and behavior and on evolutionary neuropsychology, i.e., man's biological heritage as revealed in comparative studies of brain and behavior in various species, including man. Such approaches should be brought to bear on: (a) studies of the relations between structure and function of the developing nervous system; (b) investigations of neurobehavioral plasticity, including biological mechanisms of learning and memory, the recovery of function after nervous system injury, and environmental influences on the brain; and (c) studies of behavioral effects of nervous system pathology in animals and man, and possible treatments.

In experimental psychology, studies of memory, perception, language, motivation, and learning at all age levels are highly relevant to the NIMH mission and should be increased. For example, within the past 12 years, only an occasional grant has been awarded for a project pointed directly at new instructional methods or strategies in spite of the fact that these methods could reduce the number of dropouts and possibly of delinquents. Another example of research on basic psychological processes with clearly potential usefulness is the study of memory, including memory processes in aging.

In the area of developmental psychology more research on aggressive behavior is needed to test the generalizability of experimental findings to the clinic and to society and to understand the stimuli that evoke aggressive behavior in the individual. A great deal more investigation is required in the area of rearing the developing organism and meeting the unique needs of persons at all age levels. Much more biologically and ecologically oriented research should be undertaken.

In social psychology, we need systematic research on the effects of the physical and social world on individuals. Emphasis should be placed on research on the determinants of a broad range of complex socially significant behaviors—antisocial (aggression, intergroup hostility, interpersonal

411

conflict, exploitation, and delinquency); prosocial (helping, cooperation, sharing, friendship, marriage, identification); and withdrawing responses (alienation, dependency, alcoholism, drug abuse).

Social and Cultural Processes

The Social and Cultural Processes Study Group analyzed expenditures on social science research in 1972 and found that of $12 million devoted to social processes research, only $2.4 million went to basic research while $9.6 million supported projects in categorical programs. This 4 to 1 ratio between categorical and fundamental research is regarded as seriously imbalanced. There must be increased support for basic social and cultural research aimed at improving theory, method, and conceptual foundations in this important area.

Social research methodology should be encouraged. Particular support should be given to multivariate methodology, analysis of change through time, social experimentation, and causal analysis. Other areas needing development are techniques for studying interactions, use of secondary analysis, study of unplanned events, improvements in ethnography and participant observation, computer simulation, and use of game theory.

High priority should be given to studies by sociologists, anthropologists, social psychologists, and psychiatrists on social factors bearing directly on mental health. These include problems of mental health measurement and classification, information on how psychological symptoms are identified in the population and how social factors influence who receives what kind of treatment, studies of innovative treatment settings such as halfway houses and home treatment settings. All of the recently developed group therapies and activities—encounter, sensitivity, marathon groups, etc.—deserve careful analysis and evaluation.

The relationships between social structure and psychological functioning are not well understood. It would be profitable to emphasize research that looks at social structure as the independent variable and at personality and psychological structure as the outcome variable. Especially needed are studies of the impact of organizational life and of work on the individual.

Further research in the area of ethnography is needed, including studies of sociolinguistics. Cross-cultural research is essential and must be encouraged without delay.

Mental Illness and Behavior Disorders

The Mental Illness and Behavior Disorders Study Group presented data that reveal a major imbalance in research support allocations in its area of interest. The analysis showed that in 1971, for example, more than 60 percent of all extramural research grants for investigations directly on the mental disorders went to studies in schizophrenia and the affective disorders. This was more than three times the combined total amount spent for research directly on psychosomatic illness, psychoneurosis, personality disorders, and organic psychosis. The study group recommends a careful reconsideration of this distribution in order to judge whether or not this emphasis on functional psychosis is based on scientific judgment.

412

Particularly, and indefensibly, neglected is research in organic psychosis. The victims, primarily older Americans, fill almost one-third of the total mental hospital beds in the country, and a larger, but undetermined, proportion are in nursing homes and with their families. A small amount of research is currently being conducted, for example, on the use of hyperbaric oxygen, neurosurgical shunting procedures, lipid metabolism, and virology, but most of this research arises from general medicine and geriatrics and does not readily reach the attention of researchers and clinicians in mental health. Increased support for research in organic psychoses would not only raise the level of health care for these neglected patients but might well provide basic knowledge that would be important to the whole field of mental health.

Drug Abuse

The Drug Abuse Study Group found that, in straightforward dollar terms, the expenditures for treatment, education, and training in the field of drug abuse dwarf the expenditures for research. In their view, a substantial increase in research support would significantly strengthen the service and training programs.

Among the group's specific recommendations is that NIMH make a more intensive effort to encourage better methods to evaluate treatment efficacy. Development of measuring instruments and better criteria, as well as other techniques for assessing therapeutic change, should be encouraged. Search for new chemical agents to be used in treatment is necessary, along with the various immunological approaches.

The epidemiology of drug use is especially in need of development. We know very little about the use of drugs by persons of various age groups, sex, education, family size, occupation, and other standard demographic variables. Trends in the types of drugs used by particular groups need to be studied.

Similarly, we still know very little about how to prevent drug abuse. One line of neglected research is the study of the relationship of various aspects of child development, parental attitudes and behavior, peer relationships, and other factors in development to later drug involvement.

Alcoholism

The Alcoholism Study Group recommends maintenance of balanced support between biological and psychosocial studies of alcoholism.

Study of the effects of alcohol on the central nervous system is of high priority. Biological research demanding increased support includes the interaction of alcohol and the numerous neurotransmitters in the brain and the effects of alcohol on the neuronal transmission of nervous impulses in the brain; studies of carbohydrate, amino acid and lipid metabolism, energy-linked systems, and alcohol and nerve function; studies of the effects of alcohol on electrical activity of the brain; studies of the mechansims of the action of alcohol and its metabolites on nerve membranes, and a vigorous effort to investigate the effect of alcohol on hormones.

413

Research on the effects of alcohol on other systems is absolutely essential. This includes studies of liver function, alcoholism-associated heart disease, blood disorders of alcoholics, and of the effects of alcohol on the formed elements of the blood in addition to studies on the binding proteins. Research on the effects of alcohol in decreasing the absorption of essential amino acids and vitamins should receive high priority.

Basic psychosocial research should concentrate less on individual psychopathology and should instead seek to identify and weigh pervasive influences in society, subcultures, ethnic groups, social classes, and families which influence alcohol abuse. Future research on distribution studies should test hypotheses regarding interactions between individuals and broader social forces. We need more data on alcoholism among American Indians, blacks, and women. Research on etiology should be formulated in a broad conceptual framework that clarifies the interplay of factors, and research on diagnosis should consider not only early detection as a necessary prelude to treatment but also what is an alcoholic and what distinguishes the alcohol user from the abuser. Longitudinal studies of cohorts studied early in their lives and followed for considerable periods of time should be conducted. More studies of the social consequences of alcohol abuse should be undertaken, specifically the effects of alcohol abuse on institutional efficiency, family relationships, children, and suicide.

Further research on treatment techniques should seek to determine which approach works best with what types of people, with emphasis directed to procedures increasing the utilization of proven therapy. Broad social psychological and sociological studies should define the organizational structures needed to provide these techniques. Target groups of individuals in particular need of education and prevention are often outside the social mainstream. Prevention programs should be directed to understanding and reaching these groups. Systematic studies of constructive personal strategies for using—and not abusing—alcohol should be conducted.

Social Problems

The Study Group on Social Problems emphasized that NIMH should broaden and consolidate its research on social problems, rather than attack problems piecemeal. Serious deficits in current research on social problems are: an underemphasis on causal conditions, particularly social conditions; lack of studies investigating the likely social structural commonalities in the causes and consequences of social problems; an underemphasis on change and on the interplay of social structure, psychological, and biological factors; and a lack of rigor in the evaluation of ameliorative programs. The group also concluded that it is important to conduct research on the "natural history of social problems" in order to determine how social phenomena come to be defined as social problems and how such definitions affect society's efforts to deal with these phenomena.

Also recommended is increased support of well-designed cross-national research efforts.

414

Treatment Techniques

In terms of program balance the Study Group on Treatment Techniques calls attention to the tiny proportion of NIMH funds that are devoted to research directly concerned with treatment techniques. The thrust of its report is how to remedy this imbalance.

The study group states that there is an urgent need to find answers to the question of what type of treatment is best for what type of persons with which problems. Answers to this question will provide information to help make the best use of existing facilities and personnel. They also will provide guidelines for matching health services to health needs.

Aftercare and rehabilitation strongly merit increased research. To be emphasized is research on the total rehabilitation process, inside and outside the institution, as it evolves over time and as it may be affected by crisis intervention and other short-term interventions.

Research on the interaction of drugs and psychosocial treatment is needed, as well as more studies of the outcome of family therapy.

Like the Study Group on Mental Illness, the Study Group on Treatment Techniques sees research on treatment of the nonpsychotic disorders as undersupported.

Research on the prevention of mental disorders deserves the highest priority. These studies should include early detection of problems of children and the efficacy of various modes of intervention. The group reminds us that the communtiy mental health centers have done almost no research on preventive techniques.

Mental Health Services Research

The Study Group on Mental Health Services Research stated that as an overriding priority the Institute should undertake a major epidemiological and biostatistical research effort to secure reliable data on the prevalence and incidence of mental disorders and to develop more accurate ways of measuring the need for, patterns of use of, and effectiveness of specific mental health services in a given population.

Also recommended was increased support in three areas of equal importance. The first area is research on the processes essential to delivery of services. In this group of studies, first priority should go to research on ways to ensure financing of mental health services, second priority to ways to ensure quality of care, and third to ways of improving planning and evaluation of service programs.

The second area is research on means of ensuring equity of access to mental health services and equity of services, with priority going to studies concerned with the groups in greatest need of services.

The third area is research on technological developments, with priority going to methods of transferring research results from the investigator to the potential user.

Also strongly recommended is increased research to identify, analyze, and solve systemic problems in mental health delivery systems.

Mental Health Information and Utilization

From the point of view of program planning and balance, the Study Group on Research Information and Utilization concluded that this area has been neglected by the NIMH research management and recommends that it be accorded formal recognition as an integral component of all research activities. Especially needed are more studies to evaluate the impact of the Institute's dissemination and utilization activities. These studies should be concerned with, among other matters, the quality of the informational materials, the extent of their distribtuion to appropriate audiences and potential users of the information, and the processes by which research information is put to use.

OVERALL PROGRAM BALANCE AND PRIORITIES

As stated earlier, the recommendations of the study groups, although extremely useful in identifying the many important research areas that need to be supported, do not address the problem of overall program balance and priorities.

However, certain commonalities, or clusters, of research endeavors can be discerned throughout the many specific recommendations. One recurring theme is the importance of the study of normal functioning. Although a major goal of the Institute is to conquer mental illness, a focus on illness or deviance is not recommended. Just as there is truth to the dictum that the study of abnormal behavior leads to insights about normal behavior, so it is also true that the study of normal behavior is essential to understanding abnormal behavior or mental illness.

Another overall recommendation that emerges is emphasis on a developmental perspective. Especially important here is research on the interplay of genetic and environmental influences on normal and abnormal behavior. A related series of recommendations stresses the need to study the interactions of biological, psychological and sociocultural processes underlying behavior.

Support of work on methodology and techniques is recommended for the entire mental health field. Finally, the Task Force agreed on the necessity for broad conceptual frameworks to guide all research and for assuring that the results of mental health research are put to effective use.

After many months of careful study the Research Task Force concluded that it would be unwise to attempt to set specific priorities—to say, for example, that research on schizophrenia has a higher priority than research on depression. Setting priorities of this kind could be detrimental to the research program, because, once established and announced, they become self-perpetuating. As described in the section on mission and policy, NIMH should handle the problem of priorities by flexible and continuous review of short- and long-term planning by the NIMH research managers, research scientists, and—through the peer review system—mental health scientists throughout the country.

The decision on the part of the Task Force not to establish a set of priorities was not capricious nor a shirking of responsibility. Literally hundreds of hours were spent by many people deliberating the pros and cons of setting up a priority list. It would have been relatively easy arbitrarily to designate certain areas as having higher priority than others and urge that more funds and more resources be allocated to such areas. Such a listing coming from highly prestigious authorities in the field of mental health and behavioral science would sound extremely convincing; it would appear that we had specific goals which could be attained simply by a concentration of effort, that in a matter of "x" years these problems would be solved and the pains of countless thousands of American citizens alleviated. To present such a list would be a disservice to the NIMH Director.

The Task Force appreciates the need for setting priorities but feels that this is a political process and not a scientific one. Hence, the Director will have to continue to make this kind of decision, as in the past, on the basis of the extent and severity of given problems and the amount and cogency of concern being expressed by Congress and the American people.

EVALUATION

Because evaluation of the research program is intrinsic to its administration, the Task Force examined evaluation activities throughout the Institute and formulated a series of recommendations designed to improve the evaluative process. The term "evaluation" as used in NIMH, has a number of meanings. Depending on the context, evaluation may refer to the review of grant expenditures, to the judgment of the scientific merit of a research proposal, or to the broad assessment of the potential of a scientific field for resolving a mental health problem. Study group and Task Force staff discussions of evaluation included seven different evaluative functions, as listed and exemplified below:

- Scientific evaluation: Is the research supported by NIMH of high scientific quality? Have the investigations developed new and important scientific information?

- Mission evaluation: Has the research supported by the NIMH contributed to the overall objective of the Institute?

- Evaluation of research activities: Have investigators conscientiously tried to accomplish the research plans presented in their original proposals? Have other activities been supported through use of diverted grant funds?

- Evaluation of review process: Is the requisite objectivity, balance, and thoroughness of the peer review process being maintained? Are particular review groups either unduly stringent or lenient in their judgments?

- Evaluation of program goals: Are the goals of the separate Institute research programs consistent with the overall objectives of the Institute?

- Evaluation for scientific guidance: What is the current state-of-the-art of a given field; where are the knowledge gaps or methodological stumbling blocks? Such evaluation is often undertaken in order to consolidate and integrate scientific knowledge in a field, with interested scientists as the principal beneficiaries.

417

- Evaluation for administrative guidance: The above state-of-the-art questions may also be asked for a different, management-related purpose: to identify areas that seem ripe for rapid scientific advance, and to guide the funding agency as to where and how developmental funds might be most wisely spent.

Scientific Evaluation

The responsibility for evaluation of the scientific quality of the individual research projects supported by NIMH is borne by the peer review system. The review of new applications constitutes a prospective evaluation; the review of renewal applications provides a retrospective evaluation.

The peer review process has been ably and vigorously defended in a number of NIH and NIMH documents and has been widely praised throughout the history of its operation, by both scientific and political observers. This report need not reiterate the arguments for continued reliance on the peer review system; it is sufficient to say that the consensus of those participating in the Task Force is that the basic principle of the peer review system is an absolutely essential foundation upon which a high-quality research program must rest.

From Task Force consideration of the peer review process, a number of important principles and suggestions emerged. These are summarized below:

- In the basic research areas, reliance on the peer review process, emphasizing, as it does, the criterion of scientific excellence, is appropriate for overall program guidance. In categorical research programs, however, scientific merit is a necessary but not sufficient criterion for research support. In these programs, more active participation and direction by NIMH staff are essential. A greater reliance might well be placed on the contract mechanism for research support in targeted areas of applied research.

- The peer review process should be applied to all contract research supported by the Institute.

- Research in the intramural program should be evaluated by an expanded form of peer review process (in addition to the Board of Scientific Counselors), and immediate steps should be taken to develop such a process. In this connection the Assembly of Scientists has developed a peer review proposal that will be discussed in the final section of this chapter.

- To ensure a better balance in review panel membership, and also to ensure a more objective review of research applications, greater use should be made of expert consultation in connection with specific tasks such as nominations for replacement of panel members, and for opinions on specific research proposals.

- Representatives of the population groups to be studied under proposed research grants or contracts should participate in the consideration of such factors as the social or technological impact of the research and ethical issues involved, but such aspects of the review

418

process should be clearly distinguished from the review for scientific merit. This is not to say that the regular review committees should not also consider such factors, but rather that formal consideration of them should be at a separate level of review.

Mission Evaluation

The question of the degree to which NIMH research has contributed to the overall objectives of the Institute was of central concern to the Task Force. It is also the question most often asked of the Institute by the Congress and the public. The preceding chapters give a clear answer: Research conducted or sponsored by NIMH has made outstanding contributions to the Institute's mission. To recall just a few of the highlights presented earlier, NIMH research has:

- Played a significant and in some cases a key role in vastly enlarging our understanding of the biological processes affecting the state of our mental health.

- Demonstrated the role of heredity in mental disorder.

- Helped to explain how genetic and familial factors may work together to produce schizophrenia.

- Increased our understanding of child development.

- Pioneered in assessing the effectiveness of psychotropic drugs, explaining their action, and searching for new ones.

- Contributed heavily to the revolutionizing advances known as behavior therapy and biofeedback.

- Demonstrated that many mentally ill persons can be cared for in the community.

Now that the results are in, it is clear that all the research contributing in any way to such developments was relevant to NIMH goals. However, to assess the relatedness of research to these goals beforehand—that is, before the results and all their consequences are known—is a different and greatly difficult problem. Task Force conclusions, although complete consensus was not reached, may be summed up as follows:

1. Much of the basic research in scientific fields related to the functioning of man's brain and body has no directly demonstrable, immediate relevance to a mental health problem. The goal is to develop facts that may ultimately lead to better understanding of these problems, but the nature and degree of relevance cannot be predicted. In evaluating basic research, scientific excellence is a sufficient criterion. As the chapter on the basic research activities of NIMH notes, the peer review system leads to the evaluation of proposed research on the basis not only of scientific excellence but also of relevance and of the ripeness of the field for research.

2. In applied research, where relevance can usually be assessed, the criterion of relevance as well as that of scientific excellence should be applied. At the present stage of mental health research, the assessment of relevance can be handled most effectively on an individual

basis. Each applied research program must ensure that the relevance of a proposed research project to the program's mission is scrutinized.

The Chlorpromazine History

The difficulty in evaluating beforehand—or even soon afterward—the relevance of research to the NIMH research mission is exemplified by the Institute's experience with a recently completed scientific-historical analysis of the contribution of research to the development of chlorpromazine. (See the description of this project in the chapter on NIMH's basic research activities.) The clearest implication of this history is that the ultimate relevance to mental health of most of the research that was done was not demonstrable at the time; it can be demonstrated only in retrospect. The development of chlorpromazine from an ingredient of a coal tar dye to a powerful clinical tool against schizophrenia came about, not as a result of goal-directed planning, but as a result of the apparently anarchic, but actually rigorous, self-regulating processes that guide unfettered science.

Evaluation of Research Activities

The evaluation of a grantee's responsibility and productivity in his use of research support is clearly a responsibility of program staff in the case of continuation applications, and of the review committees in the case of renewal applications. The responsibility for this kind of evaluation is additionally shared by the Grants and Contracts Management Branch in its review of expenditure reports and of final progress reports. This level of evaluation is primarily administrative, its aim being to ensure that the investigator is generally following the research plan laid out in the original proposal, and that he is not misusing grant funds.

In a pilot project carried out in 1971, the continuation applications from a randomly selected group of projects were sent to the initial review group member who had been the primary reviewer of the application when it was first submitted. The reviewer was asked to rate progress along several dimensions. The results suggest that it would not be useful to establish such an evaluation procedure on a wide and continuing basis. The procedure imposes severe demands on the time of the review committee members, and only rarely does it produce a more searching evaluation than could be provided by an informed staff member.

A system for reviewing final progress reports is currently being established by the Program Analysis and Evaluation Section of the Division of Extramural Research Programs. To facilitate adequate reviews, investigators are being requested to follow a standardized format in preparing their final reports.

Evaluation of Review Process

It is essential for NIMH to ensure that its primary scientific advisory mechanism, the peer review system, maintain the highest possible levels of objectivity, scientific balance, and thoroughness. In monitoring these committees, the Institute is concerned not only with administrative mechanisms, such as procedures for appointing new members, but also

420

with scientific issues. These last are the responsibility of the scientifically trained executive secretaries and scientist administrators who direct the programs for which the committees are evaluating research applications. In NIMH—unlike NIH, where the peer review system is centralized in the Division of Research Grants—review committees are attached to the research programs; as a result, it is possible for scientific program staff to monitor committee activities more closely and exert a corrective influence when it appears that the criteria for objective, fair, and thorough review are not being met.

In response to criticisms of the peer review process, both NIH and NIMH have subjected their procedures to a number of searching examinations. These have ranged from external analyses such as that undertaken by the Wooldridge Committee to internal staff-conducted studies of priority score distributions, approval rates, and other variables in the review process. Critics have suggested that the peer review system contains a number of weaknesses, including conflict of interest, usurpation of Federal administrative responsibility for allocation of funds, and distortion of Federal program goals. None of the rigorous NIH-NIMH evaluations has ever provided any evidence either that such weaknesses exist or that the peer review process would be improved by anything beyond rather minor procedural changes.

Task Force participants, although they have not proposed any specific measures for evaluating the work of review committees, have made two suggestions intended to enhance the committees' effectiveness. One of these, relating to procedures for appointing members, has been reported earlier in this section, in the discussion of scientific evaluation. The other, which is also concerned in part with appointment procedures, suggests that one of the functions of the proposed Inter-Divisional Research Council (discussed in a later section of this chapter) should be to advise the Director regarding the review committee structure of the Institute. This council would consider the membership of the panels, advise on the selection of new members, examine the approval rates of the panels, and make suggestions concerning the termination of committees and the establishment of new ones as needed.

Administrative Structure

Continuing scientific and administrative efforts to ensure the balance, objectivity, and thoroughness of the peer review process can best be achieved by keeping the review committees functionally placed in the Institute research programs, where the responsibility for committee evaluation can be shared by executive secretaries, scientific program staff, and committee management personnel.

Evaluation of Program Goals

This form of evaluation was second only to scientific evaluation in the emphasis given to it by Task Force participants. Evaluating goals is an exceedingly complex function, requiring simultaneous reference to statements concerning NIMH research policy, individual program philosophies, and the balance between targeted and nontargeted research. In many respects, it is the most important sort of evaluation since all research activities should be describable in terms of their rate of progress toward the stated goals of a given program. It is also the most difficult form of evaluation because of the above-mentioned interdependence with overall research policy and research philosophies.

In the basic research programs of the Institute, the evaluation of progress toward program goals is both a simple and a very complex issue. The basic programs have as their goal the development of new knowledge that will now or ultimately be relevant to mental health problems. This development can be somewhat objectively weighed through the use of such means as citation indexes and publication counts. However, it must be kept in mind that the goals of the basic research programs are only means toward Institute objectives.

There is little in the history of NIMH that can properly be called a systematic evaluation of program goals. The Institute's mission has been constantly evolving and expanding, dependent always on an interplay between political and scientific determinants. Programs have arisen in what seems, in retrospect, to have been a rather expedient manner, often without any clear rationale or relationship to the intercurrent research policies or to the readiness of the scientific field for exploitation. Establishing a new program seems to be easier than terminating an existing program; infrequently has an established Institute program been deservedly terminated.

The Research Task Force constitutes the first and only concentrated effort to deal with all of the issues inherent in the determination of research program goals. It is hoped that NIMH interest in these problems does not wane when the Task Force completes its work and presents its final report.

Evaluation for Scientific Guidance

This kind of evaluation usually takes the form of scientific conferences, which may or may not be supported by NIMH. For the basic research programs, conferences to identify knowledge gaps or methodological problems in a scientific field or topic have served a useful purpose in educating current and potential grantees, staff, and review committee members. The major purpose of NIMH support of such conferences is to upgrade the scientific quality of the research supported by the Institute.

Evaluation for scientific guidance has also been accomplished by NIMH contract or grant support to senior scholars in a particular field for the preparation of review papers or state-of-the-art assessments. Several study groups have recommended increased support for such efforts. These assessments should include recommendations for future research and direct advice about methodological or conceptual stumbling blocks.

A number of Task Force participants have suggested extension into other fields of the periodic state-of-the-art assessments that have been conducted in schizophrenia and depression. For example, an annual review of research on alcoholism has been recommended, in order to survey current research activity in the field and communicate the results to all interested scientists. The Task Force recommends the continued support of conferences and scientific reviews. The suggestion for periodic compendia of research in alcoholism could well be extended to other important research areas supported by the Institute.

A major drawback is that support of such activities diverts funds and other resources from an already restricted budget for the actual conduct of research. Such activities, therefore, should not be undertaken lightly; careful consideration should be given to the costs as well as the benefits of conferences or reviews. Conferences should be supported only when they show considerable promise for scientific advance. The identification of high-yield areas might well be one of the functions of the proposed Inter-Divisional Research Council discussed later in this chapter.

Evaluation for Administrative Guidance

The research programs of the Institute must be responsive to the dynamic nature of the scientific fields they support. Frequently, this responsiveness is built into the peer review process; however, many programs of the Institute, particularly in the applied areas, combine elements of several disciplines. The program of the Depression Section of the Clinical Research Branch, for example, supports a wide range of clinical and biological studies involving many discrete scientific disciplines, and it is important for the program's administrator to have access to informed guidance about the "mix" of research support that is likely to lead to the most rapid advance in the understanding, treatment, and prevention of depression.

Particularly in the applied research programs of the Institute, then, the scientist administrator must have counsel about the best way to balance a program in order to achieve program goals. The periodic review and assessment of the various scientific aspects of an applied program are often best accomplished through the support of conferences and workshops, in which the various disciplines involved summarize what is known, and what needs to be known, about the problem in question. Such conferences and workshops also serve the purpose of bringing together investigators in different disciplines who otherwise would have little contact with one another.

The caveats mentioned in the preceding section with regard to the diversion of funds from actual research for the support of conferences, workshops, and reviews also apply here. The programs for which these forms of evaluation are most appropriate are those programs that are multidisciplinary in nature. The Task Force recommends continued support of such interdisciplinary conferences and workshops, provided that adequate consideration be given to balancing the need for integration and summarization against the need for actual research.

ADMINISTRATION AND ORGANIZATION

This section presents a summary of the present research management structure in NIMH, and against this background a major recommendation of the Task Force and a number of study group recommendations concerning specific management issues. These recommendations are as diverse and wide-ranging as NIMH itself, but they have a common theme:

in one way or another, each manifests the need for more effective coordination and focus of the entire enterprise.

Description

In the organizational structure for NIMH research there are 30 operating branch-level units responsible for conducting or supporting research; these units are located in all but one of the seven major organizational components of the NIMH. The six with research responsibilities are the Division of Extramural Research Programs, Division of Mental Health Service Programs, Division of Special Mental Health Programs, Division of Narcotic Addiction and Drug Abuse, National Institute on Alcohol Abuse and Alcoholism, and the Mental Health Intramural Research Program. Of the six, three have both intramural and extramural components; these are the Division of Mental Health Service Programs, Division of Narcotic Addiction and Drug Abuse, and the National Institute on Alcohol Abuse and Alcoholism. Certain activities of the Division of Manpower and Training Programs might also be regarded as research activities; for example, the support of research training and fellowships, and the evaluation of experimental training programs. Additional research activities, or closely related functions, are also carried out in the Office of Program Planning and Evaluation and in the Office of Communications.

There is great diversity in the scope and size of the research enterprise among the divisions with research responsibility. For example, in fiscal year 1972, the Division of Mental Health Service Programs spent approximately $9 million for research on the delivery of mental health services, while the Division of Extramural Research Programs spent approximately $47 million for a broad spectrum of research projects ranging, for instance, from basic studies of brain mechanisms to applied research on fostering psychosocial development in children.

Considerable diversity exists, too, among the branch-level components involved in research. There are 11 branch-level units that provide extramural support, one that serves a coordinating function but has no funds for extramural support, and 18 that conduct research. These units are organized on a variety of bases, including disciplines (behavioral sciences, psychology, neurobiology), types of inquiry (clinical, applied), type of treatment (psychopharmacology), population group (children, minorities), and social problems (crime and delinquency, metropolitan problems). These branch-level components, like the divisions to which they belong, vary greatly in the breadth of their functions and the extent of resources allocated to them.

The Office of Program Planning and Evaluation has nominal responsibility for overall planning, analysis, and evaluation of all the Institute's programs, including research. In practice, however, this office has not carried out these functions in any comprehensive way for the total research effort of the Institute.

Interdivisional Research Council

The Research Task Force decided to make one major recommendation concerning the administration and organization of NIMH research programs: that the Director establish an interdivisional research council.

Several study groups recommended that the Director appoint a high-level advisory council to provide scientific and managerial advice concerning the research enterprise as a whole. Although independently formulated by the study groups, the proposal for a research-focused council is not new. For example, the need to strengthen advisory mechanisms for planning in the National Institutes of Health was addressed in "Investigation of HEW," a report of a special subcommittee of the House Committee on Interstate and Foreign Commerce (1966). This report takes the position that advisory councils of NIH do not provide adequate research policy advice in the course of their brief discussions of program plans and of the policy implications of specific grant applications. Rather than trying to add additional functions to the already overburdened advisory councils, the report suggests it

> . . . might be preferable to establish an Advisory Research Planning Council for each Institute and Division of NIH which would have as its sole assignment the responsibility for continuous scanning and review of relevant biomedical research so as to identify research areas which appear to merit greater support or a more targeted research effort. Such planning effort should be carried out, of course, in close conjunction with the respective institute or division staffs, who would do much of the spadework of collecting information on research in progress, etc., prior to meeting periodically with the Research Planning Councils.

After lengthy and intensive discussion, the Task Force concluded that the research mission and policy of NIMH could best be served by a council made up of the research managers and research scientists within the Institute. This council would meet at frequent intervals, probably weekly, discuss issues of immediate and long-range significance, weigh priorities as the need arises, and consult with and advise the Director on the entire research program.

Therefore, the Task Force recommends that the Director establish an interdivisional research council, representing the leadership of all research components of the Institute, including representation from the Assembly of Scientists, and served by an executive secretariat charged with recording and communicating its deliberations. The council could also include other Institute staff, invited by the council membership on an ad hoc basis.

While the detailed functions of the proposed council can be left open, the goals of this arrangement are clear: that the NIMH research activity be accorded a voice, support, and management time and concern equal to that enjoyed by other major components of the Institute.

Specific Recommendations by Study Groups

Each study group, working from its own vantage point, proposed certain changes in administration that it believed would enhance the effectiveness of research support in its own domain. The Task Force reports these recommendations without comment, except to mention that analysis of these proposed organizational changes could be an early agenda item for the recommended interdivisional research council. The recommendations are loosely categorized under three headings: (l) proposed new organizational entities; (2) coordination and consolidation; and (3) substantive-integrative recommendations.

Proposed New Organizational Entities

Biobehavioral Sciences Research Branch

The Biological and Physiological Processes Study Group recommends the establishment of a Biobehavioral Sciences Research Branch within the Division of Extramural Research Programs. This branch would have three major programs (or sections): Genetics—behavioral genetics and genetics of mental illness; Neurobiology—developmental neurobiology and molecular neurobiology; and Biological Bases of Social Behavior—neuroendocrines, adaptation, and ethology.

Social Sciences Research Review Committee

The Social and Cultural Processes Study Group recommends that the Social Sciences Initial Review Group be divided into two sections: a Social Psychology Section dealing with the subject matter usually treated by psychologists and those areas of sociology with heavy social-psychological relevance and a Culture and Social Structure Section. The study group also recommends that in any review panel where only a small proportion of members are expert with reference to a particular proposal, intensive use be made of ad hoc reviewers so that the requisite knowledge and expertise can be applied.

Office of Secondary Analysis

Secondary analysis refers to the examination of survey data previously collected for the purpose of testing new hypotheses or applying different analytic techniques. The Social and Cultural Processes Study Group recommends the establishment of an office, consisting of one or two people, that would maintain a data archive, arrange for data to be put on computer tape, provide codebooks and information on scales and scores, inform relevant scientific audiences of the availability of the data, and in other ways facilitate use of the data by scientists inside and outside the Institute.

Clinical Genetics Branch

The Study Group on Mental Illness recommends that a branch concerned with the full range of problems in clinical genetics be established. (See also the recommendation above for a Genetics Section as part of a recommended Biobehavioral Sciences Research Branch.)

Model Laboratory for Applied Research and Training in Psychopathology

The Mental Illness Study Group recommends that NIMH coordinate applied research in psychopathology by developing a model research and training laboratory. This laboratory would: (I) consolidate relevant methodology from different disciplines; (2) train clinical scientists; and (3) foster and collaborate in the conduct of large-scale, nationally coordinated, multidisciplinary studies of mental disorders.

Drug Abuse Intramural Facility

The Drug Abuse Study Group recommends that NIMH establish an intramural treatment facility for drug abuse and addiction. This initiative is particularly needed now that the Clinical Research Center, Lexington, Ky., has been closed.

Center for Advanced Studies of Alcoholism

The Alcohol Study Group recommends the establishment of a center with three purposes: (l) to provide opportunities for advanced study for senior investigators; (2) to foster communication among scientists in the field; and (3) to facilitate the preparation of major scholarly works in the field of alcoholism.

Interdivisional Work Group on Child Mental Health

The Committee on Child Mental Health proposes a new approach for structuring child research activities in the Institute. It recommends: establishment of an interdivisional work group to classify research efforts and set priorities in consultation with the advisory council, and establishment of a research coordination center in the Office of the Director to monitor implementation of priorities.

Center for Research on Psychosocial Treatment

The Treatment Study Group draws attention to the need for an Institute focus in the broad research field of psychosocial and behavioral treatment. It recommends the establishment of a center that would: coordinate and evaluate all NIMH research in this area; support the development of the necessary instruments, measures, and methodologies; disseminate timely research findings to the field; and emphasize new treatment approaches to nonpsychotic disorders.

Coordinating Panel on Mental Health Services Research

The Services Study Group calls for stronger and more systematic coordination among NIMH components involved in services research, including the Biometry Branch, the Center for Epidemiologic Studies, the Mental Health Services Development Branch, the Evaluation Branch, and the Division of Special Mental Health Programs. In the view of this study group, such coordination would require an Institute-wide coordinating panel with the necessary authority to integrate and administer the entire services research enterprise.

Research Information and Dissemination Staff Group

The Research Information Study Group points to a serious and costly lack of coordination and integration of the Institute's many activities aimed at research information dissemination and utilization (RIDU). The group advocates a purposeful and planned overall Institute effort in this field. The recommended first step is to assemble a RIDU staff group in the Office of the Director, with representatives from each office and division. This staff group would: serve as an advocate for RIDU at the highest management levels, and devise and promote an overall system that would coordinate the multiplicity of independent RIDU activities of the Institute, with the aim, not of controlling, but of promoting cooperation and interaction among the components of the system.

Sabbatical Center

The Mental Illness Study Group, in endorsing the pressing need for synthesis, integration, and critical reflection on the state of mental health research, recommends the establishment of a scholarship center where NIMH scientists and scholars from outside NIMH could spend a year or two with freedom and mutual stimulation to conceptualize, integrate, and innovate in problem areas relevant to mental health.

Field Stations for Population Studies

To facilitate the design and implementation of epidemiological and biostatistical activities, the Mental Health Services Study Group recommends the development of several field stations in different catchment areas of the United States to carry out population-based studies in a sufficiently intensive way to make it possible to determine the extent to which persons in need of mental health services are using the services and whether their use alters the amount of disability.

Coordination and Consolidation of Existing Components

Intramural-Extramural

Three study groups, although endorsing the historical separation between intramural and extramural research, advocate initiatives to improve communication and cooperation between the two.

The Mental Illness Study Group recommends the establishment of a bridging organizational unit that would capitalize on the separate, but related, capabilities of the two organizations. The group suggests that such a unit might: directly engage critical public health issues such as developing or evaluating new treatment modes through combined laboratory and clinical field studies; deal with clinical or social problems that span the basic and applied realms; and foster collaborative endeavors among investigators inside and outside NIMH.

The Social Problems Study Group points out that research support in its area of interest is distributed across four or more NIMH divisions with little or no coordination among them. The group recommends that new organizational arrangements be established to provide for a more integrated pattern of research support in social problems. The essential requirements are outlined as follows: all directors of components supporting research on social problems should report to one higher official; each component responsible for social problems research should be taxed 10 percent of its budget to support research on interrelationships between, and common conditions underlying, social problems; NIMH should establish interdepartmental seminars and other information exchange initiatives among components engaged in social problems research; and the NIMH computer system should be redesigned to permit researchers to retrieve information that would reveal commonalities in separate research programs on social problems.

428

The Social Problems Study Group also advocates other measures aimed at improving communication and cooperation between the two major research components. These include: flexible personnel arrangements that would permit intramural scientists to take temporary assignments in the extramural program and vice versa; the appointment of intramural scientists as liaison members to appropriate initial review groups (the Psychology Study Group also made essentially the same recommendation); the use of intramural facilities to conduct research of high priority to extramural programs; and the facilitation of this cooperation with provisions that would permit intramural investigations to be funded by other Institute components.

Combination of Clinical Facilities

The Study Group on Mental Illness recommends that the installations at St. Elizabeths, Lexington, and Bethesda be combined into one facility (housed in one location). This expanded facility would be devoted to multidisciplinary research programs in the major mental disorders, addiction, childhood psychosis, violence, and neurological problems.

Biometry and Epidemiology

The Services Study Group points out the absence of a close working relationship between the Biometry Branch and the Center for Epidemiologic Studies. They recommend that the Institute seriously consider what purposes are served by continuing the present administrative separation of these components.

Substantive Integration

Social Problem Causation

The Social Problems Study Group draws attention to the fact that most causal research in social problems is unidisciplinary in focus. Largely overlooked, it claims, is the possibility that for most social problems there may well be causal interaction among social, psychological, and biological conditions. Accordingly, the group recommends emphasis on research that is conceptualized and designed in such a way as to permit such interactions to be revealed.

Drug Abuse

The Drug Abuse Study Group views interdisciplinary collaborative studies as extremely important in the epidemiology and treatment of drug abuse problems. The group considers it highly likely that interactions between biological and social factors may distinguish drug abusers from normal users, and that, by extension, the design and evaluation of intervention measures should also take both kinds of factors into account.

Research Information

The Research Information Study Group recommends that NIMH increase its support of syntheses, state-of-the-art studies, and other such efforts to consolidate knowledge. In support of this recommendation they point to the information overload in many fields, generated by the massive proliferation of empirical research studies. Creative, synthetic, integrative theorizing about existing information is at least as important as generating new information.

The Psychology Study Group made essentially the same point. NIMH research support practices presently encourage empirical studies and discourage conceptual-integrative-theoretical work. The study group indicates the pressing need for syntheses of existing data in psychology and for high-level integrative theoretical writing, and urges that research funding policies should encourage such work.

THE ROLE OF SCIENTISTS IN ADMINISTRATION

In order to provide NIMH scientists as a whole with representation in the Task Force, the Director, NIMH, specified that the Coordinating Committee should include a representative of the Assembly of Scientists. The Assembly took an active role in the Task Force throughout, conveying its views through its representative. One of this group's major efforts was the preparation of a position paper recommending an enlarged and more effective role for scientists in the administration of NIMH research. Because the Assembly speaks for all NIMH scientists, and because the Task Force regards its effort as a genuine contribution to the work of the Task Force, its recommendations will be included in this section.

Recommendations

In the Assembly's view, research scientists are the scarcest and most valuable of the Institute's resources, and it submits that this resource is not being optimally made use of in NIMH decisionmaking. The Assembly's basic premise is that the scientists' role should not be limited to doing research in their own specialized domains, under conditions specified by higher authority, but should be expanded to include their active participation in shaping the research programs, judging the work of their peers, and helping to select scientific administrators. This principle underlies three specific recommendations that can only be summarized here but are supported by closely reasoned, detailed discussion in the original paper.

Research Support

The Assembly recommends that NIMH explicitly guarantee at least a basic minimum of research support for independent NIMH investigators with demonstrated research competence and productivity. Above the minimum level of support, administrators would still retain ample discretion in deciding which scientists should be most liberally supported. At the price of some limitation of administrative flexibility the Institute can thus provide its scientists with the freedom and security that the best scientists require in order to work productively.

Peer Review

The Assembly recommends that a modified peer review system be instituted in the intramural research program as a primary basis for evaluating the scientific accomplishments and potential of individual scientists and programs. This evaluation would provide the administration with a valuable adjunct to, though not a substitute for, administrative judgment in allocating program support and judging scientists for career advancement.

Selection of Program Directors

The Assembly views the selection of responsible program officials in NIMH as among the most consequential decisions for maintaining the excellence of its scientific programs. The Assembly further states that NIMH scientists have been underutilized in such selection procedures, and that scientists can collectively lend these decisions an unmatched degree of substantive expertise and firsthand personal and professional familiarity with candidates.

Accordingly, the Assembly proposes the use of search committees in selecting candidates for positions anywhere in NIMH that involve research program leadership. Different committee composition is proposed for different levels of responsibility, ranging from section chief to division director, but all levels of selection would involve the participation of working scientists. The appointing official would not be bound by the recommendations of the search committee, but he would be obligated to deal seriously and responsibly with these recommendations.

References

Biomedical Science and its Administration: A Study of the National Institutes of Health. Report to the President, Feb. 1965. Washington, D.C.: U.S. Govt. Print. Off., 1965.

A Framework for Government Research and Development. Presented to Parliament November 1971. London: Her Majesty's Stationery Office, 1972.

Performance Measures for Research and Development. Committee on Federal Laboratories of the Federal Council for Science and Technology. Report to the Joint GAO/OMB/CSC Project Team, May 1973.

A Policy for Biomedical Research. Report of an Ad Hoc Committee of the Council of Academic Societies, Association of American Medical Colleges. Journal of Medical Education, 46:693-739, 1971.

Rich, W.C. Accountability indices: The search for the philosopher's touchstone in mental heaith. Administration in Mental Health, Fall:6-11, 1973.

Segal, J. The evaluation of mental health research programs. In: Miller, L. 4th International Congress of Social Psychiatry: Abstract of Papers, 1972.

Smith, M.B. Is psychology relevant to new priorities? American Psychologist, 28:463-471, 1973.

The Use of Quality and Quantity of Publication as Criteria for Evaluating Scientists. Washington, D.C.: U.S. Dept. of Agr. Pub. No. 1041, Jan. 1967.

Epilog

Twenty-five years is less than an eyeblink in human history, yet in this time the National Institute of Mental Health has fostered major developments in mental health research and treatment that raise the expectations of the quality of life for all Americans. Indeed, seen in perspective, the contributions of NIMH may be regarded as an important factor in the social evolution of recent times.

Looking back, it is hard to believe that only 300 years ago, in Europe and Great Britain, stench-filled leprosariums were being transformed into dungeons serving as houses of "correction" for the mentally ill. Victims of emotional disturbances or thought disorders were likely to face chains—for example, in a rat-infested prison such as the Hospital General in France or in a British correctional facility. The possibility that mental illness need not persist for life began to be acknowledged very slowly, and only toward the end of the 19th century did scientific psychiatry begin. With its new concepts came the possibility of medical intervention, of amelioration and perhaps cure, introducing hope for the millions of people who are in some way afflicted.

More recently, in our own time, that hope has begun to be realized, and NIMH has played a critical role in the processs. The Institute has had a relatively brief existence, yet it has supported scientific inquiries and applications that now touch a large fraction of the mentally ill people who live on this planet. Today, people all over the world are being affected by the conviction that mental illness, like physical illness, has causes that can be explored, understood, and ultimately corrected. Because a medical model of emotional and behavioral disorders has become increasingly acceptable, it is possible for disturbed people to seek help rather than resign themselves to misery. But it must be emphasized that in some areas, such as alcoholism, we have only in very recent years and only in part moved away from a harsh, corrective approach and toward a therapeutic one.

The Institute is significantly responsible for this quiet revolution in the delivery of mental health services—for responding to affliction not in a punitive but in a therapeutic mode. Its policies and abiding philosophy have strongly influenced the entire mental health profession, and thus the lives of millions of Americans, present and future.

Yet, even as the Institute enters its second quarter-century, the medical model itself becomes inadequate as a universal approach, since it is clear now that a sizable proportion of the disorders resulting from the stresses of a long-industrialized society do not reflect pathology in the traditional sense. There is special value, therefore, in the exploration, with NIMH support and guidance, of the social stresses that threaten to afflict all Western people. Mental health research can hardly be expected to cure all the problems generated by society, but it can help lay bare the inner structure of such problems and thus indicate the directions of amelioration and prevention.

In scanning the many accomplishments by NIMH in 25 years, an interesting contrast emerges with the bulk of medical research. Although most major health research programs are targeted around specific pathologies such as cancer or heart disease, a large number of NIMH projects have been focused upon correlates of mental "health" rather than illness. Institute-sponsored research has correctly avoided an emphasis only on pathology, for such an emphasis leads to the misguided impression that health is something left over from the resolved problems of illness rather than the other way around.

Correctly, too, the NIMH investment in research has not been channeled into any one research area, nor has all reliance been placed on one or two specific disciplines. As this report has made clear, the quality of life—of mental health—has been nourished by many kinds of research, from the basic psychobiological studies to wide-ranging social observations and evaluations. The Institute has actively encouraged multidisciplinary programs, and it is the confluence of discoveries from previously unrelated researches that has led to the burgeoning understanding of behavior and to two decades of notable advances in biological psychiatry. The field of psychopharmacology, for example, owes much of its development to Institute programs, to the coordinated investigations that neurochemists, psychologists, and clinicians have pursued in a creative and productive partnership. Without their work through the 1960's, millions of people suffering symptoms of anxiety and depression would have no effective treatment today.

A specially important role has been played by basic biological and behavioral studies, those not specifically hinged to a particular problem area. Although such basic research offers no guarantees, no specific end-products, this report underscores its crucial role in mental health as the foundation on which all applications must rest. One of the major conclusions to be drawn from the work of the Research Task Force is that prevention or correction of pathological behavior can come only through a thorough, basic understanding of normal processes.

Basic research is forbidding to many nonscientists, and its language and procedures require an intellectual initiation that is not available to everyone. It is difficult even for the scientists to predict when an isolated and seemingly useless finding—as the discovery of serotonin may have seemed in its time—will come to fruition in an unexpected nexus, such as the present attempts to understand basic functions of the nervous system through its response to psychoactive drugs. Because such connections between the findings of science and their application are so important—to the researcher, the clinician, and the layman—this report has underscored the need for continued efforts by NIMH to widely disseminate carefully evaluated information about the outcome of its research programs.

433

This report also suggests that the availability of skilled mental health manpower in research as well as in service programs is directly attributable to the training programs established by NIMH. Without the Institute's training programs—including, for example, specialized programs providing postdoctoral fellowships and career development grants for independent work—many lines of research may not have developed.

The quality of research, it is clear, depends upon the availability of first-rate investigators. It has often been observed by researchers that creative scientific leaps take place when there is a "critical mass" of highly trained minds focused on a given area. The productivity of scientists, however, depends ultimately upon a particular kind of environment—precisely the type encouraged by the Institute's intramural research programs and its extramural research policies. The excellence of NIMH research has stemmed from a policy of selecting talented scientists and creating an atmosphere of trust, free of distractions, in an unprogramed environment. Although this approach has been difficult to defend among efficiency experts and cost accountants, the loyalty and creativity of NIMH research staff and NIMH grantees were generated exactly by this freedom.

Had NIMH policy been directed toward tightly controlled and managed research programs, the Institute would not have sustained its high-quality staff. Biomedical and behavioral scientists are not given high status in Government—if judged by laboratory space and salary limits. Many could readily double and triple their incomes in industry, and Government laboratories do often lose their best people in an unequal competition. Yet a number of extraordinarily talented researchers, including Nobel Prize winners, remain at NIMH, a fact that would be puzzling were it not for the particular environment of trust that nurtured their work. The same policies that apply to the Institute's own research projects apply also to those it sponsors. However nebulous these policies may have seemed to some, they nurtured the mental health field into its present being.

Traditional cost-effectiveness methods for evaluating major Government programs are found wanting when applied to mental health research. Improvements in mental outlook, mood, learning ability, or participation in daily life cannot readily be assayed in dollars. Moreover, attempts to evaluate human welfare in the manner, say, of a weapons system, force an inappropriate emphasis on pathology. In reporting reductions of absenteeism, crime, accident rates, or drug abuse, for example, statisticians are likely to phrase outcome in terms only of a lessening of a negative. It is more difficult to place a dollar value on the positive—on information and programs that help foster emotional well-being and self-realization even among those of our citizens who suffer no clearly defined psychopathology. Nevertheless, it must be acknowledged that concern for positive mental health, along with concern for the conquest of mental illness, is at the core of our interests. Internal misery breeds interpersonal and social trouble, and vice versa, in a cruel circle of pain—for the individual and for society.

It is instructive to look back on the last quarter-century and to ask what would have happened had there been no NIMH. Surely, the United States would have had far fewer scientists devoted to urgent mental health concerns. Many of the great universities and colleges in the United States would be without strong laboratories for a range of productive research in the biological, psychological, and social sciences. The number of psychiatrists, psychologists, sociologists, psychopharmacologists, psychobiologists, and other skilled research contributors toward the future quality of life would be substantially smaller were it not for the Institute's efforts.

Except for the Institute's programs, it is likely, too, that the process of discovery and innovation in the mental health field would have been retarded. The surge of productivity in psychopharmacology, for example, would have lagged, in all probability, if the field had waited only for industrial support.

Moreover, without the close tie fostered by NIMH between research and services, innovative approaches to mental health problems would have been diminished, and community mental health programs would remain a dream—as in fact, for lack of financial support, they do in many communities. Only a small group of affluent people might be receiving therapy, probably heavily weighted toward psychoanalysis and concentrated upon the individual rather than on families or groups, since many of the innovations in therapeutic practice have come from NIMH-trained researchers able to investigate innovative methods.

Only with NIMH support were departments of psychiatry and behavioral science established in all medical schools, and only in this way did an appreciation of the emotional and behavioral factors in every illness become part of the curriculum of all medical students. The impact of the Institute's programs has thus gone far beyond the bounds of psychiatry proper to affect every physician's approach to his patients.

The disease categories for which NIMH has the primary responsibility represent perhaps the only major category of illness that, during the first quarter-century of NIMH existence, has shown a significant major change in treatment patterns and in treatment dollar cost. In cancer and heart disease, the incidence, hospital-patient days, and cost have not receded. In contrast, the steady increase in mental hospital population which marked the early years of that period has been sharply reversed, with important savings as a result. This has been a major accomplishment even though new problems have developed in consequence.

The achievements summarized in this report suggest the Institute's impact upon the expectations of future Americans. Anyone whose life has been touched by emotional disturbance, not to mention the more acute and crippling mental problems, knows that mental health is the primary determinant of the quality of the life an individual leads. Many conditions influence our lives, but none so much as our psychological state. Since the mental outlook of a people will be reflected in their behavior, it seems rational for a Government to seek its people's healthy emotional development and well-being. That a Government agency could actually make the progress indicated by this report reflects a step forward in the evolution of human society.

Members of the Coordinating Committee, Study Groups, and Panel of Research Consultants

Coordinating Committee

James D. Isbister, Chairperson
Deputy Director, NIMH

Julius Segal, Ph.D., Chairperson (1973-)
Director, Research Task Force

Floyd E. Bloom, M.D. (1973-)
Acting Director, Division of Special Mental Health Research, NIMH

Donald S. Boomer, Ph.D.
Associate Director, Research Task Force

Robert W. Brown
Associate Administrator for Program Coordination, NIMH

William E. Bunney, Jr., M.D.
Director, Division of Narcotic Addiction and Drug Abuse, NIMH

Harry P. Cain II, Ph.D.
Director, Office of Program Planning and Evaluation, NIMH

George V. Coelho, Ph.D.
Behavioral Science Coordinator, Research Task Force

Robert A. Cohen, M.D., Ph.D.
Director, Division of Clinical and Behavioral Research, NIMH

John C. Eberhart, Ph.D.
Director, Mental Health Intramural Research Program, NIMH

Patricia S. Goldman, Ph.D.
Coordinator, Study Groups, 1, 2, and 3, Research Task Force

James A. Goodman, Ph.D.
Director, Division of Special Mental Health Programs, NIMH

David Kefauver
Assistant Director for Extramural Programs, NIMH

Melvin L. Kohn, Ph.D.
President, Assembly of Scientists

James D. Lawrence
Executive Officer, NIMH

Edwin M. Long, Jr. (1973-)
Acting Director, Office of Communications, NIMH

Ronald E. McMillan
Acting Director, Office of Communications, NIMH

Frank M. Ochberg, M.D. (1973-)
Acting Director, Division of Mental Health Service Programs, NIMH

Morris B. Parloff, Ph.D.
Coordinator, Study Groups 7, 8, and 9, Research Task Force

William Pollin, M.D.
Coordinator, Study Groups 4, 5, and 6, Research Task Force

Luther D. Robinson, M.D.
Acting Superintendent, Saint Elizabeths Hospital

Gian C. Salmoiraghi, M.D., Ph.D.
Director, Division of Special Mental Health Research, NIMH

James W. Stockdill (1973-)
Acting Director, Office of Program
Planning and Evaluation, NIMH

Claudewell S. Thomas, M.D.
Director, Division of Mental Health
Service Programs, NIMH

Francis N. Waldrop, M.D.
Director, Division of Manpower and
Training Programs, NIMH

Louis A. Wienckowski, Ph.D.
Director, Division of Extramural
Research Programs, NIMH

And the Chairpersons of the Study Groups

Study Groups

Study Group No. 1: Biological and Physiological Processes

Fred Elmadjian, Ph.D., Chairperson
Chief, Biological Science Section
Behavioral Sciences Training
Branch
Division of Manpower and Training
Programs, NIMH

Floyd E. Bloom, M.D.
Chief, Laboratory of
Neuropharmacology
Division of Special Mental Health
Research, NIMH

David Bodian, Ph.D., M.D.
Director, Department of Anatomy
Johns Hopkins University School of
Medicine

John M. Davis, M.D.
Professor of Psychiatry
Vanderbilt University School of
Medicine

Seymour Kaufman, Ph.D.
Chief, Laboratory of
Neurochemistry
Division of Biological and
Biochemical Research, NIMH

Irwin J. Kopin, M.D.
Chief, Laboratory of Clinical
Science
Division of Clinical and Behavioral
Research, NIMH

Gerald E. McClearn, Ph.D.
Director, Institute for Behavioral
Genetics
University of Colorado

Harvey S. Mudd, M.D.
Chief, Section on Alkaloid
Biosynthesis
Laboratory of General and
Comparative Biochemistry
Division of Biological and
Biochemical Research, NIMH

Phillip G. Nelson, Ph.D., M.D.
Chief, Behavioral Biology Branch
Office of the Scientific Director
National Institute of Child Health
and Human Development, NIH

437

Study Group 2: Psychological Processes

Marian R. Yarrow, Ph.D.,
Co-chairperson
Chief, Section on Developmental
Psychology
Laboratory of Socio-environmental
Studies
Division of Clinical and Behavioral
Research, NIMH

Betty H. Pickett, Ph.D.,
Co-chairperson
Deputy Director
Division of Extramural Research
Programs, NIMH

Sheldon Alexander, Ph.D.
Health Scientist Administrator,
Psychology Section
Behavioral Sciences Training
Branch
Division of Manpower and Training
Programs, NIMH

Peter L. Carlton, Ph.D.
Professor of Psychiatry
College of Medicine and Dentistry
of New Jersey
Rutgers Medical School

Dorwin P. Cartwright, Ph.D.
Professor of Psychology
Institute for Social Research
University of Michigan

Steven L. Chorover, Ph.D.
Professor of Psychology
Massachusetts Institute of
Technology

Charles N. Cofer, Ph.D.
Professor of Psychology
The Pennsylvania State University

William Hodos, Ph.D.
Professor of Psychology
University of Maryland

Julius W. Kling, Ph.D.
Chairman, Department of
Psychology
Hunter Laboratories
Brown University

David Pearl, Ph.D.
Chief, Behavioral Sciences
Research Branch
Division of Extramural Research
Programs, NIMH

H. Enger Rosvold, Ph.D.
Chief, Section on Neuropsychology
Laboratory of Psychology
Division of Clinical and Behavioral
Research, NIMH

William N. Schoenfeld, Ph.D.
Professor of Psychology
Queens College
City University of New York

Study Group No. 3: Social and Cultural Processes

Morris Rosenberg, Ph.D.,
Chairperson
Chief, Section on Social Structure
Laboratory of Socio-environmental
Studies
Division of Clinical and Behavioral
Research, NIMH

John D. Campbell, Ph.D.
Chief, Section on Personality and
Stress
Laboratory of Socio-environmental
Studies
Division of Clinical and Behavioral
Research, NIMH

Elliot Liebow, Ph.D.
Chief, Center for Studies of
Metropolitan Problems
Division of Special Mental Health
Programs, NIMH

Gillian Lindt, Ph.D.
Professor of Sociology
The American University

Bela C. Maday, Ph.D.
Administrator, Cultural
Anthropology Fellowship Program
Division of Manpower and Training
Programs, NIMH

David Reiss, M.D.
Chief, Section on Experimental
Group and Family Studies
Adult Psychiatry Branch
Division of Clinical and Behavioral
Research, NIMH

William C. Sturtevant, Ph.D.
Curator, Department of
Anthropology
Smithsonian Institution

Lorraine B. Torres
Chief, Social Sciences Section
Behavioral Sciences Research
Branch
Division of Extramural Research
Programs, NIMH

Study Group No. 4: Mental Illness and Behavior Disorders

Martin M. Katz, Ph.D., Chairperson
Chief, Clinical Research Branch
Division of Extramural Research
Programs, NIMH

William E. Bunney, Jr., M.D.,
Vice-chairperson
Director
Division of Narcotic Addiction and
Drug Abuse, NIMH

John A. Benvenuto, M.D.
Special Assistant to the Director
for Youth
Division of Narcotic Addiction and
Drug Abuse, NIMH

Stephen P. Hersh, M.D.
Special Assistant to the Director
for Children and Youth
Office of the Director, NIMH

Mary H. Lystad, Ph.D.
Special Assistant to the Director
Division of Special Mental Health
Programs, NIMH

Loren R. Mosher, M.D.
Chief, Center for Studies of
Schizophrenia
Clinical Research Branch
Division of Extramural Research
Programs, NIMH

David Rosenthal, Ph.D.
Chief, Laboratory of Psychology
Division of Clinical and Behavioral
Research, NIMH

Carmi Schooler, Ph.D.
Acting Chief, Section on
Personality and Environment
Laboratory of Socio-environmental
Studies
Division of Clinical and Behavioral
Research, NIMH

Paul H. Wender, M.D.
Research Psychologist, Laboratory
of Psychology
Division of Clinical and Behavioral
Research, NIMH

Richard Wyatt, M.D.
Acting Chief, Laboratory of Clinical
Psychopharmacology
Division of Special Mental Health
Research, NIMH

Study Group No. 5: Drug Abuse

Robert C. Petersen, Ph.D.,
Co-chairperson
Chief, Center for Studies of
Narcotic and Drug Abuse
Division of Narcotic Addiction and
Drug Abuse, NIMH

William R. Martin, M.D.,
Co-chairperson
Chief, Addiction Research Center
Division of Narcotic Addiction and
Drug Abuse, NIMH

Julius Axelrod, Ph.D.
Chief, Section on Pharmacology
Laboratory of Clinical Science
Division of Clinical and Behavioral
Research, NIMH

Mitchell B. Balter, Ph.D.
Chief, Special Studies Section
Psychopharmacology Research
Branch
Division of Extramural Research
Programs, NIMH

Richard E. Belleville, Ph.D.
Special Assistant to the Director
Division of Narcotic Addiction and
Drug Abuse, NIMH

Eleanor E. Carroll
Research Sociologist, Center for
Studies of Narcotic and Drug Abuse
Division of Narcotic Addiction and
Drug Abuse, NIMH

Leo E. Hollister, M.D.
Medical Investigator
Veterans Administration Hospital
Palo Alto, California

William H. McGlothlin, Ph.D.
Professor in Residence,
Department of Psychology
University of California at
Los Angeles

Stephen I. Szara, M.D.
Chief, Clinical Drug Studies
Section
Center for Studies of Narcotic and
Drug Abuse
Division of Narcotic Addiction and
Drug Abuse, NIMH

Abraham Wikler, M.D.
Professor of Psychiatry and
Pharmacology
University of Kentucky Medical
Center

Study Group No. 6: Alcoholism

Morris E. Chafetz, M.D.,
Chairperson
Director
National Institute on Alcohol Abuse
and Alcoholism, NIMH

H. Keith H. Brodie, M.D.
Assistant Professor of Psychiatry
Stanford University School of
Medicine

Theodore J. Cicero, Ph.D.
Assistant Professor of
Neuropsychology in Psychiatry
Washington University School of
Medicine

Thomas Harford, Ph.D.
Research Psychologist, Laboratory
of Alcohol Research
National Institute on Alcohol Abuse
and Alcoholism, NIMH

Nancy K. Mello, Ph.D.
Assistant Chief, Laboratory of
Alcohol Research
National Institute on Alcohol Abuse
and Alcoholism, NIMH

Ernest P. Noble, Ph.D., M.D.
Professor of Psychiatry and
Human Behavior
College of Medicine
University of California at Irvine

Albert A. Pawlowski, Ph.D.
Acting Chief, Extramural Research
Branch
National Institute on Alcohol Abuse
and Alcoholism, NIMH

Norman A. Scotch, Ph.D.
Visiting Fellow
Salk Institute
La Jolla, California

Louis Sokoloff, M.D.
Chief, Laboratory of Cerebral
Metabolism
Division of Biological and
Biochemical Research, NIMH

Irving C. Wolf, Ph.D.
Special Assistant to the Director
National Institute on Alcohol Abuse
and Alcoholism, NIMH

Study Group No. 7: Social Problems

Ann C. Maney, Ph.D.,
Co-chairperson
Research Sociologist, Mental
Health Study Center
Division of Mental Health Service
Programs, NIMH

Saleem A. Shah, Ph.D.,
Co-chairperson
Chief, Center for Studies of Crime
and Delinquency
Division of Special Mental Health
Programs, NIMH

James A. Goodman, Ph.D.
Director
Division of Special Mental Health
Programs, NIMH

Melvin L. Kohn, Ph.D.
Chief, Laboratory of Socio-
environmental Studies
Division of Clinical and Behavioral
Research, NIMH

Leonard I. Perlin, Ph.D.
Chief, Section on Social Process
Laboratory of Socio-environmental
Studies
Division of Clinical and Behavioral
Research, NIMH

Marguerite L. Young, Ph.D.
Executive Secretary, Social
Problems Research Review
Committee
Applied Research Branch
Division of Extramural Research
Programs, NIMH

Study Group No. 8: Treatment Techniques

Jerome Levine, M.D., Chairperson
Chief, Psychopharmacology
Research Branch
Division of Extramural Research
Programs, NIMH

Donald L. Burnham, M.D.
Research Psychiatrist, Office of the
Director
Division of Clinical and Behavioral
Research, NIMH

Thomas N. Chase, M.D.
Chief, Section on Experimental
Therapeutics
Laboratory of Clinical Science
Division of Clinical and Behavioral
Research, NIMH

David S. Horwitz, M.D.
Senior Investigator, Experimental
Therapeutics Branch
National Heart and Lung Institute,
NIH

Morris A. Lipton, Ph.D., M.D.
Chairman, Department of
Psychiatry
University of North Carolina School
of Medicine

Beryce W. MacLennan, Ph.D.
Acting Chief, Mental Health Study
Center
Division of Mental Health Service
Programs, NIMH

Chester M. Pierce, M.D.
Professor of Education and
Psychiatry
Harvard University School of
Education

Winfield H. Scott, Ph.D.
Chief, Section on Clinical
Psychology
Adult Psychiatry Branch
Division of Clinical and Behavioral
Research, NIMH

Stephanie B. Stolz, Ph.D.
Chief, Small Grants Section
Office of the Director
Division of Extramural Research
Programs, NIMH

Study Group No. 9: Mental Health Services

Henry A. Foley, Ph.D.,
Co-chairperson
Health Economist, Mental Health
Care and Services Financing
Branch
Division of Mental Health Service
Programs, NIMH

Morton Kramer, Sc.D.,
Co-chairperson
Chief, Biometry Branch
Office of Program Planning and
Evaluation, NIMH

Howard R. Davis, Ph.D.
Chief, Mental Health Services
Development Branch
Division of Mental Health Service
Programs, NIMH

William T. Tash, Ph.D.
Chief, Evaluation Branch
Office of Program Planning and
Evaluation, NIMH

Claudewell S. Thomas, M.D.
Director
Division of Mental Health Service
Programs, NIMH

Robert van Hoek, M.D.
Acting Director, National Center
for Health Services,
Research, and Development, NIMH

Study Group No. 10: Research Information and Utilization

Lorraine Bouthilet, Ph.D.,
Chairperson
Scientific Director, National
Clearinghouse for Mental Health
Information
Office of Communications, NIMH

Daniel G. Brown, Ph.D.
Consultant in Mental Health
Phoenix Area Indian Health
Service Annex

Samuel L. Buker, Ph.D.
Deputy Director
Division of Mental Health Service
Programs, NIMH

Antoinette Gattozzi
Science Writer
Berkeley, California

Mildred K. Lehman
Acting Chief, Public Information
Branch
Office of Communications, NIMH

John Osmundsen
Science Writer
New York City

Richard L. Schiefelbusch, Ph.D.
Director, Bureau of Child Research
University of Kansas

Louis A. Wienckowski, Ph.D.
Director
Division of Extramural Research
Programs, NIMH

Panel of Research Consultants

Charles I. Schottland, Chairperson
Professor, Florence Heller School
of Social Welfare
Brandeis University

Melvin Calvin, Ph.D.
Director, Laboratory of Chemical
Biodynamics
University of California at Berkeley

Irving H. Chase
Chairman, Council on Legislation
and Public Policy
National Association for
Mental Health

James S. Coleman, Ph.D.
Professor of Sociology
University of Chicago

Lloyd Elam, M.D.
President
Meharry Medical College

Daniel X. Freedman, M.D.
Chairman, Department of
Psychiatry
Pritzker School of Medicine
The University of Chicago

Norman Garmezy, Ph.D.
Professor of Psychology
University of Minnesota

David A. Hamburg, M.D.
Chairman, Department of
Psychiatry
Stanford University School of
Medicine

Ernest R. Hilgard, Ph.D.
Professor of Psychology
Stanford University

Roger E. Levien, Ph.D.
Director, Washington Domestic
Program
The RAND Corporation

Neal E. Miller, Ph.D.
Professor of Physiological
Psychology
Rockefeller University

Mildred Mitchell-Bateman, M.D.
Director
West Virginia Department of
Mental Health

Gardner C. Quarton, M.D.
Director, Mental Health Research
Institute
University of Michigan

Richard L. Sidman, M.D.
Professor of Neuroscience
Children's Hospital Medical Center
Boston, Massachusetts

Alberta E. Siegel, Ph.D.
Professor of Psychology
Stanford University School of
Medicine

Herbert A. Simon, Ph.D.
Professor of Psychology
Carnegie-Mellon University

W. Donald Weston, M.D.
Associate Dean, College of
Human Medicine
Michigan State University